Geoscience Canada, Reprint Series 1

Facies Models, Second Edition

Edited by

Roger G. Walker
Department of Geology
McMaster University
Hamilton, Ontario L8S 4M1 Canada

May, 1984

A fully rewritten version of the first edition, with several new
contributions. Most of the papers in the first edition appeared
originally in Geoscience Canada, 1976-1979, published by
the Geological Association of Canada.

D1604402

Additional copies may be obtained by
writing to:
Geological Association of Canada
Publications
Business and Economic Service Ltd.
111 Peter Street, Suite 509
Toronto, Ontario M5V 2H1

ISBN 0-919216-25-0

Geological Association of Canada
Department of Earth Sciences
Memorial University of Newfoundland,
St. John's, Newfoundland A1B 3X5
Canada

Printed by Ainsworth Press Limited,
Kitchener, Ontario

Contents

Preface to Second Edition

Johannes Walther stated in 1894 that "only the ontological method can save us from stratigraphy"; by the "ontological method" he referred to the study of modern environments and processes. In his work, he constantly advocated the investigation of events of the past through study of modern phenomena. In the study of sedimentary environments, the constant cross-comparison of the ancient and the recent leads to simplifications that are now referred to as "facies models".

The first edition of this volume was aimed at a general audience, especially students, with the view of covering the basic ideas about each environment with a minimum of jargon. Our objective remains the same in the second edition. Unfortunately, it seems to be a law of nature that Second Editions are always larger than First Editions. In this case, there is simply more literature that needs discussion, and we have decided to add some new topics which were absent in the First Edition.

This volume has been completely revised, typeset in (hopefully) a more legible typeface, and has a sewn binding rather than the (so called) "perfect" binding of the first edition. I thank John Kramers (Chairman, Publications Committee) and the Geological Association of Canada for their support in producing a second edition, for agreeing to these improvements, and for setting a price that most students will be able to afford. However, the volume would not exist without the authors, and I thank them for their contributions, and for meeting deadlines – this made my task a lot easier.

When the series was planned in *Geoscience Canada,* I asked Noel James to help select and advise on the carbonate and evaporite contributions. Maureen Czerneda has again taken a major role in the production of the volume, helping to edit the manuscripts and convey our wishes to the printer. Many McMaster students have commented on the papers over the years, and their thoughts have also found their way into this edition. For my contributions, I thank Jack Whorwood for his preparation of the photographs, and Margaret Belec and Edith Denham of the word-processing centre for typing the manuscripts. The sketches that enhance the heading of each paper are by Peter Russell, and the new cover design is by Peter Russell and Dave Bartholomew. I particularly thank our colleagues who have allowed us to use their illustrations; acknowledgements are in the captions.

Finally, although these are essentially review papers, there is a lot of original research reported in them. Over the years, much of this research has been supported by the Natural Sciences and Engineering Research Council of Canada, and by the various Universities, Government Agencies and Companies where the authors work. We hope that this volume will help "save you from stratigraphy", that is, from what Walther considered the barren cataloguing of rock and fossil sequences that sometimes passes for stratigraphy.

Roger G. Walker,
McMaster University
May, 1984

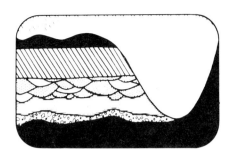

General Introduction: Facies, Facies Sequences and Facies Models

ROGER G. WALKER
Department of Geology
McMaster University
Hamilton, Ontario L8S 4M1

INTRODUCTION
In this paper, I will comment briefly on three concepts – facies, facies sequence and facies models. The intent is to simplify and de-mystify, and hence return some meaning to those misused terms, "facies", and "model". The first part of the bibliography, "basic sources of information", lists with annotations the major texts and monographs on sedimentary environments and facies.

FACIES
The term "facies" was introduced into geology by Nicholaus Steno (1669). It meant the entire aspect of a part of the earth's surface during a certain interval of geological time (Teichert, 1958). The word itself is derived from the latin *facia* or *facies*, implying the external appearance, or look of something. The modern usage was introduced by Gressly (1838), who used the term to imply the sum total of the lithological and paleontological aspects of a stratigraphic unit. Translations of Gressly's extended definition are given by Teichert (1958) and Middleton (1978).

Unfortunately, the term has been used in many different ways since 1838. In particular, arguments have focussed on: 1) whether the term implies an abstract set of characteristics, as opposed to the rock body itself; 2) whether the term should refer only to "areally restricted parts of a designated stratigraphic unit" (Moore, 1949), or also to stratigraphically unconfined rock bodies (as originally used by Gressly and other European workers); and 3) whether the term should be purely descriptive (e.g., "black mudstone facies") or also interpretive (e.g., "fluvial facies").

Succinct discussions of these problems have been given by Middleton (1978) and Reading (1978) – I will use the term in a concrete sense rather than abstractly implying only a set of characteristics, and will use it in a stratigraphically unconfined way. Middleton (1978) has also given the most useful modern working definition of the term, noting that:

"the more common (modern) usage is exemplified by de Raaf *et al.* (1965) who subdivided a group of three formations into a cyclical repetition of a number of facies distinguished by "lithological, structural and organic aspects detectable in the field". The facies may be given informal designations ("Facies A", etc.) or brief descriptive designations (e.g., "laminated siltstone facies") and it is understood that they are units that will ultimately be given an environmental interpretation; but the facies definition is itself quite objective and based on the total field aspect of the rocks themselves... The key to the interpretation of facies is to combine observations made on their spatial relations and internal characteristics (lithology and sedimentary structures) with comparative information from other well-studied stratigraphic units, and particularly from studies of modern sedimentary environments."

DEFINING FACIES
Many problems concerning the interpretation of depositional environments can be handled without the formal definition of facies. Where the method is invaluable is in stratigraphic sequences where apparently similar facies are repeated many times over (de Raaf *et al.*, 1965; Cant and Walker, 1976).

Subdivision of a rock body into constituent facies (or units of similar *aspect*) is essentially a classification procedure, and the *degree* of subdivision must first and foremost be governed by the *objectives of the study.* If the objective is the routine description and interpretation of a particular stratigraphic unit, a fairly broad facies subdivision may suffice. However, if the objective is more detailed, perhaps the refinement of an existing facies model or the establishment of an entirely new model, then facies subdivision in the field will almost certainly be more detailed.

The *scale of subdivision* is dependent not only upon one's objectives, but on the time available, and the abundance of physical and biological structures in the rocks. A thick sequence of massive mudstones will be difficult to subdivide into facies, but a similar thickness of interbedded sandstones and shales (with abundant and varied examples of ripples, cross bedding and trace fossils) might be subdivisible into a large number of distinct facies. As a general rule, I would advocate erring on the side of oversubdividing in the field – facies can always be recombined in the laboratory, but a crude field subdivision cannot be refined in the lab.

Subdivision of a body of rock into facies ideally should not be attempted until one is thoroughly familiar with the rock body. Only then will it be apparent how much variability there is, and how many different facies must be defined to describe the unit. In the field, most facies studies have relied on distinctive combinations of sedimentary and organic structures (e.g., de Raaf *et al.*, 1965; Williams and Rust, 1969; Cant and Walker, 1976). Statistical methods can also be used to define facies, especially where there is considerable agreement among workers as to the important quantifiable, descriptive parameters. In carbonate rocks, percentages of different organic constituents, and percentages of micrite and/or sparry calcite have been used as input to cluster and factor analyses, with the resulting groupings of samples (in Q mode) being interpreted as facies (Imbrie and Purdy, 1962; Klovan, 1964; Harbaugh and Demirmen, 1964; see also Chapter 7 of the book by Harbaugh and Merriam, 1968, on Computer Applications in Stratigraphic Analysis - Classification Systems). Unfortunately, statistical methods are unsuited to clastic rocks, where most of the important information (sedimentary and biological structures) cannot readily be quantified. Readers unfamiliar with the process of subdividing rock bodies into facies

2

Figure 1
Cardium Formation, facies 1 massive dark mudstones (from Walker, 1983). For comparison with Figures 2, 3 and 4, note absence of silty or sandy laminae, and absence of recognizable burrow forms. Core from well 10-33-34-6W5, 7851 feet (2293.0 m), Caroline Field, Alberta. Scale in cm.

Figure 2
Cardium Formation, facies 2 laminated dark mudstones (from Walker, 1983). Note presence of sharp-based, delicately laminated silty layers (absent in Fig. 1), which are not pervasively bioturbated (compare with Fig. 3). Core from well 8-25-34-5W5, 2098.4 m, between Caroline and Garrington Fields, Alberta. Scale in cm.

Figure 3
Cardium Formation, facies 4 pervasively bioturbated muddy sandstones (from Walker, 1983). Note total bioturbation of silty and sandy layers (compare with Fig. 2), and presence of a few distinct burrow forms - these are better developed in Figure 4. Core from well 10-17-34-7W5, 8390 feet (2557.3 m), between Caroline and Ricinus Fields, Alberta. Scale in cm.

should consult the papers listed in the annotated bibliography, to see how the general principles briefly discussed here can be applied in practise. As one brief example, consider the mudstones and siltstones shown in Figures 1 to 4 from the Upper Cretaceous Cardium Formation of Alberta (Walker, 1983). If one's objective is a detailed study of the hydrocarbon-bearing Cardium sandstones, the examples in Figures 1 to 4 could probably be lumped together as "mudstone or siltstone". But there are clear descriptive differences, involving presence of silty laminations, degree of general bioturbation, and preservation of specific burrow forms. It has turned out that mudstones of Figure 1 only overlie the Cardium "B sand", and mudstones of Figure 2 only overlie the "A sand". Detailed facies subdivision thus happened to define two regional marker horizons (Walker, 1983), which lumping all the mudstones together would not have done.

FACIES SEQUENCE

It was pointed out by Middleton (1978) that "it is understood that (facies) will ultimately be given an environmental interpretation". However, many, if not most, facies defined in the field have ambiguous interpretations – a cross-bedded sandstone facies, for example, could be formed in a meandering or braided river, a tidal channel, an offshore area dominated by alongshore currents, or on an open shelf dominated by tidal currents. Many facies defined in

Figure 4 ▶
Cardium Formation, facies 5 bioturbated sandstones (from Walker, 1983). Note excellent development of burrow forms (compare with Figure 3), including prominent Z-shaped Zoophycos burrow, and small vertical tube at top (Conichnus conicus), with later burrowing by Chondrites (white circles/-ovals). Core from well 10-20-37-7W5, 2294.1 m, between Caroline and Garrington Fields, Alberta. Scale in cm.

the field may at first suggest no interpretation at all. The key to interpretation is to analyze all of the facies communally, in context. The sequence in which they occur thus contributes as much information as the facies themselves.

The relationship between depositional environments in space, and the resulting stratigraphic sequences developed through time as a result of transgressions and regressions, was first emphasized by Johannes Walther, in his Law of the Correlation of Facies (Walther, 1894, p. 979 — see Middleton, 1973). Walther stated that "it is a basic statement of far-reaching significance that only those facies and facies areas can be superimposed primarily which can be observed beside each other at the present time". Careful application of the law, therefore, suggests that in a vertical sequence, a *gradational* transition from one facies to another implies that the two facies represent environments that once were adjacent laterally. The dangers of applying the Law in a gross way to stratigraphic sequences with cyclic repetitions of facies have been emphasized by Middleton (1973, p. 983).

The importance of clearly defining gradational facies boundaries in vertical section as opposed to sharp or erosive boundaries, has been emphasized by de Raaf *et al.* (1965) and Reading (1978, p. 5). If boundaries are sharp or erosional, there is no way of knowing whether two vertically adjacent facies represent

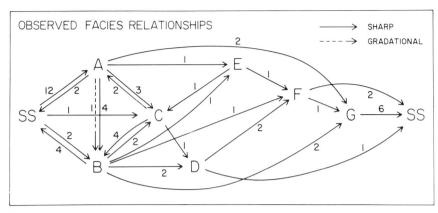

Figure 6
Facies relationship diagram for Battery Point section shown in Figure 8. Numbers indicate the observed number of facies transitions. From Cant and Walker, 1976.

environments that once were laterally adjacent. Indeed, sharp breaks between facies, especially if marked by thin bioturbated horizons implying non-deposition (Fig. 5), may signify fundamental changes in depositional environment and the beginnings of new cycles of sedimentation (see de Raaf *et al.*, 1965, and Walker and Harms, 1971, for examples of sharp facies relationships accompanied by bioturbation).

The first formal documentation of the quantitative relationships between facies was published by de Raaf *et al.* (1965; Fig. 5) in a diagram resembling the web of a demented spider. Note that sharp and gradational boundaries have been carefully distinguished. Note also that there are two "spurs" off the main trend of the web (black mudstone to oscillatory 1, and silty streak to sandy streak). These spurs imply that for the purposes of facies transitions, the facies at the end of the spur is completely contained within another facies (e.g., sandy streak within silty streak). This in turn suggests that facies were oversubdivided in the field, and that (for example) sandy streak is a subset of silty streak and could be combined with silty streak for interpretive purposes.

The spider's web is now termed a "facies relationship diagram" – examples are shown in Figures 5 and 6. As geologists have become more concerned with facies transitions, they have sought methods for simplifying the facies relationship diagram to remove the "noise". In essence, methods have involved converting the *numbers* of transitions (Figs. 5 and 6) to observed *probabilities* of transitions (see Walker, 1979, Fig. 2). The observed probabilities

are then compared with the probabilities that would apply if all the transitions between facies were *random*. It has been argued that those transitions which occur a lot more commonly than random must have some geological significance.

The problem is to derive a matrix of random probabilities. The method used by Selley (1970), Miall (1973), Cant and Walker (1976) and Walker (1979) is statistically incorrect. In the field, it is assumed that one cannot recognize a transition from one facies to itself. Consequently, a matrix of transition probabilities must have "structurally empty cells" along its main diagonal, where the transition from, say, facies A to facies A cannot be recognized in the field and therefore appears in the matrix as zero. However, Carr (1982) has pointed out that "zeros cannot result from a simple independent random process". Consequently, methods for deriving a random matrix based on absolute facies abundances (as explained by Walker, 1979, in the first edition of *Facies Models*) are incorrect.

There is not space here to explain the more complex methods of Markov chain analysis that must now be used, and the reader is referred to the work of Carr (1982) and Powers and Easterling (1982). Another problem of the "old" method, which involved substracting the random probabilities from observed probabilities, was that there was no way of evaluating the differences statistically. This aspect of facies analysis has been improved by Harper (1984) and is explained in "Improved Methods of Facies Sequence Analysis" (this volume). It applies to entries in the

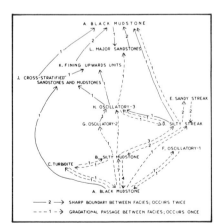

Figure 5
Facies relationship diagram for Carboniferous Abbotsham Formation, North Devon, England. Arrows show nature of transitions, and numbers indicate observed numbers of transitions. This is the first published facies relationship diagram. From de Raaf et al., 1965.

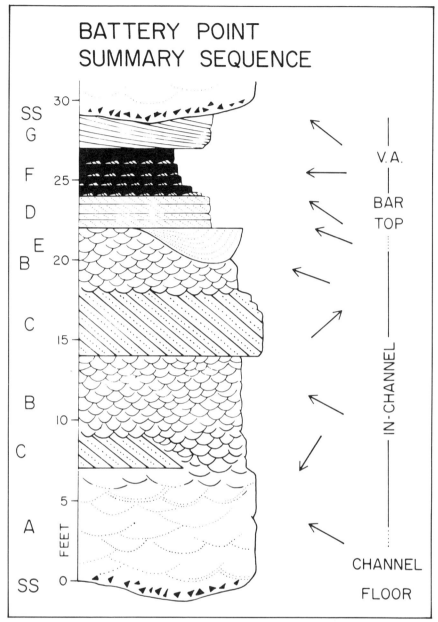

BATTERY POINT SUMMARY SEQUENCE

SS
G
F
D
E
B
C
B
C
A
SS

FEET

30
25
20
15
10
5
0

V. A.

BAR
TOP

IN-CHANNEL

CHANNEL
FLOOR

Figure 7
Summary facies sequence expressed as a vertical section. This has the advantage of visual appeal, and allows the facies to be drawn to their observed average thickness. Battery Point Formation, Quebec. From Cant and Walker, 1976.

observed-minus-random matrix that are different from zero, and assumes that a statistically valid random matrix has been derived.

Using Battery Point data from Cant and Walker (1976), Harper ("Improved Methods of Facies Sequence Analysis", this volume) has produced a set of facies transitions where the null hypothesis that the transitions occurred at random can be rejected at a given level of significance. For most of the transitions, that level of significance is less than 0.1 (Harper, this volume, Fig.

1); for E to F, and F to SS the level of significance must be set at 0.13 in order to reject the null hypothesis.

Harper's Figure 1 can be regarded as a simplified facies relationship diagram, or a "distillation" of the Battery Point data. Geologists are most accustomed to seeing transitions of this type expressed as a vertical stratigraphic sequence, and one version of the Battery Point data is shown in Figure 7. This is the original Cant and Walker (1976) version, and has *not* been corrected for the statistical problems dis-

cussed above. It should be compared with the raw Battery Point data (Figure 6) and with Harper's simplified facies relationship diagram (Figure 1 of "Improved Methods of Facies Sequence Analysis", this volume). Clearly, the transitions included in a "summary diagram" will depend on the arbitrarily set level of significance that one accepts. By gradually relaxing the level from, say, 0.1 to 0.2, one can attempt to evaluate the *geological* significance of the transitions judged to be different from random. The problems of statistical versus geological significance have been examined in the discussion of Selley's paper (1970, p. 575-581).

The columnar method of presenting the data shows not only the facies *sequence* but also the mean *thickness* of each facies (calculated from the raw data). This is one way in which data can be "distilled" into summary sequences, or "models", as discussed below.

It is now important to distinguish between a single facies sequence, and repeated sequences (or cycles). The summary sequence diagram in Figure 7, with the suggested basic interpretations, established the probably fluvial origin of the Battery Point Sandstone. The scoured surface SS can then be interpreted as the fundamental boundary between cycles, and hence individual cycles can be defined on the original complete stratigraphic section (Fig. 8). Using the summary stratigraphic sequence (Fig. 7) as an idealization of all of the Battery Point sequences (Fig. 8), each individual cycle can be compared with the summary to identify points in common and points of difference. The reader may do this with the sequences in Figures 7 and 8.

FACIES MODELS
The construction and use of facies models continues to be one of the most active areas in the general field of stratigraphy, as is demonstrated by several new books in the field (see bibliography). This emphasis is not new; many of the ideas were embodied in Dunbar and Rodgers' *Principles of Stratigraphy* in 1957, and were based on studies dating back to Gressly and Walther in the 19th Century (Middleton, 1973). Walther (1893, quoted by Middleton, 1973, p. 981) "explained that the most satisfying genetic explanations of ancient phenomena were by analogy with modern

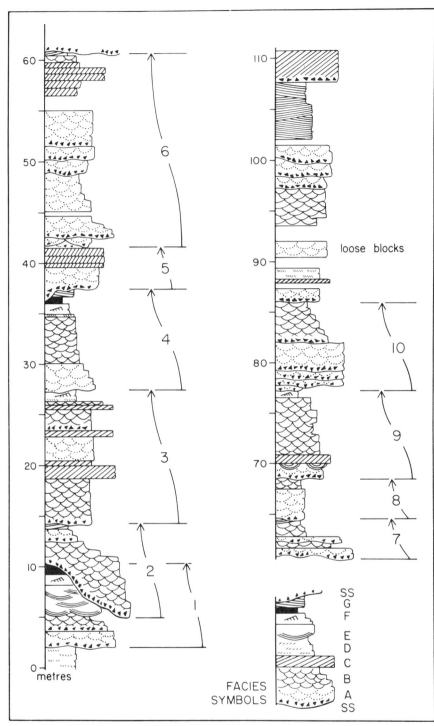

Figure 8
Measured section of the Lower Devonian Battery Point Sandstone near Gaspe, *Quebec. Numbers refer to individual channel-fill sequences. From Cant and Walker, 1976.*

geological processes". The study of modern environments and processes was termed the "ontological method" by Walther, who observed that "only the ontological method can save us from stratigraphy" (Walther, in Middleton, 1973, p. 883). Facies models similarly link modern and ancient observations into coherent syntheses, and their importance at the present time is due to an increasing need for the models, and a rapidly increasing data base on which the models are formulated.

In this volume, facies models are expressed in several different ways —as idealized sequences of facies, as block diagrams, and as graphs and equations. Examples of all of these are given in "Sandy Fluvial Deposits" (this volume). The term model here has a generality that goes beyond a single study of one formation. The final facies relationship diagram and its stratigraphic section (Fig. 7) are only local summaries, not general models for fluvial deposits. But when the Battery Point facies relationship diagram is compared and contrasted with the facies relationship diagrams from other ancient braided river deposits, and then data from modern braided rivers is incorporated (e.g., Cant, 1978), the points in common between all of these studies begin to assume a generality that can be termed a *model*.

A facies model could thus be defined as a general summary of a specific sedimentary environment, written in terms that make the summary useable in at least four different ways. The basis of the summary consists of many studies of both ancient rocks and recent sediments; the rapidly increasing data base is due at least partly to the large number of recent sediment studies in the last 20 years. The increased need for the models is due to the increasing amount of prediction that geologists are making from a limited local data base. This prediction may concern subsurface sandstone geometry in hydrocarbon reservoirs, the association of mineral deposits with specific sedimentary environments (for example, uraniferous conglomerates), or the movement of modern sand bars in shallow water (Bay of Fundy, tidal power). In all cases, a limited amount of local information plus the guidance of a well-understood facies model results in potentially important predictions about that local environment.

Our aim as geologists is partly to identify different environments in ancient rocks, and also to understand the range of processes that can operate within these environments. We must also be sure of why we want to identify environments in the first place. Is it to provide a name showing that we have thought about the origin of the unit we have mapped ("the Ordovician Cloridorme Formation consists of deep water turbidites"), or is it to provide a framework for further thought? It is the latter - the framework for further thought - that in my mind separates the

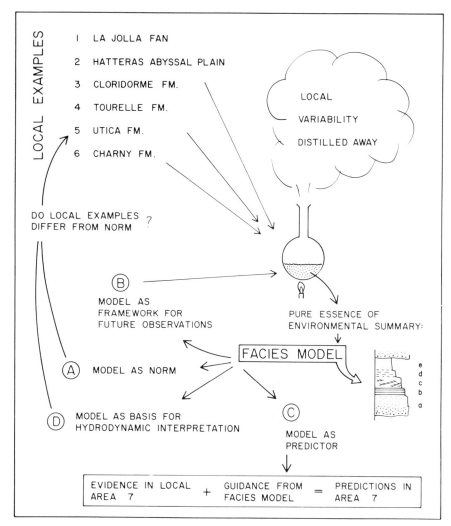

Figure 9

Distillation of a general facies model from various local examples, and its use as a NORM, FRAMEWORK for OBSERVATIONS, PREDICTOR, and BASIS for INTERPRETATION. See text for details.

art of recognizing environments from the art of FACIES ANALYSIS and FACIES MODELLING. The meaning and implication of these two terms will become apparent below.

FACIES MODELS – CONSTRUCTION AND USE

The principles, methods and motives of facies analysis are shown in Figure 9, using turbidites as an example. The principles, of course, apply to all environments. We begin by assuming that if enough modern turbidites can be studied in cores, and if enough ancient turbidites can be studied in the field, we may be able to make some *general* statements about turbidites, rather than statements about only one particular example.

The process of extracting the general information is shown diagramatically in

Figure 9, where numbers 1 and 2 represent recent sediment studies (cores from, say, La Jolla fan and Hatteras abyssal plain) and numbers 3 through 6 represent studies of ancient turbidites (for example, the Cloridorme and Tourelle Formations of Gaspe, the Utica Formation at Montmorency Falls, and the Charny Formation around Quebec City). The entire wealth of information on modern and ancient turbidites can then be distilled, boiling away the local details, but distilling and concentrating the important features that they have in common into a general summary of turbidites. If we distill enough individual turbidites, we can end up with a perfect "essence of turbidite" – now called the Bouma model. But what is the essence of any local example and what is its "noise"? Which aspects do we dismiss and which do we

extract and consider important? Answering these questions involves experience, judgment, knowledge and argument among sedimentologists, and the answers also involve the ultimate purpose of the environmental synthesis and summary. Some of the different methods for "distilling" the examples will become apparent in the papers in this volume. Facies relationship diagrams could be used if the same facies can be recognized in many different examples. Indeed, "standard" facies classifications have been proposed for turbidite (Mutti and Ricci Lucchi, 1972; Walker, 1978) and braided fluvial (Miall, 1977) environments. More commonly, models are still derived by qualitative comparison and contrast, rather than strict quantitative distillation.

I pointed out earlier that the difference between the summary of an environment and a facies model perhaps depends mainly on the use to which the summary is put. As well as being a summary, a FACIES MODEL must fulfill four other important functions:

1) it must act as a *norm*, for purposes of comparison;
2) it must act as a *framework* and *guide* for future observations;
3) it must act as a *predictor* in new geological situations; and
4) it must act as an integrated *basis for interpretation* of the environment or system that it represents.

Figure 9 has been constructed to illustrate these various functions. Using the example of the turbidite model, the numbers 1 through 6 indicate various local studies of modern and ancient turbidites. There is a constant feedback between examples – in this way the sedimentologist exercises his judgment in defining the features in common and identifying "local irregularities". This is the "distillation" process that allows the environmental summary (that will act as a facies model) to be set up.

Having constructed the facies model, it must act first as a norm (Fig. 9, A) with which individual examples can be compared. Without a norm, we are unable to say whether example 5 of Figure 9 contains any unusual features. In this example, Utica Formation turbidites at Montmorency Falls are very thin, silty, and many beds do not begin with division A of the Bouma model (Fig. 9); they begin with division B or C. Because of the existence of the norm (Bouma model), we can ask questions about example 5 that we could not otherwise have asked, and whole new avenues of productive thought can be opened up this way. Thus there is a constant feedback between a model and its individual examples – the more examples and the more distillation, the better the norm will be, and the more we must be forced into explaining local variations.

The second function of the facies model is to set up a framework for future observations (Fig. 9B). In as much as the model summarizes all the important descriptive features of the system, geologists know that similar information must be recorded when working with a new example. In Figure 9, this would include the detailed characteristics and thicknesses of the five Bouma divisions. Although the framework ensures that this information is recorded wherever possible, it can also act to blind the unwary, who might ignore some evidence because it is not clearly spelled out by the model. This leads to imprecise interpretations, and would cause a freeze on any further improvement of the facies model – hence the feedack arrow (Fig. 9B) implying that all future observations must in turn be distilled to better define the general model.

The third function of a model is to act as a predictor in new geological situations (Fig. 9C). This is hard to illustrate on the small scale of an individual Bouma bed, so let us imagine that we have a generalized facies model for automobiles – four wheels, hood, trunk, doors, etc. The new discovery of an *in situ* radiator by itself might be interesting, but without other information, one might be able to say little more than "nice radiator". With a general model, which ideally expresses the relationship of all the parts of the system, we should be able to predict the rest of the car from the discovery of a radiator. Or we might be able to predict other parts of a submarine fan from one thickening-upward prograding lobe sequence. This is obviously a vitally important aspect of facies modelling, and good surface or subsurface prediction from limited data can save unnecessary exploration guesswork and potentially vast sums of money.

The fourth major function of a facies model is to act as an integrated basis for interpretation (Fig. 9D). Again, it is important to eliminate "noise" before looking for a general interpretation, and hence, there should be feedback between the interpretation and the individual examples (Fig. 9D). This is indicated by the feedback arrow to example 5 (Fig. 9), implying the question "does the interpretation of example 5 differ from the idealized hydrodynamic interpretation?" If there is a difference (and there is), we can again ask questions that could not be asked if we had not used the facies model to formulate a general interpretation. This usage of the facies model is demonstrated particularly well by the Bouma sequence for turbidites, as discussed later in this volume.

The turbidite example of Figure 9 illustrates another point, namely that facies models can exist on different scales. The Bouma sequence for individual turbidite beds is a small scale example, but when turbidites are studied as groups of related beds, the system as a whole is referred to as a large scale submarine fan model.

The turbidite/submarine fan example has been discussed above because it is reasonably well understood, and because it illustrates the four functions of a facies model (Fig. 9). Some of the other models discussed in this volume are less well understood – because the environmental summary is weaker, so the functioning of the model is weaker. I emphasize that the construction and functioning of facies models is essentially similar for all environments, and that the turbidite example was discussed above to make the general statements about facies models a little more specific.

Just as there can never be any absolute classification of depositional environments, so there will be differing numbers and types of facies models. As very large scale systems are studied in more detail (e.g., submarine fans), models for sub-components of the system may emerge, such as depositional suprafan lobes, or channel-levee complexes on fans. However, it is probably safest at the moment to emphasize and develop the generality of existing models, rather than encouraging the proliferation of more and more very restricted models. The reason for this suggestion is that given one piece of new information, such as an *in situ* radiator, one might make fairly safe generalizations about automobiles in general. But with many different types of automobile models, one may have problems about assigning the new data to the correct model (is the radiator a Chevrolet or Ford?), and hence run the risk of incorrect predictions. But ultimately, as our understanding improves, subdivision of broad models will be both possible and desirable, as in the case of braided and sandy fluvial models; river-, wave- and tide-dominated deltaic models; and storm- and tide-dominated shallow marine models.

BASIC SOURCES OF INFORMATION

This list is not intended to be complete, but highlights some of the more recent and more important books on depositional environment, facies and facies models. The list is roughly in the order of increasing scope and complexity of coverage of the subject, with Selley as a good place to start, and Reading as the most complete and detailed source.

Selley, R.C., 1970. Ancient sedimentary environments. Ithaca, N.Y., Cornell University Press, 237 p.
Selley introduces the volume as "not a work for the specialist sedimentologist, but an introductory survey for readers with a basic knowledge of geology". The book achieves this end very well – it summarizes, it leans on classical examples, and it very briefly indicates the economic implications (oil, gas, minerals) of some of the environments. This volume is a good place to start.

Blatt, H., Middleton, G.V., and Murray, R.C., 1980. Origin of sedimentary rocks, Second Edition. Englewood Cliffs, N.J., Prentice Hall, 782 p.
Chapter 19, on facies models has been greatly expanded in the second edition, and now summarizes concisely the general principles of facies and facies analysis, and reviews all important depositional environments.

Allen, J.R.L., 1970. Physical processes of sedimentation. New York, American Elsevier, 248 p.
Chapter 11 (p. 439-543) is a review of sand bodies and environments written at a fuller and more technical level than Selley (1970), or Blatt, Middleton and Murray (1980). It considers Alluvial, Deltaic, Estuarine, Tidal Flat, Beach and Barrier, Marine Shelf, Turbidite and Aeolian environments, with separate remarks on sand body prediction. Useful follow-up reading after Selley and Blatt, Middleton and Murray in that order.

Galloway, W.E., and Hobday, D.K., 1983. Terrigenous clastic depositional systems. New York, Springer Verlag, 423 p.
This new volume also covers most important depositional environments, but in more detail than the books listed above. It deliberately is slanted toward economic applications and hence gives a different perspective from all the other books in this list.

Rigby, J.K., and Hamblin, W.K., eds., 1972. Recognition of ancient sedimentary environments. Society of Economic Paleontologists and Mineralogists, Special Publication 16, 340 p.
Contains separate papers on many important environments written at a technical level. Many of the papers are disappointing as reviews but there are excellent contributions on Alluvial Fans, Fluvial Paleochannels, Barrier Coastlines and Shorelines. Most of the authors present their environmental summaries but do not attempt to use them as models.

Reineck, H.E., and Singh, I.B., 1973. Depositional sedimentary environments. New York, Springer Verlag, 439 p.
Pages 160-439 are devoted to summaries of many modern environments. Coverage is at the graduate student – professional sedimentologist level, but is patchy and rather uncritical. Vast reference lists are given, but it is hard to single out the very important papers from the trivial. The emphasis on modern environments is useful, but the book should not be used until one is at least somewhat familiar with specific environments.

Scholle, P.A., and Spearing, D.R., eds., 1982. Sandstone depositional environments. American Association of Petroleum Geologists, Memoir 31, 410 p.
This abundantly illustrated volume contains 12 papers reviewing major depositional environments. Most are good, some excellent, one or two are poor. There is no professed overall philosophy to the volume, hence the variability of the contributions. It was suggested in one review that one should read the text of *Facies Models* and use the pictures in Memoir 31.

Reading, H.G., ed., 1978. Sedimentary environments and facies. Oxford, Blackwell, 557 p.
Excellent compilation of data on depositional environments and facies models. An indispensable reference, and the best available summary of major depositional environments.

REFERENCES CITED

I have grouped these under three headings, and then listed the references alphabetically.

FACIES

Gressly, A., 1838. Observations geologiques sur le Jura Soleurois. Neue Denkschr, allg. schweiz, Ges. ges. Naturw., v. 2, 1-112.
Gressly's work first established the concept of facies in the geological literature.

Middleton, G.V., 1973, Johannes Walther's Law of the correlation of facies. Geological Society of America Bulletin, v. 84, p. 979-988.
An excellent discussion of the use, misuse and implications of Walther's Law.

Middleton, G.V., 1978. Facies. *In* Fairbridge, R.W., and Bourgeois, J., eds., Encyclopedia of sedimentology. Stroudsburg, Pa., Dowden, Hutchinson and Ross, p. 323-325.
One of the best and most concise statements of the facies concept, discussing the various ways in which the term has been used.

Moore, R.C., 1949. Meaning of facies. *In* Longwell, C.R., ed., Sedimentary facies in geological history. Geological Society of America, Memoir 39, p. 1-34.
This paper is from the first important North American volume on facies. It emphasizes the lateral variations of facies within a designated stratigraphic unit. Historically, an important paper, but now conceptually out of date (or out of fashion).

Teichert, C., 1958. Concepts of facies. Bulletin of the American Association of Petroleum Geologists, v. 42, p. 2718-2744.
This is probably the best single review of the facies concept. It examines the history of the concept, and its influence in Europe, Britain and North America, and Russia. Teichert's twelve conclusions could be modified slightly in light of the last 20 years work, particularly in recent sediments.

Walther, J., 1893-4. Einleitung in die Geologie als historische Wissenschaft. Verlag von Gustav Fischer, Jena, 3 vols., 1055 p.
See Middleton, 1973, for a commentary on the importance of Walther's work.

FACIES SEQUENCES, FACIES MODELS, EXAMPLES

Cant, D.J., 1978. Development of a facies model for sandy braided river sedimentation: comparison of the South Saskatchewan River and the Battery Point Formation. *In* Miall, A.D., ed., Fluvial sedimentology. Canadian Society of Petroleum Geologists, Memoir 5, p. 627-639.
A detailed comparison of ancient sediments and recent sediments, emphasizing facies comparisons and the construction of a facies model.

Cant, D.J., and Walker, R.G., 1976. Development of a braided fluvial facies model for the Devonian Battery Point Sandstone,

Quebec. Canadian Journal of Earth Sciences, v. 13, p. 102-119.
Selley's difference matrix is used to help define fluvial cycles in a sandy braided system. This method is no longer statistically sound – see Carr (1982) and Powers and Easterling (1982).

Carr, T.R., 1982. Log-linear models, Markov chains and cyclic sedimentation. Journal of Sedimentary Petrology, v. 52, p. 905-912.
Explains problems of deriving a random matrix, and suggests improved methods for facies sequence analysis using Markov chain analysis.

de Raaf, J.F.M., Reading, H.G., and Walker, R.G., 1965. Cyclic sedimentation in the Lower Westphalian of North Devon, England. Sedimentology, v. 4, p. 1-52.
This paper gives the first published example of a facies relationship diagram and uses the diagram to establish cyclicity in a series of prograding shoreline sediments. Cycles are defined by black mudstones resting on bioturbated sandstones.

Harper, C.W., 1984. Facies models revisited: an improvement to the method advocated by Walker in the General Introduction to Geoscience Canada Reprint Series No. 1. Geoscience Canada, in press.
Gives details of the method used in the next paper in this volume.

Miall, A.D., 1973. Markov chain analysis applied to an ancient alluvial plain succession. Sedimentology, v. 20, p. 347-365.
An introduction to Markov chain methodology with an example from the Devonian Peel Sound Formation of Prince of Wales Island, Arctic Canada. See modifications by Carr (1982) and Powers and Easterling (1982).

Miall, A.D., 1977. A review of the braided river depositional environment. Earth Science Reviews, v. 13, p. 1-62.
Miall suggests a series of "universal" facies that could be used to describe gravelly and sandy braided systems, and shows facies relationship diagrams for several modern and ancient examples. Four "types of depositional profiles" are suggested – these make very useful reference points for future generalizations about fluvial models.

Mutti, E., and Ricci Lucchi, F., 1972. Le torbiditi dell'Appennino settentrionale: introduzione all'analisi di facies. Memorie della Societa Geologica Italiana, v. 11, p. 161-199. Translated into English by T.H. Nilsen (1978), Turbidites of the northern Appennines: Introduction to facies analysis. International Geology Review, v. 20, p. 125-166.
This paper is one of the most influential in turbidite studies in the last 15 years. It proposes a set of seven facies which have

been used successfully in Italy and other parts of the world. Although some of these facies need revising, most turbidite workers accept the idea of a "universal" set of facies that can be used to describe most turbidites, of any age, anywhere.

Powers, D.W., and Easterling, R.G., 1982. Improved methodology for using embedded Markov chains to describe cyclical sediments. Journal of Sedimentary Petrology, v. 56, p. 913-923.
A companion paper to Carr (1982). Emphasizes problems of zero entries in the transition matrix, and explains improved methods for sequence analysis and testing the significance of the results.

Selley, R.C., 1970. Studies of sequence in sediments using a simple mathematical device. Geological Society of London, Quarterly Journal, v. 125, p. 557-581.
The first discussion of the difference matrix, and its possible use in describing and interpreting facies sequences. Contains written discussions of the paper by various authors, some of which are thought-provoking. See improvements by Carr (1982) and Powers and Easterling (1982).

Walker, R.G., 1979. Facies and facies models. 1) General introduction. In Walker, R.G., ed., Facies Models. Geoscience Canada Reprint Series, 1 (first edition), p. 1-7.
The "old" method for calculating random probability matrices is given here. The correct versions are given by Carr (1982) and Powers and Easterling (1982).

Walker, R.G., 1983. Cardium Formation 3. Sedimentology and stratigraphy in the Garrington-Caroline area. Bulletin of Canadian Petroleum Geology, v. 31, p. 213-230.
This paper illustrates how mudstones, siltstones and sandstones can be subdivided into various facies using such criteria as amount and type of bioturbation, presence or absence of silty laminations, grain size, sedimentary structures, nature of bedding contacts and textures of conglomerates.

Walker, R.G., and Harms, J.C., 1971. The "Catskill Delta": a prograding muddy shoreline in central Pennsylvania. Journal of Geology, v. 79, p. 381-399.
Describes cyclic facies sequences that are defined by transgressive bioturbated sandstone horizons.

Williams, P.F., and Rust, B.R., 1969. The sedimentology of a braided river. Journal of Sedimentary Petrology, v. 39, p. 646-679.
A good example of facies definition in a modern gravelly river (the Donjek, Yukon Territory), with definition of facies sequences and expression of a local "model" in terms of block diagrams.

STATISTICAL DEFINITION OF FACIES

Harbaugh, J.W., and Demirmen, F., 1964. Application of factor analysis to petrologic variations of Americus Limestone (Lower Permian), Kansas and Oklahoma. Kansas Geological Survey Special Distribution Publication 15, 40 p.
A good example of factor analysis used to establish facies (termed "phases") in the Permian Americus Limestone (Kansas and Oklahoma). Maps show distribution of the phases, with interpretations of depositional environments.

Harbaugh, J.W., and Merriam, D.F., 1968. Computer applications in stratigraphic analysis. New York, Wiley, 282 p.
Chapter 7 is concerned with classification systems, and gives a good introduction to factor analysis and other techniques. Several useful examples are discussed.

Imbrie, J., and Purdy, E.G., 1962. Classification of modern Bahamian carbonate sediments. In Ham, W.E., ed., Classification of carbonate rocks. American Association of Petroleum Geologists, Memoir 1, p. 253-279.
A good introduction to factor analysis, with an excellent example of how it can be used to define carbonate facies (with data from the Bahama Banks).

Klovan, J.E., 1964. Facies analysis of the Redwater Reef Complex, Alberta, Canada. Bulletin of Canadian Petroleum Geology, v. 12, p. 1-100.
Defines different types of carbonate particles and uses a hierarchal representation technique to classify them.

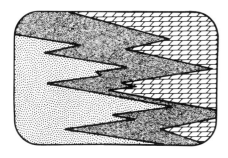

Improved Methods of Facies Sequence Analysis

CHARLES W. HARPER, Jr.
School of Geology and Geophysics
The University of Oklahoma
Norman, OK. 73019

INTRODUCTION
In the Introduction to the first edition of *Facies Models,* Walker (1979) advocated a method for constructing facies models based on transition frequencies. It is objective and powerful, yet easy to apply. The method can be improved, however, by subjecting proposed models to the following minimal constraint: for each facies transition, if we cannot (even tentatively) rule out the null hypothesis that the transition occurs at random in stratigraphic sequences, we have no basis for postulating that the transition occurs frequently (or rarely) in the depositional environment under study.

The method explained by Walker follows the work of Read (1969), Gingerich (1969), Selley (1970) and Miall (1973); like Miall, he does not recognize "multi-story lithologies" such as a sandstone overlain by a sandstone. This raises severe problems, as discussed by Carr (1982), and Powers and Easterling (1982). In essence, the method consists of: 1) tabulating observed numbers of transitions, and 2) converting these to relative frequencies relative to row totals. Then 3), a matrix is calculated assuming the null hypothesis that such transitions are random, and depend only on the relative abundance of facies in the successions sampled. Finally, 4), the random probabilities are subtracted from the observed probabilities to produce a matrix emphasizing differences from

random which are large. Selley (1970, p. 558) characterized his own method as simple and easy to use with results that may be shown in a clear, objective graphic manner. The same may be said of the method advocated by Walker, which closely follows Selley's (and Gingerich, 1969) yet excludes the nebulous case of multistorey transitions. Walker's method, particularly with improvements suggested below, is especially useful in studies of ancient biofacies patterns; unlike patterns involving lithofacies, these often cannot be established by comparison to the present-day.

IMPROVEMENTS
In subtracting the random from observed probabilities, one does not know whether a given different is significant. Consider the transition between facies SS and facies A (Walker, 1979). The difference is .48. Is .48 significant? Is the difference for facies C to B = .35 significant? Is the difference for facies C to SS = -.24 significant? Rather than answering these questions on the basis of subjective conjecture, I suggest we proceed further as follows:

1) Choose a level of significance α (.10) say).
2) For each possible transition i to j where the difference is positive, e.g., facies C overlain by facies B, compute the probability of at least the observed number of successes (observations of B over C) in N trials (observations of any facies *other* than C over C) given the *null hypothesis* that (a) the transition occurs at random and (b) the N trials are independent. By (a) I mean that the probability of observing the transition in any one trial depends only on the relative frequency of occurrences of the overlying facies amongst all occurrences of facies *other than* the underlying facies (e.g., occurrences of B amongst occurrences of all facies excepting C).
3) Tentatively reject the null hypothesis if the probability computed in step (2) is greater than or equal to the level of significance chosen. Otherwise do not reject the null hypothesis.

For each possible transition where the difference is negative, proceed as above, except compute the probability of at least the observed number or fewer

successes (i.e., use a left-sided rather than a right-sided rejection region, as the observed transition frequency appears anomalously low rather than high).

The probability of at least n_{obs} transitions in N trials is simply the binomial probability of at least n_{obs} successes in N trials, and is given by:

$$\sum_{n=n_{obs}}^{n=N} C(N,n)\, p^n\, q^{N-n}$$

where C (N,n) = the number of possible combinations of N objects taken n at a time, and is given by

$$C(N, n) = \frac{N!}{(N-n)!\, n!}$$

p = the probability of success on a single trial, given in Walker's (1979) Figure 2C, and

$$q = 1 - p$$

In the case of the transition C to B: p = the probability of success in a single trial = .22, Q = probability of failure in a single trial = 1 - .22 = .78. From the fourth row in Walker's Figure 2A (1979), we note that four successes (transitions to B) were observed in seven trials, so n_{obs} = 4 and N = 7. From Table 1 we compute that the probability ($n_{obs} > 4$)= .045 which is definitely significant at the .10 level. Similarly, for the transition SS to A: n_{obs} = 12, N = 15, p = .32, and q = .68, so the probability ($n_{obs} \geq 12$) = .0002 under the null hypothesis. For the transition B to A, n_{obs} = 1, N = 13, probability ($n_{obs} > 1$)= .051 assuming the null hypothesis. Incidentally, note here the probability of one or *fewer* successes was computed since the observed values appeared anomalously low.

Table 1
Binomial probability for at least four successes (occurrences of B over C) in seven trials (occurrences of facies other than C over C). See text for details.

n	C (7,n)	p^n	q^{7-n}	Prob (n)
4	35	.0023	.475	.038
5	21	.0005	.608	.006
6	7	.0001	.780	.0005
7	1	.00002	1.00	.00002
			TOTAL	.045

Examination of the transition E to C provides an opportunity to see how the method accommodates the occurrences of limited data. Observed minus random transition probabilities using Walker's method is .38. Sounds significant, doesn't it? Yet, only three transitions of E to other facies were observed at the sites studied. Using the method just outlined, p = .12 and probability (one or more successes in 2 trials) = 2 (.12) (.88) + (.12)^2 = .23. Hence, the observation of one or two successes in two trials should occur about 23% of the time. In other words the difference between observed and expected transition probabilities of .38 is not significant at all.

Of the 56 facies transition counts for Walker's eight Battery Point Sandstone facies, five are significantly larger than predicted for a random sequence at the 10% level of significance. Only two are significantly lower than predicted even at the 20% level. Compare Tables 2 and 3 herein with Walker's (1979) Fig. 2D. These facies relationships have been shown diagrammatically by Walker (pers. commun., and Fig. 1).

Lloyd (in Selley, 1970, discussion p. 577) questioned Selley's procedure (like

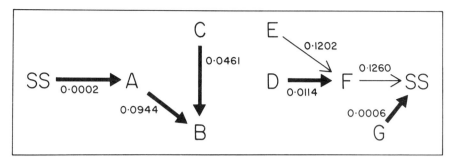

Figure 1

Facies relationship diagram for Battery Point data, derived from Table 2. Heavy lines show relationships significant at 0.1 level, light lines *at 0.13. Compare with Figure 6 of Walker ("General Introduction", this volume). From Walker (pers. commun.).*

Table 2

Battery Point Sandstone data (see Walker, 1979, Facies Models, first edition). P = transition probability for random sequence. N = No. of transitions from lower facies. M = no. of transitions from lower to upper facies. PROBABILITY = Binomial probability of M or more successes in N trials under null hypothesis of random sequence. Data for transitions with PROBABILITY greater than .20 not listed.

Facies Transition	P	N	M	PROBABILITY
SS → A	.32	15	12	.0002
A → B	.26	13	6	.094
C → B	.22	7	4	.045
D → F	.063	3	2	.011
E → F	.062	2	1	.120
F → SS	.222	13	1	.126
G → SS	.226	5	5	.0006

Table 3

Legend as in Table 2, except PROBABILITY = probability of M or fewer successes in N trials.

Facies Transition	P	N	M	PROBABILITY
B → A	.315	13	1	.051
C → SS	.237	7	0	.151

Walker's) of subtracting expected from observed frequencies and using the differences as the basis for a facies model. Lloyd notes that even if a random model has given an accurate value for the *expectation* in each cell, each of Selley's *observed* values "represent a point estimate accurate only within limits determined by an acceptable probability of error." From this he argues that each of the values in his difference matrix "must be subjected to a significance test before they can be ordered into a facies diagram". I, of course, heartily agree. Selley's only viable answer was to use a chi-square test of the whole matrix (leaving open the question of which if any of the seemingly high differences are entirely consistent with a random model).

Note that the procedure just recommended allows the explicit testing of the possibility that alleged "patterns" of facies transitions are, in fact, just chance associations. Following the procedure would *place constraints* on the facies patterns which we would allow sedimentologists/paleoecologists to postulate on a given data set. For any facies transition, the *bottom line* would be this: If we cannot rule out the null hypothesis that a given facies transition occurs at random in stratigraphic sequences, then we have no basis for postulating that the transition occurs frequently (or rarely) in the depositional environment under study.

MULTISTORY TRANSITIONS

Powers and Easterling (1982, p. 915), and others, consider transitions from a facies i to itself as merely "not observable". Indeed, at one place (p. 915) they present arguments which hinge on such an interpretation. I prefer to regard the

notion of self-transition as meaningless, or at least ill-defined. This philosophical difference does not alter procedures recommended here in any way.

TWO MINOR POINTS

In most cases, it would be prudent to test the matrix (Walker's, 1979, Fig. 2B) *as a whole* for non-randomness before proceeding as outlined above (Miall, 1973, p. 352; SAS Inst., 1982, p. 170). For a N by N facies transition matrix, the appropriate degrees of freedom for a chi-square test is (N-1)^2 - N (Powers and Easterling, 1982, p. 916). Thus, for the Battery Point Sandstone data, there are 41 degrees of freedom. Chi-Square [= Sum of (observed value i - expected value i)^2/(expected value i)] equals 51, which is significant at the 15% level.

Statistical references often state that a chi-square test is valid only if none of the cell expectations is less than five. Recent studies (Miller, 1983, p. 323; Feinberg, 1980, p. 172) show that this requirement may be relaxed so that several expected cell frequencies may in fact be less than one.

Also, if one performs a number of separate tests of significance, each at a level of .05, say, then the probability of at least one type-1 error (rejection of a null hypothesis when it is true) is, of course, considerably greater than .05. This probability can be minimized by setting the level of significance in each test low (see excellent discussion of multiple significance tests in the SAS manual (1982, p. 169-171) plus Miller, 1981). Alternatively, we might set our level of significance at, say, .05 and simply accept that up to 5% of the time, on the average (an upper bound), we will tentatively reject a transition as random when in fact it is. So if we *can* tentatively reject the null hypothesis on the basis of available data we still ought to exercise caution. However, the method outlined in the previous section has to do with how we should proceed if we *cannot* reject it.

ALTERNATIVE METHODS

In estimating expected transistion frequencies for a random sequence Walker uses counts of instances of facies rather than counts of facies *transitions*. In my opinion, it would be better to use the latter. Also, Turk (1979), Powers and Easterling (1982) and Carr (1982) argue cogently in favour of using a technique called iterative proportional fitting to estimate expected transition frequencies. Unlike Walker's method, iterative proportional fitting preserves observed column as well as row totals; tests of significance could be performed by analyzing residuals (Powers and Easterling, 1982, p. 922) perhaps using a multistep application of a chi-square test for successive extraction of residuals (Carr, 1982, p. 908). Elsewhere I discuss these points, as well as present a new way to analyze facies transition data using median tetrads and half-normal plots (Harper, in press).

ACKNOWLEDGEMENTS
I thank R.N. Hiscott, Memorial Univ. of Newfoundland for calling several key references to my attention. I wrote this paper while a visiting professor at the Univ. of Michigan.

REFERENCES
Carr, T.R., 1982. Log-linear models, Markov chains and cyclic sedimentation. Journal of Sedimentary Petrology, v. 52, p. 905-912.

Feinberg, S.E., 1980. The analysis of cross-classified data. Cambridge, Mass., Massachusetts Institute of Technology Press, p. 1-198.

Gingerich, P.D., 1969. Markov analysis of cyclic alluvial sediments. Journal of Sedimentary Petrology, v. 39, p. 330-332.

Harper, C.W., Jr., in press. Facies models revisited: possible revisions of the method advocated by Walker in the general introduction to Geoscience Canada Reprint Series No. 1. Geoscience Canada.

Miall, A.D., 1973. Markov chain analysis applied to an ancient alluvial plain succession. Sedimentology, v. 20, p. 347-364.

Miller, R.G., 1981. Simultaneous statistical inference, second edition. New York, Springer-Verlag.

Miller, S.M., 1983. A statistical method to evaluate homogeneity of structural populations. Mathematical Geology, v. 15, p. 317-328.

Powers, D.W. and Easterling, R.G., 1982. Improved methodology for using embedded markov chains to describe cyclical sediments. Journal of Sedimentary Petrology, v. 52, p. 913-923.

Read, W.A., 1969. Analysis and simulation of Namurian sediments in Central Scotland using a Markov process model. Mathematical Geology, v. 1, p. 199-219.

SAS Institute Inc., 1982. SAS users guide: Basics. Cary, North Carolina, SAS Institute Inc., p. 1-923.

Selley, R.C., 1970. Studies of sequence in sediments using a simple mathematical device. Geological Society of London, Quarterly Journal, v. 125, p. 557-581.

Turk, G., 1979. Transistion analysis of structural sequences. Discussion and reply. Geological Society of America Bulletin, v. 90, p. 989-991.

Glacial Facies

NICHOLAS EYLES AND
ANDREW D. MIALL
Department of Geology
University of Toronto
Toronto, Ontario M5S 1B3

INTRODUCTION
Basin wide investigations of glacial facies based on integrated outcrop and subsurface data from modern and ancient sequences are as yet few in number, but the field is currently experiencing vigorous growth. This late development is probably because there are few significant Phanerozoic glacial sequences in North America or Western Europe apart from the late Cenozoic glacial record. Glacial sequences are also widely suspected to be nonproductive and consequently glacial sedimentology has not caught the attention of petroleum geologists. This neglect contrasts with most other sedimentary environments, where assessment of petroleum potential and the search for modern analogs prompted much sedimentological research starting in the nineteen-fifties.

However, economic and potentially very important accumulations of glacial sediments occur in parts of Southern Asia and the Southern Hemisphere. These are of Permo-Carboniferous age, and represent a glacial episode within the former limits of the Gondwana supercontinent that lasted for about 90 million years. Representative deposits of this glaciation occur in successions up to several kilometres thick in South America, South Africa, India, Australia and parts of the Arabian Peninsula (Crowell, 1978; Hambrey and Harland, 1981; Visser, 1983). Petroleum is already produced from glaciated basins such as the Cooper Basin, and related basins of South Australia (Harris, 1981) and the Marsul Field, Oman (de la Grandville,

1982). Another thick glacial basin succession of potential hydrocarbon importance is the predominantly glaciomarine Late Cenozoic Yakataga Formation (20 to 2 Ma) of the Gulf of Alaska Tertiary Province (Plafker and Addicott, 1976; Armentrout, 1983). Exploration of these and other basins is creating a considerable stimulus for glacial basin studies and facies models.

Application of facies model concepts to glacial deposits is complicated by the fact that the only well-studied modern glacial environments are in continental settings, whereas because of selective preservation most ancient glacial sequences are glaciomarine in origin. Extensive Quaternary glaciomarine deposits exist, but with few exceptions these have not been studied using modern facies analysis methods. Considerable controversy is now arising over the interpretation of many Quaternary successions, much of which centres on the meaning and usefulness of the word "till". Space does not permit an examination of this problem here, and the reader is referred to discussions appearing elsewhere (Dreimanis, 1984; Eyles *et al.*, 1983, 1984a). We do not use the term "till" in this paper. "Diamict", and its lithified equivalent "diamictite", are employed instead as non-genetic terms for poorly sorted gravel-sand-mud deposits.

Glacial facies models must be constructed from many sources, because so-called "glacial" sequences include the deposits of many distinct environments (rivers, lakes, continental shelves and margins, oceanic abyssal plains). In fact a case could be made for eliminating "glacial facies" as a distinct category and treating them as special sub-types of those other environments, characterized by the particular influence of grounded or floating ice and by the effects of rapid sea-level change.

In this paper we treat glacial facies under two main headings, continental and marine. The final part of the paper examines a number of glaciated continental margin depositional systems.

CONTINENTAL GLACIAL FACIES
A fourfold division recognises grounded ice, glaciofluvial, glaciolacustrine and cold climate 'periglacial' facies.

Grounded Ice Facies
Under conditions of low temperature

and sufficient precipitation, ice sheets grow to continent-size proportions. A complex zonation of subglacial erosion and sedimentation develops in response to different thermal conditions across the ice base (Andrews, 1982). Facies and associated bedforms exposed by retreat depend on whether the ice sheet margin is thin, inactive and frozen to the substrate, or actively sliding over the bed lubricated by basal meltwaters. In the first case (Fig. 1) thick englacial sequences of debris and ice are built up at the ice base either by refreezing of basal meltwaters or by intense folding of basal debris layers at the ice margin (Moran *et al.*, 1980; Paul, 1983). An inactive or retreating margin of this type becomes buried under a drape of diamict formed by the melt-out of englacial debris (Figures 1 and 2). This mobile drape is resedimented down-slope by sediment gravity flow into local basins generated by the irregular melt of buried ice (Boulton, 1972; Lawson, 1982; Paul 1983: Fig. 3). Basin fills are exposed as hummocks when adjacent ice-cores, under a thinner sediment cover, melt-down more rapidly ('relief-inversion'). Typical vertical profiles through hummocks show uppermost sequences of resedimented massive, graded and stratified diamicts, variably reworked and interbedded with glaciofluvial and lacustrine facies, overlying crudely stratified diamicts which were aggregated *in situ* as the dirty ice base melted (basal melt-out; Fig. 1). These melt-out units may contain or drape over bedrock rafts that were present in the former ice base. Glacitectonised bedrock and incorporated substrate sediments may be an important component of the sedimentary sequence (Fig. 1; Moran *et al.*,1980). Englacial structures (e.g., folded basal debris sequences) survive basal melt-out as ridge-like bedforms oriented transverse to former ice flow direction (e.g., Shaw, 1979). Broad belts of hummocky topography with complex internal stratigraphies, form extensive regional facies tracts in Quaternary glaciated terrains.

In contrast, Figures 4 and 5 show a wet-based ice margin where the glacier continues to slide over the bed even during retreat. Debris is transported within a crudely stratified basal layer less than 1 m thick, with intense abrasion between particles in the base of the

16

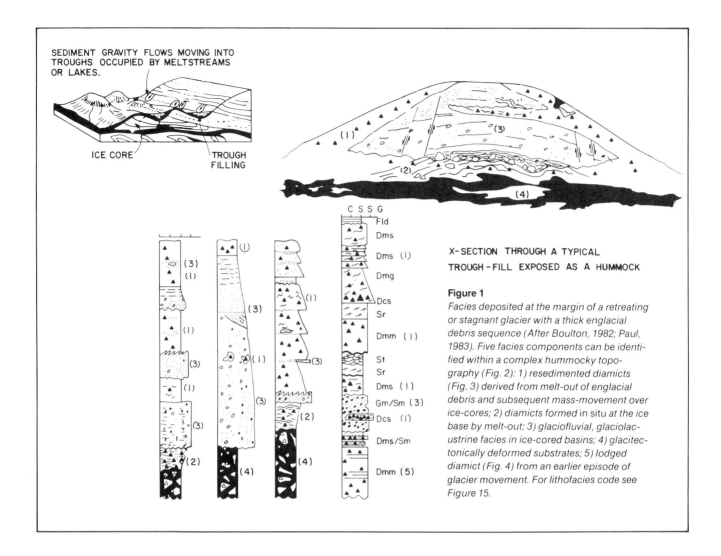

SEDIMENT GRAVITY FLOWS MOVING INTO TROUGHS OCCUPIED BY MELTSTREAMS OR LAKES.

ICE CORE TROUGH FILLING

X-SECTION THROUGH A TYPICAL TROUGH-FILL EXPOSED AS A HUMMOCK

Figure 1

Facies deposited at the margin of a retreating or stagnant glacier with a thick englacial debris sequence (After Boulton, 1982; Paul, 1983). Five facies components can be identified within a complex hummocky topography (Fig. 2): 1) resedimented diamicts (Fig. 3) derived from melt-out of englacial debris and subsequent mass-movement over ice-cores; 2) diamicts formed in situ at the ice base by melt-out; 3) glaciofluvial, glaciolacustrine facies in ice-cored basins; 4) glacitectonically deformed substrates; 5) lodged diamict (Fig. 4) from an earlier episode of glacier movement. For lithofacies code see Figure 15.

Figure 2

Avaatsmarkbreen, Spitsbergen, showing a kilometre-wide arcuate belt of hummocky topography underlain by sequences such as shown in Figure 1. Photograph courtesy of T.E. Day.

layer (the traction zone) and the substrate. Clasts that collide with the bed may beome lodged against the substrate. A characteristic and diagnostic glacially-faceted clast shape evolves as a result of dirty ice moving over the lodged clast (Boulton, 1978; Figs. 6 and 19). Continued lodgement gives rise to lenticluar beds of dense overconsolidated diamict (Fig. 4) which are massive but show many diagnostic structures indicating deposition under high basal shear stresses (Figures 4 and 7). Clasts show a strongly preferred direction of long axes aligned parallel to ice flow vectors. Measurement of a few 'shaped' clasts gives a rapid guide to former flow direction. Identification of lodged diamicts and former ice flow directions is of considerable importance in drift exploration programs in glaciated terrains where mineralised 'float' in glacial

Figure 3
Lobate flow of resedimented diamict at Matanuska Glacier, Alaska. Resedimented diamicts become interbedded with glacio-lacustrine and glaciofluvial facies (e.g., Fig. 1).

Figure 4
Basal deposition at a thawed sliding ice margin (e.g., Breidamerkurjökull, Fig. 5), with typical vertical profile and diagnostic criteria for diamicts deposited by lodgement. Lithofacies code as in Figure 15. ▼

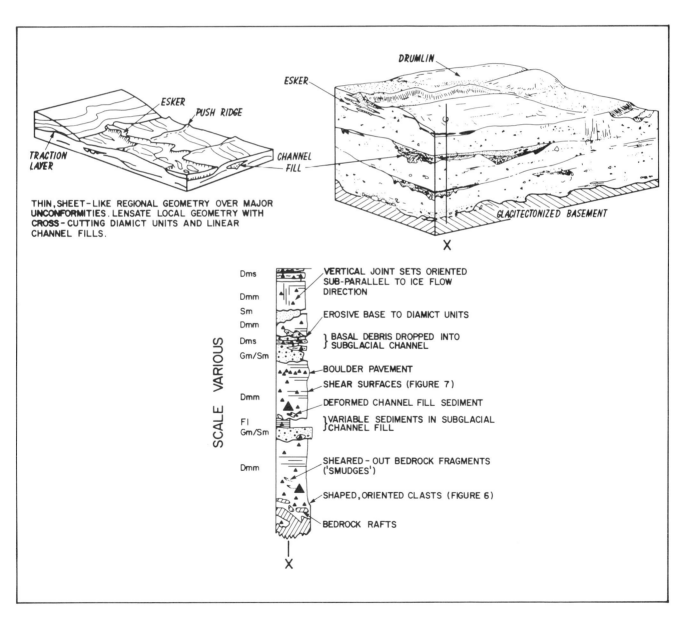

Figure 5
Glacier bed of lodged diamict exposed by the retreat of a sliding thawed glacier (Brei-
damerkurjökull, southeast Iceland). Small moraine ridges parallel to the ice margin are formed each winter by minor readvances of
the margin. Low relief drumlins impart a streamlined surface. Section exposed in middle of picture is 8 m high.

Figure 6
Large glacially streamlined clast exhumed from diamictite deposited by lodgement below a Late Proterozoic sliding ice sheet; Mauretania, West Africa. Direction of ice flow from right to left. The presence of shaped clasts with a consistent long axis orientation
is, in conjunction with other criteria (Fig. 4), an aid to identification of diamict(ite)s deposited by lodgement. In addition, it also enables a glacial source to be recognised where diamict(ite)s have been reworked or resedimented (Fig. 19).

sediment is traced to buried mineralised bedrock zones by reference to dispersal fans.

The geometry of lodged diamicts across a sedimentary basin is sheet-like lying above marked local and regional unconformities. Within this apparently simple geometry, are strongly lenticular diamict units in a cross-cutting and overlapping relationship as a result of intermittent erosion and changes in ice flow direction (Fig. 1). Lodged diamicts, containing clasts and matrix from contrasting bedrock lithologies, may be superimposed during a single glaciation emphasising the need for care in interpreting ice advance/retreat cycles from multiple stratigraphies. An integral component of the subglacial stratigraphy may be channel fills resulting from subglacial stream drainage (Davis and Mallett, 1981; Eyles *et al.*, 1982). These fills show a very wide range of lithofacies and may contain irregular diamict masses flushed from the former ice base. Channels have a planar upper surface truncated by overlying diamict, are oriented subparallel to ice flow direction and are genetically related to esker ridges (Fig. 4).

Eskers record either the infilling of

Figure 7
Shear surfaces in lodged diamict, resulting from glacial shear stress at sliding ice base: a) diamictite of the Late Proterozoic Jbeliat Formation of Mauretania, West Africa; and b) diamict of Late Pleistocene age from Northumberland, Britain.

lins and more narrow flutes formed either by selective subglacial lodgement around obstacles or erosional streamlining of bed material (Boulton, 1979).

The most spectacular example of an exposed bed of a paleo-ice sheet, outside Quaternary glaciated terrains, occurs across the 1500 km broad Taoudeni Basin of Mauretania (Deynoux and Trompette, 1981) which represents the sedimentary cover of the West African Shield. Metamorphic effects are absent and extensive Late Proterozoic glaciated surfaces with streamlined highs have been exhumed. Continental glacial facies are less than 50 m thick and contain lodgement diamictites averaging 3 to 5 m thick covering glacitectonized surfaces (Figs. 5, 6 and 7). Whereas thicker sequences may be accumulated by repeated continental glaciation, the reduced regional thickness of individual lodged diamict(ite) units (generally < 15 m) is an important criterion for distinguishing continental facies from the thicker diamict(ite) sequences deposited in glaciolacustrine and glaciomarine environments.

Glaciofluvial Facies
Continental ice sheets release large quantities of meltwater that drain broad outwash plains, reworking glacial debris into a distinctive suite of glaciofluvial lithofacies.

Aggradation at the head of outwash fans is frequently rapid enough to bury portions of the adjacent ice margin; such ice-contact depositon generates widespread deformation structures in coarse-grained crudely-bedded or massive proximal outwash gravels. 'Pitted' or 'kettled' outwash surfaces may extend over many square kilometres, and are flanked by eskers or complex ice-contact diamict sequences (e.g., Fig. 1).

Beyond the immediate ice terminus lies the outwash plain or sandur (plural: sandar, Icelandic). Modern sandar are well developed in Alaska, Arctic Canada and Iceland (Rust, 1972; Church, 1982; Boothroyd and Ashley, 1975; Boothroyd and Nummedal, 1978). Glacial outwash rivers are typically of multiple-channel (braided) type, and are normally of low sinuosity. Their morphology and sedimentology are similar to those of other braided streams, (see "Coarse Alluvial Deposits", this volume) such as those

meltwater tunnels within and under the ice mass, confined braided stream sedimentation in open ice walled channels or deposition as overlapping subaqueous fans in standing water as the ice margin retreats (Banerjee and McDonald, 1975). Tunnel-fill eskers are commonly exposed as steep sided ridges showing tabular and longitudinally extensive cross-bedded sandy lithofacies with restricted variance in paleocurrent directions. A beaded form

is typical of eskers deposited in water. These show rapid downstream transitions into fine-grained lacustrine facies with considerable variation in paleocurrent directions. Eskers show characteristic deformation structures (faults, subsidence basins) resulting from the melt of underlying and buttressing ice cores and may drape over lodged diamicts having channeled upper surfaces.

Other bedforms exposed by the retreat of wet based glaciers are drum-

occurring in arid environments (arctic to tropical), and their analysis forms part of general reviews of coarse-grained fluvial sedimentation that appear elsewhere (Miall, 1977, 1978; Bluck, 1979; "Coarse Alluvial Deposits", this volume). The braided morphology reflects an abundance of coarse bedload, variable discharge and non-cohesive channel banks. The rivers are unable to transport more than a fraction of the available bedload except during extreme floods (Ostrem, 1975), and at other times gravel and sand are deposited as a variety of bedforms and bars.

Modern sandar are up to about 100 km in length, and show gradients varying from 2 to 50 m/km. Typically there is a downstream decrease in grain size from coarse gravel to sand. Sandar commonly terminate as coastal fan deltas (e.g., Galloway, 1977) which may be flanked by barrier ridges created by seasonal pack ice-push. Deflation may strip abandoned fan surfaces and deposit blankets of wind blown coarse silt

(loess) downwind. Under more humid conditions, swamps of subarctic vegetation may become established in the proximity of water bodies. These may generate thick peat accumulations and ultimately cold-climate coals such as those of the Permo-Carboniferous coal bearing glaciated basins of the southern continents (e.g., Le Blanc Smith and Eriksson, 1979).

Glaciolacustrine Facies
Overdeepening by glacial erosion, glacial derangement of drainage and the release of large volumes of meltwater results in frequent lacustrine ponding. Lake basins vary from narrow 'alpine' basins in areas of high relief and isostatically-depressed continental interiors evacuated by ice sheets. Lake Agassiz is the most famous example of the latter, extending over a total area of some 1,000,000 km^2 in interior North America (Teller and Clayton, 1983). Many complex classifications of lake basins exist, but for the sedimentologist

working from outcrop and subsurface lithofacies data a simple distinction between 'periglacial' and 'proglacial' lake bodies may be the most useful. Periglacial lakes are not in direct contact with an ice margin and are fed by braided stream systems. In contrast proglacial lakes form in direct contact with the ice margin and receive a substantial volume of sediment direct from meltwater conduits and subaqueous fans with an additional component supplied by ice rafting (Fig. 8).

Periglacial Lakes
Sedimentation is dominated by the rapid growth of arcuate delta lobes. Incoming sediment laden and higher density meltwaters, therefore, move down these lobes as density underflows. A distinct sequence of sandy lithofacies is deposited with each melt season (Fig. 9) and records the start, later increase and ultimate decline of density underflow activity (Ashley, 1975). The sequence is bounded top

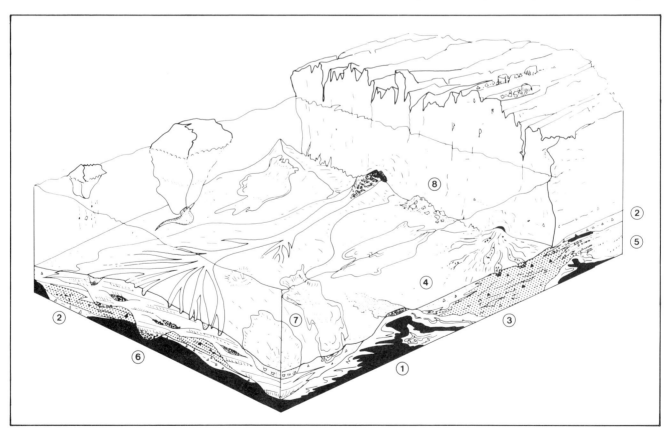

Figure 8
Proximal subaqueous sedimentation; 1) glacitectonized marine sediments; 2) lensate lodged diamict units; 3) coarse-grained stratified diamicts (Figs. 12 and 15); 4) pelagic muds and diamicts (Fig. 12); 5) coarse-grained proximal outwash; 6) interchannel cross-stratified sands with channel gravels; 7) resedimented facies (debris flow, slides and turbidites); and 8) supraglacial debris. Deformation results from ice advances (Fig. 15), melt of buried ice and iceberg turbation. Suspended sediment plumes not shown. The same model may apply with modifications to sedimentation adjacent to grounding lines of large ice shelves.

and bottom by a 'winter' clay layer. Distal equivalents of these sandy lithofacies can be identified as isolated 'starved' ripples and rare ripple-drift cross-lamination within clay/silt couplets (varves). A varve is an annually-produced couplet of silt and clay laminae and shows a sharp division between the clay and silt components (Fig. 10), each deposited in a different season and by different sedimentary processes. The light coloured silt unit (summer layer) may be graded and can show multiple laminations representing deposition by a single pulsating or intermittent density underflow with a minor contribution of pelagic material from interflows or overflow 'plumes' of suspended sediment (Banerjee, 1973). The dark clay unit (winter layer) may show normal grading recording principally the deposition of suspended sediment under a closed lake ice cover. Bioturbation and trace fossils are commonly present. Clay layer thicknesses are generally uniform across the basin but may contain massive or cross-stratified sands and laminated silts recording the winter drawdown of lake levels, delta foreslope slumping and the generation of grainflows and turbidity currents (Shaw, 1977; Fig. 9).

The term 'varve' (or 'varvite') is used unfortunately as a routine descriptive term for sediments that more correctly should be termed rhythmically-laminated, or simply laminated, sediments (rhythmites, laminites). The real significance of many 'varved' sequences as indicators of seasonally controlled sedimentation remains to be assessed rigorously in view of observations showing that many such units are not annual couplets but single or multiple graded units (silt → clay; units C,D and E of a Bouma sequence; see "Turbidites and Associated Coarse Clastic Deposits", this volume) deposited by discrete-event turbidity currents with no seasonal control (e.g., Lambert and Hsü, 1979; Fig. 10). In Pre-Quaternary sequences 'varves' are used to infer glaciolacustrine, and therefore continental environments and seasonality of climate, but new data increasingly show that many of these are discrete-event turbidites of glaciomarine origin (Fig. 10).

Diamict lithofacies are a very minor component of reported periglacial lake sequences. Graded and stratified dia-

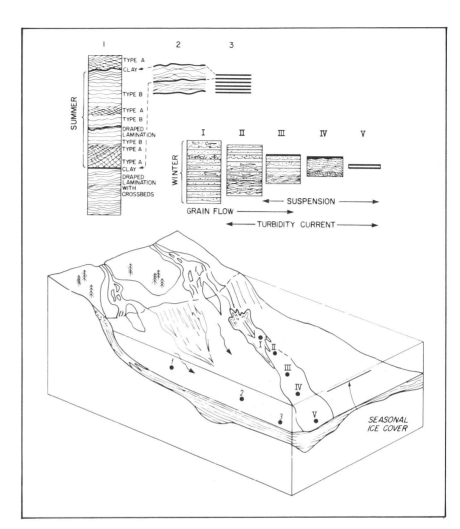

Figure 9
Annual cycles of sedimentation in a periglacial lake. 1 to 3 show lateral facies variation in varved sediments (After Ashley, 1975). I to V show sand lithofacies within winter clay layers that result from delta foreslope slumping (after Shaw, 1977).

mict lithofacies may, however, occur as thin channelised lenses within deltaic sequences and result from the mixing of fine and coarse-grained sediments by downslope resedimentation (e.g., Cohen, 1983).

Proglacial Lakes
Facies modelling in proglacial lacustrine sediments is frustrated by logistic difficulty of working on modern proglacial lakes, (Gustavson, 1975) and the small size of these lake basins compared to Pleistocene and older examples. Extensive Pleistocene proglacial sequences exposed around the modern Great Lakes in North American are of considerable significance therefore to modelling studies. Figure 11 shows a 10 km long section of a Late Pleistocene glaciolacustrine sequence from the Lake Ontario Basin, divided into three repeated lithofacies associations. Diamicts at the base of each association have a blanket-like geometry, thickening in topographgic lows and thinning over highs, and internally are complex assemblages of massive and stratified lithofacies. Massive facies result from the basin floor accumulation of suspended sediment and ice rafted debris with stratification produced by variable reworking by downslope resedimentation and traction currents, as is seen in glaciomarine environments (Figs. 12 and 13 and below). Diamict assemblages are overlain conformably, frequently with a gradational contact, by laminated silty clays of probably turbidite origin, containing dropstones. Laminated silty clays occupy broad channels (Fig. 11) illustrating the control on

(A)

(B)

(C)

Figure 10
a) Laminated and graded silty clays described as 'diamictic varves' by Banerjee (1973) with abundant ice-rafted lithic clasts, diamict pellets and angular rip-up clasts of silt and clay. The thick lower unit was probably transported as a debris flow. Don Valley, Ontario. b) Laminated argillites, consisting mainly of the deposits of dilute turbidity currents. Note scattered dropstones, and a sandy sediment gravity flow with a "flow nose" at the base of the picture. Early Proterozoic Gowganda Formation, Ontario. c) Laminated graded argillites of turbidite origin from the Gowganda Formation. Width of photograph is 1 cm; photograph courtesy of P. Fralick.

density underflow location of basin floor relief, and probably record the release of flows from a prograding delta. Coarsening-upwards ripple laminated, planar and trough cross-bedded sands complete the lithofacies association recording delta progradation over sites of diamict accumulation. The most common deltaic facies is a crudely bedded silty sand with abundant liquefaction structures indicating rapid subaqueous deposition (e.g., Rust, 1977). Sands are often loaded into diamict upper surfaces as a result of progradation across a wet diamict substrate.

The geometry of the lithofacies asso-

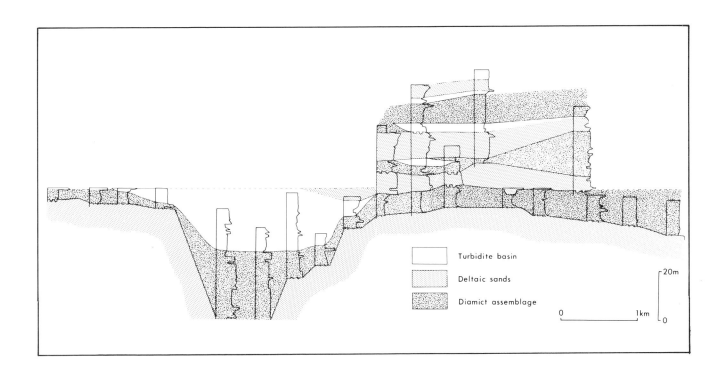

Turbidite basin

Deltaic sands

Diamict assemblage

20m

0   1km   0

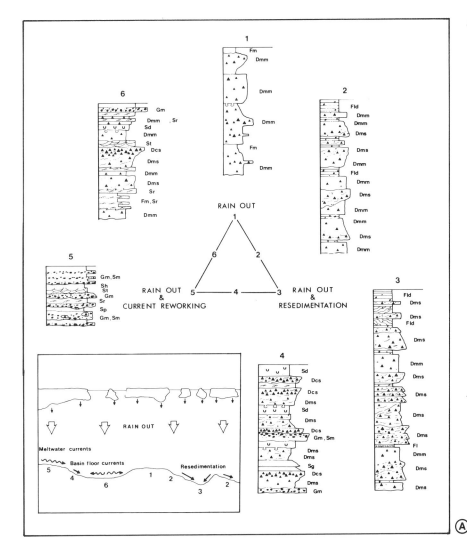

▲ Figure 11
Glaciolacustrine lithofacies associations of Late Pleistocene age exposed along the northern margin of the Lake Ontario Basin, Ontario (from Eyles et al., 1984b).

◀ Figure 12
a) Diamict lithofacies produced by ice rafting and suspension deposition on basin floors. Rain-out refers to suspension deposition and ice rafting. By allowing for changes in the relative importance of end member processes, the model integrates a wide variety of diamict assemblages deposited on marine and lake floors away from ice-proximal environments (e.g. Fig. 8). Lithofacies codes as in Figure 15.

Ⓐ

Figure 12

b) Massive diamict with starved ripples (arrowed) indicating minor traction current activity during deposition; Late Pleistocene of the Great Lakes. c) Massive diamictite with dispersed clasts and occasional out-sized boulders. Scale is 1.5 m long. Late Proterozoic Gowganda Formation, Ontario (Fig. 19). d) Stratified diamictite with traction current deposited sand stringers penetrated and deformed by ice-rafted clasts. Late Proterozoic Port Askaig formation of Scotland (Fig. 18). e) Stratified sandy diamict resulting from suspension deposition, traction current activity and ice-rafting. Late Pleistocene, Irish Sea Basin (from Eyles and Eyles, 1984; Fig. 15). f) Lithofacies continuum of sands and sandy diamicts indicating episodic traction current activity, ice rafting and suspension deposition on a proglacial subaqueous fan (Fig. 8); Late Pleistocene, Irish Sea Basin (Fig. 15).

ciations in Figure 11 is distinctly different from that shown by lithfacies deposited under and at the margin of grounded ice sheets (Figures 1 and 4). Glaciolacustrine diamicts sit in conformable sequence context with deltaic or deeper water muddy lithofacies recording sedimentation on a low relief lake floor (Eyles *et al.*, 1984b).

The architecture of the infills of other extensive lake bodies of Pleistocene age (e.g., Agassiz, Copper River Basin, many Great Lake Basins) still awaits documentation using surface and subsurface facies analysis techniques. Such data would be a significant aid to interpretation of the infills of intracratonic basins of similar dimensions dating from the Permo-Carboniferous glaciation of the Gondwana

Supercontinent (e.g., Wopfner, 1972; Thornton, 1974; Harris, 1981). These provide examples of glacial overdeepening in continental interiors and the selective preservation of continental glacial facies. We suspect that many thick sequences in other Quaternary basins in Europe and North America interpreted as grounded ice deposits

Figure 13

Resedimented subaqueous diamict lithofacies. a) Resedimented diamict lithofacies unit (2 m thick) showing inverse grading at base (arrowed) passing up into normally graded clast supported diamict (at hammer level) and normally graded coarse sands. Early Pleistocene glacially-influenced submarine channel; Upper Yakataga Formation, Alaska. b) Diamictite deposited as a subaqueous debris flow. Note inverse grading at base,

and imbrication of large clasts. The flow rests on a massive to faintly bedded, well sorted sandstone of probable liquified/fluidized flow origin. Scale is 1 m long. Early Proterozoic Gowganda Formation, Ontario. c) Stratified, resedimented glaciolacustrine diamict with graded silty clay laminations at top left. The latter are turbidites and are genetically associated with subaqueous resedimented diamicts (Fig. 12). The section above the knife contains brecciated diamict and laminations;

Late Pleistocene of Great Lakes. d) Cut slab of stratified resedimented glaciolacustrine diamict with abundant silt and clay clasts. Label is 2 cm long. e) 30 m section through 'paraglacial' fan; stratified diamicts and gravel lithofacies deposited by debris flow from valley sides during deglaciation. Late Pleistocene; Canadian Rockies. f) graded diamict units up to 1m thick recording downslope subaqueous resedimentation, Pleistocene Copper River Basin, Alaska.

26

are in fact of similar glaciolacustrine origin. Their stratigraphy reflects a very complex response to changing ice volumes, lake levels, and basin subsidence, and simplistic interpretations relating "till sheets" to climatic ice advance-retreat cycles need to be re-evaluated.

Cold Climate ('Periglacial') Structures and Facies

The term 'periglacial' is used in this section in its broadest sense identifying glacial and non-glacial cold climates. Definitions vary (Washburn, 1980).

Cold climate landscapes are characterised by aeolian activity, mass wasting processes, mechanical distrubance of surface sediments and rocks by ground icings and braided stream deposition. Periglacial structures and facies are most commonly associated with major unconformities, weathered zones and depositional hiatuses separating stratigraphic successions, and indicate subaerial exposure. Certain structures develop only under a restricted climatic range and identify 'permafrost' conditions where the ground remains perennially frozen to perhaps depths of 500 m or more, except for a seasonal surface thaw layer, under a mean annual air isotherm of below -4 to -1°C.

Modern structures diagnostic of permafrozen ground are penetrative ice wedges, formed by continued refreezing of waters in open contraction cracks, and 'pingo' mounds formed essentially as hydrolaccoliths by the upwards injection of water along a migrating freezing front. Other structures include involutions and flame structures, formed as refreezing generates high pore water pressures in summer thaw layers (cryoturbation), and collapse structures that follow the irregular melt of ground ice (thermokarst). None of these has been systematically described in section using modern facies treatments and so the interpretation of former permafrost climates from the rock record is hazardous.

Many workers report polygonal networks of fossil ice wedge casts infilled by a variety of sediments, in Pre-Quaternary diamictite sequences (Hambrey and Harland, 1981; Deynoux, 1982; Fig. 14). Possible pingos up to 350 m in diameter have been identified from exhumed surfaces of Ordovician sandar

Figure 14
a) Polygonal network of small sand-filled wedge structures in the Late Proterozoic Port Askaig Formation, Scotland, argued to be of permafrost ice-wedge origin by Spencer (1971) and discussed by Eyles et al. (1984).
b) Interseciton of large fossil sand-wedge polygons developed in diamictite; Late Proterozoic of Maurentiania, West Africa. Note v-shaped furrow between polygons marking a former thermal contraction wedge filled by wind transport in a cold climate (Deynoux, 1982).

of the central Sahara (Biju-Duval et al.,1981). Whilst 'periglacial' structures are identified and used to infer subaerial continental permafrost climates, similar structures also occur as a result of subaqueous loading, liquefaction, thermal contraction, syneresis and desiccation (Black, 1976; Mills, 1983). Identification of rapidly deposited subaqueous facies, seismically active episodes in basin histories and associated cold climate continental facies is an aid to interpretation of 'periglacial' structures.

A distinctive periglacial facies is windblown silt (loess) derived from

deflation of large braided stream networks. Extensive loess blankets are a marked feature of Quaternary periglaciated continental interiors (e.g., North America; 800,000 km[2]). Whereas total thicknesses of Quaternary loess approach 300 m in some areas of China, reports of loessite are few. Edwards (1979) reports Late Proterozoic loessite from Norway and Svalbard. There are many descriptions of the action of seasonal ice in rafting clasts, grooving and deforming soft sediments along temperate and cold climate shorelines (Dionne, 1974). These have a greater preservation potential (Rattigan, 1967; Dalland, 1977).

The predominant periglacial facies are probably coarse-grained fluvial sediments recording seasonal braided stream activity and access to large volumes of coarse debris. Other important periglacial facies are stratified diamicts, resulting from a wide variety of mass movement processes as seasonal thawed surface layers become waterlogged and are resedimented downslope. These facies frequently infill the lowest points of the topography, and are interbedded with fluvial lithofacies resulting from slopewash. It should be noted that the term 'paraglacial' has been used to refer a shortlived period immediately following deglaciation of high relief glaciated valleys, when glacial facies are resedimented downslope as debris flows over valleyside alluvial fans to be reworked along the valley floor by braided streams (Ryder, 1971; Fig. 13). Rockfall and slide debris is an associated stratigraphic component. Glacial landforms and facies deposited by valley glaciers seldom survive this

episode and glaciated valleys are preserved in the rock record as finger-like fiord troughs filled with coarse resedimented facies, braided stream, glaciomarine and glaciolacustrine sequences (e.g., Visser, 1982).

MARINE GLACIAL FACIES
Most classifications of glaciomarine sedimentation contrast proximal facies belts characterized by strong bottom currents and subaqueous fan growth with distal locations where nonglacial marine processes predominate.

Proximal Facies
A number of distinct lithofacies can be recognized within submarine ice-contact fans (Fig. 8). Cobbles and gravels accumulate at the fan apex (Rust and Romanelli, 1975) with cross-stratified sands being typical of the main fan body away from bifurcating channels (Powell, 1981). Massive, horizontally stratified and inversely graded gravels and sands accumulate within steep sided channels by sediment gravity flow as pulses of dense sediment

laden meltwater sweep down the fan (Rust, 1977; Cheel and Rust, 1982). Surface subsidence and associated faulting results from the melt of buried ice.

A wide range of diamict lithofacies (with geometries that vary from drapes and lenses to channel fills), accumulate under depositional regimes of suspended sediment deposition and berg rafting ('rain-out'), and reworking by downslope sediment gravity flow and traction current activity (Figs. 8, 12 and 13). Coarse-grained stratified diamicts with a muddy sand matrix accumulate in areas of episodic-traction current activity and rain-out. These contain ice-rafted 'outsized' clasts, abundant traction current structures and rounded clasts rolled along as bedload, and occur as part of a lithofacies continuum with pebbly sands and poorly sorted gravels (Figs. 12 and 15). Coarse grained, angular, ice rafted debris in areas of high basement relief represents former supraglacial debris derived by rockfall from valleysides. Former basal debris components may be preserved as cohesive diamict pellets (Ovenshine,

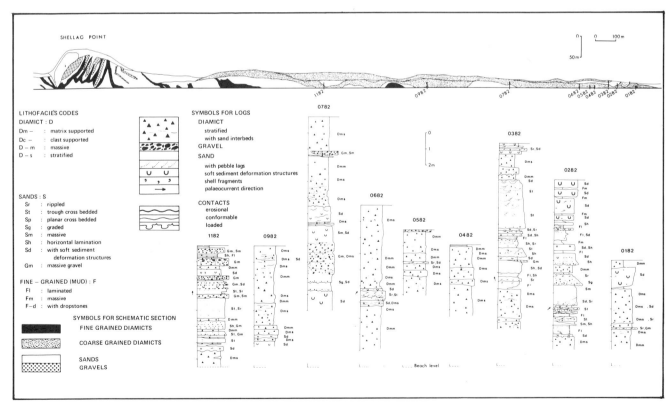

Figure 15
Lithofacies logs, from Quaternary glaciomarine sediments of the Irish Sea Basin, of sandy stratified diamicts draped over the back of a large push ridge (after Eyles and Eyles, 1984). Diamicts comprise lithofacies continuous with sand and gravel lithofacies showing ice-rafted clasts (Figs. 12e and 12f) indicating coeval traction current activity and diamict accumulation by suspension deposition and ice-rafting (Fig. 12a). Sedimentation probably occurred on a subaqueous fan (Fig. 8). Lithofacies codes from Eyles et al. (1983).

1970).

Mud belts occur where overflows or interflows dump large volumes of suspended sediment and where currents are sufficient to move ice bergs away from the ice margin (Powell, 1981; Elverhoi et al., 1983). These muds may bury wedge-shaped fan accumulations as the ice margin retreats. Finely laminated and graded silty mud and sand lithofacies result from the repeated interaction of sediment plumes and tidal currents and comprise a very significant component of fiord fills (Mackiewicz, 1982).

Downslope resedimentation of fan sediments is an important process. Gazdzicki et al., (1982) describe a Pliocene example of sediment gravity flow deposition from the distal reaches of a subaqueous outwash fan merging with a basin plain from the South Shetland Islands. Deposition is dominated by slow sedimentation of mud from suspension interrupted by repeated incursion of pebbly sands and diamict by sediment gravity flow. The flows are defined by tabular or broadly lenticular geometries, matrix-supported fabric, laminated tops and sharp, sometimes erosive, bases. Processes range from debris flows through grain flows to turbidity currents. Similar sequences are described by Visser (1983) from a Permian fjord-head setting in the Karoo Basin of South Africa. Visser et al., (1984) provide criteria for discriminating tectonic structures produced by compressional glacier overriding from those resulting from downslope (extensional) movement. Downslope resedimentation of subaqueous sediments is a common process (Nardin et al., 1979) but it is the case that evidence for downslope resedimentation in glacial environments is still simplistically interpreted as indicating the release of debris direct from an ice margin.

Glacier retreat from the marine environment results in a fining-upward sequence with the upper part of the lithofacies sequences dominated by muds and fine-grained diamicts (Elverhoi et al., 1983). However, isostatic emergence or rapid sediment accumulation may bring the sequence up above wave base, producing a coarsening-up beach or deltaic 'cap' (Andrews, 1978; Boulton and Deynoux, 1981; Boulton et al., 1982).

Deposition from ice shelves represents a special case of proximal glaciomarine sedimentation. An ice shelf forms as a result of very high ice discharges into a marine environment with subsequent 'creep' thinning from a number of pinning points. Recent data show that large areas of ice shelves may undergo basal melting. This is of major importance because the bulk of basal debris is released close to the points at which the shelf begins to float. Consequently, icebergs calved from the ice front are fairly clean (Orheim and Elverhoi, 1981). In Antarctica, for example, ice shelves do not contribute significantly to continental margin sedimentation despite making up some 45% of the Antarctic coastline.

Many publications have maintained that extensive sequences of massive diamict(ite) in conformable sequence with marine sediments required continuous uninterrupted sedimentation from floating ice which, it was argued, could only be met below the closed cover of an ice shelf. A detailed facies model for the sub-ice shelf environment awaits documentation but a recent review (Eyles et al., 1984) argues that the importance of such sedimentation in the rock record (as evidenced by the popularity of the ice shelf model) has been exaggerated beause of simplistic interpretation of massive diamictites. Such facies may be more likely to be of distal glaciomarine origin because sub-ice shelf sedimentation appears to be characterised by rapid exhaustion of basal debris, local deposition within fan-like accumulations (e.g., Drewry and Cooper, 1981) and widespread glacio-tectonism resulting from migration of grounding lines. Lack of data from modern sub-ice shelf environments frustrates detailed facies modelling.

Away from ice-proximal environments, marine processes dictate the pattern of sediment accumulation and direct glacial influence is restricted to the supply of fine-grained suspended sediment, ice-rafted detritus and deformation and reworking by iceberg grounding (iceberg turbation; Vorren et al., 1983). Sediment gravity flow and marine currents may be of considerable, even predominant, importance in generating the final depositional product.

There are problems in defining the outer limit of distal glaciomarine sedimentation which is commonly taken as the farthest extent of ice rafted debris. Definition is complicated because detritus is also rated by ice of various origins (e.g., seasonal ice on temperate and arctic coasts; see Piper, 1976; Dalland, 1977; Clarke et al., 1980; and Andres and Matsch, 1983 for diagnostic criteria).

In mud belts where there is unrestricted supply of pelagic sediment, massive fine-grained diamicts accumulate where ice-rafted debris melts out (Miller, 1953; Ferrians, 1963; Miller, 1973; Plafker and Addicott, 1976; Armstrong, 1981). These show highly variable clast fabrics (Nystuen, 1976; Domack, 1983). Assemblages of massive and stratified diamicts result from spatial and/or temporal variation in the relative importance of: 1) pelagic rain-out and ice rafting, 2) traction current activity, and 3) downslope resedimentation (Figs. 12 and 13). Traction currents serve to winnow or supplement the fine-grained component derived from suspension. These currents vary from tidal, wind-driven and storm-generated currents on shallow marine shelves, contour currents of the upper continental slope, cold bottom currents released from ice shelves, thermohaline currents produced by the formation of pack ice, and mid-depth and bottom currents in abyssal plains. The effect of these is to maintain silt and clay in suspension, allowing selective deposition of coarser ice-rafted debris. Stratified 'residual' diamicts with a muddy sand matrix are widespread on the Antarctic continental shelf (Elverhoi and Roaldset, 1983; Anderson et al., 1983). The production of surface lags is promoted by iceberg turbation and re-suspension of fines (Vorren et al., 1983). In areas of low current velocity silts may be deposited from waning traction currents to produce stratified and laminated diamicts with a silt-sized mode (Anderson et al., 1982).

Subaqueously resedimented diamicts can be recognized by the variable presence of flow noses, flow banding and folding, creep structures, incorporated rafts of associated lithologies, frequent truncation of underlying lithologies, basal grooving and flutings (which can be confused with those associated with diamicts deposited by lodgement), abundant silt and clay clasts (Fig. 13) and preferential alignment of clasts. Silt and clay clasts are probably produced by brecciation of fine-grained laminated lithofacies during slumping, creep, subaqueous dewatering or sub-aerial exposure.

Lack of sorting, grading or stratification within resedimented diamict facies may indicate proximity to the flow source (c.f. "disorganized bed model for conglomerates", Walker, 1975). Increased internal sorting by either dispersive pressures, kinetic sieving, flow boundary effects or clay rheology, results in a downslope sequence of internal grading characteristics (Walker, 1975, and "Turbidites and Associated Coarse Clastic Deposits", this volume) and may ultimately result in the transformation of large and highly concentrated sediment gravity flows into turbidites (Nardin *et al.*, 1979; Wright and Anderson, 1982; Fig. 13).

Upper and lower contacts of glaciomarine (and glaciolacustrine) diamict assemblages with associated lithofacies are particularly diagnostic (Figs. 15 and 18). Basal contacts are either interbedded over several centimetres to metres, recording episodic traction currents during suspension deposition, or are sharp, recording sudden changes in depositional regime. Contacts may also be transitional with underlying muds, showing increasing frequency of dropstones upwards in section. Upper contacts may be either loaded, or sharply eroded below shallowing-upwards marine sediments, frequently with a conglomeratic lag horizon. They may also be transitional to stone free muds or other fine grained lithofacies. Marine macro- or micro-fauna within a diamict-(ite) may also help identification. The recognition of a conformable sequence context with marine sediments is critical. Diamicts formed by ice rafting and suspension deposition may also overlie with a sharp contact diamicts deposited in the grounded ice environment, recording flooding of the depositional site. A good example of the analysis of lithofacies relationships is provided by Mode *et al.* (1983) who also show how paleoecological and age data in Quaternary glaciomarine sediments can be integrated into a depositional model.

GLACIATED CONTINENTAL MARGIN DEPOSITIONAL SYSTEMS

Typical glaciomarine facies assemblages are probably best considered within the framework of a number of glaciated continental margin depositional systems. The latter can be regarded as being composed of glacially influenced varieties of the typical marine depositional systems, e.g., continental shelf, canyon, slope, rise and abyssal plain. The facies assemblages in these settings (described elsewhere in this volume), are modified by the two major glacial influences of sediment supply and sea level change. Abundant coarse debris and suspended sediment are fed into glacially influenced marine basins by meltwaters, by sediment gravity flows and from icebergs. Sea level changes result from variations in the volume of continental ice, and from the isostatic response to the ice load. Andrews (1978) and Boulton *et al.* (1982) show how the amplitude of these two effects varies diachronously with distance from the centres of ice loading, resulting in complex migration of facies belts across the depositional basin. Thus there are severe problems involved in the interpretation of multiple sequences of glaciomarine diamicts, muds and shallow marine sands in terms of synchronous climatically-driven glacier advance/retreat cycles. Direct glacial influence in the marine environment is secondary to a number of other controls such as sea-level fluctuations and basin subsidence which are of pre-eminent significance in controlling alternations of diamict and other marine facies.

Continental Shelf Depositional System

Glacially modified continental shelves are underlain by subhorizontal, blanket-like units (e.g., Damuth, 1978; Josenhans, 1983) although this simple geometry may be complicated by basement tectonics or growth faults. A vigorous interglacial shelf circulation, scour by storms and grounded ice, and channeling by melt streams may reduce preserved thicknesses and generate widespread erosion surfaces and unconformities within stratigraphic successions (Fig. 16). A good example is the Quaternary infill of the current North Sea Basin where the sediment pile is

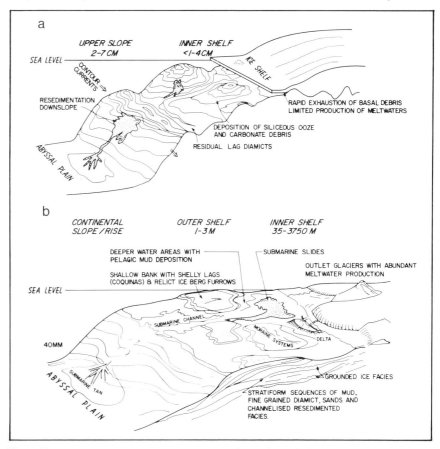

Figure 16
Contrasting types of glacially-influenced continental margin with reported deposition rates. a) 'sediment-starved' margin typical of Antarctica and other high relief margins (e.g., fiords) where cross-shelf transport is limited. b) glaciated continental margin with unrestricted sediment supply, e.g., Gulf of Alaska.

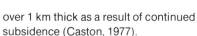

Figure 17

a) Planar units of interbedded siltstone with dropstones, pebbly and sandy dolomites and diamictites deposited on a shallow marine shelf. Regional dip to right. Boudinage and necking structures (arrowed) indicate repeated downslope movement (Disrupted Beds and Great Breccia, Fig. 18). Late Proterozoic Port Askaig Formation, Scotland. Section about 35 m. b) Coquina bank of mollusc debris within glaciomarine diamicts deposited by suspension deposition and ice rafting (Fig. 12) of the Yakataga Formation, Alaska. Photograph courtesy of B. Kaye.

over 1 km thick as a result of continued subsidence (Caston, 1977).

The Late Miocene to present history of the Gulf of Alaska provides an excellent modern analog for glacially influenced shelf sedimentation. Adjacent glaciers are wet-based and deliver large volumes of suspended sediment to the Gulf. The tectonic setting of the area is a convergent plate margin, and continued uplift of an accretionary arc complex has exposed excellent sections through the 5 km thick Yakataga Formation which contains the most complete record of Late Cenozoic glacial activity in the world. Seismic traces show that the continental shelf is underlain by planar units of marine diamict formed by ice rafting and suspension deposition in water depths between 15 and 100 m (Plafker and Addicott, 1976; Molnia and Carlson, 1978) with associated muds, submarine channel sequences and coquina bands (Figs. 13, 16 and 17).

The preservaiton of extensive coquina bands within the Yakataga Formation demonstrates that biogenic carbonates may be an integral part of Phanerozoic glaciomarine sequences. Cold water biogenic carbonates accumulate in many mid and high latitude areas at the present day (Björlykke *et al.,* 1978; Rao, 1981; Elverhoi and Roaldset, 1983).

Similar diamictite lithofacies with extensive planar geometries are well exposed over 700 km of strike in Scotland and Ireland within the 850 m thick Port Askaig Formation of the Late Proterozoic Dalradian Supergroup. Diamictite lithofacies are either massive or stratified, with traction current deposited interbeds containing dropstones (Figs. 12 and 18). Many diamictite surfaces are loaded by shallow marine conglomeratic lags or crossbedded shallow marine sands.

Glacial influence on continental shelves may also restrict sediment

supply and result in clastic starvation. The present day Antarctic continental shelf is the best studied example. Overdeepened submarine basins and fiords act as sediment traps and extreme cold prohibits meltwater transport of suspended sediment. Rapid loss of debris from basal melting ice shelves and isostatic subsidence below the Antarctic Ice Sheet also restricts deposition to landward margins, and limits cross shelf transport of sediment. As a result of sediment starvation, current-swept lag surfaces of relict ice-rafted debris occur over large areas. Siliceous oozes and biogenic carbonate accumulations (coquinas, foraminiferal debris, etc.) testify to low rates of clastic deposition. Significant sediment transport is limited to circum-continental contour current activity at the shelf break and sediment gravity flow processes in areas of irregular topography whereby older glaciomarine sediments are moved into slope

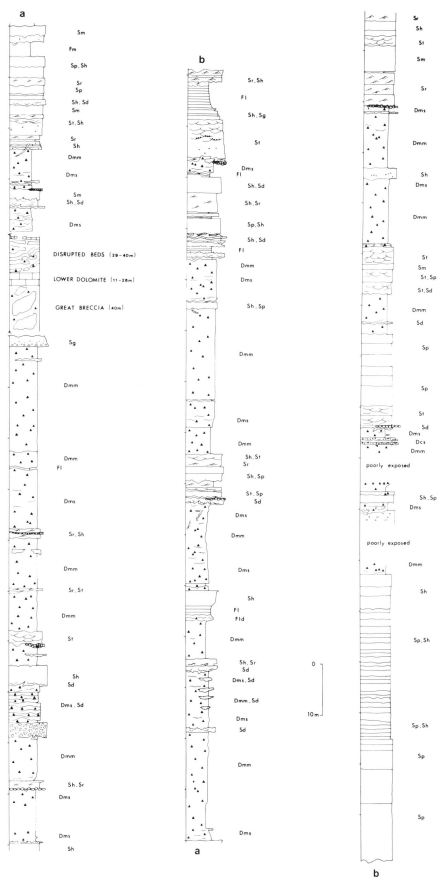

Figure 18

500 m lithofacies log from Late Proterozoic Port Askaig Formation of Scotland. Diamictites are conformably interbedded with shallow marine sandstones with a planar regional geometry (Fig. 17). Diamictite lithofacies have sharp, non-erosive lower contacts with dolomitic sandstones and loaded upper surfaces, consistent with distal glaciomarine deposition (Fig. 12d) on a shallow marine shelf undergoing episodic subsidence and subaerial exposure (Fig. 14a). The contrast in lithofacies sequences deposited by grounded glacier ice (Figs. 1 and 4) can be emphasized. From Eyles et al. (1984).

canyon and fan systems. Significant growth of slope canyon and fan systems only occurs during major glaciation when glaciers discharge directly into canyon systems or over the shelf-slope break (Anderson *et al.*, 1983).

The role of regional glaciation in producing sediment-starved continental shelves may have some bearing on the origin of mixed diamictite/carbonate successions. For example, the association of dolomite interbeds and cap rocks with Late Proterozoic diamictites, widely assumed to require either low latitude glaciation or rapid climatic change, remains a major problem following intense discussion in the mid-seventies (e.g., Schermerhorn, 1975). However, identification of detrital rather than primary dolomites (Fairchild, 1983; Fig. 17), recognition of the importance of diagnetic dolomitization of carbonates deposited on clastic-starved continental shelves following rapid post-glacial sea level rise (Deynoux and Trompette, 1976), and possible models of cold water dolomitisation all offer alternate cool climate mechanisms for dolomite formation. The debate has probably been defined too narrowly in the past because diamictite origins were ascribed simply either to glacial (from grounded ice sheets) or non-glacial origins (e.g., tectonically-triggered mud-flows: Schermerhorn, 1974). Growing evidence of the importance of diamictite accumulation by ice-rafting and pelagic deposition on glacially-influenced marine shelves and reassessment of paleolatitude data (Stupavsky *et al.* 1982) broadens the scope for investigation.

Continental Slope, Rise and Abyssal Plain Depositional Systems

Modern slopes are cut by submarine canyons, which funnel sediment down to the continental rise and abyssal plain. Canyons may be enlarged to depths of up to 2 km by submarine mass wasting, or become plugged by sediment depending on the rate of sediment supply. Climatic changes during glaciation cause rapid changes in sea level, and may result in grounded ice extending far out on to the shelf to feed coarse debris directly to the outer shelf edge and canyon systems, e.g., northern Gulf of Alaska, Gulf of St. Lawrence, Antarctica (Piper *et al.*, 1973; Stow, 1981; Carlson *et al.*, 1982; Piper and Normark,

1982; Tucholke and Laine, 1982; Anderson *et al.*, 1983).

We cannot yet generalize about facies models for these glacially-influenced continental margin environments. A preponderance of submarine fans cut by extensive channel complexes is expected to comprise the major slope and rise facies assemblages. In the ancient record the only unequivocal way to distinguish such deposits from coarse non-glacial submarine fans may be the identification of ice-rafted debris (dropstones, diamict clots) in inter-fan argillites, and striated and facetted clasts within the channel fills. Parts of the Gowganda Formation (early Proterozoic) of northern Ontario, the Dwyka "Tillite" (Permian) of South Africa (Visser 1982) and the Yakataga Formation (Miocene to Recent) of the Gulf of Alaska show such facies assemblages (Figs. 10, 12, 13 and 19).

The Gowganda Formation is a world famous "glacial" unit, traditionally interpreted as recording repeated episodes of subglacial sedimentation below grounded ice sheets and varved glaciolacustrine deposition (Lindsey, 1969, 1971). However, application of modern facies analysis methods has demonstrated that most of the formation is the product of submarine sedimentation on a continental margin (Miall, 1983, 1985; Eyles *et al.*, 1984). Sediment gravity flow and submarine fan models (Walker, this volume) are particularly pertinent.

Many varieties of sediment gravity flows can be identified, including clast-rich bouldery debris flows, sandy fluidized/liquefied flows and thin-bedded Bouma-type turbidites (Fig. 10). These probably were derived by local slope failure of basin-floor accumulations of ice-rafted debris and muds (Fig. 12). Sandy sediment gravity flows may have been produced by winnowing of debris flows by the processes identified from the modern continental slope of Antarctica by Wright and Anderson (1982) or by resedimentation of beach deposits. Massive diamictite, with dispersed unsorted clasts (Fig. 12), is volumetrically the most abundant lithofacies and probably represents relatively rapid deposition of ice-rafted detritus and pelagic mud. Where the iceberg density was low, possibly as a result of dispersal by winds or marine currents, or because of climatic amelioration or where suspended sediment input to the marine

environment was high (e.g., the situation described from the modern Gulf of Alaska by Molnia and Carlson, 1978), pelagic muds predominate over coarse ice-rafted debris. The result is argillite containing thin laminae of rafted silt and sand grains (commonly reworked into ripples), thin turbidites, and scattered dropstones (Fig. 19d).

The stratigraphic architecture of the Gowganda Formation can locally be constructed from networks of diamond drill holes (Fig. 19). Miall (1983) described a fining-upward megacycle interpreted as the deposit of a subaqueous outwash fan. Elsewhere a submarine channel, filled with laminted argillites and winnowed sandstones, can be recognized (Miall, 1985). Low-angle crossbed sets 4 to 5 m thick consist of well sorted sandstone and lenses of diamictite, and are interpreted as subaqueous point bars formed within meandering fan channels (Fig. 19).

Glacially-influenced abyssal plain sedimentation has not yet been recognised and a detailed facies model has yet to be established. The presence of extensive planar bodies of turbiditic silty clays and massive muds with ice-rafted clastics has been emphasized by Clark *et al.*, (1980) and Golstein (1983) in studies of the Arctic Ocean Basin.

FUTURE PROSPECTS

Most problems in the interpretation of glacial sequences will revolve around the origin of diamict(ite) units. Diamict(ite)s continue to be simplistically described as till(ite)s often with the implicit assumption that the direct agent of deposition was glacier ice. The assumption that massive diamict(ite) necessarily indicates subglacial deposition from grounded glacier ice can also still be found in the literature; the student should be aware that massive lithofacies do not uniquely characterise subglacial environments. Detailed field examination, laboratory slabbing, thin sectioning and x-ray analysis frequently demonstrates that 'massive' diamicts reveal structures that aid diagnosis (e.g., Fig. 12b). Diamicts deposited at an ice base for example may be massive over short core or outcrop lengths but exhibit distinct structures (Figs. 1 and 4). There are now sufficient diagnostic criteria recognised to identify diamict lithofacies deposited at an active or stagnant glacier base by virtue of substrate

33

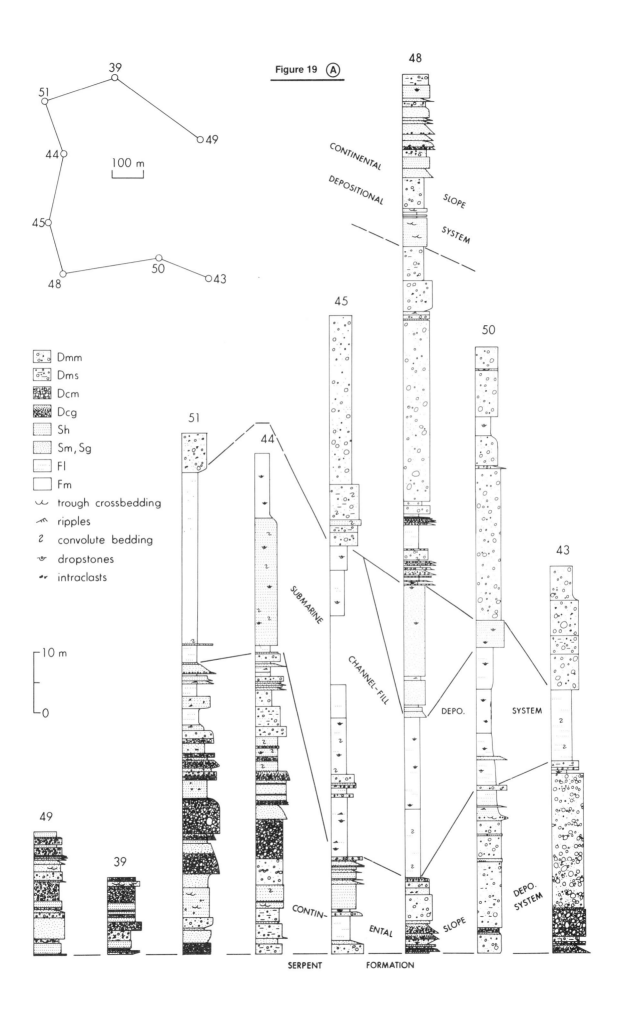

Figure 19 Ⓐ

34

Figure 19
*Lithofacies and structures from the Gow-
ganda Formation, Ontario. a) Lithofacies
logs through the lower part of the Gowganda
Formation, from diamond drill holes near
Elliot Lake, Ontario (Miall, 1985). b) Faceted
boulders in the Gowganda Formation
shaped by subglacial ice abrasion (Fig. 6)
and resedimented as a debris flow. Near
Elliot Lake. c) Grooves formed by clast rol-*
*ling or scour by floating ice in a succession
of argillites with thin-bedded turbidites. Cata-
ract Falls, near Mississagi. d) Massive diamictite, probably deposited by ice-rafting and
pelagic mud depsition (Fig. 12), containing
wispy sandstone lenses. These were formed
by current sorting or turbidity currents and
have been deformed by loading into the soft
substrate. Highway 108, near Elliot Lake.*

deformation, associated lithofacies originating when the glacier moved over the
site (Figs. 1 and 4), restricted sequence
thickness across the depositional basin,
and association with major regional
unconformities. Glacitectonic struc-

tures may be absent locally at the scale
of individual outcrops but will be clearly
evident as data are assembled from
adjacent sites.

Outside grounded ice environments,
thicker diamict sequences are depos-

ited in glacially-influenced environments (e.g., lacustrine, marine). These
diamicts commonly occur therefore in
conformable sequence context with
lithofacies charateristic of these environments and, as a result the analysis of
lithofacies relationships outlined by
Walker ("Introduction" to this volume) is
a major aid to interpretation. During the
construction of lithofacies logs (e.g.,
Figs. 1, 4, 15, 18 and 19), the description
of diamict and upper lower boundary
relations with other lithofacies is of
major importance. A critical need now
exists for detailed field descriptions of
modern and ancient glacial sequences
from a range of environments and tectonic settings, using lithofacies criteria
and facies analysis techniques.

A most important consideration with
regard to future sedimentological investigations must be that most ancient
glacial sequences accumulated and were
preserved in oceanic and continental
shelf marine environments that were
influenced not by direct glaciation, but
by the indirect glacial influence of sea-
level and oceanographic change, ice-
rafting and greatly enhanced sediment
supply. In the Late Proterozoic for
example there is a very clear association
between diamictite sequences, continental rifting and the development of
Atlantic-type trailing edge plate margins
dominated by subsidence tectonics
(Eyles *et al.*, 1984). In most cases continental glacial facies around basin
margins were not preserved. As a result
the data base from modern and Quaternary environments, overwhelmingly
biased towards observations of continental glacial facies, is unrepresentative
of much of the glacial rock record. However, knowledge of the offshore geology
of continental margins affected by Late
Cenozoic glaciations is expanding
rapidly using sonar, seismic drill-core
and down-hole data. If, as argued in this
review, glaciomarine environments are
regarded as special sub-types of the
principal continental margin environments (e.g., abyssal plain, slope etc.)
then this growing body of information
from offshore exploration forms a firm
foundation for sophisticated 'glacial'
facies models applicable to modern and
ancient sequences.

ACKNOWLEDGEMENTS
Roger Walker and Carolyn Eyles kindly
read earlier drafts of this all too brief

review of glacial facies and made many useful comments for its improvement. The authors would like to acknowledge the various funding agencies that have supported their research projects, in particular the Natural Sciences and Engineering Research Council of Canada; the senior author is partcularly grateful for the award of a NSERC University Research Fellowship in glacial sedimentology.

REFERENCES

The following reading list emphasizes the growing stimulus to integrated facies models encompasing both modern and ancient examples, provided by recent process and subsurface data from modern glacial-influenced continental margins. It is this small but expanding literature that is of greatest application to the Earth's glacial record. References cited with regard to continental environments are examples where glaciological and hydrodynamic flow regime concepts have been integrated with descriptions of sedimentary products and basin studies.

CONTINENTAL GLACIAL FACIES

Andrews, J.T., 1982. On the reconstruction of Pleistocene ice sheets: a review: Quaternary Science Reviews, v. 2, p 1-30.

Boulton, G.S., 1972. Modern arctic glaciers as depositional models for former ice sheets. Journal of the Geological Society of London, v. 127, p. 361-393.

Boulton, G.S., 1978. Boulder shapes and grain size distributions of debris as indicators of transport paths through a glacier and till genesis. Sedimentology, v. 25, p. 773-799.

Cohen, J.M., 1983. Subaquatic mass flows in a high energy ice marginal deltaic environment and problems with the identification of flow tills. In Evenson E.B., et al., eds., Tills and related deposits: Rotterdam, A.A. Balkema.

Eyles, C.H. and Eyles, N., 1983. Sedimentation in a large lake: a reinterpretation of the Late Pleistocene stratigraphy at Scarborough Bluffs, Ontario, Canada. Geology, v. 11, p. 146-152.

Eyles, N., 1979. Facies of supraglacial sedimentation on Icelandic and Alpine temperate glaciers. Canadian Journal of Earth Sciences, v. 16, p. 1341-1361.

Eyles, N., and Menzies, J., 1983. The subglacial landsystem. In Eyles, N., ed., Glacial geology: an introduction for engineers and earth scientists. Oxford, Pergamon Press, p. 19-70.

Eyles, N., Sladen, J., and Gilroy, S., 1982. A depositional model for stratigraphic complexes and facies superimposition in lodgement tills. Boreas, v. 11, p. 317-333.

Eyles, N., et al., 1984b. The application of basin analysis techniques to glaciated terrains; an example from the Lake Ontario Basin. Geoscience Canada, v. 11.

Gibbard, P., 1980. The origin of stratified Catfish Creek till by basal melting. Boreas, v. 9, p. 71-85.

Jorgensen, N.B., 1982. Turbidites and associated resedimented deposits from a tilted glaciodeltaic sequence, Denmark. Damn. Geol. Undrs., Arbog 1981, p. 47-72.

Jopling, A.V. and McDonald, B.C., eds., 1975. Glaciofluvial and glaciolacustrine sedimentation. Society of Economic Paleontologists and Mineralogists, Special Publication 23, 320 p.

Lawson, D.E., 1982. Mobilisation, movement and deposition of active subaerial sediment flows, Matanuska Glacier, Alaska. Journal of Geology, v. 90, p 279-300.

Miall, A.D., 1977. A review of the braided river depositional environment. Earth Science Reviews, v. 13, p. 1-62.

Moran, S.R., Clayton, R., Hooke, R. Le B., Fenton, M.M., and Andriashek, L.D. 1980. Glacier bed landforms of the Prairie region of North America. Journal of Glaciology, v. 25, p. 457-476.

Menzies, J., 1979. A review of the literature on the formation and location of drumlins. Earth Science Reviews, v. 14, p. 315-359.

Paterson, W.B., 1981. The physics of glaciers. Oxford, Pergamon Press.

Paul, M.A., 1983. The supraglacial landsystem. In Eyles, N., ed., Glacial geology: an introduction for engineers and earth scientists. Oxford, Pergamon Press, p. 71-90.

Postma, G., Roep, T.R., and Ruegg, G.H.J., 1983. Sandy gravelly mass flow deposits in an ice marginal lake (Saalian, Leuvenumsche Beek Valley, Veluwe, the Netherlands) with emphasis on plug-flow deposits. Sedimentary Geology, v. 34, p. 59-82.

Schlüchter, C.H., ed., 1978. Moraines and varves. Rotterdam, A.A. Balkema.

Shaw, J., 1977a. Sedimentation in an alpine lake during deglaciation, Okanagan Valley, British Columbia, Canada. Geografiska Annaler, v. 59A, p. 221-240.

Shaw, J., 1977b. Tills deposited in arid polar environments. Canadian Journal of Earth Sciences, v. 14, p. 1239-1245.

Shaw, J., 1979. Genesis of the Sveg tills and Rogen moraines of central Sweden; a model of basal melt-out. Boreas, v. 8, p. 409-426.

Symposium on Glacier Beds, 1979. The ice-rock interface. Journal of Glaciology, v. 23.

GLACIOMARINE: ICE PROXIMAL FACIES

Cheel, R.J. and Rust, B.R., 1982. Coarse-grained facies of glaciomarine deposits near Ottawa, Canada. In Davidson-Arnott, R., et al., eds., Research in glacial, glacio-fluvial and glacio-lacustrine systems. Norwich, Geo-Books, p. 279-295.

Domack, E.W., 1983. Facies of Late Pleistocene glacial-marine sediments on Whidbey Island, Washington: an isostatic glacial-marine sequence. In Molnia, B.F., ed., Glacial-marine sedimentation: New York, Plenum Press, p. 535-570.

Elverhoi, A., Lönne, O., and Seland, R., 1983. Glaciomarine sedimentation in a modern fjord environment, Spitsbergen. Polar Research, v. 1, 127-149.

Eyles, C.H. and Eyles, N., 1984. Glaciomarine sediments of the Isle of Man as a key to Late Pleistocene stratigraphic investigations in the Irish Sea Basin. Geology, v. 12, in press.

Powell, R.D., 1981. A model for sedimentation by tidewater glaciers. Annals of Glaciology, v. 2, p. 129-134.

GLACIALLY-INFLUENCED CONTINENTAL MARGIN SEDIMENTATION

Anderson, J.B., Kurtz, D.D., and Weaver, F.M., 1982. Sedimentation on the West Antarctic continental margin. In Craddock, C., ed., Antarctic geoscience. Madison, University of Wisconsin, p. 1003-1012.

Anderson, J.B., Brake, C., Domack, E.W., Meyers, N., and Wright, R., 1983. Development of a polar glacial-marine sedimentation model from Antarctic Quaternary deposits and glaciological information. In Molnia, B.F., ed., Glacial-marine sedimentation: New York, Plenum Press, p. 233-264.

Crowell, J., 1978. Gondwana glaciation, cyclothems, continental positioning and climate change. American Journal of Science, v. 278, p. 1345-1372.

Domack, E.W., 1982. Sedimentology of glacial and glacial marine deposits on the George V - Adelie continental shelf, East Antarctica. Boreas, v. 11, p. 79-97.

Elverhoi, A., and Roaldset, E., 1983. Glaciomarine sediments and suspended particulate matter, Weddell Sea Shelf, Antartica. Polar Research, v. 1, p. 1-21.

Eyles, N., Eyles, C.H., and Miall, A.D., 1983. Lithofacies types and vertical profile analysis; an alternative approach to the description and environmental interpretation of glacial diamict and diamictite sequences. Sedimentology, v. 30, p. 393-410.

36

Eyles, C.H., Eyles, N., and Miall, A.D., 1984. Models of glaciomarine sedimentation and their application to the interpretation of ancient glacial sequences: Palaeogeography, Palaeoclimatology, Palaeoecology, v. 44, in press.

Goldstein, R.H., 1983. Stratigraphy and sedimentology of ice-rafted and turbidite sediment, Canada Basin, Arctic Ocean. In Molnia, B.F., ed., Glacial-marine sedimentation. New York, Plenum Press, p. 367-400.

Minicucci, D.A. and Clark, D.L., 1983. A Late Cenozoic stratigraphy for glacial-marine sediments of the Eastern Alpha Cordillera, Central Arctic Ocean. In Molnia, B.F., ed., Glacial-marine sedimentation. New York, Plenum Press, p. 331-365.

Mode, W.N., Nelson, A.R., and Brigham, J.K., 1983. A facies model of Quaternary glacial-marine cyclic sedimentation along eastern Baffin Island, Canada. In Molnia, B.F., ed., Glacial-marine sedimentation. New York, Plenum Press, p. 495-534.

Plafker, G. and Addicott, W.O., 1976. Glaciomarine deposits of Miocene through Holocene age in the Yakataga Formation along the Gulf of Alaska margin, Alaska. In Miller, T.P., ed., Recent and ancient sedimentary environments in Alaska. Alaska Geological Society, p. 1-22.

Stow, D., 1981. Laurentian fan; morphology, sediments, processes and growth patterns. American Association of Petroleum Geologists, Bulletin, v. 65, p. 375-393.

Tucholke, B.E. and Laine, E.P., 1982. Neogene and Quaternary development of the Lower Continental Rise off the central U.S. East Coast. In Watkins, J.S., and Drake, C.L., eds., Studies in continental margin geology. American Association of Petroleum Geologists Memoir 34, p. 295-306.

Vorren, T.O., Hald, M., Edvardsen, M., and Lind-Hansen, O.D., 1983. Glacigenic sediments and sedimentary environments on continental shelfs; general principles with a case study from the Norwegian shelf. In Ehlers, J., ed., Glacial deposits in northwest Europe. Rotterdam, A.A. Balkema, p. 61-73.

Weaver, P.P.E., and Kuijpers, A., 1983. Climatic control on turbidite deposition on the Madeira Abyssal Plain. Nature, v. 306, p. 360-363.

Wright, R. and Anderson, J.B., 1982. The importance of sediment gravity flow to sediment transport and sorting in a glacial marine environment, Eastern Weddell Sea, Antarctica. Geological Society of America Bulletin, v. 93, p. 951-963.

EXAMPLES OF PRE-LATE CENOZOIC GLACIAL FACIES

Early Proterozoic

Lindsey, D.A., 1969. Glacial sedimentology of the Precambrian Gowganda Formation, Ontario, Canada. Geological Society of America Bulletin, v. 80, p. 1685-1702.

Lindsey, D.A. 1971. Glacial marine sediments in the Precambrian Gowganda formation at Whitefish Falls, Ontario (Canada). Palaeogeography, Palaeoclimatology, Paleoecology, v. 9, p. 7-25.

Miall, A.D., 1983. Glaciomarine sedimentation the Gowganda Formation (Huronian), northern Ontario. Journal of Sedimentary Petrology, v. 53, p. 477-491.

Miall, A.D., 1984. Sedimentation on an early Proterozoic continental margin; the Gowganda Formation (Huronian), Elliot Lake area, Ontario, Canada. Sedimentology, v. 31, in press.

Late Proterozoic

Bjorlykke, K., Elvsborg, A., and Hoy, T., 1976. Late Precambrian sedimentation in the central sparagmite basin of south Norway. Norsk Geol. Tidsskrift, v. 56, p. 233-290.

Christie-Blick, N., 1983. Glacial-marine and subglacial sedimentation, Upper Proterozoic Mineral Fork Formtion, Utah. In Molnia, B.F., ed., Glacial-marine sedimentation. New York, Plenum Press, p. 703-776.

Deynoux, H., 1982. Periglacial polygonal structures and sand wedges in the Late Precambrian glacial formations of the Taouden Basin in Adrar of Mauretania (West Africa). Palaeogeography, Paleoclimatology, Palaeoecology, v. 39, p. 55-70.

Edwards, M.B., 1976. Sedimentology of Late Precambrian Sveanor and Kappe Sparre Formations at Aldorsbreen, Wahlenbergfjorden, Nordaustlandet. Norsk Polarinst. Arbok 1974, p. 51-61.

Eisbacher, G.H., 1981. Sedimentary tectonics and glacial record in the Windermere Supergroup, Mackenzie Mountains, Northwestern Canada. Geological Survey of Canada, Paper 80-27.

Eyles, C.H. and Eyles, N., 1983. A glaciamarine model for Late Precambrian diamictites of the Port Askaig Formation, Scotland. Geology, v. 11, p. 692-696.

Eyles, C.H., Eyles N., and Miall, A.D., 1984. Models of glaciomarine sedimentation and their application to the interpretation of ancient glacial sequences. Palaeogeography, Palaeoclimatology, Palaeoecology, v. 44, in press.

Hambrey, M.J., 1982. Late Precambrian dia-

mictites of northeastern Svalbard. Geological Magazine, v. 119, p. 527-551.

Link, P.K. and Gostin, V.A., 1981. Facies and paleogeography of Sturtian glacial strata (Late Precambrian), South Australia. American Journal of Science, v. 281, p. 353-374.

Nystuen, J.P., 1976. Facies and sedimentation of the Late Precambrian Moelv Tillite in the eastern part of the Sparagmite Region, southern Norway. Norges Geologiske Undersokelse, v. 329, p. 1-70.

Schermerhorn, L.J.G., 1975. Tectonic framework of Late Precambrian supposed glacials. In Wright, A.E., and Moseley, F., eds., Ice ages: ancient and modern. Liverpool, Seel House Press, p. 241-274.

Spencer, A.M., 1971. Late Precambrian glaciation in Scotland. Geological Society of London, Memoir 6.

Spencer, A.M., 1975. Late Precambrian glaciation in the North Atlantic region. In Wright, A.E. and Moseley, F., eds., Ice ages: ancient and modern. Liverpool, Seel House Press, p. 217-240.

Schermerhorn, L.J.G., 1974. Late Precambrian mixtites: glacial and/or nonglacial? American Journal of Science, v. 274, p. 673-824.

Young, G.M., 1982. The late Proterozoic Tindir Group, east-central Alaska: evolution of a continental margin. Geological Society of America Bulletin, v. 93, p. 759-783.

Phanerozoic

Casshyap, S.M., and Qidwai, H.A., 1974. Glacial sedimentation of Late Paleozoic Talchir Diamictite, Pench Valley Coalfield, Central India. Geological Society of America, Bulletin, v. 85, p. 749-760.

Davis, R.A. and Mallett, C.W. 1981. Sedimentation in a Permian subglacial channel. Journal of Sedimentary Petrology, v. 51, p. 185-190.

de la Grandville, B.F., 1982. Appraisal and development of a structural and stratigraphic trap oil field with reservoirs in glacial and periglacial clastics. In Halbouty, M.T., ed., The deliberate search for the subtle trap. American Association of Petroluem Geologists, Memoir 32, p. 267-286.

Harris, W.K., 1981. Permian diamictites in South Australia. In Hambrey, H., and Harland, W.B., eds., Earth's Pre-Pleistocene glacial record. Cambridge University Press, p. 469-473.

Visser, J.N.J., 1983. Glacial-marine sedimentation in the Late Paleozoic Karoo Basin, Southern Africa. In Molnia, B.F., ed., Glacial-marine sedimentation. New York, Plenum Press, p. 667-702.

Visser, J.N.J., Collinson, W.P., and Terblanche, J.C., 1984. The origin of soft sediment deformation structures and related deposits in Permo-Carboniferous glacial and proglacial beds, South Africa. Journal of Sedimentary Petrology, in press.

OTHER REFERENCES CITED IN TEXT

Andrews, J.T., 1978. Sea level history of Arctic coasts during the Upper Quaternary. Progress in Physical Geography, v. 2, p. 375-407.

Andrews, J.T. and Matsch, C.L., 1983. Glacial marine sediments and sedimentation; an annotated bibliography. Norwich, U.K., Geo-Books.

Armentrout, J.M., 1983. Glacial lithofacies of the Neogene Yakataga Formation, Robinson Mountains, Southern Alaska Coast Range, Alaska. In Molnia, B.F., ed., Glacial-marine sedimentation. New York, Plenum Press, p. 629-666.

Armstrong, J.E., 1981. Post-Vashon Wisconsin Glaciation, Fraser Lowland, British Columbia. Geological Survey of Canada, Bulletin 322.

Ashley, G.M., 1975. Rhythmic sedimentation in glacial Lake Hitchcock, Massachusetts-Connecticut. In Jopling, A.V., and McDonald, B.C., eds., Glaciofluvial and glaciolacustrine sedimentation. Society of Economic Paleontologists and Mineralogists, Special Publication 23, p. 304-320.

Banerjee, I., 1973. Sedimentology of Pleistocene glacial varves in Ontario, Canada. Geological Survey of Canada Bulletin 226.

Banerjee, I. And McDonald, B.C., 1975. Nature of esker sedimentation, In Jopling, A.V., and McDonald, B.C., eds., Glaciofluvial and glaciolacustrine sedimentation. Society of Economic Paleontologists and Mineralogists, Special Publication 23, p. 132-154.

Biju-Duval, B., Deynoux, M., and Rognon, P., 1981. Late Ordovician tillites of the Central Sahara. In Hambey, M.J., and Harland, W.B., eds., Earth's Pre-Pleistocene glacial record. Cambridge University Press, p. 99-107.

Björlykke, K., Bue, B., and Elverhoi, A., 1978. Quaternary sediments in the northwestern part of the Barents Sea and their relation to underlying Mesozoic bedrock. Sedimentology, v. 25, p. 227-246.

Black, R.F., 1976. Perglacial features indicative of permafrost: ice and soil wedges. Quaternary Research, v. 6, p. 3-26.

Bluck, B.J., 1979. Structure of coarse grained braided stream alluvium. Transactions of the Royal Society of Edinburgh, v. 70, p. 181-221.

Boothroyd, J.C. and Ashley, G.M., 1975. Process, bar morphology, and sedimentary structures on braided outwash fans, northeastern Gulf of Alaska. In Jopling, A.V., and McDonald, B.C., eds., Glaciofluvial and glaciolacustrine sedimentation. Society of Economic Paleontologists and Mineralogists, Special Publication 23, p. 193-222.

Boothroyd, J.C. and Nummedal, D., 1978. Proglacial braided outwash: a model for humid alluvial-fan deposits. In Miall, A.D., ed., Fluvial sedimentology. Canadian Society of Petroleum Geologists Memoir 5, p. 641-668.

Boulton, G.S., 1979. Processes of glacier erosion on different substrata. Journal of Glaciology, v. 23, p. 15-38.

Boulton, G.S. and Deynoux, M., 1981. Sedimentation in glacial environments and the identification of tills and tillites in ancient sedimentary sequences. Precambrian Research, v. 15, p. 397-422.

Boulton, G.S., Baldwin, C.T., Peacock, J.P., McCabe, A.M., Miller, G., Jarvis, J., Horsfield, B., Worsley, P., Eyles, N., Chroston, P.N., Day, T.E., Gibbard, P., Hare, P.E., and Von Brunn, V., 1982. A glacio-isostatic facies model and amino-acid stratigraphy for late Quaternary events in Spitsbergen and the Arctic. Nature, v. 298, p. 437-441.

Carson, P.R., Bruns, T.R., Molnia, B.F., and Schwab, W.C., 1982. Submarine valleys in the northeastern Gulf of Alaska: characteristics and probable origin. Marine Geology, v. 47, p. 217-242.

Caston, V.N.D., 1977. A new isopachyte map of the Quaternary of the North Sea and Quaternary deposits of the Forties Field, northern North Sea. Institute of Geological Sciences, Report 77/11.

Church, M., 1972. Baffin Island sandurs: a study of arctic fluvial processes. Geological Survey of Canada Bulletin 216.

Clark, D.L.,Whitman, R.R., Morgan, K.A., and MacKay, S.D., 1980. Stratigraphy and glacial-marine sediments of the Amerasian Basin, Central Arctic Ocean. Geological Society of America, Special Paper 181.

Dalland, A., 1977. Erratic clasts in the lower Tertiary deposits of Svalbard – evidence of transport by winter ice. Norsk Polarinst. Arbok. 1976, p. 151-165.

Damuth, J.E., 1978. Echo character of the Norwegian-Greenland Sea: relationship to Quaternary sedimentation. Marine Geology, v. 28, p. 1-36.

Deynoux, M. and Trompette, R., 1976. Late Precambrian mixtites: glacial and/or nonglacial? Dealing especially with the mixtites of West Africa. American Journal of Science, v. 276, 1302-1324.

Deynoux, M. and Trompette, R., 1981. Late Precambrian tillites of the Taoudeni Basin, West Africa. In Hambrey, M.J., and Harland, W.B., eds., Earth's Pre-Pleistocene glacial record. Cambridge University Press, p. 123-131.

Dionne, J-C., 1974. Polished and striated mud surfaces in the St. Lawrence Tidal Flats. Canadian Journal of Earth Sciences, v. 11, p. 489-494.

Dreimanis, A., 1984. Lithofacies types and vertical profile analysis: comments on the paper by Eyles, N., Eyles, C.H., and Miall, A.D. Sedimentology, v. 31, in press.

Drewry, D.J., and Cooper, A.P.R., 1981. Processes and models of Antarctic glaciomarine sedimentation. Annals of Glaciology, v. 2, p. 117-122.

Edwards, M.B., 1979. Late Precambrian glacial loessites from North Norway and Svalbard. Journal of Sedimentary Petrology, v. 49, p. 85-92.

Eyles, N., Eyles, C.H., and Miall, A.D., 1984a. Lithofacies types and vertical profile models: reply to Dreimanis et al. Sedimentology, v. 31, in press.

Fairchild, I.J., 1983. Effects of glacial transport and neomorphism on Precambrian dolomite crystal sizes. Nature, v. 304, p. 714-716.

Ferrians, O.J., 1963. Glaciolacustrine diamicton deposits in the Copper River Fan-Delta, Alaska. United States Geological Survey, Professional Paper 475 C, p. C120-C125.

Galloway, W.E., 1977. Sediments and stratigraphic framework of the Copper River Fan-Delta, Alaska. Journal of Sedimentary Petrology, v. 47, p. 726-737.

Gazdzicki, A., Gradzinski, R., Porebski, S., and Wrona, R., 1982. Pholadid Penitella borings in glaciomarine sediments (Pliocene) of King George Isalnd, Antarctica. N. Jb. Geol. Palaont. Mh., v. 12, p. 723-735.

Hambrey, M.J. and Harland, W.B., eds., 1981. Earth's Pre-Pleistocene glacial record. Cambridge University Press.

Josenhans, H.W., 1983. Evidence of pre-late Wisconsinian glaciations on Labrador Shelf – Cartwright Saddle. Canadian Journal of Earth Sciences, v. 20, p. 225-235.

Lambert, A., and Hsu, K.J., 1979. Non-annual cycles of varve-like sedimentation in Walensee, Switzerland. Sedimentology, v. 26, p. 453-461.

Lindsey, D.A., 1969. Glacial sedimentology of the Precambrian Gowganda Formation, Ontario, Canada. Geological Society of America Bulletin, v. 80, p. 1685-1702.

38

Mackiewicz, N., 1982. Laminated ice-proximal glacimarine sediments. International Association of Sedimentologists, 11th International Congress on Sedimentology, Hamilton, Ontario, Abstracts, p. 74.

Miall, A.D., 1977. A review of the braided river depositional environment. Earth Science Reviews, v. 13, p. 1-62.

Miall, A.D., 1978. Lithofacies types and vertical profile models in braided rivers: a summary. In Miall, A.D., ed., Fluvial sedimentology. Canadian Society of Petroleum Geologists Memoir 5, p. 597-604.

Miller, J.D., 1953. Late Cenozoic marine glacial sediments and marine terraces of Middleton Island, Alaska. Journal of Geology, v. 61, p. 17-40.

Miller, R.D., 1973. Gastineau Channel Formation, a composite glaciomarine deposit near Juneau, Alaska. United States Geological Survey, Bulletin 1394C.

Mills, P.C., 1983. Genesis and diagnostic value of soft-sediment deformation structures – a review. Sedimentary Geology, v. 35, p. 83-104.

Molnia, B.F. and Carlson, P.R., 1978. Surface sedimentary units of Northern Gulf of Alaska continental shelf. American Association of Petroleum Geologists, Bulletin, v. 62, p. 633-643.

Nardin, T.R., Hein, F.J., Gorsline, D.S., and Edwards, B.D., 1979. A review of mass movement processes, sediment and acoustic characteristics and contrasts in slope and base of slope systems versus canyon-fan-basin floor systems. In Doyle, L.J., and Pilkey, O.H., eds., Geology of continental slopes. Society of Economic Paleontologists and Mineralogists, Special Publication 27, p. 61-73.

Ostrem, G., 1975. Sediment transport in glacial meltwater streams. In Jopling, A.V., and McDonald, B.C., eds. Glaciofluvial and glaciolacustrine sedimentation. Society of Economic Paleontologists and Mineralogists, Special Publication 23, p. 101-122.

Ovenshine, A.T., 1970. Observations of iceberg rafting in Glacier Bay, Alaska and the identification of ancient ice-rafted deposits. Geological Society of America Bulletin, v. 81, p. 891-894.

Piper, D.J.W., Von Huene, R., and Duncan, J.R., 1973. Late Quaternary sedimentation in the active Eastern Aleutian Trench. Geology, v. 1, p. 19-22.

Piper, D.J.W., 1976. The use of ice rafted marine sediments in determining glacial conditions. La Revue de Geographie de Montreal, v. 30, p. 207-212.

Piper, D.J.W., and Normark, W.R., 1982. Acoustic interpretation of Quaternary sedimentation and erosion on the channelled upper Laurentian Fan, Atlantic margin of Canada. Canadian Journal of Earth Sciences, v. 19, p. 1974-1984.

Rao, C.P., 1981. Cementation in a cold-water bryozoan sand, Tasmania, Australia. Marine Geology, v. 40, p. 23-33.

Rattigan, T.H., 1967. Depositional, soft sediment and post-consolidation structures in a Palaeozoic aqueoglacial sequence. Journal of the Geological Society of Australia, v. 14, p. 5-18.

Rust, B.R., 1972. Structure and process in a braided river. Sedimentology, v. 18, p. 221-246.

Rust, B.R., 1977. Mass flow deposits in a Quaternary succession near Ottawa, Canada; diagnostic criteria for subaqueous outwash. Canadian Journal of Earth Sciences, v. 14, p. 175-184.

Rust, B.R. and Romanelli, R., 1975. Late Quaternary subaqueous outwash deposits near Ottawa, Canada. In Jopling, A.V., and McDonald, B.C. eds., Glaciofluvial and glaciolacustrine sedimentation. Society of Economic Paleontologists and Mineralogists, Special Publication 23, p. 172-192.

Ryder, J.M., 1971. The stratigraphy and morphology of paraglacial alluvial fans in south-central British Columbia. Canadian Journal of Earth Sciences, v. 8, p. 279-298.

Stupavsky, M., Symons, D.T.A., and Gravenor, C.P., 1982. Evidence for metamorphic remagnetisation of Upper Precambrian tillite in the Dalradian Supergroup of Scotland. Royal Society of Edinburgh Transactions, Earth Sciences, v. 73, p. 59-65.

Shaw, J., 1975. Sedimentary successions in Pleistocene ice-marginal lakes. In Jopling, A.V., and McDonald, B.C., eds., Glaciofluvial and glaciolacustrine sedimentation. Society of Economic Paleontologists and Mineralogists, Special Publication 23, p. 281-303.

Teller, J.T., and Clayton, L., eds. 1983. Glacial Lake Agassiz. Geological Association of Canada Special Paper 26.

Thornton, R.C.N., 1974. Hydrocarbon potential of western Murray Basin and infrabasins. Department of Mines, Geological Survey, 5th Australian Report of Investigation, 41 p.

Visser, J.N.J., 1982. Upper Carboniferous glacial sedimentation in the Karoo Basin near Prieska: South Africa. Palaeogeography, Palaeoclimatology, Palaeoecology, v. 38, p. 63-92.

Walker, R.G., 1975. Generalized facies models for resedimented conglomerates of turbidite association. Geological Society of America, Bulletin, v. 86, p. 737-748.

Washburn, A.L., 1980. Permafrost features as evidence of climatic change. Earth Science Reviews, v. 15, p. 327-402.

Wopfner, H., 1982. Depositional history and tectonics of South Australian sedimentary basins. Mineral Resources Review, South Australia, v. 144, p. 32-50.

Volcaniclastic Rocks

JEAN LAJOIE
Département de géologie
Université de Montréal
Montréal, Québec H3C 3J7

INTRODUCTION

The first edition of *Facies Models* has been used primarily by students and workers of ancient rocks. Recent volcanoes and volcaniclastic sediments are rare in Canada, and workers have to interpret ancient volcaniclastic rocks by comparison with recent accumulations. My object is to present the major characteristics of volcaniclastic deposits that may help such workers in their day-to-day endeavours.

The realm of volcaniclastic rocks is changing rapidly and to write on facies in these rocks is ambitious. In the first edition of *Facies Models,* I noted that the subject was in its infancy. Four years later the child may have grown out of proportion and, to paraphrase Fisher (1982a), we seem to have at present a plethora of incompletely tested models and a dearth of data!

In the General Introduction to this volume, Walker suggests that models can be used as a framework for future observations, as norms and predictors, and as a basis for interpretation. The models discussed in the present paper should be used as general frameworks for future observations. They may be used to initiate interpretations, but more work needs to be done before they can be considered norms and predictors.

The present paper is not a review and, therefore, the reference list is not exhaustive. I have tried to use general comprehensive studies of all subjects that are treated.

TERMINOLOGY

Volcaniclastic rocks include all frag-
mental volcanic rocks that result from any mechanism of fragmentation. The classification most commonly used in North America is that of Fisher (1961, 1966). *Epiclastic* fragments result from the weathering of volcanic rocks. *Autoclastic* fragments are formed by the mechanical breakage or gaseous explosion of lava during movement. *Hyaloclastic* fragments, a variety of autoclastic, are produced by quenching of lava that enters water, water-saturated sediments, or ice. *Pyroclastic* fragments are formed by explosion and are projected from volcanic vents. Showers of pyroclastic fragments produce *fall deposits.* Clasts that are ejected from vents and are transported en masse on land or in water form *flow deposits.* Pyroclastic fragments are primary if ejected from a vent, and secondary if they are recycled from unconsolidated primary deposits. In ancient deposits it may be very difficult, if not impossible, to distinguish between primary and secondary pyroclastic debris.

Wentworth and Williams (1932) introduced a grain-size classification for *pyroclastic* fragments, similar to the classification used for other clastic sediments. The classification was adopted by Fisher (1961; Fig. 1).

PREDOMINANT GRAIN SIZE (mm)	EPICLASTIC FRAGMENTS	PYROCLASTIC FRAGMENTS	PYROCLASTIC ROCKS
	COBBLE	BLOCK AND BOMB	PYROCLASTIC BRECCIA
— 64 —	PEBBLE	LAPILLUS	LAPILLISTONE
— 2 —	SAND	COARSE ASH	TUFF
— 1 — ⅟₁₆	SILT	FINE ASH	

Figure 1
Grade size for epiclastic and pyroclastic fragments, and terms for pyroclastic rocks. From Fisher (1961, 1966).

Volcaniclastic sedimentation is such a vast subject, and has so many variables that it will not be possible to treat all of its aspects. Epiclastic rocks which do not differ except in composition from other clastic rocks will not be treated. In this paper, I shall describe briefly the characteristics of autoclastic and pryoclastic rocks. I shall then discuss the observed and possible variations in time and space of the fundamental characteristics (facies). Due to space limitations, fragment petrography will not be discussed. The reader will find good descriptions of the morphology and petrography of volcaniclastic fragments in Ross and Smith (1961), and in Heiken (1972, 1974).

AUTOCLASTIC ROCKS

Flow breccias and hyaloclastites, the two autoclastic rocks that will be discussed in this paper, are formed by the fragmentation of lava by friction, by rapid cooling as it flows in water or under ice, or by fragmentation of magma that is injected in water-saturated volcaniclastic sediments. Flow breccias occur in both subaerial and subaqueous environments. Hyaloclastites are for some authors synonymous with aquagene tuffs, but this usage of the word tuff has been criticized.

Flow breccias and hyaloclastites are common in basaltic sequences, and rare in acid sequences because basic magmas flow more readily than acid ones due to their lower viscosity. In these two types of autoclastic rocks, the clasts are generally monogenetic with most fragments being derived from the same parent magma. Lava may scrape vent walls or rip up fragments as it flows, but such exotics are rarely reported in descriptions of flow breccias. In basaltic sequences, the breccias commonly consist of complete pillows and (or) pillow fragments set in a matrix of devitrified glass shards and lumps (Carlisle, 1963; Dimroth *et al.,* 1978; Figs. 2, 3 and 4). Acid flow breccias are made up of abundant angular blocks with coarse and fine sand-size fragments set in a glassy matrix (Pichler, 1965).

Facies in Flow Breccias and Hyaloclastites

Due to their mode of origin one would expect *in situ* flow breccias and hyaloclastites to show little or no systematic lateral and vertical variations in clast content, size, and composition. Autoclastic associations, however, are much more complex.

The vertical variations in a typical flow breccia of basaltic composition are summarized in Figures 5 and 6. The pillowed lava grades upward into an isolated-pillow breccia that is overlain and transitional with a broken-pillow breccia. In the Archean of the Noranda region,

40

Figure 2
Flow breccia that consists of pillows and pillow fragments set in a matrix of hyaloclastite. *Mount Etna, Sicilia. Photo courtesy of John Ludden.*

Figure 3
Basaltic flow breccia in the Archean of Rouyn-Noranda, Quebec, Canada, overlain by graded pyroclastic deposits. The lava *flowed from left to right, and the fabric is due to the orientation of the brecciated pillows in shear planes. Photo courtesy of Pierre Trudel.*

Figure 4
Brecciated basaltic flow in the Archean of *Rouyn-Noranda. Coin is 2 cm in diameter. Photo courtesy of Pierre Trudel.*

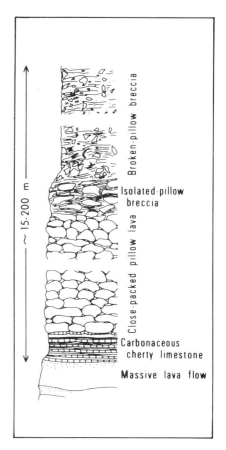

Figure 5
Typical pillow breccia-hyaloclastite sequence in the Triassic of Quandra Island, British Columbia. From Carlisle, 1963.

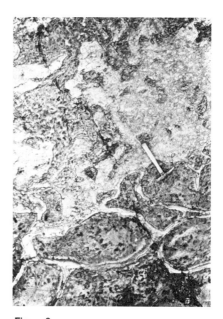

Figure 6
Hyaloclastite transitional with pillow lava, Rouyn-Noranda region, Quebec. Photo courtesy of Léopold Gélinas.

similar sequences are exceptionally overlain by fine-grained hyaloclastites. In this model, clast size decreases from base to top. This grain size variation cannot properly be called graded-bedding because there is no bedding to begin with. The clasts are formed *in situ* rather than being transported and deposited. The distinctive characteristics of this type of breccia are the monogenetic composition of the clasts and the transitional contact with the underlying flow. Since the fragmentation is formed by quenching, the shards are not welded.

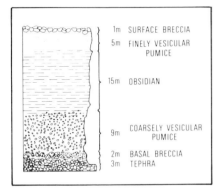

Figure 7
Schematic cross section of rhyolitic obsidian flow. After Fink, 1980.

Subaerial lava flows of acid composition commonly have flow breccias which occur underlying and/or overlying the flows. Fink (1980) presented a schematic cross section (Fig. 7) of subaerial rhyolitic obsidian flows based on measurements from California, New Mexico, and Lipari. The 32 metre-thick flow has a 2 metre-thick breccia at the base and a 1 metre-thick flow-top breccia. The texture and composition of the fragments are similar to that of the associated parent, but compared to flow breccias of basaltic composition, the breccias of acid flows are thinner, the transition with the parent lava is more abrupt, and the fragments are large and chaotic.

There are no modern examples of submarine acid flows, and they are rare and poorly known in the rock record. Sigurdsson (1982) cites two cases where fragmental deposits of volcanic rocks were generated by the nonexplosive extrusion of rhyolitic lavas in the subaqueous environment. One is from the Archean of Rouyn-Noranda (Rosen-Spence *et al.* (1980), where the

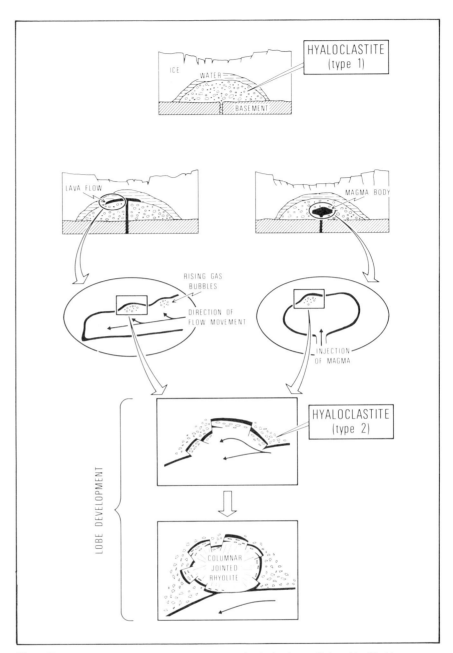

Figure 8
Evolutionary model of the two types of acid hyaloclastite and lobes. Modified from Furnes et al., 1980.

fragmentation was interpreted as pyroclastic by Gélinas *et al.* (1978). The other is from subglacial formations on Iceland (Furnes *et al.*, 1980). The Icelandic acid hyaloclastites show a greater lithological diversity than basaltic hyaloclastites. They are made of structureless to strongly flow-banded fragments of pumice and obsidian, commonly associated with large (long axes average 7 m) irregular to subspherical bodies (lobes) of vesicular to nonvesicular rhyolite. Two genetically different types of hyaloclastites can be

described (Fig. 8). Type 1 hyaloclastite, which is by far the most common, consists entirely of pumiceous fragments that vary considerably in size and shape and are said to result from "violently explosive events". Most authors might refer to this type of fragmentation as pyroclastic in origin. Type 2 hyaloclastites consist of fragments of obsidian, flow-banded/flow-folded pumice and lithic rhyolite invariably associated with ellipsoidal to irregularly shaped bodies (*lobes*) that may commonly reach 70 m in length. These lobes, which are mineralogically and chemically similar to the pumice, consist of an outer shell of obsidian adjacent to a zone of flow-banded and flow-folded vesiculated and glassy rhyolite, with a core of "lithic" rhyolite (Furnes *et al.*, 1980). Type 2 hyaloclastites are derived from the lobes during their development from the breaking up of lava flows or magma bodies (Fig. 8) that have intruded water-saturated volcaniclastic material. It should be noted that the Type 2 hyalo-clastites of Furnes *et al.* (1980) are closely related, are in sharp contact with a parental magma, and have no internal structures indicative of transport.

Autoclastic fragments may be reworked by bottom currents or resedi-mented from density flows. In certain cases the deposit may show some of the characteristics of pyroclastic rocks. These secondary hyaloclastites may be difficult to distinguish from pyroclastites as both types of fragmentation may form similar textures. However, pu-miceous fragments should be more common in pryoclastic deposits. Also, fragments in reworked hyaloclastic rocks are commonly polygenetic and may be welded. Honnorez and Kirst (1975) have shown that the relative per-centages of concave, convex and planar grain boundaries can be used to distin-guish a hyaloclastic from a pyroclastic origin.

The model proposed for basaltic flow breccias and hyaloclastites is suffi-ciently well established to be used as a norm, but is is safe to say that a model cannot yet be constructed for acid hyaloclastites.

PYROCLASTIC ROCKS

Pyroclastic debris (pumice, shards, crystals, and lithics) is ejected from vents and then falls or flows in air and/or water under the influence of gravity. The settling velocities are proportional to fragment size, shape, and density. Therefore, the priniciples that govern the sedimentation of pyroclastic frag-ments are identical to those controlling the deposition of other clastic debris.

The lateral extent and geometry of pyroclastic deposits are influenced in part by magma composition, and the environment in which the eruption takes place. Basaltic subaerial eruptions gene-rally produce cones of scoria and ash of limited areal extent around or down-wind of the cones. Basaltic eruptions

that take place in shallow water or where water has access to the vent are more strongly explosive, and produce ash rings and ash layers that may have considerable areal extent. Eruptions of acid and intermediate composition are generally explosive due to the higher volatile content of the magma. These eruptions may project very large volumes of pyroclastic debris to heights well in excess of 25 km, and may pro-duce thick fall and flow deposits.

Walker (1973) classified recent pyro-clastic-fall deposits using the suface of dispersal limited by a fixed isopach con-tour, and the degree of fragmentation (the percentage of material finer than 1 mm, obtained at a second fixed iso-pach contour). Fall deposits are termed *hawaiian, strombolian, sub-plinian, pli-nian,* and *ultraplinian* with increasing surface of dispersal and degree of frag-mentation. In ancient volcanic terranes where rocks have gone through much erosion and deformation, the classifi-cation cannot be used as there is little or no chance to find the dispersal surface or the grain size values at the fixed iso-pach contour.

Facies in Pyroclastic Fall Deposits

The showering of pyroclastic debris is governed by the settling velocities. It follows that size, composition, and thick-ness of the deposit should vary with dis-tance from the vent. Figure 9, modified from Walker (1971), is an example of such lateral variations of the size and composition in an air-fall unit. In this example, size decreases for all com-positions and the relative abundance of fragment-type varies in the direction of

transport. Due to their low density, pumicious fragments make poor pro-jectiles and are, therefore, more abun-dant near the vent whereas crystals may travel greater distances. This zonation of textures is common in many air-fall deposits of the world (Walker, 1971; Kuno *et al.*, 1964; Lacroix, 1904). Pumi-ces may be lighter than water and thus float; deposition may occur only when the pumiceous fragments become waterlogged. It follows that in such deposits, the distribution of pumices may be very erratic.

Any particular fall deposit becomes finer-grained as the distance from the vent increases. However, fine-grained deposits may also form near the vent if the eruption is weak. Even if coarse-grained fall deposits are reliable indi-cators of vent proximity, fine-grained deposits do not necessarily indicate dis-tance from the vent.

In fall deposits, the dispersion of the graphic standard deviation ($\sigma\phi$) is con-siderable near the vent. This results from the differences in settling veloci-ties; small and dense clasts fall at veloci-ties similar to those of larger and lighter clasts. Figure 10 suggests that a high $\sigma\phi$ could indicate proximity of an eruptive center. The scale is important on this diagram. Sorting improves with dis-tance from the vent (Fig. 10), but it appears that the improvement is detec-table only in deposits that are close to the vent. Brazier *et al.* (1982) have shown significant increase in sorting in the fall deposits of St. Vincent, but at Mount St. Helens, the fall deposits show no significant sorting variations

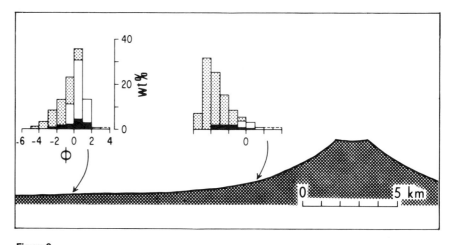

Figure 9
Lateral variations in size and contents of pumice (stippled), crystals (blank), and lithic

(black) in a pyroclastic fall deposit in the Azores. Modified from Walker (1971).

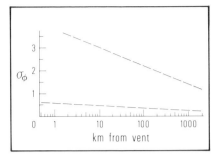

Figure 10
Variation of sorting (σφ) with distance from the vent for pyroclastic fall deposits. The two lines represent the lower and upper limits of the analytical results. From Walker (1971).

Figure 11
Stratification in air-fall deposits. Crude bed- *ding, La Palma, Canary Islands; notebook is 20 cm long.*

Figure 12
Stratification in air-fall deposits. Crude laminations, San Lorenzo de Gran Canaria, Canary Islands; arrow is 50 cm. Courtesy of Pierre Verpaelst.

between 57 and 620 km from the vent (Sarna-Wojcicki *et al.*, 1981).

The downwind decrease in thickness of pyroclastic fall deposits is particularly well illustrated by the recent eruptions of Mount St. Helens (Sarna-Wojcicki *et al.*, 1981). Some windborne ash may be transported over extensive areas and makes an excellent marker horizon. Fall deposits may be poorly stratified: because stratification may be a result of discontinuity in the volcanic activity rather than a change in composition or grain size, beds and laminations may be crudely defined (Figs. 11 and 12). Walker and Croasdale (1971) gave some characteristics of basaltic fall deposits. According to these authors, ashes from subaqueous eruptions are well strati-

fied, and beds are extremely thin (1 mm). Deposits due to rhythmic ejections of incandescent cinder and lapilli are thicker, rarely less than 1 cm, and commonly more than 5 cm. Pyroclastic fragments of acid and intermediate compositions may be ejected in very large volumes, and bed thickness may easily reach 4 m near the vent.

Bedding in fall deposits is poorly defined close to the vent but becomes very well defined in more distal sections. In subaerial deposits, bomb-sags and accretionary lapilli are common. Accretionary lapilli are small spherical masses generally between 2 and 10 mm in diameter, composed of concentrically layered ash or fine lithic particles, formed chiefly through accretion by condensed moisture. They usually fall within a few kilometres of the vent and accumulate only on land or in shallow water (Williams and McBirney, 1979, p. 131). Ejecta do not produce sags if they fall in deep water.

Grading is common within beds of fall deposits because settling is a function of size and density. It may be normal or reverse (Bond and Sparks, 1976). Reverse density-grading has been documented by Koch and McLean (1975). It results from the progressive evacuation of a compositionally stratified magma chamber with increasing intensity of eruption. In subaerial falls, all fragments are heavier than the fluid whereas in

subaqueous falls, pumices may float, and may not be present in the deposit, or may only occur at or near the top of the bed.

Due to the great variety of eruption types and of initial size distributions, vertical variations of facies are unpredictable in pyroclastic fall deposits. Self (1982) notes that primary air-fall textures are subject to modification by many factors. Reverse grading can be produced by changing conditions in the vent and eruption column. Increasing vent size promotes higher eruption columns which leads to reversely graded deposits. Brazier *et al.* (1982) documented an inverse relationship at St. Vincent where median diameters decrease with increasing time of eruption.

Pyroclastic-Flow Deposits
In order to relate pyroclastic-flow deposits in space, it is first necessary to introduce the nomenclature use by volcanologists for the deposits and to describe them briefly. I shall then present models that have been proposed for recent deposits, and discuss their application to ancient sequences.

Wright *et al.* (1980) and Fisher (1982a, p. 71) recognized two basic types of pyroclastic-flow deposit: *flow* deposits, originating from laminar transport, and *surge* deposits that accumulate from turbulent transport. The terminology is

44

ambiguous since both pyroclastic flow and surge are flows, but it is however, well entrenched in the literature. In order to avoid confusion I shall always use italics when referring to *pyroclastic* or *flow* deposits in the sense of Fisher (1982a). The problem is not only one of terminology as there is little agreement among workers as to what are flow and surge deposits. This is well illustrated by the nomenclature used by three groups of authors that described the same surge deposit of the May 18th, 1980 eruption of Mount St. Helens. It was necessary for the editors (Lipman and Mullineaux, 1981, p. 378) to introduce a table correlating the terminology from one paper to the other. This recent eruption of Mount St. Helens had many witnesses, and it does raise a few questions as to the applicability of the proposed nomenclature to ancient deposits.

Pyroclastic flows are defined as hot, high-concentration mixtures where the fluid is gas. The deposits are poorly sorted, massive or reversely graded. These features characterize laminar flows. They are also found in *lahars* (discussed below) where the interstitial fluid is water rather than gas.

Surges are turbulent low-concentration density currents (sedimentologists would probably call them *turbidity* currents). They are subdivided into *base* surge, *ground* surge, and *ash-cloud* surge, depending on the volcanic processes. Base surges are formed by the collapsing of phreatomagmatic eruptions, ground surges from the collapsing of the margin of magmatic eruptions, whereas ash-cloud surges form by elutriation of fines by gases escaping from the top of the cloud.

The characteristics of the three types of surge deposit are very similar. The thin-bedded deposits are commonly laminated and cross-bedded, characteristics which most authors use for their recognition. Surge deposits are made of tuff and lapilli composed of pumice, crystals, and lithic clasts in various proportions (Figs. 13 and 14). Ground-surge deposits occur below the *pyroclastic flow* deposit, and are commonly in sharp contact with it (Fig. 14). Ash-cloud surge deposits are generally finer grained, and are found above the *flow* deposit, in immediate contact with it. Fisher *et al.* (1980) stretched the definition of ash-cloud surge deposits to

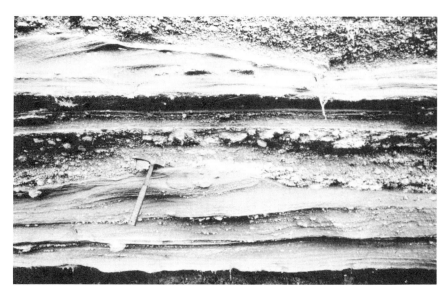

Figure 13
Base-surge deposits, Guadeloupe. Courtesy of Léopold Gélinas.

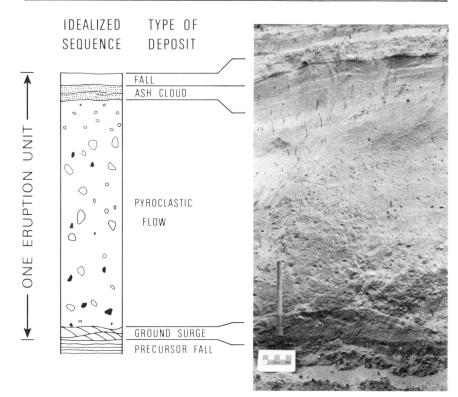

Figure 14
Idealized depositional sequence of one erup- *tion unit modified from Fisher (1979), with an* *example from Mount Pelée, Martinique.*

include coarse-grained, massive to normally graded deposits found at the base of the sequence.

Lahars are subaerial or subaqueous debris-flow deposits composed of poorly sorted volcanic fragments which range in size from clay to boulders. They may make up a large volume of the volcaniclastic pile around volcanoes. Their characteristics, which are well summarized by Fisher (1982c, 1983), are those of sedimentary debris-flow deposits resulting from laminar transport controlled by gravity. The deposits are massive or reversely graded, with sharp, non-erosive basal contacts

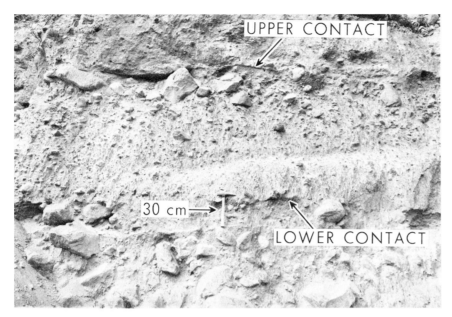

Figure 15
Coarse-tail reverse grading in a subaerial debris-flow deposit (lahar) 4 km from the vent, Mount Pelée, Martinique. Hammer is 30 cm long.

Figure 16
Normally graded "surge" deposit from the May 18, 1980, eruption of Mount St. Helens. Near locality 13 of Moore and Sisson (1981).

(Fig. 15), and since they are controlled by gravity, they commonly fill large or small valleys.

Facies in Pyroclastic-Flow Deposits
Many authors have presented "standard" depositional sequences resulting from one eruptive event (Sparks *et al.*, 1973; Fisher, 1979; Sheridan, 1979). These standard beds should not be taken as norms. Due to the wide range of eruption type, flow thickness, density, temperature, and clast composition, no single model can encompass all types of pyroclastic accumulations (Sheridan, 1979).

The idealized depositional sequence proposed by Fisher (1979) for subaerial flow deposits (Fig. 14) shows a basal relatively thin, cross-bedded, surge deposit resting sharply on an underlying fall deposit. The surge is overlain by a thicker *flow* deposit. The top of the sequence consists of a thin, cross-bedded ash-cloud deposit overlain by falls. The *flow* "division" may be massive or reversely graded (Fisher, 1982b). Alternatively, in the model proposed by Sparks *et al.* (1973), the lithic clasts, concentrated at the base, are normally graded whereas the size of the pumiceous fragments increases upward to reach a maximum at the top of the bed. These two "standard" sequences contrast with those observed in the surge deposits of Mount St. Helens (Fig. 16), and in subaqueous deposits described

by Fiske and Matsuda (1964), Fiske (1969), Bond (1973), and Tassé *et al.* (1978), where the accumulation is normally graded by size and (or) density and the cross-bedded surge "division" underlying the flow is not present. Normal grading of lithic clasts is a frequent feature of many ancient and recent deposits of the world (Sparks *et al.*, 1973). Pumice clasts may be either reversely or normally graded. In many subaerial deposits the pumices are reversely graded, and normal grading of pumices seems rare. In such deposits, the pumice size may increase gradually from base to top (true reverse grading), or the larger pumices may be concentrated in an upper horizon within the bed (Sparks, 1976). The reverse grading of pumices is explained by flotation, the matrix being denser than the fragments. In beds of subaequeous deposits, the pumices and the lithic fragments may be concentrated in different horizons but both types of fragment commonly show similar grading trends, reverse or normal (Fiske and Matsuda, 1964; Yamada, 1973; Bond, 1973; Tassé *et al.*, 1978).

From the above descriptions, it seems clear that "standard" beds do not exist in pyroclastic flow deposits. I believe most workers would agree with this opinion. The characteristics of the deposit vary with the type of eruption, and the velocity, density, and viscosity of the flow.

Deposits close to vent will have different characteristics from those observed more distally.

In pyroclastic deposits that originate from flows, grain size and bed thickness may either decrease or increase downflow depending on the origin of the deposit. The maximum radial distance where base-surge deposits have been recognized is about the same as the diameter of the vent (Fisher, 1982a, p. 84). Ashcloud surges do not occur near the vent, and their thickness increases down flow (Fisher, 1979; Fig. 17).

Wohletz and Sheridan (1979) proposed a model for lateral variations in base-surge deposits (Fig. 17A) in which a proximal, cross-bedded facies passes down-flow within some 500 m (the scale is important) to a massive and reversely graded facies. Bed thickness decreases very rapidly in the direction of transport in the cross-bedded facies but not in the massive facies where there is no systematic varations. Sorting is poor ($\sigma\phi$ ranging from 1.6 to 1.88) for the entire deposit, but grain size *increases* from a mean of 2.6 ϕ (0.177 mm) in the cross-bedded facies to -0.48 ϕ (30 mm) in the more distal massive beds. According to Wohletz and Sheridan (1979), the surge is inflated (fluidized) by the volatiles on

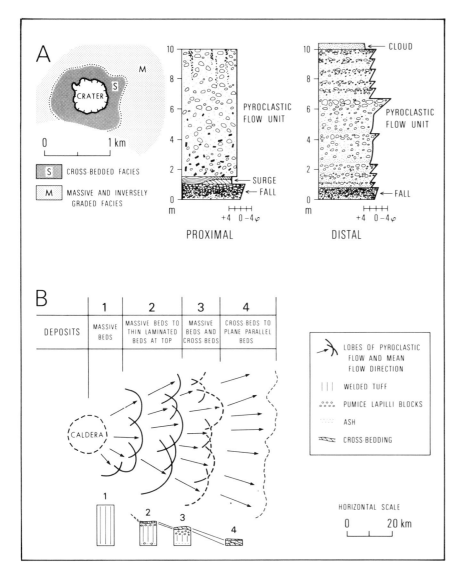

Figure 17
Lateral variations in thickness and primary structures in some pyroclastic surges, and flow deposits.
A: Facies in pyroclastic surges, and in intermediate to large flows; modified from

Wohletz and Sheridan (1979), and Sheridan (1979).
B: Ash-cloud surge (2,3,4) developed from pyroclastic flow (1) showing relative thicknesses. Modified from Fisher (1979).

the surge (Fig. 17A), the lithic fragments are normally graded whereas pumiceous fragments may either be ungraded, normally, or reversely graded (Sheridan, 1979; Sparks et al., 1973). Gas-escape pipes are common. In distal sections, the surge is absent; the flow deposits have few lithic clasts, and pumiceous fragments are concentrated near the top of layers (beds) which may represent individual flow pulses (Sheridan, 1979).

The thickness of ash-cloud-surge deposits increases away from the vent (Fig. 17B), and their bedforms vary from plane bed to dune. The ash-cloud deposits of Mt. Pelée are normally graded; the mean size of the larger clasts decreases in the direction of transport, whereas the median and sorting $(\sigma\phi)$ do not have significant variations (Fisher and Heiken, 1982).

Pyroclastic-Flow Deposits in The Stratigraphic Record
Can any of the facies just described be recognized in the stratigraphic column as far back even as the Archean? What are the characteristics which would permit the identification of a base-surge deposit rather than an ash-cloud surge in the absence of the *pyroclastic-flow* "division"? How does one distinguish between the massive facies of base-surge deposits and massive *pyroclastic-flow* deposits? What is the probability of finding a section as close as 500 m to the original position of a vent, now folded and eroded? Are subaqueous deposits similar to subaerial? What is the basal portion of an eruptive event in deposits that lack paleosols, and burned vegetation debris? These are some of the questions that come to mind when dealing with older sequences, and none can as yet be satisfactorily answered. One cannot call all cross-bedded deposits surges, nor everything that is massive a *flow* or a lahar. If one did, the basin analysis might prove to be difficult. The object of mapping facies in volcaniclastic rocks is fundamental for paleogeographic reconstructions. It also has an important economic implication, because many sulphide deposits are associated with volcaniclastic rocks, particularly with the coarse facies. The identification of these coarse facies and the prediction of their position in the stratigraphic sequences is therefore important for many geologists.

eruption to such an extent that velocities are extremely high and viscosities very low. Therefore, turbulence sets in close to the vent, resulting in traction that produces the observed primary structures. The cloud travels horizontally down-slope, away from the vent, aided by gravity. Gases escape rapidly and the cloud deflates, resulting in a higher concentration of grains, leading to the laminar flow responsible for the massive and reversely graded distal facies. Cloud deflation, however, cannot explain the large lateral increase in grain size from fine sand to coarse pebbles. Fisher (1982a) suggested that the dis-

tinction between the two facies occurs where the flow segregates by gravity into a laminar bed load, and an overlying turbulent flow. Many base-surge deposits have characteristics that suggest a decrease in flow power away from the vent. Fisher (1982a, p. 84) gives examples of deposits in which grain size decreases with increasing sorting. In some of these deposits bedforms vary from antidune to plane bed (Schmincke et al., 1973). This leaves us with two very contrasting models of base-surge deposits.

In the proximal sections of the *pyroclastic-flow* deposit found above

The solution to the problem is to map volcaniclastic rocks as sediments, which they are. Most are transported as mass flows for which models of accumulation are well established. In many types of flow, the fluid is gas rather than water. In these flows, gases play a major role in the suspension of volcaniclastic material, but elutriation is considered to be active in areas close to the vent so that gravity becomes imprtant in the mobility of pyroclastic flows early in their history. Air cushioning has been suggested as a suspension agent, but Sheridan (1979) notes that the available data argue against incorporation of large volumes of air by the flow, and that the air cushion remains to be proved as an effective suspension agent. Lacroix (1904) showed quite conclusively that gravity plays an important role in the mobility of pyroclastic flows, a conclusion that many workers accept as fact. It follows that the physics which applies to these flows should be similar, if not identical, to those of other density flows. Given similar flow parameters (density, viscosity, velocity, and thickness), and grain size, deposits of all types of flow will have similar sedimentary characteristics, which is well illustrated by the preceding examples. There is therefore little or no chance of defining only one model that will characterize subaqueous or subaerial flows.

In most models of volcaniclastic deposits that originate from density flows, the characteristics may be explained in terms of decrease in flow power and/or by an increase in turbulence due to flow dilution or segregation in the direction of transport. In such deposits primary structures that are controlled both by flow parameters and by grain size are certainly the best tool to define and map

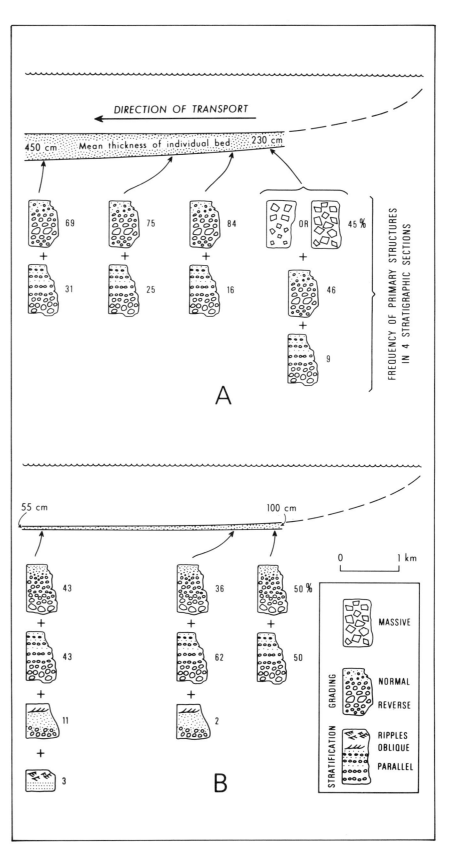

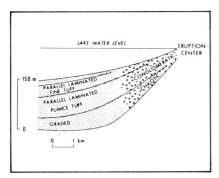

Figure 18
Lateral variations of size and primary structures in a Pleistocene pyroclastic flow deposit in Japan. Modified from Yamada (1973).

Figure 19
Lateral variations of mean bed thickness and primary structure sequences with distance of transport, in an Archean subaqueous pyroclastic flow deposit. High concentration (A) and low concentration (B) suspension deposits are shown (see text). The frequency distributions of structure sequences are in percentages, and total 100% for each section. Modified from Tassé et al., (1978).

Figure 20
Grading in Archean pyroclastic deposits. Reversely graded lithics of intermediate composition; Renault, Rouyn-Noranda, Québec; top is to left; notebook is 30 cm long.

Figure 21
Primary-structure sequence in a type B bed, Rouyn-Noranda, Quebec. From Tassé et al. (1978).

facies. What I am suggesting here is that one should characterize and map one's own facies as defined by combinations of what one sees locally in the field rather than trying to fit in with the "facies" of pyroclastic flows and falls as defined earlier. Yamada (1973) proposed a model (Fig. 18) for lateral variations of primary structures for a subaqueous deposit of Pleistocene age. Tassé et al. (1978) used a similar approach for Archean rocks, and Figure 19 is a simplified version of the model that they proposed. The rocks that were studied are intermediate in composition and not welded. The sections show two distinct bed types that have different mean-thickness, grain size, and primary structures. The two types are therefore treated in two different assemblages (A and B, Fig. 19). Type A beds (Fig. 20) are thicker than type B (Fig. 21) and mean bed thickness increases with distance of transport in type A whereas it decreases in type B. In both bed types, primary structure sequences vary systematically away from the vent, but the sequences are somewhat different in the two types. In type A beds, the most abundant structure is grading, and parallel lamination is relatively rare. The proximal section has a high proportion of massive or reversely graded beds whereas the distal section is characterized by normal grading, and a higher number of beds that show parallel lami-

nations. The two intermediate sections suggest a gradation from the proximal to the distal facies. Grading is also very common in type B beds, and is generally normal. Traction structures, such as parallel and oblique laminations (dunes and ripples) are more abundant than in type A, and their proportion increases with distance of transport.

Tassé et al. (1978) interpreted the lateral variation of facies by analogy with sedimentary density flows. Type B beds most probably result from the accumulation of decelerating turbulent suspensions of low density such as turbidity currents. Most of the flows responsible for type A beds appear to have been turbulent in the distal regions, but almost half (45%) of the deposits in the more proximal section probably accumulated from laminar suspensions such as debris flows, as suggested by the reverse grading and massive beds. It follows that different transporting mechanisms acted at different stages of the flows. This may be caused by an increase in flow velocity due to gravity, coupled with a decrease in viscosity.

In the subaqueous deposits of Noranda the ratio between lithic fragments and pumice decreases with distance from the vent. This relationship has also been observed in some Japanese deposits (Kuno et al., 1964), and is opposite to the pumice-lithic ratio commonly found in pyroclastic fall

deposits. This is due to the lower density of the pumice which settles at lower velocities, and is therefore found further down flow.

Grain orientation may also be used along with other lateral variations such as grain size, bed thickness, and primary structures to help locate vents and proximal facies. The grain orientation technique is described by Elston and Smith (1970), and was used successfully in Archean pyroclastic sequences of northwestern Ontario (Teal, 1979).

Subaerial flow deposits may show facies that are similar to those of subaqueous flows, but because of the higher temperature of the mass and, in certain cases the higher viscosities, they may exhibit different characteristics. Rhyolitic flows have fragments that are commonly deformed, stretched, and welded. The eutaxitic "texture" that results from the parallel arrangement and alternation of layers of different textures or composition may be common in these rocks. The structures are found in deposits that accumulated from laminar suspensions (Schmincke and Swanson, 1967) but they also occur in turbulent flow deposits (Lock, 1972).

There is reason to believe that, given similar flow properties, subaerial deposits would show lateral variations similar to those described by Tassé et al. (1978) in subaqueous deposits. The deposit of the May 18, 1980 eruption of Mount St. Helens described by Moore and Sisson (1981) is an example. The deposit (Fig. 22) consists of a coarse basal unit that is massive or normally graded, channelized in the flow axis. It is overlain by a

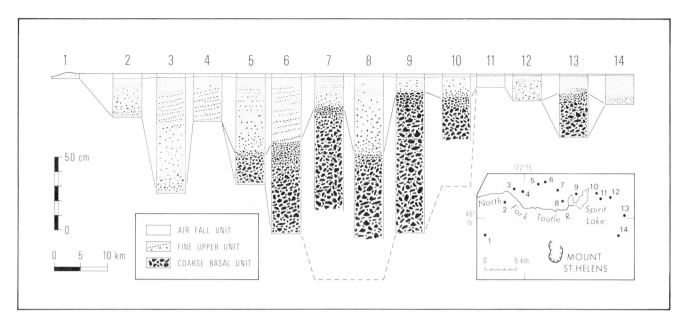

Figure 22
Lateral variations of bed thickness and primary structures in the May 18, 1980 surge deposit of Mount St. Helens. From Moore and Sisson (1981).

finer upper unit with a massive or normally graded lower portion which grades upward into laminated or cross-laminated ash. The thickness of the lower graded "division" of this upper unit decreases away from flow axis, and lamination and cross lamination become increasingly well developed. This suggests accumulation from a decelerating turbulent suspension, not unlike some of the Type B beds described by Tassé *et al*. (1978).

Little is known of vertical facies sequences in pyroclastic-flow deposits. Most workers have focussed their attention on eruptive cycles (e.g., Aramaki and Yamasaki, 1963; and Sparks *et al*., 1973). In pyroclastic-flow deposits, bed thickness and maximum grain size are greatly influenced by the intensity of the eruptive event so that vertical sequential evolutions will not follow fining and coarsening models that are presented elsewhere in this volume for other types of sedimentary deposits.

The distinction between subaerial and subaqueous deposits is not always easy because evidence is commonly indirect. Primary structures, and structure sequences are not valid criteria. Accretionary lapilli found at the top of many flows suggest a subaerial environment and bomb-sags do not occur in deep water deposits, but workers must often rely on fossils or the presence of pillows in the sequence. A word of cau-

tion here; pillows form under water, but it is not necessary for the entire sequence in which they occur to be subaqueous. Pillows are present 1000 m above sea level in Guadeloupe, and the recent overlying accumulations are subaerial. Welding of fragments has been used as evidence for subaerial deposition, but there are known occurrences of subaqueous deposits that are welded.

Distinction Between Pyroclastic-Flow and Fall Deposits

Table 1 sums up the differences that may be observed between beds of fall and flow deposits. Many of these particular characteristics are discussed in preceeding sections. Mantle bedding is commonly observed in fall deposits and is very characteristic. Like a blanket, the deposit drapes irregularities in the underlying surface with little or no bed-

Table 1
Differences that may be observed between beds of fall and flow deposits.

	Fall	Flow
Sorting	Relatively well sorted (see text)	Relatively poorly sorted.
Bed thickness	Regular and drapes the underlying surface (mantle bedding).	Irregular. Thins over highs, thickens in depressions. Thins laterally towards channel margins.
Grading and laminations	Massive beds are rare; normal grading of size and density is common; reverse grading is rare. Absence of traction structures such as parallel and oblique laminations.	Massive beds and reverse grading are common in beds that have accumulated from laminar suspensions (debris flows). Normal grading is common in deposits from turbulent suspensions, but it is generally found underlying or overlying a laminated division.
Other primary structures	Bomb-sags and accretionary lapilli are common in subaerial or shallow-water deposits. Gas-escape pipes are absent.	Both structures are rare or absent. Gas-escape pipes are common.
Primary structure sequences	Absent.	Common; may be similar to those observed in turbidites or to models discussed in text (see Fig. 14).

50

thickness variations even on steep slopes.

Much work has been done on statistical parameters of grain size distribution to help make the distinction between flow and fall deposits (Walker, 1971; Sheridan, 1971). The most commonly used diagram (Fig. 23) is that of Walker (1971) which shows some differences in sorting between the two deposits, but with considerable overlap. The sorting coefficient that is used, Inman's graphic sorting coefficient, may not be the best

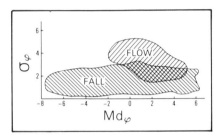

Figure 23
Grain-size characteristics of pyroclastic flow and fall deposits. From Walker, 1971.

method to evaluate sorting in such deposits. The inclusive deviation of Folk and Ward (1957) could give better results. Needless to say, the method can only be used in recent deposits that can be sieved, because measurements from thin sections cannot be correlated with sieve equivalents in such deposits.

Primary structures and particularly structure sequences are used successfully to distinguish the two deposit types. Flows leave imprints that are different from falls.

SUMMARY
The purpose of this article has been to present what is known of facies relationships in some autoclastic rocks, and in pyroclastic fall and flow deposits. Autoclastic fragments that are formed *in situ* are monogenetic and not welded. The clastites may be transitional with the parent magma, and have the same composition. The internal structures of these deposits indicates the absence or near absence of transport.

Pyroclastic fall deposits are well stratified. They commonly show a systematic lateral decrease in grain size and bed thickness. In such deposits, sorting is poorest close to the source due to settling of fragments of different densities. In fall deposits, the vertical variations

are controlled by eruption intensity, and are therefore unpredictible.

In flow deposits, bed thickness and grain size commonly decrease down flow, but close to vent the variations are not systematic. Beds deposited from flows are commonly graded. In subaqueous deposits the grading of all fragments is generally normal but in many subaerial flows, pumices are commonly reversely graded. The primary structure sequences vary systematically downflow, and depict the changing flow conditions (density, viscosity, velocity) and the grain size that is transported. Vertical variations of size and thickness are poorly known in these deposits.

Statistical parameters of grain size have been used extensively to distinguish pyroclastic flows from falls. Primary structure sequences are also a powerful tool that can help make this distinction.

The assemblage of characteristics presented for pyroclastic flows and falls can be used as a norm or predictor, and thus define these two groups of deposits in the stratigraphic record. However, the models proposed for recent pyroclastic-flow deposits are incompletely tested and insufficiently documented, and thus cannot be used as predictors or norms for older deposits. Most recent work has been done on volcanoes or in areas in their immediate vicinity so that much emphasis has been placed on characteristics that are near the vent. In the rock record where there has been much folding and erosion, the models derived from these recent deposits have probably been lost. With our present state of knowledge, it is futile to try to correlate models for recent deposits to ancient rocks, and it is suggested that one should characterize and map one's own facies as defined by combinations of what one sees locally in the field. In short, treat these rocks as sediments, which is what they are!

ACKNOWLEDGEMENTS
Léopold Gélinas, John Ludden, and Roger G. Walker kindly read earlier versions of this manuscript and offered many helpful suggestions for its improvement.

REFERENCES

GENERAL

Heiken, G.H., 1972. Morphology and petrography of volcanic ashes. Geological Society of America Bulletin, v. 83, p. 1961-1988.
Petrography, chemical analyses, and scanning electron microscopy of ashes to characterize different types of volcanic eruptions, and to relate morphology to magma composition. Good description with examples.

Heiken, G.H., 1974. An atlas of volcanic ash. Smithsonian Contributions to the Earth Sciences, No. 12, 101 p.
An expanded version of the above. Descriptions of three-dimensional forms, and of this sections of a large number of ash samples. Excellent descriptions and photographs.

Ross, C.S., and Smith, R.L., 1961. Ash-flow tuffs: their origin, geologic relations and identification. United States Geological Survey, Professional Paper 366, 81 p.
A good text with abundant photographs. Excellent review of the literature. Excellent descriptions.

Williams, H., and McBirney, A.R., 1979. Volcanology. San Francisco, Freeman, Cooper and Company, 397 p.
A good and recent introduction to the subject.

NOMENCLATURE AND CLASSIFICATION

Fisher, R.V., 1961. Proposed classification of volcaniclastic sediments and rocks. Geological Society of America Bulletin, v. 72, p. 1409-1414.

Fisher, R.V., 1966. Rocks composed of volcanic fragments and their classification. Earth Science Reviews, v. 1, p. 287-298.

Walker, G.P.L., 1973. Explosive volcanic eruptions — a new classification scheme. Geologische Rundschau, v. 62, p. 431-446.

Wentworth, C.K. and Williams, H., 1932. The classification and terminology of the pyroclastic rocks. National Research Council Bulletin, v. 89, p. 19-53.

Wright, J.V., Smith, A.L. and Self, S., 1980. A working terminology of pyroclastic deposits. Journal of Volcanology and Geothermal Research, v. 8, p. 315-336.

AUTOCLASTIC ROCKS

Carlisle, D., 1963. Pillow breccias and their aquagene tuffs. Quadra Island, British Columbia. Journal of Geology, v. 71, p. 48-71.

Dimroth, E., Cousineau, P., Leduc, M., and Sanschagrin, Y., 1978, Structure and organization of Archean subaqueous basalt flows, Rouyn-Noranda, Québec,

Canada. Canadian Journal of Earth Sciences, v. 15, p. 902-918.

Fink, J., 1980. Surface folding and viscosity of rhyolite flows. Geology, v. 8, p. 250-254.

Furnes, H., Fridleifsson, I.B., and Atkins, F.B., 1980. Subglacial volcanics – on the formation of acid hyaloclastite. Journal of Volcanology and Geothermal Research, v. 8, p. 95-110.

Honnorez, J. and Kirst, P., 1975. Submarine basaltic volcanism: morphometric parameters for discriminating hyalocastites from hyalotuffs. Bulletin Volcanologique, v. 39, p. 441-465.
A good review of the literature, origin, and characteristics of hyaloclastites.

Pichler, H., 1965. Acid hyaloclastites. Bulletin Volcanologique, v. 28, p. 293-311.

PYROCLASTIC FALL AND FLOW

Ayres, L.D., ed., 1982. Pyroclastic volcanism and deposits of Cenozoic intermediate to felsic volcanic islands with implications for Precambrian greenstone-belt volcanoes. Geological Association of Canada, Short Course Notes, v. 2, 365 p.
Contains excellent reviews of Cenozoic pyroclastic deposits in contributions by Fisher. Inexpensive.

Bond, A. and Sparks, R.S.J., 1976. The Minoan eruption of Santorini, Greece. Journal of the Geological Society, v. 132, p. 1-16.

Brazier, S., Davis, A.N., Sigurdsson, H., and Sparks, R.S.J., 1982. Fall out and deposition of volcanic ash during the 1979 explosive eruption of the Soufrière of St. Vincent. Journal of Volcanology and Geothermal Research, v. 14, p. 335-359.

Elston, W.E., and Smith, E.-I., 1970. Determination of flow direction of rhyolitic ash flow tuffs from fluidal textures. Geological Society of America Bulletin, v. 81, p. 3393-3406.
Grain-orientation measurements are described and used for determinatin of flow direction.

Fisher, R.V., 1979. Models for pyroclastic surges and pyroclastic flows. Journal of Volcanology and Geothermal Research, v. 6, p. 305-318.

Fisher, R.V., 1982a. Pyroclastic surges. In Ayres, L.D., ed., Pyroclastic volcanism and deposits of Cenozoic intermedite to felsic volcanic islands with implications for Precambrian greenstone-belt volcanoes. Geological Association of Canada, Short Course Notes, v. 2, p. 71-110.

Fisher, R.V., 1982b. Pyroclastic flows. In Ayres, L.D., ed., Pyroclastic volcanism and deposits of Cenozoic intermedite to felsic volcanic islands with implications for Pre-

cambrian greenstone-belt volcanoes. Geological Association of Canada, Short Course Notes, v. 2, p. 111-132.

Fisher, R.V., 1982c. Debris flows and lahars. In Ayres, L.D., ed., Pyroclastic volcanism and deposits of Cenozoic intermediate to felsic volcanic islands with implications for Precambrian greenstone-belt volcanoes. Geological Association of Canada, Short Course Notes, v. 2, p. 136-190.

Fisher, R.V., and Heiken, G., 1982. Mt. Pelée, Martinique: May 8 and 20, 1902, pyroclastic flows and surges. Journal of Volcanology and Geothermal Research, v. 13, p. 339-371.

Fisher, R.V., Smith, A.L., and Roobol, M.J., 1980. Destruction of St. Pierre, Martinique by ash-could surges, May 8 and 20, 1902. Geology, v. 8, p. 472-476.

Fisher, R.V. and Schmincke, H.-U., 1984. Pyroclastic rocks. New York, Springer-Verlag, 528 p.
A new textbook by two experts in the field.

Fiske, R.S., 1969. Recognition and significance of pumice in marine pyroclastic rocks. Geological Society of America Bulletin, v. 80, p. 1-8.

Fiske, R.S., and Matsuda, T., 1964. Submarine equivalents of ash flows in the Tokiwa Formation, Japan. American Journal of Science, v. 262, p. 76-106.

Gélinas, L., Lajoie, J., Bouchard, M., Simard, A., Verpaelst, P., et Sansfaçon, R., 1978. Les complexes rhyolitiques de la région de Rouyn-Noranda. Ministère des richesses naturelles du Québec, rapport DPV,-583, 49 p.

Kuno, H., Ishikawa, T., Yagi, K., Yamasaki, M., and Taneta, S., 1964. Sorting of pumice and lithic fragments as a key to eruptive and emplacement mechanism. Japan Journal of Geology and Geography, v. 35, p. 223-238.

Lacroix, A., 1904. La montagne pelée et ses éruptions. Paris, France, Masson et Cie, 662 p.
A classic study with excellent descriptions of nuées ardentes. A must for anyone interested in pyroclastic flows.

Lipman, P.W., and Mullineaux, D.R., 1981. The 1980 eruptions of Mount St. Helens, Washington. United States Geological Survey, Professional Paper 1250, 844 p.

Moore, J.G., and Sisson, T.W., 1981. Deposits and effects of the May 18 pyroclastic surge. In Lipman, P.W., and Mullineaux, D.R., eds., The 1980 eruptions of Mount St. Helens, Washington. United States Geological Survey, Professional Paper 1250, p. 421-438.
Perhaps the only published analysis of lateral variations in subaerial pyroclastic flow

deposits.

Schmincke, H.-U., and Swanson, D.A., 1967. Laminar viscous flowage structures in ash-flow tuffs from Gran Canaria, Canary Islands. Journal of Geology, v. 75, p. 641-664.
Good descriptions of textures and structures.

Sheridan, M.F., 1979. Emplacement of pyroclastic flows: A review. In Chapin, C.E., and Elston, W.E., eds., Ashflow tuffs. Geological Society of America, Special Paper 180, p. 125-136.
One of the best papers to come out on the subject in recent years.

Sparks, R.S.J., 1976. Grain size variations in ignimbrites and implications for the transport of pyroclastic flows. Sedimentology, v. 23, p. 147-188.

Sparks, R.S.J., Self, S., and Walker, G.P.L., 1973. Products of ignimbrite eruptions. Geology, v. 1, p. 115-122.

Tassé, N., Lajoie, J., and Dimroth, E., 1978. The anatomy and interpretation of an Archean volcaniclastic sequence, Noranda region, Quebec. Canadian Journal of Earth Sciences, v. 15, p. 874-888.
One of the rare analysis of lateral variations in subaqueous pyroclastic flow deposits.

Teal, P.R., 1979. Stratigraphy, sedimentology, volcanology, and development of the Archean Manitou Group, Northwestern Ontario, Canada. Hamilton, Canada, McMaster University, Unpublished Ph.D. Thesis, 291 p.

Walker, G.P.L., and Croasdale, R., 1971. Characteristics of some basaltic pyroclastics. Bulletin Volcanologique, v. 35, p. 303-317.
A relatively good description of fall deposits.

Wohletz, K.H., and Sheridan, M.F., 1979. A model of pyroclastic surge. In Chapin, C.E., and Elston, W.E., eds., Ash-flow tuffs. Geological Society of America, Special Paper 180, p. 177-194.

Yamada, E., 1973. Subaqueous pumice flow deposits in the Onikobe Caldera, Miyagi Prefecture, Japan. Journal of the Geological Society of Japan, v. 79, p. 585-597.

DISTINCTION BETWEEN PYROCLASTIC FLOW AND FALL

Sheridan, M.F., 1971. Particle-size characteristics of pyroclastic tuffs. Journal of Geophysical Research, v. 76, p. 5627-5634.

Walker, G.P.L., 1971. Grain-size characteristics of pyroclastic deposits. Journal of Geology, v. 79, p. 696-714.
An excellent review of size characteristics of more than 1000 samples of flow and fall deposits.

52

OTHER REFERENCES CITED

Aramaki, S., and Yamasaki, M., 1963. Pyroclastic flows in Japan. Bulletin Volcanologique, v. 26, p. 89-99.

Bond, G.A., 1973. A late Paleozoic volcanic arc in the Eastern Alaska Range, Alaska. Journal of Geology, v. 81, p. 557-575.

deRosen-Spence, A., Provost, G., Dimroth, E., Gochnauer, G., and Owen, V., 1980. Archean subaqueous felsic flows, Rouyn-Noranda, Quebec, Canada and their Quaternary equivalents. Precambrian Research, v. 12, p. 43-77.

Folk, R.L., and Ward, W.C., 1957. Brazos River Bar: a study in the significance of grain size parameters. Journal of Sedimentary Petrology, v. 66, p. 3-27.

Koch, A.J., and McLean, H., 1975. Pleistocene tephra and ash-flow deposits in the volcanic highlands of Guatemala. Geological Society of America Bulletin, v. 86, p. 529-541.

Lock, B.E., 1972. A lower Paleozoic rheoignimbrite from White Bay, Newfoundland. Canadian Journal of Earth Sciences, v. 9, p. 1495-1503.

Sarna-Wojcicki, A.M., Waitt, R.B., Jr., Woodward, M.J., Shipley, S., and Rivera, J., 1981. Premagmatic ash erupted from March 27 through May 14, 1980 – extent, mass, volume, and composition. *In* Lipman, P.W., and Mullineaux, D.R., eds., The 1980 eruptions of Mount St. Helens, Washington. United States Geological Survey, Professional Paper 1250, p. 569-576.

Self, S., 1982. Deposits of the vent area and air-fall deposits. *in* Ayres, L.D., ed., Pyroclastic volcanism and deposits of Cenozoic intermediate to felsic volcanic islands with implications for Precambrian greenstone-belt volcanoes. Geological Association of Canada, Short Course Notes, v. 2, p. 64-70.

Schmincke, H.-U., Fisher, R.V., and Waters, A.C., 1973. Antidune and chute and pool structures in the base-surge deposits of the Laacher See area, Germany. Sedimentology, v. 20, p. 553-574.

Sigurdsson, H. 1982. Volcanic sediments in island arcs. *In* Ayres, L.D., ed., Pyroclastic volcanism and deposits of Cenozoic intermediate to felsic volcanic islands with implications for Precambrian greenstone-belt volcanoes. Geological Association of Canada, Short Course Notes, v. 2, p. 221-293.

Coarse Alluvial Deposits

BRIAN R. RUST
Department of Geology
University of Ottawa
Ottawa, Ontario K1N 6N5

EMLYN H. KOSTER
Alberta Geological Survey
4445 Calgary Trail South
Edmonton, Alberta T6H 5R7

INTRODUCTION

Alluvial conglomerates are minor components of the stratigraphic record, but their tectonic and paleoclimatic significance give them an importance far greater than their abundance implies. They are indicators of the sharp terrestrial relief resulting from lithospheric uplift at continental margins and from intra-cratonic faulting. They are also indicative of climatic extremes, for the production of large lithic fragments is maximized on steep slopes in semi-arid or paraglacial/alpine settings (Wilson, 1973). The study of alluvial conglomerates can, therefore, reveal important tectonic or paleoclimatic influences on sedimentation and basin evolution.

Coarse-grained alluvial deposits also have economic importance, notably the Witwatersrand placer gold and uranium ores of South Africa (Minter, 1978; Smith and Minter, 1980) and the similar uraniferous conglomerates of the Blind River-Elliot Lake area, Canada (Pienaar, 1963). Robertson *et al.* (1978) noted that uranium placer deposits are confined to rocks between 3.0 and 2.2 billion years old, because their formation ceased when the atmosphere became oxygenic. Thick, laterally impersistent coals are associated with intermontane alluvial deposits, some conglomeratic, as described by Heward (1978) and Long (1981).

Compared with studies of sandy fluvial systems, those on alluvial gravels are hampered by problems of scale in flume work, and by the high energy and rarity of natural flows capable of transporting large clasts. In addition, clast size is not necessarily a function of flow competence alone; availability from the source terrane may also be a factor. For these reasons, experimental studies have not contributed greatly to gravel models, although notable exceptions are the work of Koster (1978b) and Southard *et al.* (1984).Studies of modern gravel systems are mainly geomorphic, because of the difficulty of observing active gravel transport, and of coring or trenching gravel. Another problem is the strong influence of Quaternary glaciation on present-day alluvial gravel transport in many parts of the world, an influence present only intermittently in the past. The recognition and interpretation of structures in gravels and conglomerates requires extensive, good quality exposure, which is rare in modern gravels. Both gravels and conglomerates are hard to interpret from cores, and commonly cannot be distinguished from sandstones using borehole logs (Cant, "Subsurface Facies Analysis", this volume).

From the discussion above it is evident that there are abundant data on the geomorphic features of alluvial gravels, but we rely heavily on the ancient record for evidence of stratal type and stratification sequence. This means that coarse alluvial facies models have rather limited use for hydrodynamic interpretation (Walker, 1979). Their function as guides and predictors relates to varia-

tions in external factors, largely climatic and tectonic. Recent reviews which provide useful insights are those of Miall (1977), Collinson (1978), Nilsen (1982) and Chapter 6 of Harms *et al.* (1982). Symposium volumes edited by Miall (1978a), Collinson and Lewin (1983) and Koster and Steel (1984) include additional reviews, case histories and discussions of alluvial models.

TERMINOLOGY

The facies terminology used here (Table 1) is that of Miall (1978b). We restrict the term coarse-grained to successions that contain at least 50% gravel, which are therefore dominated by facies prefixed G in Table 1. Sand facies are also present, but in subordinate amounts. In effect, this limits the discussion to braided alluvium, characterised by multiple, low-sinuosity, relatively unstable channels (Rust, 1978a). Various authors, for example McGowen and Garner (1970) and Jackson (1976, 1978) have described meandering-fluvial deposits containing gravel. However, the coarse sediment is restricted to lag accumulations within channels, constituting less than half the total succession. Exceptions are the deposits of streams like the Little Wind River (Jackson, 1978) and the Jarama River, Spain (Arche, 1983), which contains gravel in large-scale cross-strata formed by lateral migration of meander bars. Smith and Smith (1980) reported gravel-filled channels in the anastomosing Columbia River, but Smith (1983, p. 161) showed that these channel sediments are mainly coarse sand and granules. The valley fill is dominated by finer overbank deposits,

Table 1
Facies typical of fans and braidplain deposits (Miall, 1977; as modified by Miall, 1978 and Rust, 1978).

Major facies —	Gm:	Clast-supported, commonly imbricate gravel with poorly defined sub-horizontal bedding.
	Gms:	Muddy matrix-supported gravel without imbrication or internal stratification
	Gt:	Trough cross-bedded clast-supported gravel
	Gp:	Planar cross-bedded gravel, transitional from clast-supported gravel through sand matrix-supported gravel to sand (Sp)
Minor facies —	Sh:	Horizontally stratified sand
	St:	Trough cross-stratified sand
	Sp:	Planar cross-stratified sand
	Fm:	Massive fine sandy mud or mud
	Fl:	Laminated or cross-laminated very fine sand, silt or mud
	P:	Pedogenic concretionary carbonate

Table 2
Descriptive parameters for gravels/conglomerates.

- maximum clast size vs. bed thickness relationship

MATRIX
- size, sorting
- mineralogy
- pedogenic modification

COARSE FRACTION
- size, sorting
- shape, sorting } textural maturity
- fabric
- lithotypes and compositional maturity

- clast or matrix-supported
- diagenetic changes
- porosity and permeability

INDIVIDUAL BEDS
- boundaries
- distribution and thickness
- preserved bedforms, stratification
- grading
- fossil content

SUCCESSION
- temporal trends in bed character
- stratigraphic relationships with associated facies

Figure 1
Planar cross-stratified conglomerate (facies Gp) in the Middle Devonian Malbaie Formation, Pte. St-Pierre, Quebec. Notebook 19 cm long. Note sorting on cross-strata and sparry calcite cement filling voids in openwork conglomerate (arrowed). See Rust (in press, b).

so that the overall proportion of gravel is small (Smith, 1983, Fig. 5).

An important descriptive parameter for gravels and conglomerates is the relationship between framework (clasts greater than 2 mm in diameter) and matrix (sand- and mud-sized particles) (Table 2). Framework-supported gravel results from deposition of gravel bedload by an energetic aqueous flow that keeps sand in suspension. As flow velocity decreases, the sand infiltrates the spaces between the framework particles (Smith, 1974; Eynon and Walker, 1974; Beschta and Jackson, 1979). Openwork gravel is less common, and results from incomplete matrix infiltration, which ocurs mostly during the rapid accumulation of gravel on cross-strata (Fig. 1). There are two types of matrix-supported gravel: those with stratified sand matrix, and those with unstratified matrix, commonly of muddy sand. The former type indicates aqueous transport, but at an energy level lower than for framework gravel, so that sand and fine gravel are deposited together. The second type of matrix-supported gravel is typified by facies Gms (Table 1), which, in the alluvial context, forms mainly by debris flow deposition.

Other descriptive parameters include particle shape and fabric (Koster *et al.,* 1980) and stratification and stratal sequence (Table 2 and Harms *et al.,* 1982). Aqueous deposition commonly forms a fabric in which maximum projection *(ab)* planes dip upstream at ` moderate angles, and *a* axes are perpendicular to flow, due to rolling on the bed (Rust 1972b, 1975). Fabrics with *a* parallel to flow are less common, and apparently result from more energetic aqueous transport, in which elongate pebbles saltate longitudinally (Johansson, 1965). Stratification boundaries are commonly gradational, but may be abrupt or erosional. In contrast, debris flow deposits normally lack internal stratification and fabric.

DEPOSITIONAL ENVIRONMENTS

Alluvial gravels accumulate in two related depositional environments: 1) *fans,* and 2) *braided rivers and braidplains.*

Alluvial fans form where streams confined by narrow valleys emerge onto a plain or major trunk valley (Fig. 2). Related gravel-bearing landforms are the steep talus cones that accumulate below mountain gullies (Church *et al.,*

Figure 2
Block diagram of alluvial fans tributary to a braided river in a trunk valley. D) debris flows.

1979; White, 1981), and pediment mantles. Pediments are sloping surfaces cut on bedrock by streams emerging from mountain valleys, which are normally covered by a thin alluvial mantle (Denny, 1967; Twidale, 1979). Sedimentation under these conditions, particularly alluvial fan development, occurs in response to a sharp decrease in transport efficiency as the stream emerges from its confined valley. A semi-conical landform is built, with slopes and transport directions radiating from the mouth of the source valley. Grain size decreases rapidly down fan (Figs. 3 and 4), and roundness of gravels increases, whereas the proportion of finer facies increases distally (Fig. 3). Conditions on the steep valley slopes adjacent to alluvial fans commonly give rise to debris flows, particularly in proximal fan reaches (Fig. 2).

In contrast, *braided rivers and braid-plains* (Allen, 1975) have two-dimensional depositional surfaces with lower slopes. Drainage patterns are essentially parallel, although they may radiate or converge locally due to increasing or decreasing space at the margins of the river or braidplain (Fig. 5). Downslope decrease in grain size and attendant facies changes occur over a considerable distance, generally an order of magnitude greater than that required for equivalent facies changes on alluvial fans (Fig. 4). Debris flows are rarely deposited, and if so, are unlikely to survive reworking by aqueous flows.

Some authors have extended the term fan to what are regarded here as braidplains, for example the Scott fan of Boothroyd and Ashley (1975). Boothroyd and Nummedal (1978) referred to coastal outwash plains in Iceland as alluvial fans. These landforms are morphologically unlike fans, and their sediment dispersal patterns and facies fit the braidplain model.

Alluvial fans that are tributary to braided rivers enter them perpendicularly, have significantly higher slopes and are readily distinguished from them (Fig. 5). For example, Spring Creek fan is one of the larger tributary fans of the Donjek River, Yukon, and has a slope of 0.019, whereas that of the trunk river at the same locality is 0.006 (Rust, 1972b). In contrast, a series of laterally contiguous fans formed adjacent to a mountain front may be transitional downslope to a braidplain on which the radiating flow

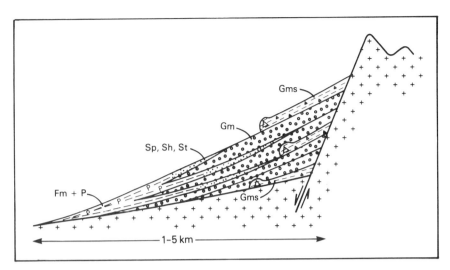

Figure 3
Diagrammatic cross-section of an alluvial fan, showing proximal-distal facies variation.

See Table 1 and text for explanation of facies codes.

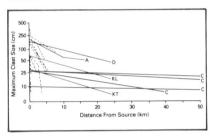

Figure 4
Variation in maximum grain size (i.e., mean

of ten largest clasts at each site) versus distance downslope for various alluvial gravels. Modified after Figure 11 of Wilson (1970) and Figure 19 of Schultheis and Mountjoy (1978). Dashed lines are trends on alluvial fans, solid lines are trends on braided rivers and braid-plains: A: Arroyo Seco (Krumbein, 1942), D: Donjek River (Rust, 1982a), KL: Knik River, lag gravel (Bradley et al., 1972), KT: Knik River, transported gravel, C: Cadomin Formation (McLean, 1977).

Figure 5
Vertical air photograph (A15517-19) of upper reach of Slims River, Yukon (61° 55'N, 138° 38'W), showing marked contrast between tributary alluvial fans and braided trunk river. Note the entrenchment features of the lower left fan (see Bull, 1977, Fig. 20b),

and the constriction of the river by fans. Dark areas on fans are vegetated. Original photo supplied by the Surveys and Mapping Branch, Department of Energy, Mines and Resources, Canada. Width of view about 7.5 km, north toward top of photograph. Flow in trunk river left to right.

56

Figure 6
Block diagram of alluvial fans transitional downslope to a braidplain as the fans coalesce and lose their morphological identity. D) debris flow.

Figure 7
Horizontally stratified conglomerate (facies Gm) in Middle Devonian Malbaie Formation, *Paradise Cove, Quebec. Notebook (arrowed) 19 cm long.*

Figure 8
Bedding-plane view of imbricate, horizontally *stratified conglomerate in Malbaie Formation, Belle Anse, Quebec. Scale 30 cm.*

patterns of the individual fans are lost, but the mean drainage direction is the same (Fig. 6). The distinction between a braided river and a braidplain is one of confinement by a valley in the former case (Kraus, 1984). However, the width of the river is normally sufficient that the influence of the valley walls is minimal, so that the processes and sediments of braided rivers and braidplains are essentially identical.

ALLUVIAL FAN SEDIMENTATION

Modern Alluvial Fans
The classic descriptions of modern alluvial fans are mostly from the mountainous semi-arid regions of the southwestern United States (Bull, 1963, 1964, 1972, 1977; Hooke 1967). Fans of this type are uncommon in Canada, but paraglacial fans (those associated with retreat of valley glaciers) are relatively abundant (Ryder, 1981a,b; Church and Ryder, 1972). In each case the fans form adjacent to regions of high relief, which are rapidly denuded to provide the sediment which builds the fans. In semi-arid environments the relief is commonly a faulted mountain front, and denudation is promoted by sparse vegetation and occasional intense rainfall.

Paraglacial fans form where tributary valleys enter a major glaciated valley (Figs. 2 and 5), in which case sediment production is promoted by seasonal temperature fluctuations and the high spring runoff. According to Ryder (1971b), paraglacial fans differ from arid-region fans by having steeper gradients and weaker correlations between

fan and basin parameters. This is because their deposits derive from earlier glacially-eroded detritus, in contrast to the concurrent nature of denudation and sedimentation in tectonically-controlled systems. Fans in humid tropical settings are less common, because the climate induces chemical weathering rather than mechanical production of coarse detritus, and dense vegetation protects slopes. However, tropical storms in alpine areas can cause catastrophic mass movements, as illustrated by Bell's (1976) study of the effects of Cyclone Allison on South Island, New Zealand.

Most fans are dominated by water-laid deposits, predominantly facies Gm (horizontally stratified gravel, commonly imbricate) in proximal reaches (Figs. 7 and 8). Bull (1972, p. 66-9) divided water-laid gravels into stream channel, seive and sheetflood deposits, the latter defined in more detail by Hogg (1982). Sheetflood and stream channel deposits can be considered intergradational, for the surfaces on which sheetflood deposits accumulate are in fact composed of numerous shallow channels and bars. Sieve deposits are comparatively rare, forming as gravel lobes that receive little sand or mud from their source areas (Bull, 1977, Fig. 7). The broad, shallow channels on alluvial fans of humid climates commonly contain periodic accumulations of coarse, imbricate gravel, known as transverse ribs. They are interpreted as antidune bedforms, and can be used to estimate paleodepth, velocity and Froude number (Koster, 1978a). Rust and Gostin (1981) recognised fossil transverse ribs in Holocene fan gravels in semi-arid South Australia, and showed how paleohydraulic parameters could be estimated, using equations given by Koster (1978a).

On many fans the main channel is entrenched in the fanhead (proximal) region, but reaches the general level at a location downfan known as the intersection point (Hooke, 1967). Some authors attribute fanhead entrenchment to external causes such as climatic change (Lustig, 1965) or faulting (Bull, 1965), but others regard it as an intrinsic part of fan development. Wasson (1977b) suggested that both circumstances may prevail. Downcutting that contributes sediment to a lower part of the fan is part of fan construction, whereas down-cutting that results in sedimentation beyond, but not on the fan, constitutes destruction by external causes.

The nature of water-laid deposits shows progressive change down-fan. There is an increase in the abundance of cross-stratal sets, chiefly planar (Fig. 1) with transitions from coarse gravel through clast-supported fine-grained gravel, sand matrix-supported gravel to sand (Gm to Gp to Sp). These changes reflect gradual decrease in the particle size to water depth ratio as stream competence decreases down-fan. Minor deposits of horizontally laminated sand (facies Sh) and laminated or massive mud (Fl, Fm) also increase in abundance down-fan (Fig. 3). Fans formed entirely of sand and finer sediment are not part of our topic, but they are in any case rare, because they need a high-relief source of poorly consolidated sand or finer material, which is a short-lived feature of the landscape (Legget *et al.*, 1966).

Debris flow (or mudflow) deposits are the other principal component of most alluvial fan successions in both semi-arid and paraglacial environments (Fig. 3). Middleton and Hampton (1976) pointed out that debris flows are one member of a continuous range of sediment gravity flows. According to Bull (1977, p. 236) debris flows are promoted

Figure 9
Leveed edge of debris flow on west side of Donjek Valley between Spring Creek and

Donjek Glacier. Pack (mid-ground, circled) and figure (behind) give scale.

by steep slopes, lack of vegetation, short periods of abundant water supply and a source providing debris with a muddy matrix. Johnson (1970) discussed debris flows, providing eyewitness accounts, as did Sharp and Nobles (1953), Curry (1966) and Winder (1965). The flows may be confined to channels, but commonly spread out as lobate sheets on lower reaches of fans. The lobate distal terminations are distinctive, and commonly concentrate the larger clasts at the steep outer margin of the flow, forming levees (Fig. 9). The flows lack internal stratification, but commonly show reverse or reverse-to-normal grading (Nilsen, 1982, Figs. 17 and 34C,D). In contrast with the imbricate fabric of waterlaid gravel, the clasts in debris flow deposits commonly lack an organised fabric. Bull (1963, p. 245) noted that more fluid (that is, proximal) debris flows may show subhorizontal orientation of megaclasts, whereas more viscous (distal) flows tend to have larger clasts in predominantly vertical orientations, due to matrix support. However, according to Shultz (1983), some flows of relatively low viscosity may be able to reach distal reaches of fans.

Schumm (1977, p. 246) recognized two types of alluvial fans: "... dry or mudflow fans formed by ephemeral stream flow, and wet fans formed by perennial stream flow". This implies that "wet" fans do not develop debris flows.

It is true that evenly distributed rainfall favours steady erosional processes rather than mass movements, but short term fluctuation in precipitation can undoubtedly produce debris flows in humid areas (Curry, 1966; Broscoe and Thompson, 1969; Winder, 1965). Schumm (1973) suggested that initiation of debris flows requires accumulation of a threshold amount of loose detritus, a concept further elaborated by Heward (1978). Beaty (1970) estimated an average depositional rate of approximately 2400 m³/yr on a debris flow-dominated fan of 4.4 km radius on the California-Nevada border.

Alluvial fans prograde into lakes or seas where high coastal topography causes alluvium to be shed directly into the water (Friedman and Sanders, 1978, Fig. 10-29; Gvirtzman and Buchbinder, 1978). These fans have been termed fan-deltas by several authors (Holmes and Holmes, 1978, p. 358-9; Wescott and Ethridge, 1980). However, because of the steep alluvial slope, the typical deltaic features of break in slope and facies change at the water plane are not well developed, and the term coastal alluvial fan seems more appropriate (Hayward, 1983). Modification of coastal fans by marine processes was described by Ethridge and Wescott (1984), who noted that they form mainly along continental and island-arc collision zones where continental shelves are narrow and relatively steep.

58

Ancient Alluvial Fan Deposits

The principal features of modern alluvial fans - debris flow deposits and rapid downslope facies changes - are also recognisable in ancient fan successions. Many of these successions are thick, indicating formation in a tectonically-influenced setting, for example the Devonian Peel Sound Formation of Arctic Canada (Miall, 1970). The stratigraphic record also shows vertical changes in facies type. For example, when faulting gives rise to source elevation or basin subsidence, the alluvial system is rejuvenated, and the fan progrades. Areas on which proximal facies accumulate migrate down-fan, so that the succession at any given location shows upward increase in grain size and bed thickness (Fig. 10a). This upward coarsening/thickening trend may be overlain by a thinner upward fining/thinning sequence (Fig. 10b) as the effects of rejuvenation wear off (Mack and Rasmussen, 1984). Repeated faulting gives rise to cyclic repetition of coarsening/thickening units or the asymmetric coarsening then fining units descirbed above. Heward (1978) suggested that simple fining-upward sequences may result when faulting causes retreat of the scarp front (Fig. 10c).

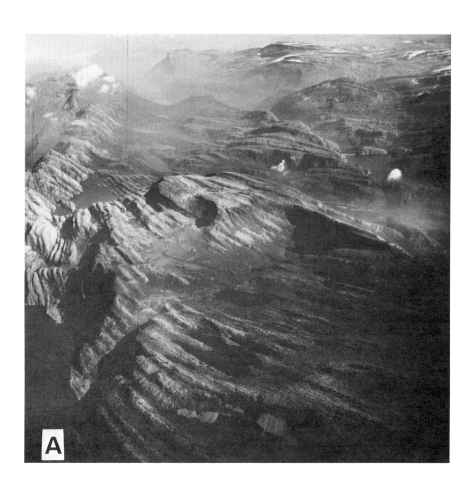

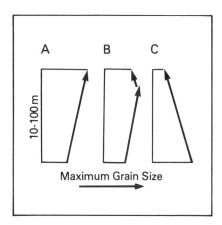

Figure 10
Allocyclic grain size/bed thickness trends in alluvial fan successions subject to periodic tectonic rejuvenation. a) Coarsening/thickening upward due to periodic fault uplift of source or subsidence of basin. b) Coarsening/thickening followed by fining/thinning in asymmetric cycles. Same mechanism as in a), but spacing between fault movements allows system to move toward equilibrium before renewed faulting. c) Fining/thining upward, ascribed to back-stepping of boundary fault (Heward, 1978).

Figure 11
The Devonian Hornelen Basin, Norway, with its spectacular exposure of coarsening-upward cycles in alluvial fan deposits (Steel et al., 1977). A) Northern edge of the basin with successive scarps, ca. 100 m high, relating to each cycle. B) A steeply tilted, south-ern part of the basin showing three cycles which thin upwards (i.e., towards the basin centre) and interfinger with floodbasin/lake depostis. Photos kindly supplied by R.J. Steel who obtained 'A' from Fjellanger Wideroe A-5, Oslo.

Well exposed successions of ancient alluvial fan deposits were described from the Devonian of Norway by Steel *et al.* (1977), Steel and Gloppen (1980) and others (Fig. 11). They contain coarsening-upward sequences about 100 m thick, with coarsening-upward subcycles in the 10 to 25 m range, all attributed to allocyclic (tectonic) causes. Cycles of internal (autocyclic) origin are also present in these and other fan deposits. They result from major floods, or from the switching of deposition from one fan lobe to another. Repetitive units of this type are thinner, commonly a few metres thick, and fine upwards or coarsen then fine symmetrically (Muir and Rust, 1982).

Another feature which has been recognised mainly from studies of ancient fan successions is the relationship between maximum particle size (MPS, mean of 10 largest clasts) and bed thickness (BTh). Bluck (1967) demonstrated for both water-laid and debris flow conglomerates that these parameters commonly correlate, both decreasing downslope. Gloppen and Steel (1981) showed for debris flow deposits that the MPS:BTh ratio also decreases downfan, indicating that competence decreases more rapidly than other attributes of the flow. Bluck (1969) suggested that MPS:BTh ratios are higher for subaerial than for subaqueous flows, which would permit identification of submerged parts of coastal alluvial fans. In most cases, however, fossils and other subaqueous facies provide better environmental indicators.

Ancient debris flow deposits have been recognised in the Quaternary of Tasmania (Wasson, 1977a) and Spain (Harvey, 1984), the Miocene of Switzerland (Burgisser, 1984), the Permo-Triassic of Scotland (Steel, 1974) and in numerous other successions. Surface features such as lobate terminations are rarely preserved because of subsequent erosion or lack of exposure. However, Daily *et al.* (1980) recognised an example in Cambrian coastal fan deposits, in which a lobate termination with upward coarsening was apparent (Fig. 12). Commonly preserved features include a lack of internal stratification and imbrication, and a sheet-like form, in contrast with the common channel forms of water-laid deposits (Wasson, 1977a; Wells, 1984).

Red colouration and evaporitic paleo-

Figure 12
30 cm scale rests on top of coarsening-upward debris flow deposit wih boulders emergent from its upper surface. The debris flow deposit forms a lobe, whose base is parallel to horizontal stratification in overlying shallow marine sandstones. Coastal alluvial fan deposits in the Lower Cambrian Boxing Bay Formation of Kangaroo Island, South Australia (see Daily et al., 1980).

Figure 13
Paleosol of nodular calcrete in finer upper part of fining-upward sequence formed by flood deposition on an alluvial fan. Lower Member, Carboniferous Cannes de Roche Formation, Barachois-de-Malbaie, Quebec. Tape open 20 cm.

sols (facies P, Table 1) occur in several ancient alluial fan deposits, and point to a semi-arid paleoclimate (Williams, 1973). Canadian examples are the Carboniferous Cannes de Roche Formation of eastern Gaspé (Rust, in press, a) and the Bonaventure Formation of Gaspé and New Brunswick (Zaitlin and Rust,

1983). The paleosols are predominantly nodular limestones (calcretes) within finer lithologies (Fig. 13). Other types of paleosol can provide paleoclimatic evidence, although with less confidence (Retallack, 1983). According to Bown and Kraus (1981), paleosols are the rule rather than the exception in ancient alluvial deposits, and therefore have considerable potential for paleoclimatic interpretation.

Ancient successions containing coastal fan deposits were recognised in the Miocene of Turkey (Hayward, 1983), the Devonian of Norway (Steel and Gloppen, 1980) and Arctic Canada (Muir and Rust, 1982), and the Cambrian of South Australia by Daily *et al.* (1980). In the Devonian example discussed by Steel and Gloppen (1980), the basin sediments are lacustrine. Repetitive cycles in marginal alluvial fan deposits were also recognised in the lacustrine succession, indicating that the cause of cyclicity was basin-wide subsidence. Daily *et al.* (1980) described a Cambrian fan succession that prograded across shallow marine environments. The unidirectional alluvial paleocurrents provide a clear indication of the orientation of the ancient coastline and therefore help in understanding the multipolar nature of the marine paleocurrents. For example, longshore currents can be distinguished from those induced by onshore wave attack, and by offshore flows such as rip currents.

Depositional Models for Fans

Miall (1977, 1978b) used a study of the modern Trollheim fan, California (Hooke, 1967) as the principal basis for his alluvial fan model. The Trollheim is a small fan with abundant debris flow deposits. Sedimentation is strongly influenced by two factors: the semi-arid climate and the active tectonic setting. It has been suggested that fans in humid climatic settings produce relatively fewer debris flows, and are therefore dominated by water-laid deposits (Schumm, 1977). This is probably true, but the concept has not been demonstrated quantitatively, and some humid-region fans contain abundant debris flow deposits (Broscoe and Thomson, 1969; Winder, 1965).

Other indicators of paleoclimatic influence in the ancient record are paleosols (discussed earlier), associated facies and biota. The facies indicative of a dry paleoclimate are evaporites in lacustrine or tidal flat deposits associated with coastal alluvial fans. Eolian deposits are less diagnostic, because they could be formed in paraglacial as well as arid climatic conditions (Brookfield, "Eolian Facies", this

volume). However, the association of paraglacial alluvium with ancient glacigenic deposits has strong interpretive value. These include deposits from glacier ice (tillites), as well as characteristic facies assemblages of glaciomarine or glaciolacustrine environments (Eyles and Miall, "Glacial Facies", this volume). Paraglacial alluvial successions show upward-coarsening during periods of glacial advance and fining during retreat. The situation is complicated by the fact that coarse detritus results not only from proximity to glaciers, but also from the isostatic uplift consequent on the retreat of continental ice sheets. In general, alluvial successions generated in response to episodic glacial advance should show approximately symmetric coarsening-up, fining-up cycles, but such a situation has not been documented.

The preservation potential of fossils is not high in coarse-grained alluvium. However, Gostin and Rust (1983) described vertebrate and insect burrows and large upright tree trunks buried in Holocene alluvial fan gravels in South Australia. The preservation of xerophytic plant stems and associated faunal traces is likely to leave a permanent stratigraphic record of the semi-arid climatic conditions.

As described previously, tectonic influence can be recognised in the form of repetitive cycles of grain size and bed

thickness variation with alluvial fan successions. However, the absence of such cyclicity should not be taken as evidence that tectonic influence was lacking. Small, frequent movements on faults maintain transport energy within fluvial systems, without being individually large enough to induce repeated trends.

Coastal alluvial fans are distinguished from their purely terrestrial counterparts largely by the presence of marine or lacustrine fossils. The effects of reworking by waves and subaqueous slumping may also be recognized (Kleinspehn *et al.*, 1984), but if the water body is small and protected, the resultant subaqueous deposits may be hard to detect.

BRAIDED RIVERS AND BRAIDPLAINS

Modern Examples

Gravelly braided rivers are common features of modern paraglacial environments (Rust, 1982a, 1975; Church and Gilbert, 1975). Gravelly braidplains are less common to-day, but their lateral extent gives them a high preservation potential, and they are more abundant in the ancient record.

The most abundant facies of coarse-grained proximal braided rivers and braidplains is horizontally bedded, imbricate gravel, which may appear massive where bedding is thick and texture uniform (Figs. 7, 8 and 14). This

Figure 14
Middle Devonian Malbaie Formation at Petite Pte. St-Pierre, Quebec, showing horizontally strafitied conglomerate (facies Gm), planar cross-stratified conglomerate (Gp) and horizontally stratified sandstone (Sh). Notebook (arrowed) is 19 cm long.

facies dominates proximal braided rivers of paraglacial environments (Boothroyd and Ashley, 1975; Church and Gilbert, 1975; Rust 1972a, 1975) as well as braided gravels not influenced by glacial melting (Ore, 1964, p. 9; Smith, 1970, p. 2999). The dominance of facies Gm reflects the low ratio of mean particle size to water depth, in turn a function of the relatively low relief of bars and channels in proximal reaches. The bars are mostly longitudinal, that is, elongate parallel to flow, with gentle slopes into surrounding low sinuosity channels. Diagonal bars are similar, but oblique to flow (Smith, 1974, p. 210). Leopold and Wolman (1957) proposed that longitudinal bars start as a nucleus of the coarsest bedload fractions deposited in mid-channel as flow diminishes, and grow by addition of finer sediment mainly downstream from the nucleus. Smith (1974) observed similar processes during diurnal stage fluctuations in the Kicking Horse River, British Columbia: lateral and downstream growth of 'unit bars' with predominantly depositional morpholoy. In the same river Hein and Walker (1977) observed an initial stage of bar formation as 'diffuse gravel sheets' a few pebble diameters thick. They postulated that the sheets evolve into longitudinal or diagonal bars with horizontal stratification, or transverse bars with cross-strata. The latter, however, are rare in gravel-bed braided streams (Smith, 1974, p. 218).

It is clear that falling-stage modifications of gravel bars occur by depositional and erosional processes, but observations during flood stage are hampered by turbid water and the impossibility of walking across bars, let alone channels. Remote sensing is also impracticable under these circumstances. Rust (1978b, p. 614-5) suggested that longitudinal bars are stable bedforms at flood stage, when all the bedload is in motion. An indication that this is so comes from the giant longitudinal bars (1.4 to 2.5 km long, 15 to 45 m high) of catastrophic Pleistocene floods in eastern Washinton (Bretz et al., 1956; Malde, 1968). Giant cross-bed sets with boulders up to 3 m diameter formed in estimated water depths up to 100 m (Malde, 1968), and longitudinal bar forms were preserved. Preservation of such large bars implies stability under the conditions prevailing. A possible analogy may be with the apparent bar forms in channels on Mars (Baker, 1978; Komar, 1983).

Sand facies are uncommon in proximal braided gravels, but where present include planar cross-stratified sand (facies Sp) and horizontally stratified sand (facies Sh, Fig 14.) Mud facies are rarely preserved. All these facies increase in abundance downstream, but unlike alluvial fan deposits the change is very gradual (Fig. 4). For example, clast-supported gravel is the principal lithotype of the Donjek River 50 km from its glacial source (Area 2, Rust 1972a).

Like alluvial fans, braidplains may also accumulate gravel in coastal environments (Leckie and Walker, 1982). Examples are the paraglacial coastal outwash plains of Alaska and Iceland (Boothroyd and Ashley, 1975; Boothroyd and Nummedal, 1978).

Ancient Braidplain Deposits
Like their modern counterparts, ancient successions formed in braided rivers and braidplains are characterised by gradual facies change and decreasing grain size in the downstream direction (Fig. 4). Examples of both confined and unconfined braided river deposits are known (Kraus, 1984), as well as close genetic relationships with neighbouring alluvial fan successions (Middleton and Trujillo, 1984; Rust, 1981). Although coarse-grained braidplain successions are generally thinner than those of alluvial fans, their extent parallel to paleslope may approach 500 km. Vonhof (1965) has documented cobble-grade Oligocene gravels at the Alberta-Saskatchewan border derived from the Montana area across a relatively steep foreland slope. Similarly, the Lower Cretaceous Cadomin Formation of the Cordilleran Foothills in Alberta and Montana (McLean, 1977; Schultheis and Mountjoy, 1978) is sheet-like, extending up to 300 km downslope from its source (McLean, 1977, Fig. 4). Maximum clast size decreases in the transport direction (northeastward) very gradually (McLean, 1977, Fig. 4). Plotted on Figure 4, these data are comparable with maximum clast size trends in modern braided rivers, but differ markedly from size trends on modern alluvail fans. In proximal reaches these deposits are characterised by an abundance of facies Gm (Fig. 7).

Other examples of proximal braidplain conglomerates in the ancient record include Triassic conglomerates in England (Steel and Thompson, 1983), conglomerate units within the Lower Paleozoic Piekenier Formation of South Africa (Vos and Tankard, 1980) and the Middle Devonian Malbaie Formation of Eastern Gaspé, Canada (Rust, 1978b, in press, b). Essentially continuous coastal sections of the Malbaie Formation expose braidplain conglomerates for about 4 km in the downslope direction and about 5.5 km across the slope of the plain. Within this area grain size does not vary appreciably, and paleocurrents determined from clast imbrication (Fig. 8) are essentially uniform (Rust, in press, b). This suggests that the rate of grain size reduction down the Malbaie braidplain was similar to that in the Cadomin conglomerate, and in modern equivalents. As with the other examples, Gm is the predominant facies of Malbaie conglomerate units. Planar cross-stratified conglomerate (facies Gp) makes up about 20% of the conglomerate, a much higher proportion than in the modern equivalents described above (Figs. 1 and 14).

Proximal braidplain deposits form in response to major glacial or tectonic events. However, they are not organised into smaller scale cycles that might represent individual tectonic episodes, as is the case with alluvial fans. It appears that the influence of individual tectonic episodes is lost when the resulting detritus has been transported away from the fans adjacent to the mountain front. Hence stratification and grain size changes are a response to major floods rather than tectonic events.

Distal gravelly braided fluvial deposits are not well represented in the ancient record. An example is the Upper Member of the Carboniferous Cannes de Roche Formation of Eastern Quebec (Rust, 1981; in press, a). Trough cross-stratified clast-supported conglomerate occurs in multiple sets above a sharp erosional base (Fig. 15). This facies (Gt) fines upwards to trough cross-stratified sandstone (St), commonly through intermediate units of horizontally bedded conglomerate (Gm) (Figs. 14 and 15). This succession is interpreted as a response to shallowing of water over bars and active gravelly channels as they accrete, accompanied by, or in response to migration of the active tract. The sequence ends with mudstone and organic material deposited as the tract

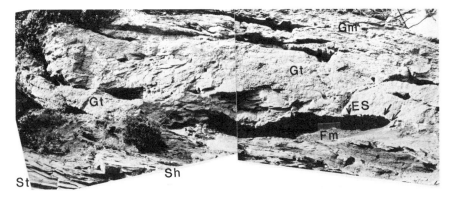

Figure 15
Repetitive stratification sequence in Upper Member of Carboniferous Cannes de Roche Formation, Coin-du-Banc, Quebec. Base of sequence is an irregular erosion surface (ES), overlain by trough cross-bedded conglomerate (Gt), comprising a coset in which some of the trough sets are sandstone-filled.

These in turn are overlain by horizontally stratified conglomerate (Gm) and sandstone (Sh). Sandstone sets (Sh and shallow trough: St) are best seen at top of underlying sequence; in turn they pass upward into mudstone (Fm), cut into by erosional surface. Scale (arrowed) 1 m long.

became inactive and started to support vegetation (Figs. 16 and 17).

Models for Braided River and Braidplain Deposition
Two models, proximal and distal, are required to describe the sedimentary characteristics of braided rivers and braidplains.

Miall (1977, 1978b) based his proximal model on proximal reaches of the Scott outwash. The model is essentially the same as facies assemblage G_{II} of Rust (1978b). Imbricate, horizontally-stratified gravel is dominant (facies Gm), with minor amounts of planar cross-stratified gravel (Gp) and sand facies (Sp and Sh). This assemblage (Fig. 18a) characterises their proximal outwash gravels, such as the Donjek

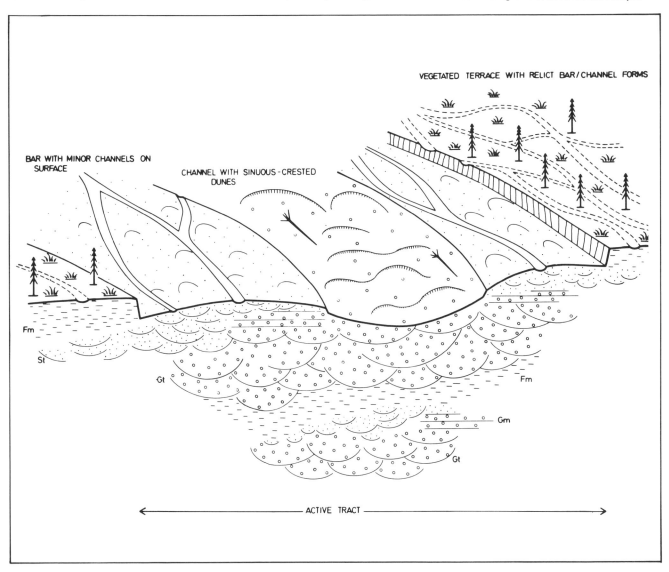

Figure 16
Repetitive stratification sequence in Upper Member of Cannes de Roche Formation, as related to facies assemblage G_{III} of Rust (1978b) and the Donjek model of Miall (1978b).

63

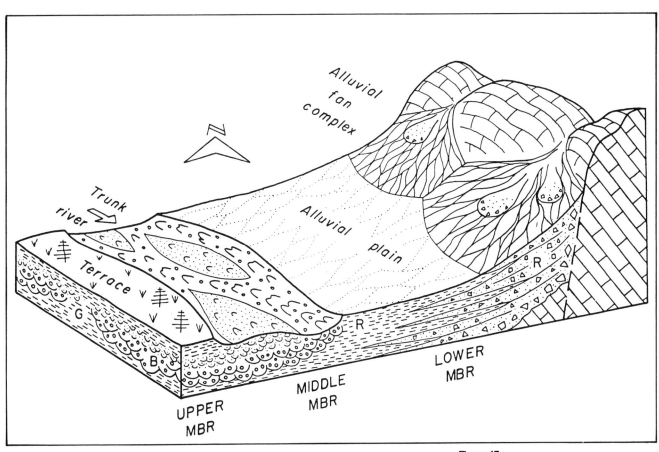

Figure 17
Depositional model for Cannes de Roche Formation, showing distal braided river deposits (Upper Member) in trunk valley confined by tributary alluvial fan deposits (Lower and Middle Members). R) red, B) buff, G) grey-green. See Rust (in press, a).

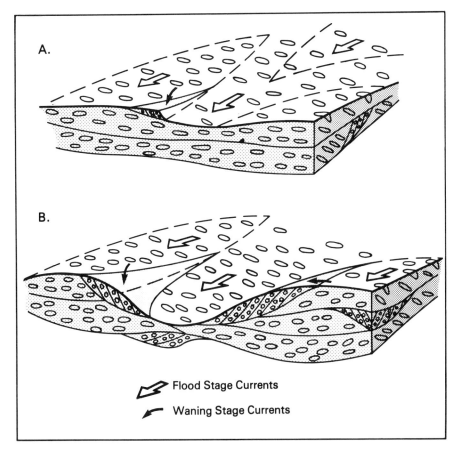

Flood Stage Currents

Waning Stage Currents

Figure 18
Depositional models for proximal gravelly braidplain/braided river deposits. A) Modern deposition, in which facies Gm is strongly dominant because of shallow flow in semi-arid or paraglacial settings. B) Ancient (Paleozoic) deposition, in which Gm is still the dominant facies, but Gp is more prominent, because the bar/channel relief is greater. This results from commonly recurring deep flood flows, due to formation under humid climatic environments.

(Rust, 1975) and gravelly braided rivers of non-glacial settings (Ore, 1964; Smith, 1970).

In the modern setting, deposits of this type are characteristic of climatic extremes (semi-arid or paraglacial), in which large amounts of coarse detritus are produced, and plant cover is sparse. In the Paleozoic, however, vegetation was confined to well-watered low-lying valleys or coastal plains. Hillslopes were unprotected, so upland gravels were generated abundantly in humid climates, forming extensive braidplains. Unlike modern counterparts, these floods were deeper and more frequent, so large-scale units of planar cross-stratified gravel (facies Gp) formed, together with falling-stage sequences of sand facies. In this sense the input into the model from modern and ancient deposits differs, but the difference is relatively minor (Fig. 18b).

The facies model for distal braided gravels discussed here (G$_{III}$ of Rust, 1978b) is not as well established as that for proximal equivalents: it is offered as a guide for further investigation (Fig. 16). Miall (1977, 1978) chose the middle reaches of the Donjek River (Area 2 of Rust, 1972a, about 50km from its glacial source) as the type example of his facies assemblage for distal gravelly braided rivers. Clast-supported gravel is the dominant lithotype in this reach of the river, and is abundant in the active channel tract. In a similar setting in the Knik River, Alaska, Fahnestock and Bradley (1973, p. 241) identified dunes of fine gravel by echo sounding. They probably resemble the crescentic gravel bedforms observed in the North Saskatchewan River by Galay and Neill (1967), and would generate sets of trough cross-strata (facies Gt) by migration in flood. An alternative possibility in shallower rivers is the formation of transverse gravel bars (Hein and Walker, 1977, Fig. 3) which would generate principally planar cross-strata (facies Gp) on migration.

The mid reaches of the Donjek are also characterised by inactive tracts on levels or terraces above the active tract (Williams and Rust, 1969). The inactive tract is primarily subject to vertical accretion of fine sediment, and supports abundant vegetation. In flood, however, minor channels transport sand and fine gravel across the inactive tract. In time, migration of the active and inactive

tracts can be expected to deposit a sequence which fines upward from trough cross-stratified clast-supported gravel through sand to mixtures containing mud and plant material, both transported and *in situ* (Fig. 16 and 17).

The depositional model described above is also representative of facies assemblage G$_{III}$ of Rust (1978b). It has not been recognised in modern braidplain deposits, perhaps because confinement by valley walls is a necessary requirement for development of this facies sequence. The Upper Member of the Carboniferous Cannes de Roche Formation serves as an ancient example of facies assemblage G$_{III}$ (Rust, 1981; in press, a). Paleogeographic reconstruction based on paleocurrents in alluvial fan deposits in the Lower and Middle Members suggests that the braided river deposits were confined to a paleovalley (Fig. 17) with tributary fans on either side. In this sense the Cannes de Roche Formation closely resembles the Donjek River, although the paleoclimatic setting is quite different. Abundant calcretes and red colouration in the Cannes de Roche fan deposits indicate a relatively dry paleoclimate.

TECTONISM AND ALLUVIAL FACIES MODELS

Miall (1981) recognised twelve plate tectonic settings for alluvial basins, in which most conglomeratic sequences were deposited as fault-bounded fan accumulations in forearc or foreland basins, or in intermontane successor or pull-apart basins. Most ancient fan successions show distinct cyclicity, ascribed to periodic tectonism, and ancient braidplain deposits also owe their origin to tectonic causes. The question remains: is there any fundamental difference between the tectonic framework of alluvial fan and braidplain successions?

Ancient braidplain successions are widespread deposits that form in response to major tectonic uplifts. For example, the Cadomin Conglomerate formed in response to Cretaceous uplift of the Cordillera (McLean, 1977; Schultheis and Mountjoy, 1978). The Malbaie Formation and other time-equivalent molasse deposits of the Appalachian and Caledonian belts accumulated in response to the mid-Paleozoic Acadian and late Caledonian Orogenies (Rust, 1981; Allen and Friend, 1968; Allen,

Dineley and Friend, 1967). Such major episodes of deformation call for extensive compression, such as that caused by collision of an outboard terrane with a continental margin (Keppie, in press).

In contrast, alluvial fan deposits are more localised accumulations formed adjacent to active fault scarps. Fans may develop in relation to several tectonic situations. In extensional rifting the alluvial successions are relatively thin, because once the continental plates separated or the rift failed, the fault scarps were worn down and became inactive. An example of this scenario was described by Hobday and Von Brunn (1979). An alternative setting for alluvial fan conglomerates is a strike-slip plate margin. In this case, fan accumulations continue to form along the fault complex as it continues to slip, and may reach considerable thicknesses. For example, about 12,000 m of Cenozoic fan deposits accumulated in the Ridge Basin, California, in response to largely strike-slip movement on faults of the San Andreas System (Crowell, 1974). Crowell (1974, p. 300) cited the post-Acadian (Carboniferous) rift basins of Maritime Canada as a similar example in which thick alluvial fan deposits accumulated adjacent to a predomonantly strike-slip fault complex. The Devonian deposits in Western Norway described by Steel and Gloppen (1980) represent a similar depositional situation. In terms of plate tetonics, these phenomena can be explained by the activity of a transform fault, causing strike-slip displacement of parts of two adjacent continental plates.

The coarse alluvial deposits of eastern Canada can be divided into pre-Upper Devonian rocks, dominated by braidplain deposits, and Upper Devonian and Carboniferous alluvial fan successions. Rust (1981) suggested that this change in alluvial style was a response to oblique continental collision during the Acadian (mid-Devonian) Orogeny, followed and partly overlapped by transcurrent shearing along the former continental margin during the Carboniferous. There is nothing unusual about such a deformation sequence, because continental collision, or docking of outboard terranes commonly takes place at an olique angle to the original continental margin. Hence initial compression is followed by transcurrent shearing, and the change in alluvial style described above is to be expected.

SUMMARY

Alluvial Fans

The basic model for alluvial fan deposition (the "norm" of the "General Introduction", this volume) is characterised by rapid fining in the downslope direction and by the presence of debris flow deposits (Fig. 3). An additional feature, which may not always be recognisable in the ancient record, is a radiating pattern of paleocurrents. This model can be used as a guide and predictor for understanding reasons for variations from the norm. These variations include:

i)   Features associated with a semi-arid paleoclimate: arid-zone paleosols and biota, and association with evaporitic facies such as playa lake sediments.

ii) Features associated with a paraglacial setting: association with glacigenic sediments: tillites, glaciomarine and glaciolacustrine assemblages

iii) Coastal fan features: evidence of reworking by subaqueous processes; lacustrine or shallow marine biota.

iv) Sedimentary responses to tectonism: repetitive sequences of grain size and bed thickness trends on scales of around 10 to 100 m. Commonly they coarsen and thicken upwards, but asymmetric coarsening then fining, and thinning upward sequences are also encountered. A lack of such cyclicity does not necessarily indicate a lack of tectonic influence.

Braided Rivers and Braidplains

Deposits of these environments are essentially identical, and can be characterised by two models, which consititute norms for proximal and distal deposition, respectively (Fig. 17 and 18). The proximal model is simple, and is reasonably well established on several modern and ancient examples. The distal model is based on few case histories, and must be regarded as tentative.

1) *Proximal* deposits of gravel-dominated braided rivers and braidplains are characterised by an abundance of horizontally-stratified gravel deposited by vertical accretion on longitudinal bars. Planar cross-stratified gravel is the next most abundant facies, particularly in Paleozoic and older deposits. Debris flow deposits and tectonically-induced cyclicity are lacking, and the downstream transition to distal deposits typically occurs over a distance of several tens of kilometres.

2) *Distal* assemblages are characterised by autocyclic fining-upward sequences from gravel, chiefly trough cross-stratified, through sandstone to mudstone. The latter facies may include remains of *in situ* vegetation.

ACKNOWLEDGEMENTS

The work on which this paper is based was supported by grant A2672 from the Natural Sciences and Engineering Research Council of Canada, which is gratefully acknowledged. We would also like to thank Roger Walker for comments on the manuscript, Edward Hearn and Ian Magee for drafting, and Julie Hayes for typing.

REFERENCES

BASIC REFERENCES

Bull, W.B., 1977. The alluvial fan environment. Progress in Physical Geography, v. 1, p. 222-270.
The latest review by an author who has contributed much to our understanding of alluvial fans. Mainly deals with morphology and deposits of modern fans, but ancient equivalents are also discussed.

Collinson, J.D., 1978. Alluvial sediments. *In* Reading, H.G., ed., Sedimentary environments and facies. Oxford, Blackwell Scientific Publications, p. 15-60.
An excellent discussion of the whole spectrum of alluvial deposits.

Collinson, J.D., and Lewin, J., eds., 1983. Modern and ancient fluvial systems. International Association of Sedimentologists, Special Publication 6, 575 p.
A volume of papers on fluvial sedimentology published following an international symposium held at Keele, U.K., 1982.

Harms, J.C., Southard, J.B., and Walker, R.G., 1982. Structures and sequences in clastic rocks. Society of Economic Paleontologists and Mineralogists, Short Course No. 9.
Chapter 'Conglomerate, Emphasizing Fluvial and Alluvial Fan Environments' provides a good overview of descriptive features, processes and facies.

Koster, E.H., and Steel, R.J., eds., 1984. The sedimentology of gravels and conglomerates. Canadian Society of Petroleum Geologists, Memoir 10, in press.
A compilation of some of the most recent work on processes and facies in the complete range of gravel-dominant environments: several of its studies are reference material for this paper.

Miall, A.D., 1977. A review of the braided-river depositional environment. Earth Science Reviews, v. 13, p. 1-62.
A review of modern and ancient braided alluvial deposits, which introduces the facies code used in this paper.

Miall, A.D., ed., 1978a. Fluvial sedimentology. Canadian Society of Petroleum Geologists, Memoir 5, 859 p.
Papers resulting from the first international symposium on fluvial sedimentolgoy, held at Calgary in 1977.

Nilsen, T.H., 1982. Alluvial fan deposits. *In* Scholle, P.A., and Spearing, D.R., eds., Sandstone depositional environments. American Association of Petroleum Geologists, Memoir 31, p. 49-86.
A review of alluvial fan deposits with lavish colour illustrations. Despite the "sandstone" of the volume title, conglomerates are thoroughly discussed.

Rust, B.R., 1978b. Depositional models for braided alluvium. *In* Miall, A.D., ed., Fluvial sedimentology. Canadian Society of Petroleum Geologists, Memoir 5, p. 605-625.
A concise review of the facies sequences that characterise alluvial fan and braidplain environments and guide the basic treatment of the subject in this paper.

Steel, R.J., Maehle, S., Nilsen, H., Roe, S.L., and Spinnangr, A., 1977. Coarsening-upward cycles in the alluvium of Hornelen Basin (Devonian), Norway: sedimentary response to tectonic events. Geological Society of America, Bulletin, v. 88, p. 1124-1134.
A well illustrated account of a remarkable succession of ancient alluvial fan conglomerates and their tectonic setting.

GENERAL

Allen, J.R.L., Dineley, D.L., and Friend, P.F., 1967. Old Red Sandstone basins of North America and Northwest Europe. *In* Oswald, D.H., ed., International Symposium on Devonian System, v. 1, p. 69-98.

Arche, A., 1983. Coarse-grained meander lobe deposits in the Jarama River, Madrid. *In* Collinson, J.D., and Lewin, J.D., eds., Modern and ancient fluvial systems. International Association of Sedimentologists, Special Publication 6, p. 313-321.

Beschta, R.L., and Jackson, W.L., 1979. The intrusion of fine sediments into a stable gravel bed. Journal of the Fisheries Research Board of Canada, v. 36, p. 204-210.

Bluck, B.J., 1967. Deposition of some upper Old Red Sandstone conglomerates in the Clyde Area. A study in the significance of bedding. Scottish Journal of Geology, v. 3, p. 139-167.

Bown, T.M. and Kraus, M.J., 1981. Lower Eocene palesols (Willwood Formation, Northwest Wyoming, U.S.A.) and their significance for paleoecology, paleoclimatology, and basin analysis. Paleogeography, Palaeoclimatology, Paleoecology, v. 34, p. 1-30.

Friedman, G.M., and Sanders, J.E., 1978. Principles of sedimentology. New York, Wiley, 792 p.

Johansson, C.E., 1965. Structural studies of sedimentary deposits. Geologiska Föreningens i Stockholm Förhandlingar, v. 87, p. 3-61.

Keppie, J.K., in press. The Appalachian Collage. In The Caledonain Orogen, International Geological Correlation Project, Uppsala.

Komar, P.D., 1983. Shapes of streamlined islands on earth and mars: experiments and analysis of the minimum-drag form. Geology, v. 11, p. 651-654.

Koster, E.H., 1978b. A flume study of fluvial gravel fabric (Abst). In Miall, A.D., ed., Fluvial sedimentology. Canadian Society of Petroleum Geologists, Memoir 5, p. 853.

Koster, E.H., Rust, B.R., and Gendzwill, D.J., 1980.The ellipsoidal form of clasts with practical applications to fabric and size analyses of fluvial gravels. Canadian Journal of Earth Sciences, v. 17, p. 1725-1739.

Long, D.G.F., 1981. Dextral strike-slip faults in the Canadian Cordillera and depositional environments of related fresh-water intermontane coal basins. In Miall, A.D., ed., Sedimentation and tectonics in alluvial basins. Geological Association of Canada, Special Paper 23, p. 153-186.

Miall, A.D., 1978b. Lithofacies types and vertical profile models in braided river deposits: a summary. In Miall, A.D., ed., Fluvial sedimentology. Canadian Society of Petroleum Geologists, Memoir 5, p. 597-604.

Miall, A.D., 1981. Alluvial sedimentary basins: tectonic setting and basin architecture. In Miall, A.D., ed., Sedimentation and tectonics in alluvial basins. Geolgoical Association of Canada, Special Publication 23, p. 1-33.

A comprehensive classification of alluvial basins with respect to their plate tectonic setting.

Minter, W.E.L., 1978. A sedimentological synthesis of placer gold, uranium and pyrite concentrations in Proterozoic Witwatersrand sediments. In Miall, A.D., ed., Fluvial sedimentology. Canadian Society of Petroleum Geologists, Memoir 5, p. 801-829.

Pienaar, P.J., 1963. Stratigraphy, petrology and genesis of the Elliot Group, Blind River, Ontario, including the uraniferous conglomerate. Geological Survey of Canada, Bulletin, v. 83, 140 p.

Retallack, G.J., 1983. A paleopedological approach to the interpretation of terrestrial sedimentary rocks: the mid-Tertiary fossil soils of Badlands National Park, South Dakota. Geological Society of America, Bulletin, v. 94, p. 823-840.

Robertson, D.S., Tilsley, J.E., and Hogg, G.M., 1978. The time-bound character of uranium deposits. Economic Geology, v. 73, p. 1409-1419.

Rust, B.R., 1978a. A classification of alluvial channel systems. In Miall, A.D., ed., Fluvial sedimentology. Canadian Society of Petroleum Geologists, Memoir 5, p. 187-198.

Schumm, S.A., 1977. The fluvial system. New York, Wiley-Interscience, 335 p.

Smith, N.D., and Minter, W.E.L., 1980. Sedimentological controls of gold and uranium in two Witwatersrand paleoplacers. Economic Geology, v. 75, p. 1-14.

Walker, R.G., 1979. Facies models 1, General introduction. Geoscience Canada, v. 3, p. 21-24.

Wilson, L., 1973. Variations in mean annual sediment yield as a function of mean annual precipitation. American Journal of Science, v. 273, p. 335-349.

ALLUVIAL FANS

Beaty, C.B., 1970. Age and estimated rate of accumulation of an alluvial fan, White Mountains, California, U.S.A. American Journal of Science, v. 268, p. 50-77.

Bell, D.H., 1976. High intensity rainstorms and geological hazards: Cyclone Allison, March 1975. Kaikoura, New Zealand. Bulletin of the International Association of Engineering Geology, no. 14, p. 189-200.

Bluck, B.J., 1969. Old Red Sandstone and other palaeozoic conglomerates of Scotland. American Association of Petroleum Gelogists, Memoir 12, p. 609-629.

Broscoe, A.J. and Thomson, S., 1969. Observations on an alpine mudflow, Steele Creek, Yukon. Canadian Journal of Earth Sciences, v. 6, p. 219-229.

Bull, W.B., 1963. Alluvial fan deposits in Western Fresno County, California. Journal of Geology, v. 71, p. 243-251.

Bull, W.B., 1964. Alluvial fans and near-surface subsidence in Western Fresno County California. United States Geological Survey, Professional Paper 437-A, 71 p.

Bull, W.B., 1972. Recognition of alluvial-fan deposits in the stratigraphic record. In Hamblin, W.K., and Rigby, J.K., eds., Recognition of ancient sedimentary environments. Society of Economic Paleontologists and Mineralogists, Special Publication 16, p. 63-83.

Burgisser, H.M., 1984. A unique mass flow marker bed in a Miocene streamflow molasse sequence, Switzerland. In Koster, E.H., and Steel, R.J., eds., The sedimentology of gravels and conglomerates. Canadian Society of Petroleum Geologists, Memoir 10, in press.

Church, M. and Ryder, J.M., 1972. Paraglacial sedimentation: a consideration of fluvial processes conditioned by glaciation. Geological Society of America, Bulletin, v. 83, p. 3059-3072.

Church, M., Stock, R.F., and Ryder, J.M., 1979. Contemporary sedimentary environments on Baffin Island, N.W.T., Canada: debris slope accumulations. Arctic and Alpine Research, v. 2, p. 135-144.

Crowell, J.C., 1974. Origin of Late Cenozoic basins in Southern California. In Dickinson, W.R., ed., Tectonics and sedimentation. Society of Economic Paleontologists and Mineralogists, Special Publication 22, p. 190-204.

Curry, R.C., 1966. Observation of alpine mudflows in the Tenmile Range, Central Colorado. Geological Society of America, Bulletin, v. 77, p. 771-776.

Daily, B., Moore, P.S., and Rust, B.R., 1980. Terrestrial-marine transition in the Cambrian rocks of Kangaroo Island, South Australia. Sedimentology, v. 27, p. 379-399.

Denny. C.S., 1967. Fans and pediments. American Journal of Science, v. 265, p. 81-105.

Ethridge, F.G., and Westcott, W.A., 1984. Tectonic setting, recognition and hydrocarbon reservoir potential of fan-delta deposits. In Koster, E.H., and Steel, R.J., eds., The sedimentology of gravels and conglomerates. Canadian Society of Petroleum Geologists, Memoir 10, in press.

Gloppen, T.G., and Steel, F.J., 1981. The deposits, internal structure and geometry in six alluvial fan – fan delta bodies (Devonian, Norway) – a study in the significance of bedding sequence in conglomerates. *In* Ethridge, F.G., and Flores, R.M., eds., Recent and ancient nonmarine depositional environments: models for exploration. Society of Economic Paleontologists and Mineralogists, Special Publication 31, p. 64-69.

Gostin, V.A., and Rust, B.R., 1983. Sedimentary features of some Quaternary alluvial fan successions, South Australia. *In* Williams, B.P.J., and Moore, P.J., eds., Fluvial sedimentology workshop. Australasian Sedimentologists Specialists Group, p. 37-55.

Gvirtzman, G. and Buchbinder, B., 1978. Recent and Pleistocene coral reefs and coastal sediments of the Gulf of Elat. International Congress of Sedimentologists, Postcongress Guidebook, p. 161-191.

Harvey, A.M., 1984. Debris flow and fluvial deposits in Spanish Quaternary alluvial fans: implications for fan morphology. *In* Koster, E.H., and Steel, R.J., eds., The sedimentology of gravels and conglomerates. Canadian Society of Petroleum Geologists, Memoir 10, in press.

Hayward, A.B., 1983. Coastal alluvial fans and associated marine facies in the Miocene of S.W. Turkey. *In* Collinson, J.D., and Lewin, J., eds., Modern and ancient fluvial systems. International Association of Sedimentologists, Special Publication 6, p. 323-336.

Heward, A.P., 178. Alluvial fan sequence and megasequence models: with examples from Westphalian D – Stephanian B coalfields, Northern Spain. *In* Miall, A.D., ed., Fluvial sedimentology. Canadian Society of Petroleum Geologists, Memoir 5, p. 669-702.

Hobday, D.K., and Von Brunn, V., 1979. Fluvial sedimentation and paleogeography of an Early Paleozoic failed rift, southeastern margin of Africa. Palaeogeography, Palaeoclimatology, Palaeoecology, v. 28, p. 169-184.

Hogg, S.E., 1982. Sheetfloods, sheetwash, sheetflow, or ... ? Earth-Science Reviews, v. 18, p. 59-76.

Holmes, A., and Holmes, D.L., 1978. Principles of physical geology. Sunbury-on-Thames, Nelson, Third Edition, 730 p.

Hooke, R.L.B., 1967. Processes on arid-region alluvial fans. Journal of Geology, v. 75, p. 438-460.

Johnson, A.M., 1970. Physical processes in geology. San Francisco, Freeman, 575 p.

Kleinspehn, K.L., Steel, R.J., Johannessen, E. and Netland, A., 1984. Conglomeratic fan-delta sequences, Late Carboniferous – Early Permian, western Spitsbergen. *In* Koster, E.H., and Steel, R.J., eds., The sedimentology of gravels and conglomerates. Canadian Society of Petroleum Geologists, Memoir 10, in press.

Koster, E.H., 1978a. Transverse ribs: their characteristics, origin and paleohydraulic significance. *In* Miall, A.D., ed., Fluvial sedimentology. Canadian Society of Petroleum Geologists, Memoir 5, p. 161-186.

Legget, R.F., Brown, F.J.E. and Johnson, G.H., 1966. Alluvial fan formation near Aklavik, Northwest Territories, Canada. Geological Society of America, Bulletin, v. 77, p. 15-30.

Lustig, L.K., 1965. Clastic sedimentation in Deep Springs Valley, California. United States Geological Survey, Professional Paper 352-F, p. 131-192.

Mack, G.H., and Rasmussen, K.A., 1984. Alluvial fan sedimentation of the Cutler Formation (Permo-Pennsylvanian) near Gateway, Colorado. Geological Society of America, Bulletin, v. 95, p. 109-116.

Miall, A.D., 1970. Devonian alluvial fans, Prince of Wales Island, Arctic Canada. Journal of Sedimentary Petrology, v. 40, p. 556-571.

Middleton, G.V., and Hampton, M.A., 1976. Subaqueous sediment transport and deposition by sediment gravity flows. *In* Stanley, D.J., and Swift, D.J.P., eds., Marine sediment transport and environmental management. New York, Wiley, p. 197-218.

Muir, A.D., and Rust, B.R., 1982. Sedimentology of a Lower Devonian coastal alluvial fan complex: the Snowblind Bay Formation of Cornwallis Island, Northwest Territories, Canada. Bulletin of Canadian Petroleum Geology, v. 30, p. 245-263.

Rust, B.R., and Gostin, V.A., 1981. Fossil transverse ribs in Holocene alluvial fan deposits, Depot Creek, South Australia. Journal of Sedimentary Petrology, v. 51, p. 441-444.

Ryder, J.M., 1971a. The stratigraphy and morphology of paraglacial alluvial fans in south-central British Columbia. Canadian Journal of Earth Sciences. v. 8, p. 279-298.

Ryder, J.M., 1971b. Some aspects of the morphometry of paraglacial fans in south-central British Columbia. Canadian Journal of Earth Sciences, v. 8, p. 1252-1264.

Shultz, A.W., 1983. The deposits, internal structure and geometry in six alluvial fan-fan delta bodies (Devonian, Norway) – a study in the significance of bedding sequence in conglomerates – discussion. Journal of Sedimentary Petrology, v. 53, p. 325-327.

Schumm, S.A., 1973. Geomorphic thresholds and complex response of drainage systems. *In* Morisawa, M., ed., Fluvial geomorphology. State University of New York, Binghampton, Publications in Geomorphology, v. 4, p. 299-310.

Steel, R.J., 1974. New Red Sandstone flood plain and piedmont sedimentation in the Hebridean Province, Scotland. Journal of Sedimentary Petrology, v. 44, p. 336-357.

Steel, R.J., and Gloppen, T.G., 1980. Late Caledonian (Devonian) basin formation, Western Norway: signs of strike-slip tectonics during infilling. *In* Ballance, P.F., and Reading, H.G., eds., Sedimentation in oblique-slip mobile zones. International Association of Sedimentologists, Special Publication 4, p. 79-103.

Twidale, C.R., 1979. The character and interpretation of some pediment mantles. Sedimentary Geology, v. 22, p. 1-20.

Wasson, R.J., 1977a. Last-glacial alluvial fan sedimentation in the Lower Derwent Valley, Tasmania. Sedimentology, v. 24, p. 781-799.

Wasson, R.J., 1977b. Catchment processes and the evolution of alluvial fans in the lower Derwent Valley, Tasmania. Zeitschrift für Geomorphologie, v. 21, p. 147-168.

Wells, A., 1984. Sheet debris flow and sheet-flood conglomerates in Cretaceous cool-maritime alluvial fans, South Orkney Islands, Antarctica. *In* Koster, E.H., and Steel, R.J., eds., The sedimentology of gravels and conglomerates. Canadian Society of Petroleum Geologists, Memoir 10, in press.

Wescott, W.A., and Ethridge, F.G., 1980. Fan-delta sedimentology and tectonic setting - Yallahs fan delta, Southeast Jamaica. American Association of Petroleum Geologists, Bulletin, v. 64, p. 374-399.

White, S.E., 1981. Alpine mass movement forms (noncatastrophic): classification, description and significance. Arctic and Alpine Research, v. 13, p. 127-137.

Williams, G.E., 1973. Late Quaternary piedmont sedimentation, soil formation and paleoclimates in arid South Australia. Zeitschrift für Geomorphologie, v. 17, p. 102-125.

Winder, C.G., 1965. Alluvial cone construction by alpine mudflow in a humid temperate region. Canadian Journal of Earth Sciences, v. 2, p. 270-277.

Zaitlin, B.A., and Rust, B.R., 1983. A spectrum of alluvial deposits in the Lower Carboniferous Bonaventure Formation of western Chaleur Bay area, Gaspé and New Brunswick, Canada. Canadian Journal of Earth Sciences, v. 20, p. 1098-1110.

RIVERS AND BRAIDPLAINS

Allen, J.R.L., and Friend, P.F., 1968. Deposition of the Catskill facies, Appalachian Region: with notes on some other Old Red Sandstone Basins. In Klein, G. de V., ed., Late Paleozoic and Mesozoic continental sedimentation, northeast North America. Geological Society of America, Special Paper 106, p. 21-74.

Allen, P., 1975. Wealden of the Weald: a new model. Proceedings of the Geological Association, v. 86, p. 389-437.

Baker, V.R., 1978. The Spokane flood controversy and the Martian outflow channels. Science, v. 202, p. 1249-1256.

Boothroyd, J.C. and Ashley G.M., 1975. Processes, bar morphology, and sedimentary structures on braided outwash fans, northeastern Gulf of Alaska. In Jopling, A.V., and McDonald, B.C., eds., Glaciofluvial and glaciolacustrine sedimentation. Society of Economic Paleontologists and Mineralogists, Special Publication 23, p. 193-222.

Boothroyd, J.C., and Nummedal, D., 1978. Proglacial braided outwash: a model for humid alluvial fan deposits. In Miall, A.D., ed., Fluvial sedimentology, Canadian Society of Petroleum Geologists, Memoir 5, p. 641-668.

Bradley, W.C., Fahnestock, R.K. and Rowekamp, E.T., 1972. Coarse sediment transport by flood flows in Knik River, Alaska. Geological Society of America, Bulletin, v. 83, p. 1261-1284.

Bretz, J.H., Smith, H.T.U., and Neff, G.E., 1956. Channelled scabland of Washington: new data and interpretations. Geological Society of America, Bulletin, v. 67, p. 957-1049.

Church, M. and Gilbert, R., 1975. Proglacial fluvial and lacustrine environments. In Jopling, A.V., and McDonald, B.C., eds., Glaciofluvial and glaciolacustrine sedimentation. Society of Economic Paleontologists and Mineralogists, Special Publication 23, p. 22-100.

Eynon, G., and Walker, R.G., 1974. Facies relationships in Pleistocene outwash gravels, southern Ontario: a model for bar growth in braided rivers. Sedimentology, v. 21, p. 43-70.

Fahnestock, R.K., and Bradley, W.C., 1973. Knik and Matanuska rivers, Alaska: a contrast in braiding. In Morisawa, M., ed., Fluvial geomorphology. State University of New York, Binghampton, Publications in Geomorphology, v. 4, p. 220-250.

Galay, V.J., and Neill, C.R., 1967. Discussion of "Nomenclature for bed forms in alluvial channels". Journal of Hydraulics Division, American Society of Civil Engineers, v. 93, p. 130-133.

Hein, F.J. and Walker, R.G., 1977. Bar evolution and development of stratification in the gravelly, braided, Kicking Horse River, British Columbia. Canadian Journal of Earth Sciences, v. 14, p. 562-570.

Jackson, R.G., 1976. Depositional model of point bars in the Lower Wabash River. Journal of Sedimentary Petrology, v. 46, p. 579-594.

Jackson, R.G., 1978. Preliminary evaluation of lithofacies models for meandering alluvial streams. In Miall, A.D., ed., Fluvial sedimentology. Canadian Society of Petroleum Geologists, Memoir 5, p. 543-576.

Kraus, M.J., 1984. Sedimentology and tectonic setting of early tertiary quartzite conglomerates, northwest Wyoming, U.S.A. In Koster, E.H., and Steel, R.J., eds., The sedimentology of gravels and conglomerates. Canadian Society of Petroleum Geologists, Memoir 10, in press.

Krumbein, W.C., 1942. Flood deposits of Arroyo Seco, Los Angeles County, California. Geological Society of America, Bulletin, v. 53, p. 1355-1402.

Leckie, D.A., and Walker, R.G., 1982. Storm- and tide-dominated shorelines in Cretaceous Moosebar-Lower Gates interval – outcrop equivalents of Deep Basin gas trap in western Canada. American Association of Petroleum Geologists, Bulletin, v. 66, p. 138-157.

Leopold, L.B. and Wolman, M.G., 1957. River channel patterns: straight, meandering and braided. United States Geological Survey, Professional Paper 232-B, p. 39-85.

Malde, H.E., 1968. The catastrophic Late Pleistocene Bonneville flood in the Snake River Plain, Idaho. United Stated Geological Survey, Professional Paper 596.

McGowen, J.H., and Garner, L.E., 1970. Physiographic features and stratification types of coarse-grained point bars: modern and ancient examples. Sedimentology, v. 14, p. 77-111.

McLean, J.R., 1977. The Cadomin Formation: stratigraphy, sedimentology and tectonic implications. Bulletin of Canadian Petroleum Geology, v. 25, p. 792-827.

Middleton, L.T., and Trujillo, A.P., 1984. Sedimentology and depositional setting of the Upper Proterozoic Scanlan conglomerate (Central Arizona). In Koster, E.H., and Steel, R.J., eds., The sedimentology of gravels and conglomerates. Canadian Society of Petroleum Geologists, Memoir 10, in press.

Ore, H.T., 1964. Some criteria for recognition of braided stream deposits. University of Wyoming, Contributions to Geology, v. 3, p. 1-14.

Rust, B.R., 1972a. Structure and process in a braided river. Sedimentology, v. 18, p. 221-245.

Rust, B.R., 1972b. Pebble orientation in fluvial sediments. Journal of Sedimentary Petrology, v. 42, p. 384-388.

Rust, B.R., 1975. Fabric and structure in glaciofluvial gravels. In Jopling, A.V., and McDonald, B.C., eds., Glaciofluvial and glaciolacustrine sedimentation. Society of Economic Paleontologists and Mineralogists, Special Publication 23, p. 238-248.

Rust, B.R., 1981. Alluvial deposits and tectonic style: Devonian and Carboniferous successions in eastern Gaspé. In Miall, A.D., ed., Sedimentation and tectonics in alluvial basins. Geological Association of Canada, Special Paper 23, p. 49-76.

Rust, B.R., in press (a). The Cannes de Roche Formation: Carboniferous alluvial deposits in eastern Gaspé, Canada. Comptes Rendus, 12th International Carboniferous Congress, Urbana, Illinois.

Rust, B.R., in press (b). Proximal braidplain deposits in the Middle Devonian Malbaie Formation of eastern Gaspé, Canada. Sedimentology.

Schultheis, N.H., and Mountjoy, E.W., 1978. Cadomin conglomerate of western Alberta – a result of Early Cretaceous uplift of the Main Ranges. Bulletin of Canadian Petroleum Geology, v. 26, p. 297-342.

Southard, J.B., Smith, N.D., and Kuhnle, R.A., 1984. Chutes and lobes: newly identified elements of braiding in shallow gravelly streams. In Koster, E.H., and Steel, R.J., eds., The sedimentology of gravels and conglomerates. Canadian Society of Petroleum Geologists, Memoir 10, in press.

Smith, D.G., 1983. Anastomosed fluvial deposits: modern examples from western Canada. In Collinson, J.D., and Lewin, J., eds., Modern and ancient fluvial systems. International Association of Sedimentologists, Special Publication 6, p. 155-168.

Smith, D.G., and Smith, N.D., 1980. Sedimentation in anastomosed river systems: examples from alluvial valleys near Banff, Alberta. Journal of Sedimentary Petrology, v. 50, p. 157-164.

Smith, N.D., 1970. The braided stream depositional environment: comparison of the Platte River with some Silurian clastic rocks, North-Central Apalachians. Geological Society of America, Bulletin, v. 81 p. 2993-3014.

Smith, N.D., 1974. Sedimentology and bar formation in the upper Kicking Horse River, a braided outwash stream. Journal of Geology, v. 82, p. 205-223.

Steel, R.J., and Thompson, D.B., 1983. Structures and textures in Triassic braided stream conglomerates ('Bunter' Pebble Beds) in the Sherwood Sandstone Group, North Staffordshire, England. Sedimentology, v. 30, p. 341-367.

Vonhof, J.A., 1965. The Oligocene Cypress Hills Formation and its reworked deposits in southwestern Saskatchewan. Alberta Society of Petroleum Geologists, 15th Annual Field Conference Guidebook Part 1, Cypress Hills Plateau, p. 142-161.

Vos, R.G., and Tankard, A.J., 1981. Braided fluvial sedimentation in the Lower Paleozoic Cape Basin, South Africa. Sedimentary Geology, v. 29, p. 171-193.

Williams, P.F., and Rust, B.R., 1969. The sedimentology of a braided river. Journal of Sedimentary Petrology, v. 39, p. 649-679.

Wilson, M.D., 1970. Upper Cretaceous-Paleocene synorogenic conglomerates of southwestern Montana. American Association of Petroleum Geologists, Bulletin, v. 54, p. 1843-1867.

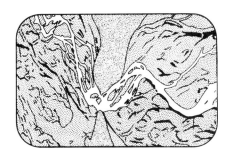

Sandy Fluvial Systems

ROGER G. WALKER
Department of Geology
McMaster University
Hamilton, Ontario L8S 4M1

DOUGLAS J. CANT
Alberta Geological Survey
4445 Calgary Trail South
Edmonton, Alberta T6H 5R7

INTRODUCTION
Sandy rivers can be subdivided into four types, straight, meandering, braided and anastomosed. Natural straight rivers are very uncommon, and there is probably a spectrum of types from meandering to braided. The anastomosed type has only recently been emphasized, and a model would probably be premature. We will therefore concentrate on the *meandering* and *braided* end members of the spectrum mentioned above. Comparison of new situations with our meandering and braided *norms* should help to establish the range of variation between the end members; it will also help to define better the end members themselves.

HISTORY OF SANDY FLUVIAL STUDIES
A full historical review has been given by Miall (1978a) – our purpose here is to introduce the reader to the development of ideas during the last 40 years. Before doing so, it is important to note that Barrell (1913, p. 458) had identified fining-upward sequences in the Devonian Catskill Formation of New York State, as had Dixon (1921, p. 32) in the South Wales coalfield. Dixon commented that the sequence: flaggy sandstone grading up into red marl is "repeated interminably and in all parts of the series".

The post-war period of about 1944-1960 was devoted mostly to the study of modern rivers, rather than the sediments therein. Classic work is that of Fisk (1944) on the Mississippi, and of the geomorphologists on various U.S. rivers (notably Leopold, Schumm and Wolman; references in Miall, 1978a).

In about 1960, two separate lines of study began to develop, namely recent sediments in rivers, and ancient fluvial sediments.

Recent sediments were studied by the Shell Oil Company in legendary but mostly unpublished work on Brazos River point bars in Texas (see Bernard *et al.*, 1970), where the classic fining-upward sequence was documented, along with vertical changes in sedimentary structures (giant ripple bedding, overlain by horizontal bedding, overlain by small ripple bedding).

Excavations in the Mississippi Old River Locksite were described by Frazier and Osanik (1961). In the early 1960s, the geometry of various sedimentary structures was still being determined, and this is the emphasis of Frazier and Osanik's work, as well as that of Harms *et al.* (1963),in the Red River of Louisiana. The relationship of fluvial bed forms, stratification and flow phenomena were further emphasized by Harms and Fahnestock (1965) from the Rio Grande near El Paso, Texas. The most significant addition to this work was probably that of Jackson (1976), who related in detail flow phenomena, bed forms and stratification sequences in meanders of the Wabash River.

Studies of *ancient meandering sandstones* blossomed along with the work on recent sediments. Fining-upward sequences were described in detail by Bersier (1968), and in classic work by Allen (1964) which has continued to this day (e.g., Allen, 1983). Low sinuosity streams were discussed by Moody-Stewart (1966) from Spitsbergen, but interpretations of *ancient braided sandstones* have been relatively few (Smith, 1970; Campbell, 1976; Cant and Walker, 1976; Allen, 1983). This may be due to the fact that relatively few *modern braided sandy rivers* have been described sedimentologically; classic studies include the Brahmaputra (Coleman, 1969), Platte (Smith, 1970; Blodgett and Stanley, 1980), Tana (north Norway, Collinson, 1970), and South Saskatchewan (Cant and Walker, 1978).

These studies constitute the core of the data base for the models we present below. For the meandering model, there seems to be much more data from ancient rocks than well-studied modern rivers. The emphasis on Devonian Old Red Sandstone/Catskill examples may bias the model toward smaller meandering streams. The data base for braided systems is much smaller – the four or five rivers mentioned above, together with a very small (but growing) number of interpretations of ancient braided sandstones.

MEANDERING SYSTEMS
The main elements of a modern meandering system (exemplified by the Mississippi or Brazos rivers) are shown in Figure 1. Sandy deposition is normally restricted to the main channel, or to partially or completely abandoned meander loops; deposition of fines (silt and clay) occurs on levees and in flood basins.

Basis For The Model
The model has been developed from both modern and ancient sediments. The most important papers on modern meandering streams used in developing the model are those of Sundborg (1956; River Klaralven), Harms *et al.* (1963; Red River), McGowen and Garner (1970; Colorado (Texas) and Amite rivers) and Jackson (1976; Wabash River), five in all.

Investigations of larger-scale processes such as meander loop migration, rates and patterns of channel switching and aggradation remain sparse. Many descriptions of ancient meandering stream deposits have also been integrated into the model, to the extent that the model is one of the most broadly based facies models in terms of numbers of modern and ancient examples used. However, much remains to be done in terms of documenting and understanding variations of the model.

The Channel And Point Bar
Meandering of the channel is maintained by erosion on the outer banks of meander loops, and deposition on the inner parts of the loops. The main depositional environment is the point bar, which builds laterally and downstream across the flood plain.

The channel floor commonly has a coarse "lag" deposit of material that the river can only move at peak flood time.

72

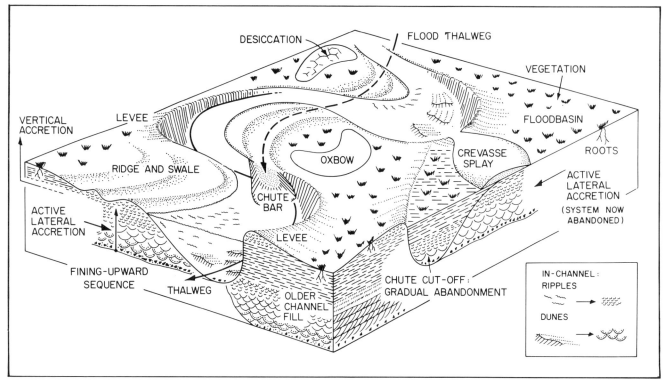

Figure 1

Block diagram showing morphological elements of a meandering river system. Erosion on the outside bend of a meander loop leads to lateral accretion on the opposite point bar. The dunes and ripples in the channel give rise to trough cross bedding and ripple cross lamination respectively (inset, lower right), which are preserved in a fining-upward sequence. See text for details.

This material includes the gravelly component of the clastic load, together with water-logged plant material and partly consolidated blocks of mud eroded locally from the channel wall. Above the lag, sand is transported through the system as bedload. During average discharge, the typical bedform on the channel floor consists of sinuous-crested dunes (Fig. 1) ranging in height from about 30 cm to one metre. Preservation of these dunes results in trough cross-stratification. In shallower parts of the flow, higher on the point bar, the bedform is commonly ripples (preserved as trough cross lamination, Fig. 1). As a broad generalization, we may propose that the preserved deposits of the active channel will pass from trough cross-bedded coarser sands to small scale, trough cross-laminated finer sands upward (Fig. 1).

The development of a plane bed (without ripples or dunes) is favoured

by higher velocities, shallow depths and finer grain sizes. Deposition on the plane bed results in horizontal lamination. The particular combinations of depth and velocity required to produce a plane bed can occur at various river stages, and hence parallel lamination can be formed both low and high on the point bar. It can therefore be preserved interbedded with trough cross-bedding, or small scale trough cross-lamination (Figs. 2 and 3).

The sequence shown in Figure 2 is typical of Devonian Old Red Sandstone/ Catskill deposits, but does not necessarily characterize deeper or flashier rivers. Very little attention has been given to the response of the sedimentary structure sequence to stage changes in meandering rivers. Also, many modern point bars appear to be terraced (Fig. 4), perhaps due to incision and erosion, or perhaps due to different levels of deposition at various flood stages. The relationship of structure sequence to terracing has not been investigated.

The fining-upward grain size change is a response to spiralling flow through the meander loop. Slightly higher water elevations on the cut-bank side drive a flow down toward the bed and up onto the point bar – the combination of this cross-channel flow with downchannel flow results in spiral flow. Gradually

decelerating flow components up the point bar result in the transport of finer and finer sediment, and the general transition from sinous crested dunes (in channel) to small current ripples (near top of point bar).

Erosion of the cut bank and deposition on the point bar result in a gradual lateral and downcurrent shift in position of the point bar. The fining-upward sequence of grain sizes, and accompanying vertical sequence of sedimentary structures, is therefore preserved by LATERAL ACCRETION of the point part (Fig. 1). If the lateral accretion is episodic, or if there are periods of erosion during overall accretion, former positions of the point bar surface can be preserved within the sedimentary sequence. These surfaces are characteristically sigmoid (flat on top of the point bar, steepening down the point bar, and flattening again into the channel floor), with dips of a few degrees up to a maximum of around 15°. They are termed *lateral accretion surfaces* or *epsilon* cross beds (Fig. 5).

Channel Abandonment

Meander loops can be abandoned gradually (chute cut-off) or suddenly (neck cut-off) (Allen, 1965, p. 118-9, 156). During chute cut-off, the river gradually re-occupies an old swale, and

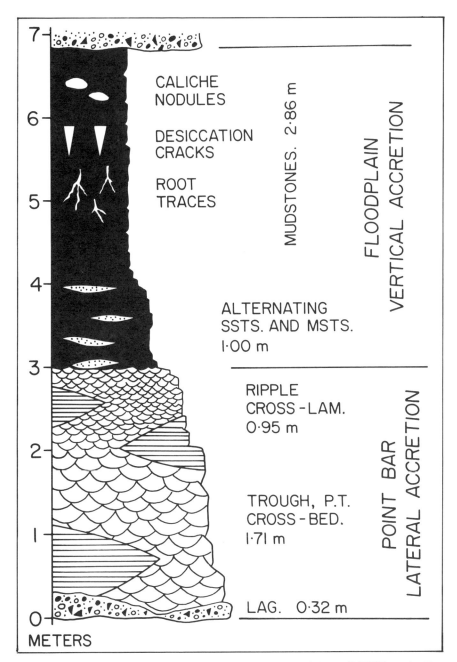

Figure 2

Model for lateral and vertical accretion deposits of meandering rivers. Data on facies sequence and fining upwards cycles summarized here are from the Devonian Old Red Sandstone of Britain and the Catskill rocks of the eastern U.S.A. (Allen, 1970). The average lateral accretion deposit is 2.98 m thick, and the vertical accretion deposit averages 3.86 m. Thus the average sequence is 6.84 m thick. Compare with braided stream sequences in Figures 17 and 19. Note that parallel lamination can replace trough cross bedding or ripple cross lamination, or both. The average thickness of parallel lamination is 1.30 m.

Figure 3

Fining-upward sequence, Cretaceous Belly River Formation, on Trans-Canada Highway between Calgary and Morley Road. Note sharp base to sand body, and cross bedding (by notebook) in lower part. Upper part of sand body (by geologist) is ripple cross laminated and overlain by fines.

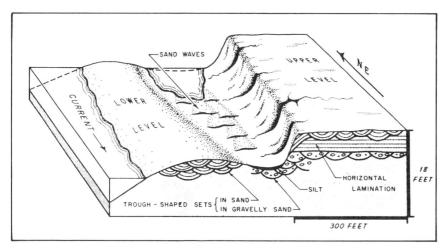

Figure 4
Block diagram showing upstream part of Beene Point Bar, Red River, Louisiana, from Harms et al. (1963). Note terracing (2 levels) on the point bar, and interbedding of various sedimentary structures.

Figure 5
Lateral accretion surfaces (epsilon cross strata), Gate Canyon (near Nine Mile Canyon, Utah). In these fluvial Eocene sandstones and shales, note erosive base of sand body. Superbly developed lateral accretion surfaces (L.A.), with overall aggradation during lateral accretion, and cut bank (C.B.) on opposite side. Main sand body about 5 m thick.

simultaneously flow gradually decreases in the main channel. Gradual abandonment thus results in gradual flow decrease, and this could be reflected in the sediments by the development of a thick sequence of low-flow sedimentary structures – essentially ripple cross-lamination (Fig. 6). After complete abandonment, forming an ox-bow lake, sedimentation would be restricted to fines (silt, mud) introduced into the ox-bow during overbank flooding from the main stream (Fig. 1).

Neck cut-off involves the breaching of a neck between two meanders, and the sudden cut-off of an entire meander loop. Both the entrance to and exit from the loop tend to be rapidly plugged with sand. Flow diminishes to zero rather quickly and the resulting sequence of deposits is dominated by later, flood-introduced silts and muds (Fig. 6).

Vertical Accretion Deposits
Outside the main channel, deposition in the flood basins, ox-bows and levees takes place by addition of sediment during flood stage when the river overtops its banks (Fig. 1). In contrast to the lateral accretion within the main channel, overbank deposition causes upbuilding of the flood plain, hence the term VERTICAL ACCRETION. Near to the main channel, where the flood waters sweep along as a stream, the vertical accretion deposits tend to be silty, and are commonly cross-laminated. In some cases, it appears that the levee is breached catastrophically, and the resulting splay bed has a sharp base and begins with parallel lamination. This may pass upward into ripple cross lamination, producing a bed which is descriptively and hydrodynamically akin to a turbidite. It can be distinguished from a deep marine turbidite (see "Turbidites and Associated Coarse Clastic Deposits", this volume) by its context, and the possible root traces in the top of the splay bed.

Farther from the river, flood waters may stagnate and only mud is deposited. After retreat of the flood, the mud and silt commonly dry out, and desiccation cracks are formed. The flood basins and levees of most river systems (post-Silurian) tend to be abundantly vegetated, and hence the deposits commonly contain root traces. In some climatic regimes, the vegetation may grow sufficiently abundantly to form coal seams. In semi-arid environments, the fluctuating water table and drying at the surface favour the formation of caliche-like nodules within the vertical accretion deposits.

The only other deposits that may rarely be preserved as part of the vertical accretion sequence are windblown, and may be either loess, or coarser sandy deposits blown in as large dunes (see "Eolian Facies", this volume).

Meandering River Facies Sequence
The distillation of observations from a large number of modern meandering streams, and from many ancient formations interpreted as meandering-fluvial, allows a general facies sequence to be formulated. One version of this sequence is shown in Figure 2; it was distilled statistically by Allen (1970) and is redrawn to scale here. In its simplest form, the sequence is FINING-UPWARD and consists of in-channel deposits (lateral accretion), followed by overbank fines (vertical accretion) (Figs. 7 and 8).

In this particular sequence, the facies relationships were determined statistically for a large number of Devonian outcrops in Britain and North America, but application of the model has demonstrated that it can be used appropriately in many other areas. The lag

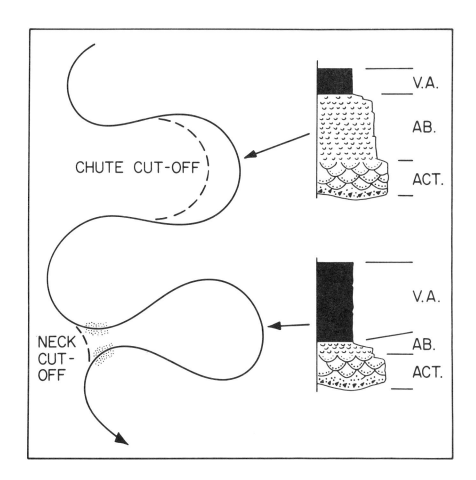

Figure 6

Meander loops can be abandoned by chute or neck cut-off. Old channel shown solid, new channels dashed. Chute cut-off involves reoccupation of an old swale and gradual abandonment of the main channel. The stratigraphic sequence will consist of some trough cross-bedded deposits of the active river (ACT) and a thick sequence of ripple cross-laminated fine sands representing gradual abandonment (AB). After cut-off, the sequence is completed by vertical-accretion (V.A.) deposits. By contrast, after neck cut-off, the meander loop is suddenly abandoned and sealed off by deposition of sand plugs (stipple). After the active deposits, the ripple cross-laminated fine sands representing low flow during abandonment (AB) are very thin, and the bulk of the sequence consists of vertical-accretion (V.A.) deposits washed into the abandoned loop at flood time. Compare with the active lateral-accretion sequence (Fig. 2).

Figure 7

A complete fining-upward sequence from the Pennsylvanian Maringouin Formation, Nova Scotia. Note sharp base, and interbedding of sandstones and shales toward top of sand body. Vertical accretion fines separate the interbedded sandstones and shales from the next sand body (top left). Directly above geologist's head is a small mud-filled channel that cuts out the interbedded sandstones and shales – it may represent an abandoned swale on a point bar.

Figure 8

Photomosaic of a multistory sand body with well-developed lateral accretion surfaces in lower part (LA). Sand body is about 15.5 m thick; Lower Cretaceous Gladstone Formation at Bighorn River, Alberta. The upper part of the sand body is inaccessible, but possibly contains smaller lateral accretion sets, or possibly huge wide shallow troughs dipping toward the reader in the left-hand half of the uppermost sand body.

deposits are overlain by trough cross-bedding, which is in turn overlain by small scale trough cross-lamination. Horizontal lamination can occur at several places within this sequence (Fig. 2), depending on the river stage at the time when the depth/velocity/grain size criteria for plane bed were met.

After the channel migrated away laterally, the facies sequence continued with vertical accretion deposits introduced at flood stage. The diagram (Fig. 2) shows root traces, desiccation cracks and caliche-like concretions. Using the data presented by Allen (1970, Table 9), it can be seen that the vertical and lateral accretion deposits in the meandering model are on average roughly equal in thickness.

Allen's model serves excellently as a norm with which to compare other fining-upward sequences. Comparison of sequences such as those in Figure 6 with Allen's norm immediately shows that the trough cross-bedding is very reduced in thickness, that the chute cut-off sequence contains an abnormal thickness of ripple trough cross-lamination, and that both contain unusual thicknesses of vertical accretion deposits. The comparison with Allen's model suggests the interpretations shown in Figure 6; without the model, we would not be so conscious that the

sequences in Figure 6 differed significantly from the sequence developed by lateral accretion in an active channel.

The rocks in Figure 8 also emphasize the role of Allen's model as a norm. In Figure 8, both the sandstones and mudstones are much thicker than suggested by the norm. There are possibly two superimposed sets of lateral accretion deposits in the sandstone, suggesting two superimposed channel sands rather than one extremely thick sand body. The apparently unusual thickness of vertical accretion fines will be discussed again below.

Comparison of the models with some sequences developed for meandering rivers with slightly coarser loads also reveals some differences. Where coarse bedload is funnelled by flood waters through a swale on the top of a point bar, a much straighter thalweg is formed. The coarse material is dumped at the downstream end of the swale forming a chute bar adjacent to the point bar (Fig. 2; McGowen and Garner, 1970). In other rivers, coarser sediment and less mud deposition leads to a sequence without a really well developed fining-upward trend (Jackson, 1976). These variations from the standard point bar model must be recognized and allowed for in the study of ancient sediments.

Sand Body Geometry And Flood-Plain Aggradation

One of the essential components of a meandering model is the fact that meander loops are cut off, abandoned, and ultimately filled with fines – silt and clay. Through time, these clay plugs, along with thick back-swamp clays, may become abundant because the plugs are relatively hard to erode. Once

confined, the entire meander belt may become raised above the general level of the flood plain by vertical accretion (Fig. 9A). This situation can persist until one catastrophic levee break results in the sudden switch of the entire river to a lower part of the floodplain ("avulsion", Fig. 9A). Thus the overall sand body geometry of a highly sinuous meandering stream will be essentially elongate ("shoestring"), bounded below and on both sides by flood-basin fines. The shoestring will also stand a good chance of being covered by overbank fines from the active river in its new position. Thus the *high sinuosity meandering model* predicts that, given continuing supply and basin subsidence, a series of point bar sand sheets interbedded with shales should be developed within the overall shoestring geometry. The internal structure of the point bar sands themselves should conform roughly to the pattern shown in Figure 1. A single-sequence sand body should be about as thick as the river was deep; however, if clay plugs restrain the river to the meander belt, multistory sand bodies should be common (Figs. 8 and 9A). Sequences of overbank fines thicker than those predicted by Allen's model could form if the river is confined in this way – compare the mudstones in Figure 8 with those in Figure 2. Conversely, using this model as a predictor, we suggest that unusually thick sequences of vertical accretion fines (10 m +) might predict (along strike) stacked sand bodies in a meander belt confined by clay plugs. The vertical scale in Figure 9A is considerably exaggerated, and individual shoestrings will probably be many times wider than they are thick.

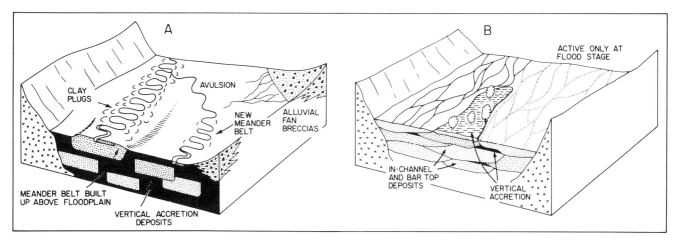

Figure 9

A) block diagram of flood plain aggradation with very sinuous rivers. Shoestring sands are preserved, and are surrounded by vertical accretion siltstones and mudstones. If the river is confined by clay plugs, very thick vertical accretion deposits can form without erosion. B) block diagram of sandy braided system with low sinuosity channels. Vertical accretion can occur during flood stage, but deposits are rarely preserved. Diagrams modified from Allen (1965).

Figure 10

Correlation of well logs (SP, resistivity) across Coyote Creek field (location in Fig. 11), with interpretation in terms of meander belt facies below. Note thickness of sand body – about 50 to 75' (15 to 23 m); channel width is about 1500 to 2000' (460 to 610 m). From Berg (1968).

Meandering Rivers In The Subsurface

There are many examples: we highlight two to illustrate how well-log data (see "Subsurface Facies Analysis", this volume) can be used in fluvial reconstructions. In the Lower Cretaceous sandstones in the Powder River basin, Wyoming, Berg (1968) has shown well-log correlations which can be interpreted in terms of: 1) porous point bar sands; 2) sands, silts and shales of swale-fill origin; and 3) shale and silt representing the fill of the abandoned channel (Fig. 10). Note the thickness of the point bar sand – up to about 75 feet, or 23 m. In the isopach map (Fig. 11), the shapes of the meander loop and swales are apparent. The isopach map does not suggest superimposed separate sand bodies – it appears to be one

system 23 m deep which accreted laterally toward the NE. The size of this meander loop (radius of curvature about 2130 m) is comparable with loops in the modern Mississippi and Missouri rivers, which helps to explain the unusually great depth of this Cretaceous river.

In a second example, Hopkins *et al.* (1982) have presented subsurface data for Lower Cretaceous Mannville Group sands in southern Alberta (Figs. 12 and 13). Here, the Mannville channels are incised into older units (Ostracod Limestone and Bantry Shale, Fig. 13), and at least the lower ones were probably not freely meandering. Part of the line BB' (Fig. 12) is shown in Figure 13, and can be interpreted in terms of a laterally accreted sandstone about 20 m

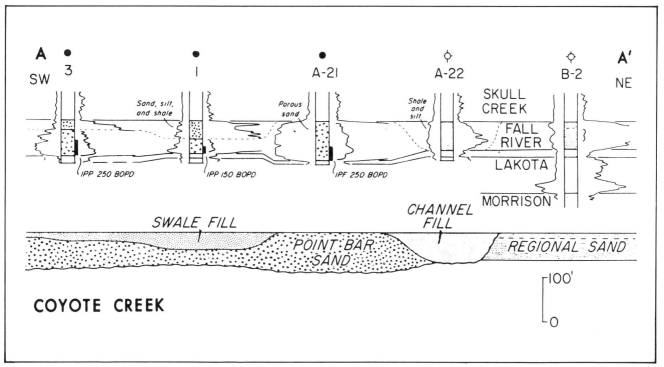

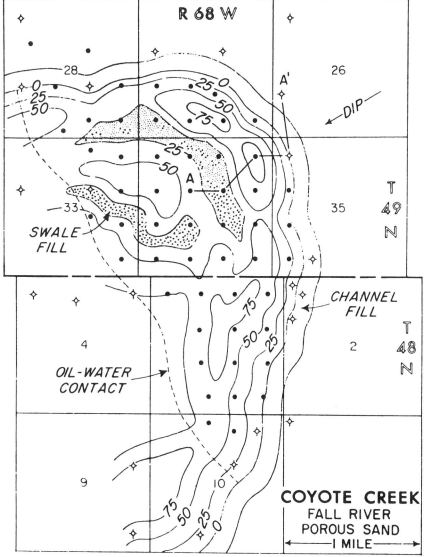

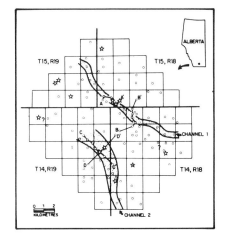

◄ Figure 11

Isopach map of Coyote Creek field, north-eastern Wyoming. Note location of cross-section AA' (Fig. 10). Swale fills show thinner sands, and the abandoned meander loop itself has no sand. This can be seen both in the sand isopach (values down to zero) and the location of dry holes (open circles) as opposed to oil wells (black circles). From this isopach map, Berg (1968) made the following estimates: channel width 1500 to 2000' (460 to 610 m), meander radius 7000' (2130 m) and meander wavelength 40000' (about 12,200 m). Note that the regional dip is southwestward, and hence the shaly fill of the abandoned meander loop is the updip stratigraphic trap. From Berg (1968).

Figure 12

Location map of Little Bow area, southern Alberta. Location of two channels shown. Figure 13 shows cross section BB', omitting the wells at each end of the line. Glauconitic Member of the Mannville (Albian), from Hopkins et al., 1982.

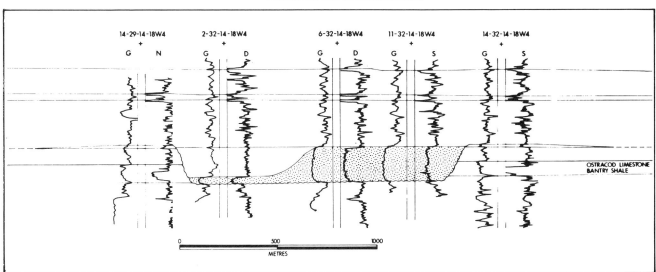

Figure 13

Part of cross-section BB' (see Fig. 12) from the Glauconitic member of the Mannville (Albian), from Hopkins et al. (1982). From the correlations shown, note the laterally accreting sand body from well 11-32 to 6-32, and then abandonment of the system with subsequent mud filling of the empty channel (well 2-32). The laterally accreted sand is about 20 m thick, the empty channel about 500 m wide, subsequently filled with about 16 to 17 m of fines.

thick (wells 6-32 and 11-32), with a channel some 500 m wide that filled with 16 to 17 m of mud after cut-off of this meander system (? by avulsion). The overall, incised channel width (Fig. 12) is about 1 km, suggesting that the 500 m quoted above (Fig. 13) represents the width of a meandering channel within the overall, straighter incised channel. This channel width (500 m) is comparable to the narrower parts of the present Missouri River.

In both examples, the simple models of Figures 1 and 2 must be use with caution in prediction, because the models are based upon much smaller rivers than those in Figures 11, 12 and 13, and because of the problem of river incision into older rocks.

Point Bar Reconstructions

Since earlier versions of this paper, several excellent reconstructions of ancient point bars have been made, particularly those of Nami (1976), Nami and Leeder (1978), Nijman and Puigdefabregas (1978) and Edwards et al. (1983). In some of these studies, the sand bodies are a little thicker than those in the sequence of Figure 2 (Nami and Leeder quote 3 to 9 m, and Nijman and Puigde-fabregas quote a maximum of 11 m), although the 2 to 3 m thick epsilon cross beds quoted by Edwards et al. (1983) are very comparable with Figure 2. The importance of these studies is that three dimensional reconstructions of channel, point bar and swales can be made from excellent outcrops, allowing a direct link between modern point bars and preser-vability of facies in the geological record.

SANDY BRAIDED SYSTEMS

The fundamental processes that control whether a river has a braided or meand-ering pattern are not completely under-stood but we do know that braiding is favoured by rapid discharge fluctua-tions of a greater absolute magnitude than in meandering rivers. Braided riv-ers also tend to have higher slopes, a heavy load of coarse sediment, and more easily erodible banks. In combina-tion these features would suggest that braiding is more characteristic of the upstream reaches of a river, with meandering becoming more common downstream as the slope and coarse-ness of load decreases. Braiding would also be more common in semi-arid or arid areas.

Basis For The Braided Model

In contrast to meandering rivers, sandy braided systems have received relatively little study. The best known rivers include the Durance and Ardeche (Doeglas, 1962), Brahmaputra (Cole-man, 1969), Platte (Smith, 1970; Blod-gett and Stanley, 1980), Tana (Collin-son, 1970) and South Saskatchewan (Cant and Walker, 1978).

Few studies of braided rivers have been detailed and comprehensive enough to contribute to the models. The scale of the rivers studied varies enor-mously, from the Platte (1 to 2 m deep, hundreds of metres wide) to the Brah-maputra (up to 25 m deep, several kilometres wide). Relatively few ancient studies have been integrated as yet into braided stream models. The best doc-umented studies include those of Moody-Stewart (1966, Devonian of Spitsbergen), Kelling (1968, Coal Mea-sures, South Wales), Conaghan and

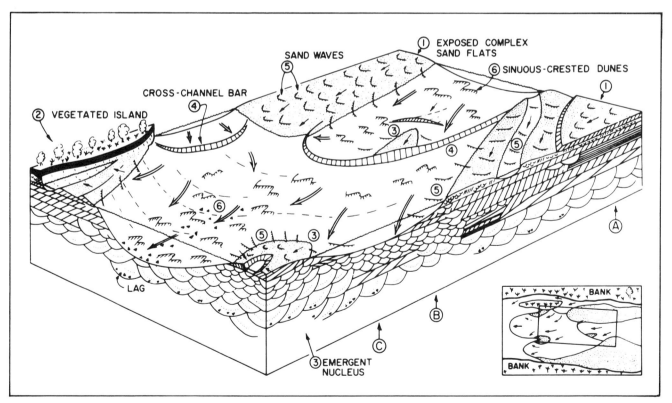

Figure 14
Block diagram showing elements (num-bered) of a braided sandy river, based on the South Saskatchewan. Stippled areas exposed, all other areas underwater. Bar in left corner is being driven laterally against a vegetated island, but is separated form the island by a slough in which mud is being deposited. Large sandflats (e.g., right-hand corner) may develop by growth from an emergent nucleus on a major cross-channel bar (see Figs. 15 and 16). Vertical fining-upward sequences A, B and C are shown in Figure 17 and include in-channel and bar top* deposits. See text for details.

Jones (1975), and Jones and Rust (1983, both on the Hawkesbury Sandstone, Australia), Campbell (1976, Morrison Formation, New Mexico), Cant and Walker (1976, Devonian Battery Point Formation, Quebec), Allen (1983, Devonian Brownstones, Welsh Borderlands) and Haszeldine (1983, Upper Carboniferous, north-eastern England). However, the data presented in these studies are diverse, and modern and ancient studies cannot yet be fully integrated into a coherent model.

Braid Bars And Channels
The morphological elements of these rivers (Fig. 14) are complex, and include (in increasing scale) individual bedforms, small "unit" bars, bar complexes (or sandflats), and mature vegetated islands. The river itself flows over and between these sand accumulations in a constantly branching and rejoining braided pattern. The finer material (silt and clay) tends to be transported through the system without accumulation.

The channels tend to be very variable in depth and width, and do not conform to the simple pattern shown by meandering rivers. The channel floor commonly has a lag deposit, and above the lag, sand is transported through the system as bedload. Bedforms in the deeper channels (3 m or deeper) tend to be sinuous crested dunes that give rise to trough cross-bedding. Deposition within channels during waning flood stage can cause channel beds to aggrade, preserving flood stage sedimentary structures. In shallower channels, and on bar tops when they are submerged at flood stage, small dunes and straight-crested to rhomboid sandwaves (Harms *et al.* 1982) are common (Fig. 14, number 5).

Also in the channels are wedge-shaped foreset-bounded transverse or oblique bars. In the South Saskatchewan these can extend across the entire widths of channels, and are termed cross-channel bars (Fig. 15; Cant and Walker, 1978). They form where 1) a smaller channel discharges into a deeper one (as a microdelta), 2) where the flow spreads laterally, or 3) where the flow is forced by channel patterns upstream to flow obliquely across the main river system. This can result in a bar near the bank of the river, generally elongated parallel to the channel trend,

Figure 15
Cross channel bar linked to bank in foreground. Nucleus (N) has given rise to two simple horns, and the entire cross channel bar has apparently migrated downstream by a distance equal to the length of the horns. Note smaller nuclei (n) near bank in foreground.

Figure 16
Evolution of a large sand flat by the coalescing of two nuclei (N) with extensive horns. Note that even the low-stage channel (C) does not have erosive margins, and appears to be aggradational. South Saskatchewan River, flow toward bottom left.

but with foresets facing the channel bank (left hand end of Fig. 14). In the Platte and Tana rivers many bars have a more regular linguoid pattern, commonly in an en-echelon arrangement, but this may reflect only a more complete remolding of the bed by high stage floods than in the South Saskatchewan.

Many of the cross-channel bars in the South Saskatchewan have a higher area which is emergent at low stages (Figs. 14 and 15; Cant and Walker, 1978). This high area may act as a "nucleus" for further deposition. The nucleus grows by lengthening downstream as sand is swept around in two "horns" (Fig. 15), and it also grows in the upstream direction as dunes and sand waves are driven up from the channel floor. As the nucleus grows, possibly with other bars coalescing onto it, the original unit bar expands into a large sandflat (Cant and Walker, 1978; Fig. 16). The South Saskatchewan sandflats are complex, and their original shape has been obscured by dissection and redeposition during changing river stage (Fig. 14). They are one to two km long in the South Saskatchewan, three km in the Tana (Collinson, 1970) and up to 10 km in the Brahmaputra (Coleman, 1969). In the South Saskatchewan, they remain constant for at least five to six years, and because of their size, they would seem likely parts of the braided system to be preserved in the stratigraphic record.

From our understanding of the South Saskatchewan (Cant and Walker, 1978), we propose a series of stratification sequences (Fig. 17) that might characterise the deposits of this type of river. The channel sequence (Fig. 17) would consist of a lag, overlain by trough cross stratification formed by migrating sinuous-crested dunes. Sandflat development appears to be initiated by the development and emergence (during falling stage) of a cross channel bar, which would be represented by a thick (0.5 to 2 m) set of planar-tabular cross bedding (Fig. 14, number 4). Nucleus aggradation, and horn growth and modification during a series of floods and falling stages (Fig. 18) would give rise to a complex set of small (tens of cm) planar tabular cross beds. A spectrum of sequences between channel aggradation and sandflat development probably exists, depending on where the sequence developed – in a deep channel, or in the immediate vicinity of a nucleus (compare Figs. 14 and 17).

The sandy tops of all of these sequences are composed of smaller planar and trough cross beds, and rippled sands, making up the feature termed bar top* in Figure 14. The bar top* (with asterisk) implies that deposition and modification are not restricted to the exposed bar tops, but may also take place in shallow dissection channels. The terminology of in-channel and bar top* was first used for ancient rocks (Cant and Walker, 1976; Fig. 19); it is important that the same terms be used for ancient and recent sediments where possible.

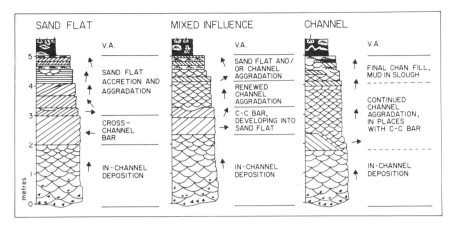

Figure 17
Three proposed sequences of sedimentary structures based on the South Saskatchewan. "Sand flat" corresponds to A (Fig. 14), *"channel" to C, and "mixed influence" to B. Arrows indicate generalized paleoflow directions, and sequences are explained in the text.*

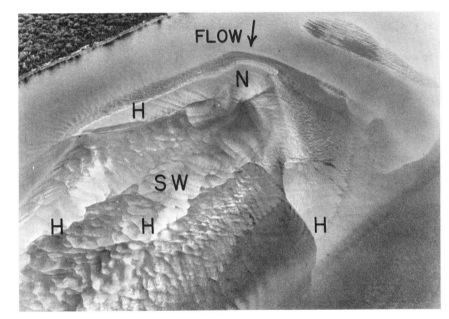

Figure 18
Large sand bar in the South Saskatchewan river; the original position of the nucleus (N) can only be estimated. Several horns (H) have developed from the nucleus, and relict positions of the inward facing sharp, steep crests of the horns can be seen. However, *during stages of higher flow, the horns have been modified into a series of straight-crested sand waves (SW); the sand wave crests strike across the horns, and indicate downchannel flow at high stage, not flow expansion during falling stage in the lee of the nucleus (see Figs. 15 and 16).*

Vertical Accretion Deposits
In contrast to meandering streams, the vertical accretion deposits of braided streams are less commonly deposited and only rarely preserved. Only during major floods does the river spill from its main channel system onto the surrounding flood plain. In the South Saskatchewan, the braided portion is essentially confined between Pleistocene bluffs. Consequently, the narrow flood plain and the vegetated islands can be relatively easily submerged and receive vertical accretion deposits. In the Platte River, a great deal of sand is swept into the overbank area.

The Brahmaputra spills into its flood basins every year, but the clays settling from the flood waters are deposited slowly, with thickness of two cm or less per annum. However, vegetation is abundant in these flood basins and peat deposits one to four metres in thickness are forming (Coleman, 1969, p. 232-3). These various sub-environments of the braided sandy system are sketched in

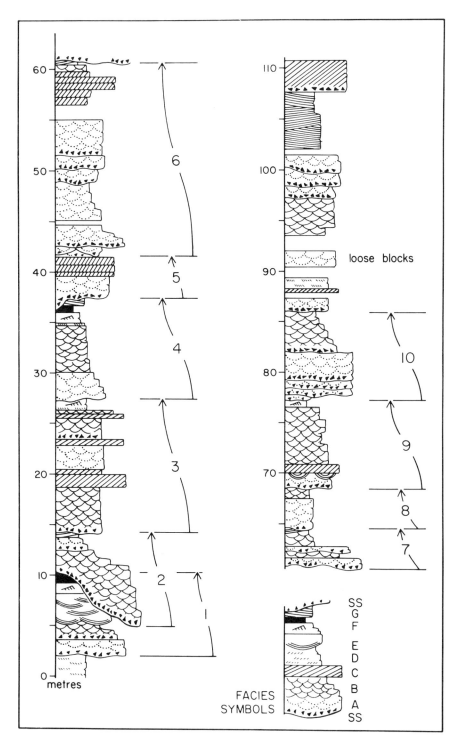

Figure 19
Measured section of the Devonian Battery Point Sandstone, Quebec (from Cant and Walker, 1976). Numbers indicate individual fluvial sequences, and letters define facies: SS = scoured surface; A = poorly-defined

trough cross bedding; B = well-defined trough cross bedding; C = large planar tabular cross beds; D = small planar tabular cross beds; E = isolated scour fills; F = ripple cross laminated silts and muds; and G = low angle inclined stratification.

Figure 14, but there is certainly more complexity in the deposits than is indicated in the diagram.

Ancient Sandy Braided Fluvial Deposits
We will discuss in some detail the Battery Point Sandstone of Gaspé, Quebec and the Brownstones of Wales as examples of ancient sandy braided fluvial deposits.

The Battery Point section studied (Cant and Walker, 1976) could be subdivided into 8 facies based on sedimentary structures and grain sizes. At least 10 fluvial sequences of the type summarized in Figure 19 could be identified in the measured section. The order of occurrence of facies was "distilled" (Walker, "General Introduction" to this volume) in order to look for a general facies sequence that could act as a basis for interpretation – see also Miall (1973) and Cant and Walker, 1976, p. 111-114). The end result of the Battery Point distillation is the sequence shown here in Figure 20. It is *not* a model – it is only a summary of a local example that could, in the future, be re-distilled with local examples from other areas to produce a general facies model. In the Battery Point summary sequence, we identified a channel-floor lag overlain by poorly defined trough cross-bedding (Facies A, Fig. 20). The in-channel deposits consisted of well-defined trough cross-bedding (B) and large sets of planar-tabular cross-bedding (C) that commonly showed a large paleocurrent divergence from the trough cross-bedding (Figs. 14 and 20; Cant and Walker, 1976, Fig. 7). The bar-top* deposits consisted mainly of small sets of planar-tabular cross-bedding (D), and the thin record of vertical accretion included cross-laminated siltstones interbedded with mudstones (F), and some enigmatic low-angle cross-stratified sandstones (G).

Upon developing this summary sequence, our first reaction was to compare it to the existing fluvial (meandering) norm (Fig. 2). Although both sequences showed channelled bases, followed by fining-upward sequences, there appeared to be sufficient differences that the norm would *not* act reliably as a basis for interpretation (Walker, "General Introduction" to this volume). In other words, the meandering model of Figure 2 seemed

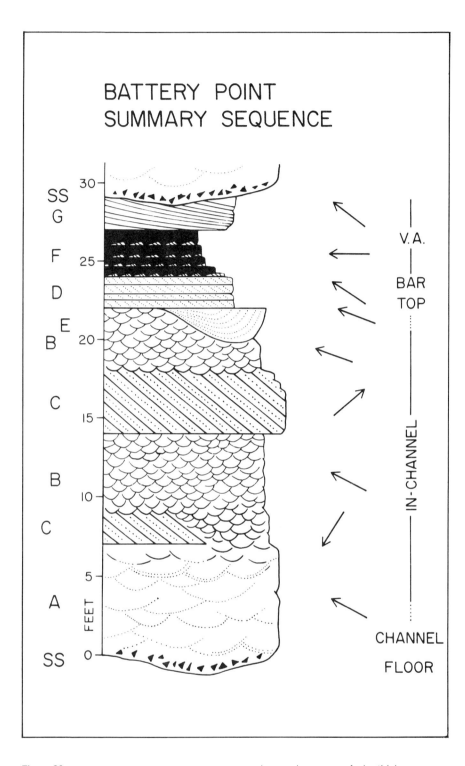

Figure 20
Summary sequence for the Devonian Battery Point Sandstone, Quebec. This sequence was developed by Markov analysis of the facies relationships (see "General Introduction" to this volume), and the preferred facies relationships were drawn as a stratigraphic column using average facies thicknesses. Arrows show paleoflow directions, letters indicate facies (see Cant and Walker, 1976). Compare the Battery Point system, interpreted as braided, with the South Saskatchewan (Fig. 17) and with Allen's (1970) sequence for meandering rivers (Fig. 2).

inappropriate for the Battery Point Sandstone of Figure 20.

Comparison with the norm nevertheless highlighted the major differences, and this gave us added understanding of the Battery Point. Similar comparisons of other systems with the squences in Figures 2 and 20 should also give added understanding. For example, the vertical-accretion deposits in the Battery Point are very thin compared with the meandering norm, both in absolute terms, and in proportion to the amount of in-channel sandstone. The in-channel sandstones do not contain parallel lamination, but planar-tabular sets of cross-bedding are common, and show high paleocurrent divergences from the main channel trend. All of these points of comparison aided in making our "braided" interpretation (Cant and Walker, 1976, p. 115-118). Refer also to annotated comments on the paper by Campbell (1976) in references.

Allen (1983) has interpreted the Devonian Brownstones of Wales as a series of sandy braided stream deposits. These are organized into a series of hierarchical units contained within intraclast-strewn scour surfaces. The 2 to 5 m thick units consist of parallel laminated and trough and planar cross-bedded sandstones and minor conglomerate. Traced laterally, the vertical sequence of sedimentary structures in each unit is extremely variable. The most striking aspect of these units is the almost ubiquitous inclination of planar cross-bed sets. Allen (1983) interprets this as slipface-bounded bars (Fig. 21) accreting laterally onto sandflats in a South Saskatchewan-like mechanism (Fig. 22). This study documents dramatically in 11 long profiles how much local lateral variability we should expect to find in braided stream sequences, as implied in studies of modern streams such as the South Saskatchewan.

Sand Body Geometry And Flood-Plain Aggradation
One major point of contrast with the meandering system is that braided rivers tend to have easily erodible banks, and no clay plugs. The area occupied by the braided river may therefore be very wide (see Campbell, 1976), and coalescing bars and sandflats will result in a laterally continuous and extensive sand sheet unconfined by shales (Fig.

84

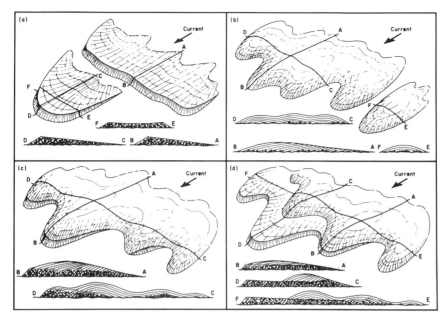

Figure 21

Superb outcrops in the Welsh Borderlands allowed Allen (1983) to reconstruct these four bar types for the Devonian Brownstones. A –

cross bedded simple bars; B – plane bedded *simple bars; C –* a compound bar; D – a composite compound bar.

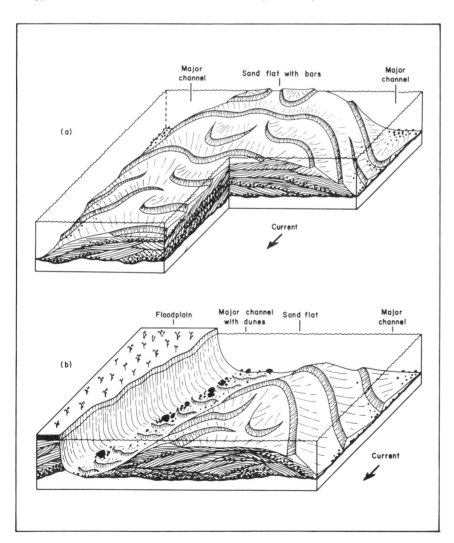

9B). Vertical accretion deposits (if formed) will tend to be quickly eroded because of the comparatively rapid lateral migration of channels. Consequently, any shales preserved in the section will tend to be patchy, laterally discontinuous, and relatively ineffective barriers to vertical hydrocarbon migration. This will not be the case for meandering systems.

Anastomosed Rivers

During the last five years, the anastomosed river has emerged as a type distinct from braided and meandering (Smith and Smith, 1980; Smith and Putnam, 1980; Putnam and Oliver, 1980; Putnam, 1982a; Smith, 1983). There are relatively few documented examples of modern anastomosed rivers (see Smith, 1983), and even fewer ancient examples (see Putnam and Oliver, 1981 and the discussion of this paper by Wightman *et al.*, 1981).

Smith and Smith (1980, p. 157) "use the term anastomosed river for an interconnected network of low-gradient, relatively deep and narrow, straight to sinuous channels with stable banks composed of fine-grained sediment (silt/clay) and vegetation . . . separating the channels are floodplains consisting of vegetated islands, natural levees, and wetlands".

Such streams differ from braided sandy rivers by having stable channel patterns and abundant areas in which fine-grained sediment is deposited and preserved.

Depositional Environments In Anastomosed Systems

Smith and Smith (1980) recognized six main facies in gravelly anastomosed rivers in western Canada (Mistaya, Alexandra, North Saskatchewan, in Alberta).

1) Peat bog facies, containing up to 98% vegetal matter, in layers a few cm to 1.5 m thick.

◄ **Figure 22**

Local facies models for sheet sandstones in the Devonian Brownstones, Welsh Borderlands, from Allen (1983). A – wide sand flat; minor channels related to falling stage may be expected to cross the top of the flat but are not shown. B – proximal part of a sand flat and its structure in strike section, together with a major channel and adjacent flood plain (vegetated island, valley flat). Vertical scales greatly exaggerated in both diagrams.

2) Backswamp facies, composed of silty mud or muddy silt, with variable amounts of organic debris.

3) Floodpond facies, consisting of laminated clay and silty clay with sparse vegetal material. Thickness is up to 6 m.

4) Levee facies, consisting of sandy silt and silty sand containing 10-22% roots by volume. This facies grades into the wetland facies (peat bog, backswamp and floodpond).

5) Crevasse splay facies, making up less than 5% of the vertical accretion facies (1 to 5, above), and consisting of thin layers of sand and/or fine gravel.

6) Channel facies, consisting of gravel and coarse sand, of unknown thickness due to limitations of augering.

These environments are controlled by a rapidly elevating base level at the downstream end of the anastomosed system, causing high rates of aggradation, deposition of fines, and stabilization of river channel patterns. In the geological record, thick vertically accreted sand bodies bounded by wetland facies would be predicted, and a block diagram emphasizing channel confinement and lack of lateral accretion is given in Figure 23. It is emphasized that the data base for this block diagram consists of augered holes a little more than 10 m deep; the aggradational history of these systems is not yet fully documented.

Ancient Anastomosed Systems

The only ancient system interpreted to be anastomosed is part of the Upper Mannville Group (Albian) of east-central Alberta (Putnam and Oliver, 1980; Putnam, 1980; Putnam, 1982a, 1982b). Here, a pattern of branching and rejoining channels has been illustrated (although it is not clear that all of the channels shown are exactly contemporaneous), and channel sandstones up to 35 m thick can be seen in cores and well-logs. Between the channel sands are "siltstones, shales, coals, and thin (generally less than 6 m thick) sheet-like sandstones which pinch out with increasing distance from the main channel fill" (Putnam, 1982a, p. 438). Some of the ideas and data presented by Putnam and Oliver (1980) have been

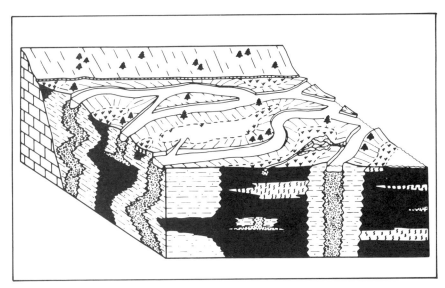

Figure 23
Block diagram of an anastomosed river, from Smith and Smith (1980). In this typical reach, channel sediments (gravel symbol) are bounded by sandy silt (dash, dot symbol) of the levees, which in turn grade into muds and silty muds of the wetlands (black). Peats are shown by small vertical wiggles. Note channel aggradation without significant lateral accretion, the channel pattern being stabilized by the muds and organic material of the wetlands, which are hard to erode.

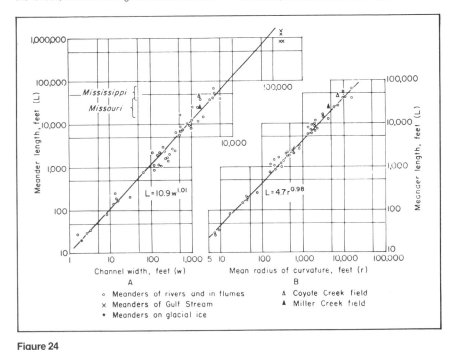

Figure 24
Relationships between meander length, channel width and meander loop radius of curvature. Original data for modern meandering streams from Leopold and Wolman (1960), with Coyote Creek and Miller Creek data plotted by Berg (1968). Note that both Coyote Creek and Miller Creek lie about as far from the regression line as any of the data, suggesting that these two fields differ somewhat from the meandering river "norm", which is represented by the regression line. From Berg (1968).

challenged by Wightman et al. (1981), with a reply by Putnam and Oliver (1981). It seems clear that it is premature to propose a general anastomosed fluvial *model* on the basis of so few modern and ancient examples. However, it is important to bear in mind that this type of stream may help to explain or interpret as-yet-undescribed ancient examples that do not fit braided or meandering norms.

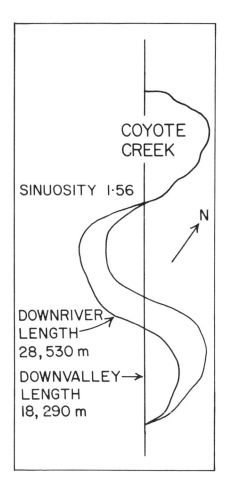

Figure 25

Extrapolation of Coyote Creek meander loop. Assuming a downvalley direction, a downvalley length of 18,290 m (60,000') was plotted. The calculated sinuosity is 1.56 (see text), so the equivalent downriver length is 28,530 m. Two possible river patterns are shown southeast of the Coyote Creek loop – many other patterns are possible, and can be estimated using a scale length of string laid over the diagram and bent into appropriate meander patterns. Details in text.

Fluvial Geomorphological Models And Paleohydraulic Reconstructions

There appears to be a direct and predictable relationship between many meandering river parameters, such as channel width (W), depth (D), sinuosity (P), meander wavelength (L), meander radius (R), slope (S) and mean annual discharge (Q). These relationships were developed by geomorphologists (especially Schumm and Leopold; references in Miall, 1978 and Ethridge and Schumm, 1978), and can be expressed by a series of regression equations (Fig. 24).

The regression equations state in a general way the relationship between parameters based on a large number of examples – that is, the regression lines are *norms*. The equations are likewise *predictors*, but beyond here, the analogy with facies models breaks down. The regression lines are not guides for future observations, nor can they be used as a basis for interpretations.

Earlier in this paper, we discussed the Coyote Creek subsurface point bar (Berg, 1968). Channel depth (roughly equal to point bar thickness) can be estimated at about 23 m (Fig. 10), and channel width (about 460 m), radius of curvature (about 2130 m) and meander length (about 12,200 m) can be estimated from Figure 11. It is important to see whether the Coyote Creek example lies close to the norm – if it does, it can be considered "typical", and one might have some confidence in using other regression equations. However, note in Figure 23 that the Coyote Creek data point lies far from the regression lines, implying that it does *not* closely resemble the "norm". The following calculations involve comparisons of Coyote Creek parameters with various other norms, and hence the results may not be too reliable. They are given here simply to illustrate the possibilities.

Mean annual discharge is estimated by

$$Q = W^{2.43}/18\ F^{1.13} \quad \text{(Imperial units)} \qquad (1)$$

where F is the width/depth ratio (here 460/23 = 20). The discharge of the Coyote Creek river is thus estimated as 98,280 cubic feet/second, or 2783 m³/sec.

Sinuousity P is given by

$$P = 3.5\ F^{-0.27} \quad \text{(Imperial Units)} \qquad (2)$$

and works out to 1.56. This number could be very useful in predicting the position and size of the next meander loop upstream or downstream from Coyote Creek, which is of obvious significance in exploration for hydrocarbons; this prediction is attempted in Figure 25, again for the sole purpose of illustrating *how* a model can be used in prediction.

The reconstructed meander loops in Figure 25 were drawn in the following way:

1) using a downvalley distance of 60,000 feet, the river length is simply 60,000 x sinuosity = 93,600 feet (28,530 m),

2) a piece of string scaled to 93,600 feet was placed over the Coyote Creek meander loop. Its far end was placed at a downvalley distance of 60,000 feet, thus defining the rough size and position of the second and third meander loops,

3) apart from problems of whether it is valid to reconstruct Coyote Creek using the meandering river norm (Fig. 24), note that we also do not know the downvalley paleoslope orientation. We also assume that the Coyote Creek meander loop (Fig. 11) is of average size for this reach of the river, because the downriver distance used to measure sinuosity in the field should normally be taken through as many meanders as possible, not just one.

Meander wavelength (L) is estimated by

$$L = 18\ (F^{0.53}\ W^{0.69}) \quad \text{(Imperial units)} \qquad (3)$$

and is about 13,687 feet (4172 m).

In Figure 11, note that the estimated meander wavelength is actually 40,000 feet (12,192 m), very different from the 13,687 feet calculated above. There are at least three possible reasons for this discrepancy; 1) Coyote Creek is so different from the norm that this type of analysis is not valid; 2) the channel width has been underestimated, and is closer to 2000 feet (610 m) (Berg, 1968, p. 151); and 3) the point bar thickness is closer to 50 feet (15 m) and the 75 foot (23 m) isopachs represent unusually deep channel floor scours during lateral accretion of the point bar (Fig. 11). Thus with W = 2000 feet and D = 50 feet, equation (2) gives a sinuosity of 1.29 and equation (3) gives a value for L of 24,103 feet (7347 m). This is still much less than the 40,000 feet estimated in Figure 11, and suggests that the Coyote Creek river is too far from the meandering river norm (Fig. 24) for this type of analysis to be valid. The reader can pursue this problem by trying to reconstruct meander loops in Figure 25 using P = 1.29 and L = 24,103 feet.

CONCLUSIONS

The meandering model seems well established and is reasonably well understood. It is a good example of a facies model in that the relationships shown in a block diagram (Fig. 1) are well known from ancient and recent sediments. Also, the simplest vertical facies sequence (Fig. 2) is well established by Markov analysis. Furthermore, numerical predictions based on channel patterns may be possible using a series of regression equations – the equations themselves are a form of model.

Braided streams have a much smaller data base, both in recent and ancient sediments. There are few well-established ancient examples, and there appear to be no convincing and well-documented subsurface examples. Anastomosed systems are even less well understood, and the only proposed ancient example is somewhat controversial.

REFERENCES

BASIC READING

The papers cited here are all listed in the alphabetic reference list below. General review papers include those of Collinson (1978) and Cant (1982). The first papers to consult on meandering streams would probably be Allen (1965, 1970) and Jackson (1976); on braided sandy streams one should begin with Allen (1983) and Cant and Walker (1976, 1978). Miall's (1977) review of the braided system is also very useful, but considers gravelly systems as well as sandy ones.

For a historical review, the most useful paper is that of Miall (1978a), and for papers on exploration, and the subsurface significance of fluvial models, see Horne *et al.* (1978), Berg (1968), Hopkins *et al.* (1982) and Putnam (1982a, 1983).

There are three recent collections of papers which, although written at the technical research level, give an unsurpassed entry into the fluvial literature – see Miall (ed., 1978b), Collinson and Lewin (eds., 1982), and Ethridge and Flores (eds., 1981).

REFERENCES

Allen, J.R.L., 1964. Studies in fluviatile sedimentation: six cyclothems from the Lower Old Red Sandstone, Anglo-Welsh Basin. Sedimentology, v. 3, p. 163-198.
Classic descriptions and interpretations of six fining-upward sequences.

Allen, J.R.L., 1965. A review of the origin and characteristics of Recent alluvial sediments. Sedimentology, v. 5, p. 89-191.
This remains a classic work, and forms the basis for most point bar models.

Allen, J.R.L., 1970. Studies in fluviatile sedimentation: a comparison of fining-upwards cyclothems, with special reference to coarse-member composition and interpretation. Journal of Sedimentary Petrology, v. 40, p. 298-323.
Presents the results of Markov analysis of sedimentary structure sequence in fining-upward cyclothems (see Fig. 2 of this paper), and continues with a full discussion of lateral accretion.

Allen, J.R.L., 1983. Studies in fluviatile sedimentation: bars, bar-complexes and sandstone sheets (low sinuosity braided streams) in the Brownstones (L. Devonian), Welsh Borders. Sedimentary Geology, v. 33, p. 237-293.
Thorough descriptions of excellent outcrops, with reconstructions of bar patterns within channels.

Barrell, J., 1913. The Upper Devonian delta of the Appalachian geocyncline. American Journal of Science, v. 36, p. 429-472.
Classic descriptions and interpretations of fluvial and deltaic rocks. Recognized fining-upward sequences and their repetitive nature.

Berg, R.R., 1968. Point-bar origin of Fall River sandstone reservoirs, northeastern Wyoming. American Association of Petroleum Geologists, Bulletin, v. 52, p. 2116-2122.
Excellent description of two subsurface point bars. See Figures 10, 11 and 23 of this paper.

Bernard, H.A., Major, C.F., Jr., Parrott, B.S., and LeBlanc, R.J., Sr., 1970. Recent sediments of southeast Texas. Texas Bureau of Economic Geology, Guidebook 11, variously paginated.
First part of guidebook presents some of the Shell work on the Brazos point bars. Illustrates fining-upward sequence and change in sedimentary structures.

Bersier, A., 1968. Sequences detritiques et divagations fluviales. Eclogae Geologicae Helvetiae, v. 51, p. 854-893.
Recognizes in-channel and overbank sequences, and discussed stacking of one channel sequence on top of another. A classic work that deserves more attention.

Blodgett, R.H., and Stanley, K.O., 1980. Stratification, bedforms and discharge relations of the Platte braided river system, Nebraska. Journal of Sedimentary Petrology, v. 50, p. 139-148.
Describes bar types and bar evolution and proposes a thin (1.5 m) idealized vertical structure sequence.

Campbell, C.V., 1976. Reservoir geometry of a fluvial sheet sandstone. American Association of Petroleum Geologists, Bulletin, v. 60, p. 1009-1020.
Describes lateral extent of sandbodies in part of the Morrison Formation. Proposes

a sequence of structures that is dominated by trough cross bedding, and hence one that is very different from the South Saskatchewan sequences.

Cant, D.J., 1982. Fluvial facies models and their application. *In* Scholle, P.A., and Spearing, D.R., eds., Sandstone depositional environments. American Association of Petroleum Geologists, Memoir 31, p. 115-137.
A useful and well illustrated review, and a very good follow-up to this paper.

Cant, D.J., and Walker, R.G., 1976. Development of a braided fluvial facies model for the Devonian Battery Point Sandstone, Quebec. Canadian Journal of Earth Sciences, v. 13, p. 102-119.
Describes facies and establishes a summary facies sequence using Markov chain analysis. The data are used in the "General Introduction" of this volume, and the study is one of the better-documented braided fluvial examples.

Cant, D.J., and Walker, R.G., 1978. Fluvial processes and facies sequences in the sandy braided South Saskatchewan River, Canada. Sedimentology, v. 25, p. 625-648.
Describes the morphological features of the river, and establishes a sequence of sand flat development from small bars. Proposes facies sequences for sand flat and channel aggradation (see Figs. 14-19, this paper).

Coleman, J.M., 1969. Brahmaputra River: channel processes and sedimentation. Sedimentary Geology, v. 3, p. 129-239.
Full description of the Brahmaputra, with preliminary discussion of sand flat development.

Collinson, J.D., 1970. Bedforms of the Tana River, Norway. Geografiska Annaler, v. 52A, p. 31-56.
Classic description of the Tana, emphasizing sand bars. Discusses changes due to reactivation, but does not propose an overall sedimentary structure sequence.

Collinson, J.D., 1978. Alluvial sediments. *In* Reading, H.G., ed., Sedimentary environments and facies. Oxford, Blackwell, p. 15-60.
An excellent general review of alluvial sediments.

Collinson, J.D., and Lewin, J., eds., 1982. Modern and ancient fluvial systems. International Association of Sedimentologists, Special Publication 5, 535 p.
Very useful collection of papers, grouped into sections on Hydrodynamics and Bedforms, Present Day Channel Processes, Facies Models, and Economic Aspects. A very useful source of data and references.

Conaghan, P.J., and Jones, J.G., 1975. The Hawkesbury Sandstone and the Brahmaputra: a depositional model for continental sheet sandstones. Journal of the Geological Society of Australia, v. 22, p. 275-283.
Proposes a braided fluvial origin for the Hawkesbury, and gives an idealized vertical sedimentary structure sequence.

Doeglas, D.J., 1962. The structure of sedimentary deposits of braided rivers. Sedimentology, v. 1, p. 167-190.
Classic descriptions of the Durance and Ardeche Rivers in France. The paper has perhaps been overlooked in the last few years because it does not present overall sedimentary structure sequences – nevertheless, the descriptions remain extremely useful.

Dixon, E.E.L., 1921. The geology of the South Wales coalfield; Part XII: the country around Tenby. Geological Survey of Great Britain, Memoir.
In this paper, the repetitive nature of what we now call a fining-upward sequence was recognized and stated more clearly than by Barrell. This paper, therefore, contains the first explicit statement of repetitive, superimposed fluvial sequences.

Edwards, M.B., Eriksson, K.A., and Kier, R.S., 1983. Paleochannel geometry and flow patterns determined from exhumed Permian point bars in north-central Texas. Journal of Sedimentary Petrology, v. 53, p. 1261-1270.
Reconstruction of flow associated with obliquely-oriented ripples on point bar surfaces.

Ethridge, F.G., and Flores, R.M., eds., 1981. Recent and ancient nonmarine depositional environments: models for exploration. Society of Economic Paleontologists and Mineralogists, Special Publication 31, 349 p.
Contains a series of papers, written at the full technical level, grouped into: 1) recent and ancient nonmarine depositional models; 2) alluvial fan and fluvial deposits; 3) lacustrine deposits; and 4) eolian deposits.

Ethridge, F.G. and Schumm, S.A., 1978. Reconstructing paleochannel morphologic and flow characteristics: methodology, limitations and assessment. In Miall, A.D., ed., Fluvial sedimentology. Canadian Society of Petroleum Geologists, Memoir 5, p. 703-721.
A very useful summary of paleohydraulic reconstruction methods, with all assumptions spelled out, and equations and their sources given.

Fisk, H.N., 1944. Geological investigation of the alluvial valley of the lower Mississippi River. Vicksburg, Miss., Mississippi River Commission, 78 p.
A classic description of the river pattern of the lower reaches of the Mississippi.

Frazier, D.E., and Osanik, A., 1961. Point bar deposits, Old River locksite, Louisiana. Gulf Coast Association of Geological Societies, Transactions, v. 11, p. 121-137.
One of the first large excavations within a fluvial system, with discussions of the geometry of stratification.

Harms, J.C., and Fahnestock, R.K., 1965. Stratification, bed forms and flow phenomena (with an example from the Rio Grande). In Middleton, G.V., ed., Primary sedimentary structures and their hydrodynamic interpretations. Society of Economic Paleontologists and Mineralogists, Special Publication 12, p. 84-115.
Classic paper relating flow phenomena to bed forms, and bed forms to the resulting sedimentary structures.

Harms, J.C., Mackenzie, D.B., and McCubbin, D.G., 1963. Stratification in modern sands of the Red River, Louisiana. Journal of Geology, v. 71, p. 566-580.
One of the first descriptions of the internal structure of point bars, emphasizing the development of stratification from bed forms.

Harms, J.C., Southard, J.B., and Walker, R.G., 1982. Structures and sequences in clastic rocks. Society of Economic Paleontologists and Mineralogists, Short Course 9, variable pagination.
Revised version of Short Course 2, with important introductory chapters by Southard and Harms on flow, bed forms and stratification.

Haszeldine, R.S., 1983. Fluvial bars reconstructed from a deep, straight channel, Upper Carboniferous coalfield of northeast England. Journal of Sedimentary Petrology, v. 53, p. 1233-1247.
Excellent and detailed reconstruction of the internal form of stratification within a bar 10 m high and 200 m wide. Lobate sandwaves 20 m wide descended the lee face of the bar.

Hopkins, J.C., Hermanson, S.W., and Lawton, D.C., 1982. Morphology of channels and channel-sand bodies in the Glauconitic Sandstone Member (Upper Mannville), Little Bow area, Alberta. Bulletin of Canadian Petroleum Geology, v. 30, p. 274-285.
Reconstruction of channel patterns from subsurface data. See Figures 12 and 13 of this paper. Well logs supported by core photographs.

Horne, J.C., Ferm, J.C., Caruccio, F.T., and Baganz, B.P., 1978. Depositional models in coal exploration and mine planning in Appalachian region. American Association of Petroleum Geologists, Bulletin, v. 62, p. 2379-2411.
An excellent and well illustrated study of how fluvial (and marginal marine) models can be used in exploration.

Jackson, R.G., 1976. Depositional model of point bars in the lower Wabash River. Journal of Sedimentary Petrology, v. 46, p. 579-594.
Describes point bar migration, and relates grain size and sedimentary structure sequences to their position within the meander loop. Possibly the most detailed description of a North American meandering river since Fisk, 1944.

Jones, B.G. and Rust, B.R., 1983. Massive sandstone facies in the Hawkesbury Sandstone, a Triassic fluvial deposit near Sydney, Australia. Journal of Sedimentary Petrology, v. 53, p. 1249-1259.
Relates massive sandstone to liquefaction during foreset failure at low flow. At flood flows, the foresets may have been up to 15 m high.

Kelling, G., 1968. Patterns of sedimentation in Rhondda Beds of South Wales. American Association of Petroleum Geologists, Bulletin, v. 52, p. 2369-2386.
Describes two types of vertical stratification sequence, and interprets the Rhondda beds as having been deposited both from low and high sinuosity streams.

McGowen, J.H., and Garner, L.E., 1970. Phisiographic features and stratification types of coarse-grained point bars: modern and ancient examples. Sedimentology, v. 14, p. 77-111.
Very useful descriptions of the Amite (La.) and Colorado (Tx.) Rivers, and comparisons with Eocene and Pleistocene deposits. Stratification and internal structure sequences emphasized.

Miall, A.D., 1973. Markov chain analysis applied to an ancient alluvial plain succession. Sedimentology, v. 20, p. 347-364.
Applies Markov chain analysis to Devonian fluvial rocks in arctic Canada, and proposes a test of significance for the probability matrices as a whole. Harper's method tests each entry in the matrix (see "Improved Methods of Facies Sequence Analysis" in this volume).

Miall, A.D., 1977. A review of the braided river depositional environment. Earth Science Reviews, v. 13, p. 1-62.
Miall reviews sandy and gravelly braided systems, and proposes a standard set of facies for their description. Distillation of these facies into sequences suggests four main types – the Scott, Donjek, Platte and

Bijou Creek. Others have been added subsequently (see Miall, 1978b).

Miall, A.D., 1978a. Fluvial sedimentology: an historical review. In Miall, A.D., ed., Fluvial sedimentology. Canadian Society of Petroleum Geologists, Memoir 5, p. 1-47.
Undoubtedly the most thorough historical review of fluvial sedimentology, beginning with observations in prehistoric times and continuing to the present day. An invaluable source for older references.

Miall, A.D., ed., 1978b. Fluvial sedimentology. Canadian Society of Petroleum Geologists, Memoir 5, 859 p.
Collection of many papers, written at the technical research level, and grouped into Texture and Structure, Bedforms and Bars, Modern Rivers, Ancient Fluvial Systems, Fluvial Facies Models, Paleohydraulics, and Economic Applications. Overall an extremely useful source of data and references.

Moody-Stewart, M., 1966. High- and low-sinuosity stream deposits, with examples from the Devonian of Spitsbergen. Journal of Sedimentary Petrology, v. 36, p. 1102-1117.
Comparison of low and high sinuosity streams and their deposits. Does not go into details of stratification sequences.

Nami, M., 1976. An exhumed Jurassic meander belt from Yorkshire. Geological Magazine, v. 113, p. 47-52.
Brief description of an exhumed meander belt, with epsilon cross strata and plan views of the channel pattern. More detail in Nami and Leeder (1978), below.

Nami, M., and Leeder, M.R., 1978. Changing channel morphology and magnitude in the Scalby Formation (M. Jurassic) of Yorkshire, England. In Miall, A.D., ed., Fluvial sedimentology. Canadian Society of Petroleum Geologists, Memoir 5, p. 431-440.
Documents upward change from low to high sinuosity channels within one formation. Shows internal structure sequences and plan views of exhumed channels.

Nijman, W., and Puigdefabregas, C., 1978. Coarse-grained point bar structure in a molasse-type fluvial system, Eocene Castisent Sandstone Formation, south Pyrenean basin. In Miall, A.D., ed., Fluvial sedimentology. Canadian Society of Petroleum Geologists, Memoir 5, p. 487-510.
Describes a well-exhumed coarse grained point bar near Castisent, showing cut bank, point bar, chutes, and bed forms. Presents vertical stratification sequences and map views.

Putnam, P.E., 1982a. Fluvial channel sandstones within Upper Mannville (Albian) of Lloydminster area, Canada – geometry, petrography and paleogeographic implications. American Association of Petroleum Geologists, Bulletin, v. 66, p. 436-459.
Subsurface description of a possibly anastomosed fluvial system.

Putnam, P.E., 1982b. Fluvial deposits and hydrocarbon accumulations: examples from the Lloydminster area, Canada. In Collinson, J.D., and Lewin, J., eds., Modern and ancient fluvial systems. International Association of Sedimentologists, Special Publication 6, p. 517-532.
Subsurface description of a possibly anastomosed fluvial system.

Putnam, P.E., 1980. Fluvial deposition within the Upper Mannville of west-central Saskatchewan: stratigraphic implications. In Beck, L.S., et al., eds., Lloydminster and beyond: geology of Mannville hydrocarbon reservoirs. Regina, Saskatchewan Geological Society, Special Publication 5, p. 197-216.
Subsurface description of Mannville channels in Saskatchewan – a possible anastomosed system.

Putnam, P.E., and Oliver, T.A., 1980. Stratigraphic traps in channel sandstones in the upper Mannville (Albian) of east-central Alberta. Bulletin of Canadian Petroleum Geology, v. 28, p. 489-508.
Description of subsurface Mannville channels, and an explicit interpretation in terms of anastomosed channels. But see discussion by Wightman et al. (1981) and reply by Putnam and Oliver (1981).

Putnam, P.E., and Oliver, T.A., 1981. Stratigraphic traps in channel sandstones in the upper Mannville (Albian) of east-central Alberta: Reply. Bulletin of Canadian Petroleum Geology, v. 29, p. 626-629.
Authors reply here to the criticisms of Wightman et al. (1981).

Smith, D.G., 1983. Anastomosed fluvial deposits: modern examples from western Canada. In Collinson, J.D., and Lewin, J., eds., Modern and ancient fluvial systems. International Association of Sedimentologists, Special Publication 6, p. 155-168.
Comparison of the Columbia (B.C.) and Saskatchewan (Sask.) Rivers, with very useful data from coring (up to 15 m) the floodplains, and the facies relationships thus revealed.

Smith, D.G., and Putnam, P.E., 1980. Anastomosed fluvial deposits: modern and ancient examples from Alberta, Canada. Canadian Journal of Earth Sciences, v. 17, p. 1396-1406.
Comparison of several ancient sandstones (Upper Mannville, Brazeau-Paskapoo, Kootenay) with the Alexandra (Alberta), Columbia (B.C.) and Saskatchewan (Sask.) rivers; emphasizes the anastomosed model.

Smith, D.G., and Smith, N.D., 1980. Sedimentation in anastomosed river systems: examples from alluvial valleys near Banff, Alberta. Journal of Sedimentary Petrology, v. 50, p. 157-164.
Describes three anastomosed rivers (Mistaya, N. Saskatchewan, Alexandra) and suggests six sedimentary facies.

Smith, N.D., 1970. The braided stream depositional environment: comparison of the Platte River with some Silurian clastic rocks, north-central Appalachians. Geological Society of America, Bulletin, v. 81, p. 2993-3014.
A classic study contrasting longitudinal and transverse bars in the Platte River, and comparing the results with stratification sequences in the Shawangunk Conglomerate.

Sundborg, A., 1956. The River Klaralven, a study of fluvial processes. Geografiska Annaler, v. 38, p. 217-316.
A classic study of fluvial processes and flood plain geomorphology. Predates the "sedimentological" approach to fluvial studies of the 1960s, so does not discuss in detail the internal structures or sequences.

Wightman, D.M., Tilley, B.J., and Last, W.M., 1981. Stratigraphic traps in channel sandstones in the upper Mannville (Albian) of east-central Alberta: Discussion. Bulletin of Canadian Petroleum Geology, v. 29, p. 622-625.
Criticism of Putnam and Oliver's (1980) paper, questioning the application of the anastomosed model to the Upper Mannville, and questioning the validity of the channel sandstone trends. See reply by Putnam and Oliver (1981).

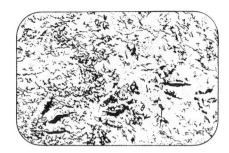

Eolian Sands

MICHAEL E. BROOKFIELD
Department of Land Resource Science
Guelph University
Guelph, Ontario N1G 2W1

INTRODUCTION

The beautiful large-scale crossbedding of ancient wind-blown sandstones has often fascinated sedimentologists, but until recently no-one has attempted to construct facies models for eolian deposits in any detail. Perhaps this is due to the difficulty of connecting modern surface structures and morphology with the form of cross-bedding seen in sections of ancient eolian sandstones. However, similar problems have not hindered the development of turbidite fan models. Perhaps, as noted in an earlier version of this chapter (Walker and Middleton, 1979), there is no preferred vertical sequence or consistent lateral change. I do not believe that this is the case, and in this paper I will first note the basis of eolian facies models, including the major problems; then look at some features of modern eolian sands, develop some facies models, and see how they can be applied to ancient eolian sandstones.

BASIS FOR EOLIAN MODELS

The facies models are based on the idea of migrating hierarchies of eolian bedforms 'climbing' over one another (Allen, 1963; Banks, 1973; Brookfield, 1977; Rubin and Hunter, 1982). Different types of bedforms in modern deserts show different types and proportions of stratification (Hunter, 1977). These bedforms, when allowed to migrate, generate assemblages of strata whose sections can then be compared with actual sections of ancient eolian sandstones.

Unfortunately there are some major problems with this approach. Recent

large eolian bedforms commonly rest on alluvium, and are usually post-Pleistocene in age (Wilson, 1973). No thick eolian deposits comparable to some ancient examples seem to be forming at present. Due to changes of wind circulation patterns during the Quaternary glacial epoch, and to the enormous lag time of the larger eolian bedforms, it seems likely that many, if not most, recent large bedforms are not in equilibrium with the present wind pattern (Wilson, 1973). The stratification types of Hunter (1977), which are used to determine the locus of deposition of an ancient eolian sandstone (described below), were described from small coastal dunes. McKee's (1966) trench sections through dunes, often used to interpret ancient eolian sandstone sections, were in small gypsum dunes which are easily stabilized by occasional wetting during rain. Thus, we do not know if the stratification types and cross-sections can be applied to the internal structures of large quartz sand eolian bedforms. Recent work (Clemmensen and Abrahamson, 1983) indicates that the stratification types are similar in recent and ancient quartz sand dunes, and that, with some modification, McKee's (1966) sections provide a guide to dune type - though not to bedform size or complexity. Direct comparison between recent dune trenches and ancient eolian sandstone sections suffers from an additional problem, namely, that only the lowest parts of eolian bedforms are usually preserved. Thus we have to reconstruct the large bedforms almost entirely from structures formed at their basal lee slopes.

MODERN EOLIAN SANDS

Modern eolian sands occur in two main settings: sandy deserts and coastal dunes. Deposits in deserts are by far the most extensive. Arid and semi-arid regions occupy about one third of the present land surface and include three main sedimentary environments: alluvial fans and ephemeral streams, inland sabkhas or playas, and sandy deserts - also called "sand seas" or ergs (Fig. 1).

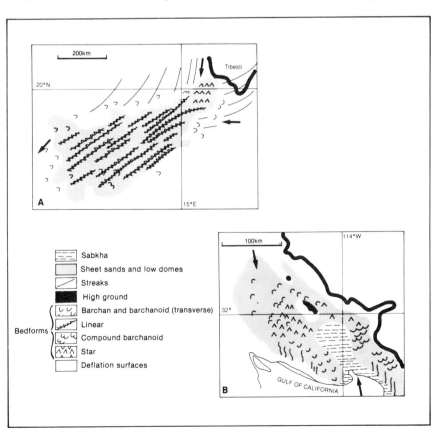

Figure 1
Bedform map of: A) the Fachi Bilma Erg, southeastern Sahara (after Mainguet and Callot, 1974; B) El Gran Desierto, Sonora, *Mexico (M. Brookfield unpub.). Note difference in scale: Mexican desert is only one quarter the size of the Fachi Bilma erg. Arrows are dominant wind directions.*

Sandy deserts form only about twenty per cent of the area of modern deserts. The rest is composed of eroding mountains (40%) and stony areas or serirs (10 to 20%) and desert flats (10 to 20%) with smaller areas of dry washes, volcanic cones and badlands, where erosion rather than deposition takes place (Cooke and Warren, 1973, p. 53). Since our ideas about modern environments tend to be strongly influenced by personal observation, it is worth noting that the desert areas of North America (with the exception of El Gran Desierto, Sonora, Mexico; Fig. 1b) are atypical. In America, alluvial fans are much more important (30%) and sandy deserts much less important (less than 1%) than in other major deserts.

The largest desert in the world is the Sahara (7 million km²). It has several major ergs arranged in three belts. Individual ergs cover areas as large as 500,000 km² (twice the area of Nevada). They are generally located in physiographic or structural basins, with long histories of sediment accumulation, including extensive Tertiary and Pleistocene fluvial sediments. The modern eolian deposits, however, are rarely more than 100 m thick (see Mainguet, 1976; Mainguet and Callot, 1974; Wilson, 1971, 1972, 1973). The main reason for the accumulation of sand in an erg seems to be the presence of a topographic depression. Once formed, the dunes themselves can trap more sand (Bagnold, 1941). Mainguet and Callot (1974) made a study of the Fachi-Bilma erg, based on air and satelite photography, with some features checked in the field. This erg (Fig. 1a) is situated in the southern Sahara. The easterly trade winds are deflected by the Tibesti massif, and the erg is situated where the winds converge again. Within the erg, there is a definite spatial zonation of dune types. Barchans occur on all sides of the erg, marking zones of intermittent deposition. Inwards, these coalesce into larger, less mobile, sinuous longitudinal (seif) dunes and then into larger, fully developed, compound longitudinal draa (silks). In the upwind part of the erg (in the 'wind shadow' of the Tibesti massif, a zone of variable winds) is a zone of large pyramidal draas (star draa) over 100 m high and 0.5 to 1.5 km wide: these star draas are themselves arranged in regular geometric patterns or rows. This erg is fairly typical. For comparison, the

only large American erg is shown on Figure 1b. We will use these two ergs as motifs for the development of facies models based on deserts with dominantly longitudinal and dominantly transverse bedforms. Breed et al. (1979) show bedform maps, based on satellite photography of many of the major ergs in the world, in which similar patterns can be seen.

Wilson's (1971, 1972) studies of Saharan bedforms led him to propose three main scales of eolian bedforms; ripples, dunes and draas. Ripples are flatter than those in water and usually have more regular crest lines (Sharp, 1963). Dunes have transverse and longitudinal morphologies and vary from 0.1 to 100 m in height. Draas are large sand bedforms between 20 and 450 m high, characterized by the superimposition of smaller

dunes on them. Nevertheless, the dune-draa distinction is not universally accepted, and a descriptive classification based on form and complexity should probably be used (Table 1).

Dune form has been related by Fryberger (1979) to wind variability and sand transport ability (Fig. 2). Drift potential (D.P.) is the relative amount of sand *potentially* moved by the wind for a stated period of time, weighted for the wind velocity. Sand drift roses are then calculated for the different wind directions. The sum of these sand drifts for all wind directions is the drift potential. The resultant drift direction (R.D.D.) is the direction of the vector resultant of all drift potentials: similarly the resultant drift potential (R.D.P.) is the vector sum of the drift potentials. High R.D.P./D.P. values indicate low directional variabil-

Table 1

Morphology and classification of eolian bedorms (after McKee, 1979)

Morphology	Name	Associations
Sheet-like	Sheet sands	
Thin elongate strips	Streaks	COMPOUND – two or more of the same type combined by overlap or superimposition (Wilson's draa).
Circular to elliptical mound, dome-shaped	Dome	
Crescent in plan	Barchan	
Connected crescents	Barchanoid (akle)	COMPLEX – two different basic types occuring together, either superimposed (Wilson's draas), or adjacent.
Asymmetrical ridge	Transverse (Reversing)	
Symmetrical ridge	Linear (seif)	
Central peak with arms	Star (pyramidal)	
U-shaped	Parabolic	

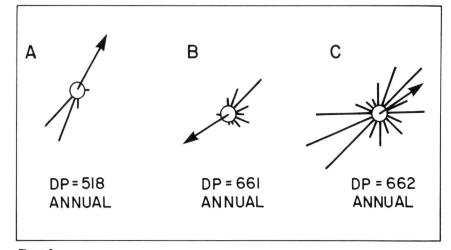

Figure 2

Characteristic high-energy wind regimes.
A) narrow unimodal; barchanoid dunes, Peru.   B) bimodal; linear dunes, Mauritania.

C) complex; star dunes, Libya. Arrows indicate resultant drift direction (RDD) (After Fryberger, 1979).

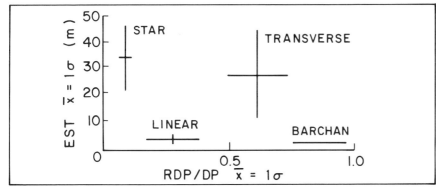

Figure 3
Statistically significant (P = 0.001) separation of the four elemental dune types by means of two variables: equivalent sand thickness (EST) and a measure of wind directional variability (RDP/DP). The x̄ ± 1 σ for EST in barchans is 0.02 ± 0.005 m (n = 8) (from Wasson and Hyde, 1983a).

ity. Barchanoid and transverse dunes occur in areas of low directional variability; linear dunes in more variable wind regimes; and star bedforms in very variable regimes. Wasson and Hyde (1983a) found that various bedforms plotted in separate fields if wind variability was plotted against 'spread out' sand thickness (Fig. 3), indicating that the form of the dunes may be controlled both by wind regime and availability of sand.

Ahlbrandt (1979) summarized the textural parameters of eolian sand in terms of three sub-environments: well-sorted to very well-sorted fine coastal dune sands; moderately sorted to well-sorted fine to medium grained inland dune sands; and poorly-sorted interdune and serir sands. The dune samples vary in mean grain-size from 0.68 phi (1.6 mm) to 3.4 phi (0.1 mm). Most interdune and serir samples are bimodal in the sand fraction and have higher silt and clay contents when compared with adjacent dune samples from dunes formed under different wind regimes. In inland dune fields, with predominantly unidirectional winds, there is progressively improved sorting and finer mean grain-size downwind from the sand source in a sequence of dome, transverse, barchanoid and parabolic dunes. In reversing and multidirectional wind regimes, sand accumulates in dunes that have little net lateral migration. The clastic material in these dunes is a combination of available source material, and because of the fluctuating conditions crest and base tend to have more divergent means than in unidirectional wind regimes. Wilson (1972, 1983) attempted to show that differing bedform hierarchies could be separated by plotting the coarsest 20th

percentile of the sand against the bedform wavelength – which would be nice if true, since we could then estimate the size of the ancient bedforms from grain-size and bounding surface data (discussed below). Unfortunately, his results have not been confirmed; and one study on Australian deserts shows no such relationship (Wasson and Hyde, 1983b).

Surface structures on eolian bedforms are among their more characteristic features and include ripple marks (really themselves a bedform), adhesion structures, animal tracks and trails, marks made by vegetation and rain or hail. All may be preserved by ripple climbing and grainfall deposition (see Kocurek and Fielder, 1982; Ahlbrandt and Fryberger, 1981; McKee, 1982; Steidtmann, 1973). Examples of these structures are shown in Figure 4.

Internal structures are difficult to study in modern dunes. Large-scale cross-bedding was formerly considered typical of eolian sandstones, but in fact also occurs in submarine bedforms, (commonly less than about 4 m; see "Shelf and Shallow Marine Sands", this volume) where it may closely resemble eolian cross-bedding (cf. Allen, 1982). The detailed structures of the laminae do, however, differ. Hunter (1977) proposed four main types of eolian laminae from study of small coastal dunes (Fig. 5).

Planebed lamination is produced by wind velocities too high for ripple formation and is analogous to upper flat bed in aqueous deposits.

Climbing ripple lamination closely resembles similar aqueous varieties, but because of the difficulty of recognizing the ripple foresets in eolian ripples (due

to their low relief), Hunter (1977) distinguished two main types. *Translatent strata* occur where only the bounding surfaces between ripples are visible: *rippleform strata* occur when the ripple foresets can be identified. Both are inversely graded and relatively closely packed (porosity average 39%).

Grainfall lamination is produced in zones of flow separation by deposition from suspension. Grain segregation is relatively poor and laminae difficult to see. Packing is intermediate between the closely-packed traction deposits above and the loosely-packed sandflow strata below (average porosity 40%).

Sandflow cross-stratification (avalanche cross-bedding) is caused by slumping and consequent grain flow down slopes. Sandflow cross-strata are loosely packed (average porosity 45%), interfinger with grainfall laminae near their base, and form lenses in horizontal exposures.

Examples of all these stratification types have now been found in ancient eolian sandstones (Hunter, 1981; Fryberger and Schenk, 1981; Clemmensen and Abrahamsen, 1983). Each type is found in different parts of a dune, and can be recognized even where the dune has been deflated (Fig. 6). In this example, we can recognize the basic features of a simple barchanoid form; the slipfaces (sandflow cross-strata), the saddles (climbing translatent strata) and the passage between the slipfaces and saddles (grainfall laminae). Further information on stratification types and their relationship to dune morpholpgy is given by Hunter and Rubin (1983), Rubin and Hunter (1983) and Hunter (1981).

Our knowledge of the larger internal structures of modern dunes is still limited and due almost entirely to the work of McKee (McKee, 1966; McKee and Douglass, 1971; McKee and Tibbitts, 1964; McKee and Moiola, 1975) and Bigarella (Bigarella, 1972; Bigarella et al., 1969). These studies are summarized in McKee (1979). The most detailed studies were done in the White Sands dune field of New Mexico which is not analogous to most ancient eolian deposits. The dunes are composed of gypsum and are easily stabilized by occasional wettings by rain. Although a close study of these sections is enlightening, space precludes their detailed consideration.

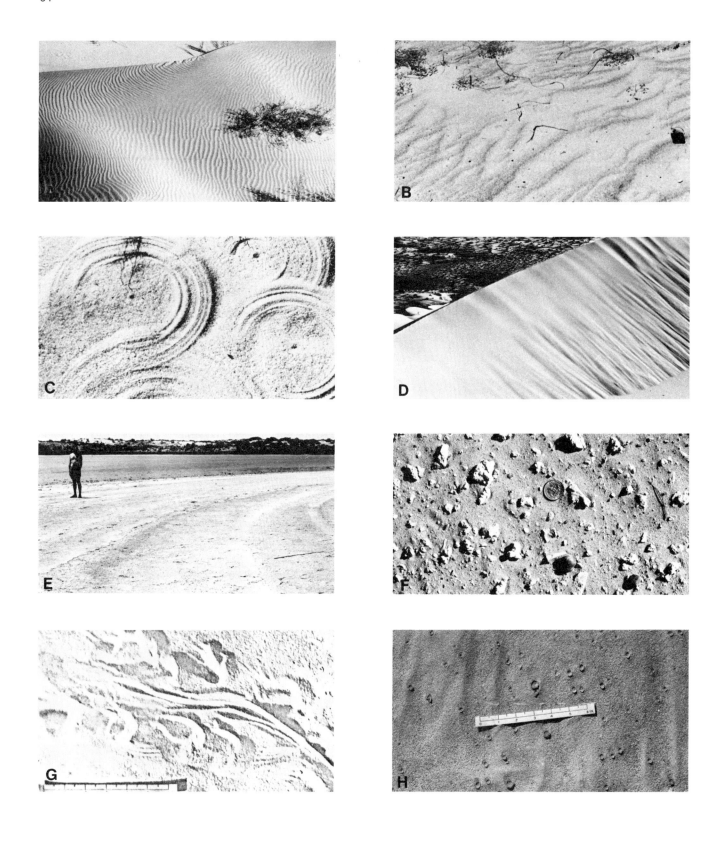

Figure 4

Surface structures on dunes. A) Fine sand ripples. B) Coarse sand ripples (compass is 5 cm across). C) Concentric grooves, 0.5 to 1.0 m in diameter created by plants, Cape Cod (courtesy of Rodney Stevens and Jour. *Sed. Petrol.). D) Grainfall burying sand-flows on arm of star beform: slipface is 10 m high. E) Adhesion structures at margin of perman- ent saline Lake. F) Lag surfaces: pebbles are dominantly deflated caliche. Coin is 2 cm/di- ameter. G) Uphill track of chuckwalla lizard* *on dry foreset slope. Scale in inches. H) Pits of raindrops in modern sand. Scale in inches. (G and H, courtesy of E.D. McKee and Uni- ted States Geological Survey) (A,B,D,E,F- from El Grand Desierto, Mexico).*

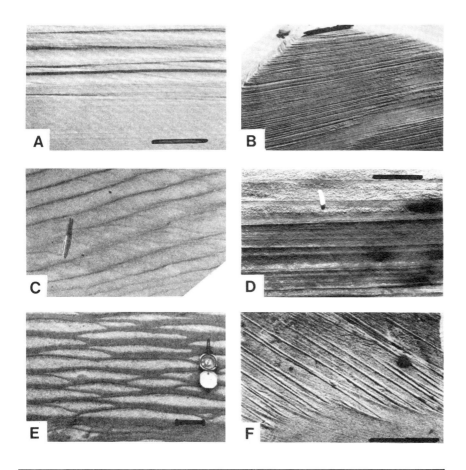

Figure 5
Stratification types.
A - Planebed lamination passing up into climbing ripple structure. Vertical section.
B - Typical subcritically climbing translatent stratification. Vertical section.
C - Subcritically to supercritically climbing translatent stratification: supercritical in centre of photo. Horizontal section.
D - Grainfall lamination, with interbedded sandflow at top. Vertical section.
E - Sandflow cross-strata: simple horizontal section.
F - Intertonguing of sandflow cross-strata and grainfall lamination near the base of a slipface. Vertical section.
Pen and bar scale all approx. 10 cm. All from Padre Island recent dunes (after Hunter, 1977, with permission), except D, which is from Permian of Arran (photo M.B., cf. Clemmensen and Abrahamson, 1983).

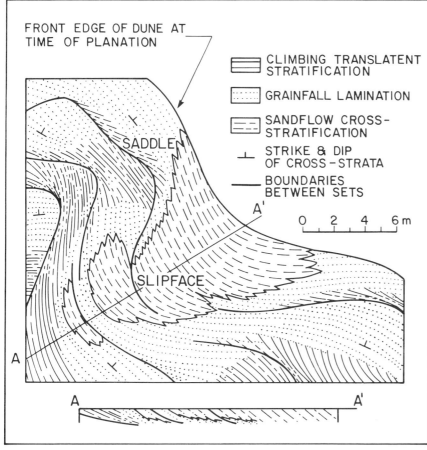

Figure 6
Map and cross-section of dune-foreset cross-strata exposed on a planed-off sinuous transverse or barchanoid dune, showing distribution of types of internal structure. Somewhat simplified from an exposure on Padre Island, Texas (from Hunter, 1977).

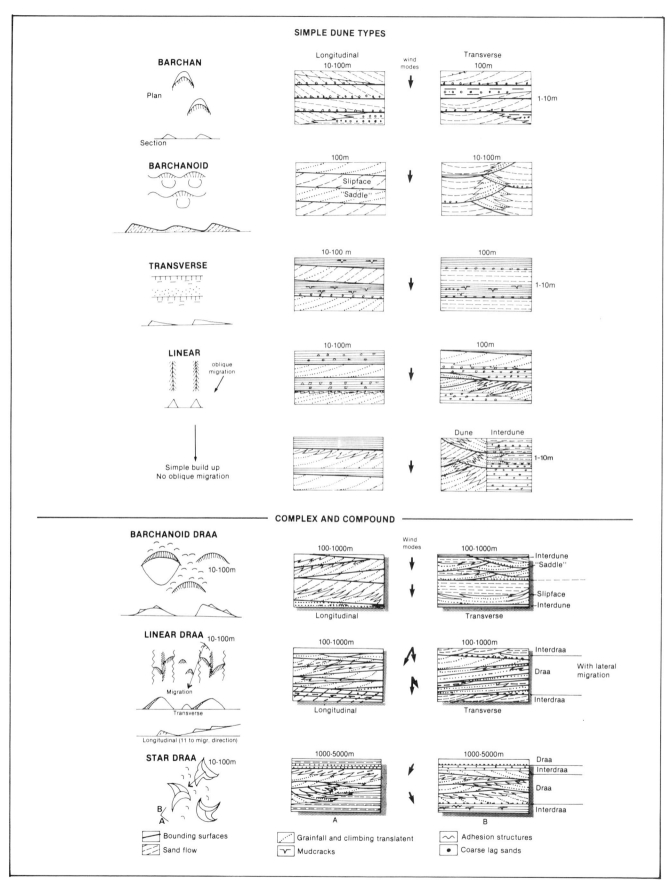

Figure 7
Stratification models for different dune types: *both simple and complex/compound. Transverse sections are perpendicular to resultant* *wind direction: longitudinal sections are parallel to resultant wind directions.*

Interdunes are an integral part of the eolian bedform system and must be taken into account when attempting to characterize, or determine the nature of the system (Ahlbrandt and Fryberger, 1981; Kocurek, 1981b). In deserts in which sand supply is limited, interdunes consist of lag deposits, coarse sand sheets, and small isolated dunes and sabhkas where the water table often reaches the surface (Stokes, 1964). Because of the way the sand is transported through the dune system, linear bedforms tend to have coarse lag and coarse sand sheets and dunes in the interdune areas; whereas transverse bedforms tend to have sabkhas and fine sand dunes between them (Glennie, 1970; Sharp, 1979). The size of the interdunes is also dependent on sand supply and on the stage of development of the erg in which they occur. Thus, most modern deserts have extensive interdunes because of their relatively recent development (Mainguet and Chemin, 1983).

Thus, as a basis for a facies model of ancient eolian sandstones, we have static features such as the textural parameters, distribution of stratification types on different parts and types of bedforms, and distributions of dunes and interdunes in modern deserts. We now need a dynamic dimension in order to see how thick, extensive ancient eolian sandstones may have formed.

STRATIFICATION MODELS BASED ON MIGRATING BEDFORMS

These are analogous to the Bouma sequence for turbidites, in that they attempt to describe the internal structures of the sand units. In this case, the internal structure is due to the migration of a packet of bedforms and not to an intermittent current.

Theoretical stratification models for transverse, longitudinal and star bedforms are shown in Figure 7. These assume *unidirectional climbing of ideal bedforms* in a fully developed draa-dune-interdune system. Migration of the dunes or dune-draa combination over interdunes leads to the development of bounding surfaces (Brookfield, 1977) (Figs. 8 and 9A).

First order surfaces are flat-lying bedding planes cutting across all other eolian structures and are attributed to the migration of draas.

Second order surfaces lie between first order surfaces, and usually dip downwind, though their inclination varies a great deal. These are attributed to dunes climbing down the lee slopes of draas, or to lateral migration of longitudinal dunes across the draa lee slope.

Third order surfaces bound bundles of laminae within cosets of cross laminae and are attributed to erosion fol-

lowed by renewed deposition due to local fluctuations in wind direction and velocity. They are reactivation surfaces.

Simple dune systems should lack the second order surfaces: but in fact, dunes periodically overtaking dunes, and especially reversing dunes, are likely to show them (Fig. 9B). All dune-draa systems show a resultant sand drift, and unidirectional climbing is thus likely. But some star draa systems, due to their very slow rates of migration, could plausibly change their migration directions due to a change in wind regime over a long period of time. The models mostly show very low rates of bedform climbing, since most eolian sandstones seem to have preserved only a very small basal part of the original bedforms. Nevertheless, the models can be modified for supercritical climbing where necessary (Rubin and Hunter, 1982).

These stratification models are for uniform assemblages of one type of dune-interdune or dune-draa-interdune system. In deserts, many different systems are present. The next stage is to consider the possible stacking of different systems during the evolution of a desert. For this, we must consider the typical areal distribution of bedform types in a desert and note the vertical and lateral variations in stratification as they migrate and as the desert evolves.

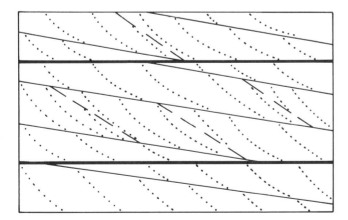 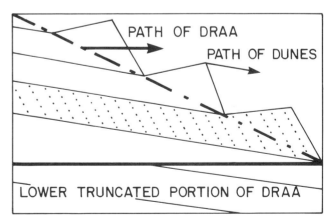

Figure 8
Relationship and origin or orders of bounding surface (after Brookfield, 1977). On left: synthetic section of ancient eolian sandstone parallel to bedform migration. Heavy lines – first order bounding surfaces; thin lines – second order bounding surfaces: dashed lines – third order bounding surfaces; dotted lines – eolian lamination. On right: origin of bounding surfaces by dunes climbing down draa lee slope. Bulk of draa is truncated by migration of succeeding draa.

98

Figure 9
A) bounding surfaces in Permian eolian sandstone, Mauchline, Scotland. Scale – 1m.
B) reversing barchanoid dunes between rows of large star draa. One large draa being traversed by truck, others in distance. Note deflation surfaces on present lee slopes of both draa and dunes. These would form third and possibly second order surfaces in preserved section.
C) bounding surfaces (mostly first order), Navajo Sandstone (Jurassic), Page, Arizona. Note decrease in thickness upwards towards contact with overlying fluviatile Carmel Formation, suggesting decrease in size of bedforms with time. Scale bar, lower right, is 20m.

FACIES MODELS FOR EOLIAN SANDS

Two different models are shown on Figures 10 and 11, based on deserts with predominantly transverse and predominantly longitudinal bedforms respectively. These may be considered simplifications of the eastern part of El Gran Desierto (Fig. 1b) and of the Fachi-Bilma erg (Fig. 1a).

The transverse bedform model (Fig. 10) is based on unidirectional winds and upward and lateral accretion of sand within an enclosed basin with marginal fans. The fans allow us to keep the first order surfaces horizontal: in a wide extensive plain, these bounding surfaces would be convex upward on a large scale and resemble successive shells. The model involves the initial development of sand patches and barchan dunes with the onset of aridity, followed by the development of, successively, transverse dunes and compound transverse draa at the climax of aridity. With decreasing aridity, reduction in sand supply or both, there would be gradual contraction of the erg and eventual covering over by fluvial or lacustrine sediments.

The longitudinal bedform model follows the same pattern, except that in this case the early sand patches and barchans are followed by linear dunes and linear complex draas and eventually star draas. These longitudinal patterns have rarely been observed in ancient eolian sandstones, probably because such bedforms are characteristic of deserts with net through-flow of sand with little net deposition. The bedforms, as in the Fachi-Bilma erg, rest on

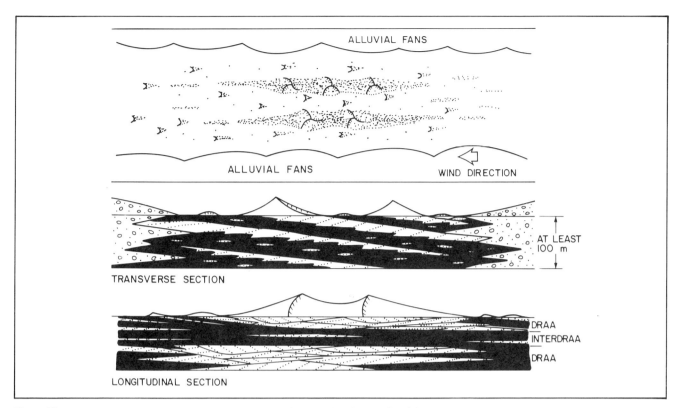

Figure 10
Synthetic model for desert with transverse bedforms. Note that bedforms are shown climbing far too steeply in the longitudinal cross-section, and that the troughs of the transverse section are too concave. Only first order surfaces are shown on the transverse section: some second order surfaces are shown on the longitudinal section. For details of stratification see Figure 7. Scale: basin is at least 5 km across.

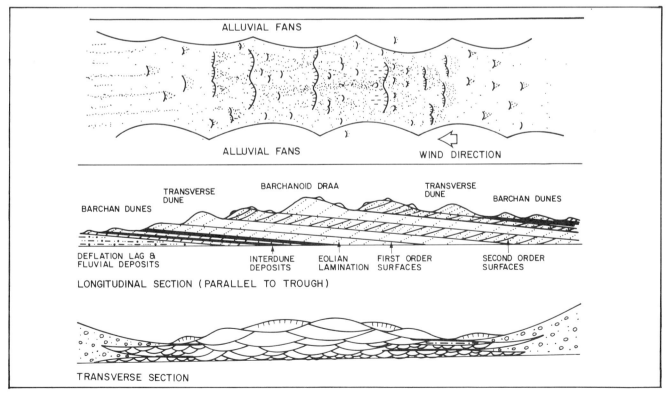

Figure 11
Synthetic model for desert with longitudinal bedforms in an enclosed basin. Note that some lateral migration of large longitudinal-star draas is permitted: without migration vertical stacks of longitudinal-star draa deposits would be separated by thick interdraa lag, barchan dune and fluviatile deposits. Black pattern includes all interdraa lag, small barchan dune, lacustrine and fluviatile sediment. For details of stratification see Figure 7. Scale: basin is at least 5 km across.

100

alluvium and lag deposits. Change in climatic conditions over a long period of time would probably lead to almost complete deflation, with perhaps isolated sand lenses left as the only remnant of the large star draas.

Note that the internal structures of the individual sets can not be shown at this scale: they are shown in Figure 7.

Similar models have been used by Kocurek (1981a) and Ross (1983) in their studies respectively of the Jurassic Entrada erg and the Precambrian Bigbear erg. Kocurek (1981a) used stratification types, bounding surfaces, foreset dip dispersion and interdune characteristics to reconstruct the central Entrada erg as shown in Figure 12. He estimated the wavelengths of the draas as between 900 and 1000 m from the intersection of first order bounding surfaces with supposed synchronous horizons. These wavelengths for the type of draa represented indicate draa heights approaching 100 m. At the edges of the Entrada erg, simple dune systems are indicated by the presence of only two orders of bounding surface.

Both models reflect growth and decay during slow environmental changes. In actual deserts, relatively sudden environmental change may cause major breaks in evolution. Thus, in the southern Sahara (Sahel), climatic change since the last ice age has led to vegetation overgrowing the dunes and preserving them intact in the full flower of their development (Talbot, 1980). Glennie and Buller (1983) studied the Permian Yellow Sands of northeast England which preserve much of a linear (seif) dune or draa system (see also Steele, 1983). This unusual preservation of a linear bedform assemblage was due to the extremely rapid inundation by the Zechstein Sea; so rapid in fact that the rounded profiles of individual dunes up to 50 m high are preserved below the overlying Marl Slate. Such feedback from ancient examples allows us to modify the models for specific cases. It would seem that such major breaks in the development of an erg – what might be called mega-bounding surfaces – should occur in the ancient; but I know of none yet described. They may be difficult to recognize except in very large continuous exposures.

Dynamic interpretations of ancient ergs are difficult, since we still do not know the exact cause for eolian bed-

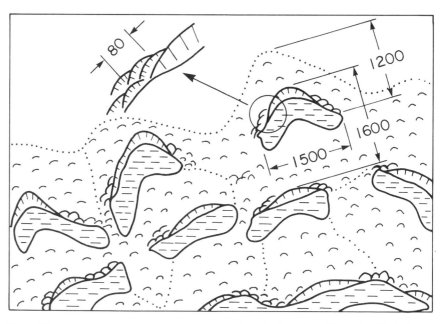

Figure 12
Interpretation of the overall structure and dimensions of bedforms and interdune areas in the central erg facies of the Entrada Sandstone (redrawn from Kocurek, 1981a). Draa slipfaces up to 110 m high: individual barchanoid dune slipfaces up to 8 m high. All measurements in metres.

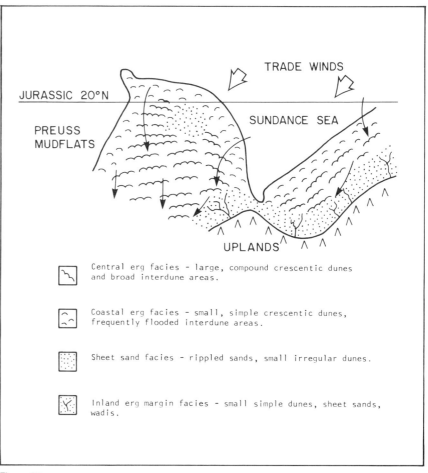

Figure 13
Reconstruction of the Entrada erg over the study area in N.E. Utah and N.W. Colorado. The region has been rotated to conform to the Jurassic paleolatitude position. Arrows indicate inferred erg circulation pattern (redrawn from Kocurek, 1981a).

form morphology and distribution in modern deserts. However, using the empirical results of bedform distribution from the Sahara, the concept of wind strength and directional variability and its effects on the nature of cross-stratification, some idea of wind regime for ancient ergs is possible. Glennie (1982) studied the paleowinds of the Permian Rotliegendes of the North Sea, and inferred that the Permian wind system was very simple. It matched that of the southern part of a modern northern hemisphere tradewind desert. A striking reversal of paleowinds around the Mid North Sea High was attributed to a 'wheel-around', similar to that seen in the Sahara and Arabia, and due to centres of high barometric pressure. A more detailed interpretation of the wind regime of the Jurassic Entrada erg is shown on Figure 13 (Kocurek, 1981 a; Kocurek and Dott, 1983).

THE EOLIAN MODEL AS A PREDICTOR

In an ideal desert, we would expect that thick compound superimposed cross-strata would characterize the interior. Towards the margins would be increasing numbers and thicker interdune deposits with smaller, simpler cross-strata, and possibly interbeds of fluvial deposits. In the two ideal sequences shown on Figure 14, we would expect "A" to have been deposited near the centre of the erg, and "B" closer to its margins. Depending on the paleowinds reconstructed from the cross-bedding, we could then try and predict in which directions the eolian sandstones would thicken and thin (Fig. 14C).

In terms of vertical sequence, I will show a possible interpretation based on a composite sequence in the Permian Thornhill and Dumfries basins of southwestern Scotland (Brookfield, 1977, 1980) shown on Figure 15. Note that the interpretation is based not only on the eolian sandstones, but also on the interdune and fluvial alluvial fan sequences with which they are interbedded.

These models do not take into account major changes, such as complete deflation of an erg due to climatic change, complete change in wind regime, or substantial lag in the response of large bedforms to changing conditions. I hope, nevertheless, that they at least illustrate that facies models

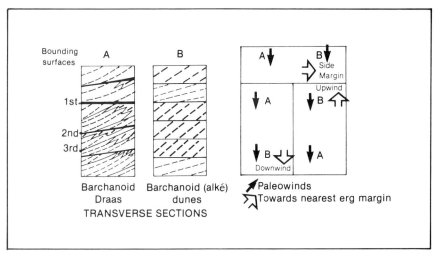

Figure 14
Two synthetic sections (A,B) (on left): inferred nearest erg margins based on loca- *tions of sections in relation to resultant wind direction (on right).*

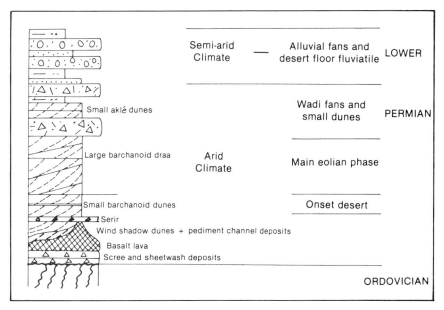

Figure 15
Section through Lower Permian deposits of *the Thornhill and Dumfries intermontane basins, with interpretation of lithologies.*

for eolian sandstones are possible. Soon, eolian facies models will no doubt be as comprehensive as those for other sedimentary environments.

ACKNOWLEDGEMENTS
I thank Lars Clemmensen and Roger Walker for criticism of earlier drafts of this manuscript.

REFERENCES

GENERAL AND VITAL
Bagnold, R.A., 1941. The physics of blown sand and desert dunes. London, Methuen, 265 p.
Still a marvellous, thought-provoking study of recent dunes and processes.

Bigarella, J.J., 1972. Eolian environments: their characteristics, recognition and importance. In Rigby, J.K., and Hamblin, W.K., eds., Recognition of ancient sedimentary environments. Society of Economic Paleontologists and Mineralogists, Special Publication 16, p. 12-62.
A bit dated but still useful.

Brookfield, M.E., and Ahlbrandt, T.S., 1983. Eolian sediments and processes. Amsterdam, Elsevier, 660 p.
A compilation of many diverse studies.

Cooke, R.V., and Warren, A., 1973. Geomorphology in deserts. London, Batsford, 394 p.

102

The best introduction to recent deserts.

Glennie, K.W., 1970. Desert sedimentary environments. Amsterdam, Elsevier, 222 p.

McKee, E.D., ed., 1979. A study of global sand seas. United States Geological Survey Professional Paper 1052, 429 p. Lots of good stuff.

Walker, R.G. and Middleton, G.V., 1979. Facies Models 4. Eolian Sands. In Walker, R.G., ed., Facies models. Geoscience Canada Reprint Series 1, p. 33-41.

Walker, T.R. and Harms, J.C., 1972. Eolian origin of flagstone beds, Lyons Sandstone (Permian), type area, Boulder County, Colorado. Mountain Geologist, v. 9, p. 279-288.
A beautifully written paper, with good illustrations – start your eolian reading here.

Wislon, I.G., 1973. Ergs. Sedimentary Geology, v. 10, p. 77-106.
The origin of much of what is contained in this summary.

MODERN EOLIAN SANDS

Ahlbrandt, T.S., 1979. Textural parameters of eolian deposits. In McKee, E.D., ed., A study of global sand seas. United States Geological Survey Professional Paper 1052, p. 21-51.

Ahlbrandt, T.S. and Fryberger, S.G., 1981. Sedimentary features and significance of interdune deposits. Society of Economic Paleontologists and Mineralogists, Special Publication 31, p. 293-314.

Andrews, S., 1981. Sedimentology of Great Sand Dunes, Colorado. Society of Economic Paleontologists and Mineralogists, Special Publication 31, p. 279-291.

Bigarella, J.J., Becker, R.D. and Duarte, G.M., 1969. Coastal dune structures from Parana (Brazil). Marine Geology, v. 7, p. 5-55.

Breed, C.S., et al., 1979. Regional studies of sand seas using Landsat (ERTS) imagery. United States Geological Survey Professional Paper 1052, p. 305-397.

Fryberger, S.G., 1979. Dune form and wind regime. In McKee, E.D., ed., A study of global sand seas. United States Geological Survey Professional Paper 1052, p. 137-169.

Fryberger, S.G. and Ahlbrandt, T.S., 1979. Mechanisms for the formation of eolian sand seas. Zeitschrift fur Geomorphologie N.F., v. 23, p. 440-460.

Fryberger, S.G., Ahlbrandt, T.S., and Andrews, S., 1979. Origin, sedimentary features and significance of low-angle eolian "sand-sheet" deposits, Great Sand Dunes National Monument and Vicinity, Colorado. Journal of Sedimentary Petrology, v. 49, p. 733-746.

Fryberger, G.S. and Schenk, C.J., 1981. Wind sedimentation tunnel experiments on the origin of eolian strata. Sedimentology, v. 28, p. 805-821.

Hanna, S.R., 1969. The formation of longitudinal sand dunes by large helical eddies in the atmosphere. Journal of Applied Meteorology, v. 8, p. 874-883.

Hunter, R.E., 1977. Basic types of stratification in small eolian dunes. Sedimentology, v. 24, p. 361-387.

Kocurek, G. and Fielder, G., 1982. Adhesion structures. Journal of Sedimentary Petrology, v. 52, p. 1229-1241.

Mainguet, M., 1976. Propositions pour une nouvelle classification des edifices sableux eoliens d'apres les images des satellites Landsat 1, Geminin, NOAA 3. Zeitschrifte fur Geomorphologie, v. 20, p. 275-296.

Mainguet, M. and Callot, Y. 1974. Air photo study of typology and interrelations between the texture and structure of dune patterns in the Fachi-Bilma Erg, Sahara. Zeitschrifte fur Geomorphologie, Suppl. Bd. 20, p. 62-69.

Mainguet, M. and Chemin, M.C., 1983. Sand Seas of the Sahara and Sahel – an explanation of their thickness and sand dune type by the sand budget principle. In Brookfield, M.E., and Ahlbrandt, T.S., eds., Eolian sediments and processes. Amsterdam, Elsevier, p. 353-364.

McKee, E.D., 1966. Structure of dunes at White Sands National Monument, New Mexico (and a comparison with structures of dunes from other selected areas). Sedimentology, v. 7, p. 1-70.

McKee, E.D., 1979. Introduction to a study of global sand seas. In McKee, E.D., ed., A study of global sand seas. United States Geogical Survey Professional Paper 1052, p. 1-19.

McKee, E.D., 1982. Sedimentary structures in dunes of the Namib desert, Southwest Africa. Geological Society of America, Special Paper 108, 64p.

McKee, E.D., and Douglas, J.R., 1971. Growth and movement of dunes at White Sands National Monument, New Mexico. United States Geological Survey Professional Paper 750-D, p. 108-114.

McKee, E.D. and Moiola, R.J., 1975. Geometry and growth of the White Sands dune field, New Mexico. Journal of Research, United States Geological Survey, v. 3, p. 59-66.

McKee, E.D. and Tibbits, G.C., Jr., 1964. Primary structures of a seif dune and associated deposits in Libya. Journal of Sedimentary Petrology, v. 34, p. 5-17.

Sharp, R.P., 1963. Wind ripples. Journal of Geology, v. 71, p. 617-636.

Sharp, R.P., 1979. Intradune flats of the Algodones Chain, Imperial Valley, California. Bulletin of the Geological Society of America, v. 90, p. 908-916.

Steidtmann, J.R., 1973. Ice and snow in eolian sand dunes of southwestern Wyoming. Science, v. 179, p. 796-798.

Talbot, M.R., 1980. Environmental repsonse to climatic change in the West African Sahel over the past 20,000 years. In Williams, M.A.J., and Faure, H., eds., The Sahara and the Nile; Quaternary Environments and prehistoric occupation in northern Africa. Rotterdam, Balkema, p. 37-62.

Tsoar, H., 1982. Internal structure and surface geometry of longitudinal (seif) dunes. Journal of Sedimentary Petrology, v. 52, p. 823-831.

Wasson, R.J. and Hyde, R., 1983a. Factors determining desert dune type. Nature, v. 304, p. 337-339.

Wasson, R.J. and Hyde, R., 1983b. A test of granulometric control on desert dune geometry. Earth Surface Processes and Landforms, v. 8, p. 301-312.

Wilson, I.G., 1971. Desert sandflow basins and a model for the origin of ergs. Geographical Journal, v. 137, p. 180-199.

Wilson, I.G., 1972. Aeolian bedforms - their development and origin. Sedimentology, v. 19, p. 173-210.

Wilson, I.G., 1973. Ergs. Sedimentary Geology, v. 10, p. 77-106.

ANCIENT EOLIAN SANDSTONES BEDFORM CLIMBING AND STRATIFICATION

Allen, J.R.L., 1963. Asymmetrical ripple marks and the origin of water-laid cosets of cross-strata. Liverpool Manchester Geological Journal, v. 3, p. 187-236.

Allen, J.R.L., 1982. Mud drapes in sand wave deposits: a physical model with application to the Folkstone Beds (Early Cretaceous, southeast England). Philosophical Transactions of the Royal Society of London, v. A306, p. 291-345.

Banks, N.L., 1973. The origin and significance of some downcurrent dipping cross-stratified sets. Journal of Sedimentary Petrology, v. 43, p. 423-427.

Brookfield, M.E., 1977. The origin of bounding surfaces in ancient eolian sandstones. Sedimentology, v. 24, p. 303-332.

Hunter, R.E., and Rubin, D.M., 1983. Interpreting cyclic cross-bedding with an example from the Navajo Sandstone. In Brookfield, M.E., and Ahlbrandt, T.S., eds.,

Eolian sediments and processes. Amsterdam, Elsevier, p. 429-454.

Kocurek, G., 1981b. Significance of interdune deposits and bounding surfaces in aeolian dune sands. Sedimentology, v. 28, p. 753-780.

Rubin, D.M. and Hunter, R.E., 1982. Bedform climbing in theory and nature. Sedimentology, v. 29, p. 121-138.

Rubin, D.M. and Hunter, R.E., 1983. Reconstructing bedform assemblages from compound cross-bedding. *In* Brookfield, M.E., and Ahlbrandt, T.S., eds., Eolian sediments and processes. Amsterdam, Elsevier, p. 407-427.

DESCRIPTIONS

Brookfield, M.E., 1980. Permian Intermontane basin sedimentation in Southern Scotland. Sedimentary Geology, v. 27, p. 167-194.

Clemmenson, L.B. and Abrahamsen, K., 1983. Aeolian stratification and facies association in desert sediemtns, Arran basin (Permian), Scotland. Sedimentology, v. 30, p. 311-339.

Glennie, K.W., 1982. Early Permian (Rotliegendes) paleowinds of the North Sea. Sedimentary Geology, v. 34, p. 245-265.

Glennie, K.W. and Buller, A.T., 1983. The Permain Weissliegend of N.W. Europe: the partial deformation of aeolian dune sands caused by the Zechstein transgression. Sedimentary Geology, v. 35, p. 43-81.

Hunter, R.E., 1981. Stratification styles in eolian sandstones; some Pennsylvanian to Jurassic examples from the western Interior, U.S.A. Society of Economic Paleontologists and Mineralogists, Special Publication 31, p. 315-329.

Kocurek, G., 1981a. Erg reconstruction: the Entrada Sandstone (Jurassic) of northern Utah and Colorado. Palaeogeography, Palaeoclimatology, Palaeoecology, v. 36, p. 125-153.

Kocurek, G. and Dott, R.J., Jr., 1983. Jurassic paleogeography and paleoclimate of the central and southern Rocky Mountain Region. *In* Reynolds, M.W., and Dolly, E.D., eds., Mesozoic paleogeography of West-central United States, Rocky Mountain Section, Society of Economic Paleontologists and Mineralogists, Denver, Colorado. p. 101-116.

Ross, G.M., 1983. Bigbear Erg: a Proterozoic intermontance eolian sand sea in the Hornby Bay Group, Northwest Territories, Canada.

Sanderson, I.D., 1974. Sedimentary structures and their environmental significance in the Navajo Sandstone, San Rafael Swell, Utah. Brigham Young University Geological Studies, v. 21, p. 215-246.

Steidtmann, J.R., 1974. Evidence for eolian origin of cross-stratification in sandstone of the Casper Formation, southermost Laramie Basin, Wyoming. Geological Society of America, Bulletin, v. 85, p. 1835-1842.

Steele, R.P., 1983. Longitudinal draa in the Permian Yellow Sands of north-east England. *In* Brookfield, M.E., and Ahlbrandt, T.S., eds., Eolian sediments and processes. Amsterdam, Elsevier, p. 543-550.

Stewart, W.D., and Walker, R.G., 1980. Eolian coastal dune deposits and surrounding marine sandstone, Rocky Mountain Supergroup (Lower Pennsylvanian), southeastern British Columbia. Canadian Journal of Earth Sciences, v. 17, p. 1125-1140.

Thompson, D.B., 1969. Dome-shaped aeolian dunes in the Frodsham member of the so-called "Keuper" Sandstone Formation (Scythian-Anisian; Triassic) at Frodsham, Cheshire (England). Sedimentary Geology, v. 3, p. 263-289.

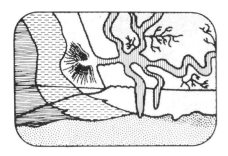

Deltas

ANDREW D. MIALL
Department of Geology
Unviersity of Toronto
Toronto, Ontario M5S 1A1

INTRODUCTION
Deltaic depositional models differ from most others in that their construction has not depended on a distillation of observations on ancient rocks but has arisen largely from a study of depositional processes on modern deltas. There are at least three distinct delta models or "norms" to consider in interpreting ancient rocks, but these are end members of a broad spectrum of delta types, and many modern and ancient deltas combine features of all three.

DEFINITION
The concept of the delta is one of the oldest in geology, dating back to about 400 B.C. when Herodotus observed that the alluvial plain at the mouth of the Nile was similar in shape to the Greek letter Δ. The term has been used for similar geographic features ever since.

We now define a delta, geologically, as "a deposit, partly subaerial, built by a river into or against a permanent body of water" (Barrell, 1912). The result is an irregular progradation of the shoreline directly contolled by the river. The sediments are formed under subaerial and shallow marine or lacustrine environments and typically show a gradation into finer-grained offshore facies. A crucial part of the definition is that the influence of a river or rivers as the main sediment source should be recognized. In the ancient record this is best accomplished by mapping lithofacies distributions, which should show the presence of a significant thickening of the clastic succession close to presumed locations of riverine sediment input into the sedimentary basin. However, in many deltas the fluvial influence is masked strongly by waves, ocean currents, tidal currents or winds. Ancient deltaic deposits of this type may be hard to recognize, and it seems likely that many have been interpreted, in the past, in terms of these modifying processes as wave-formed beach complexes or tidal flat deposits.

A SHORT HISTORY OF DELTA STUDIES
Modern work in the English-speaking world commenced with the classic studies of Gilbert on the deltas in Lake Bonneville. Gilbert was the first to attempt a hydrodynamic explanation of delta formation, and his ideas dominated thinking on the subject for many years. A classic paper by Barrell (1912) on the ancient Catskill delta also had a far-ranging influence.

Since the 1920s interest in deltas has been stimulated by the fact that the sediments of many ancient deltas contain extremely large deposits of coal, oil and gas. Nowhere is this more true than in the hydrocarbon-rich Gulf Coast of Texas and Louisiana, and research into deltaic sedimentation during the last forty years has been overwhelmingly dominated by studies of Holocene Gulf Coast deltas and their Quaternary and Tertiary antecedents. Most attention became focused on the Mississippi, which rapidly replaced the Lake Bonneville deltas of Gilbert as the standard model delta in geology textbooks.

Sedimentological research into the Mississippi commenced with the monumental work of Fisk, who established the depositional framework of the modern delta with the aid of many thousands of shallow boreholes. Subsequently the American Petroleum Institute funded a major research effort (Project 51), the objective of which was the study of modern sediments along the northwest margin of the Gulf of Mexico. The publication which summarizes this work (Shepard *et al.,* 1960) contains landmark papers on depositional processes in the Mississippi by Shepard and by Scruton. Further publications on the depositional environments and cyclic sedimentation in the Mississippi were provided by Kolb and Van Lopik (1966), by Frazier (1967) and by Coleman and Gagliano (1964, 1965).

The other deltas that were studied extensively at this time were those of the Niger(Allen, 1970; Oomkens, 1974), the Orinoco (Van Andel, 1967) and the Rhône (Oomkens, 1970).

Useful compilations of papers on ancient and modern deltas include those of Morgan (1970), Broussard (1975) and Le Blanc (1976a, 1976b). The basis of the modern three-fold classification of deltas (Fig. 1) was established

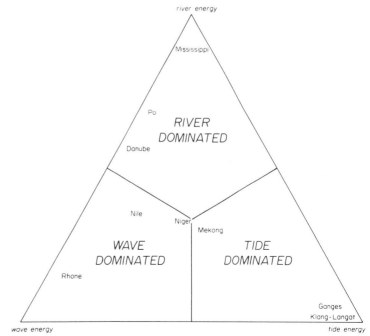

Figure 1
A classification of deltas based on variations in transportation patterns on the delta (after Galloway, 1975).

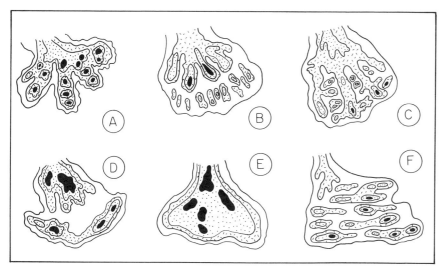

Figure 2
Delta models of Coleman and Wright (1975). A) River-dominated with low wave and tide energy, low littoral drift; B) River-dominated with low wave energy, high tide range, low lit-toral drift; C) Intermediate wave energy, high tide, low littoral drift; D) Intermediate wave energy, low tide range; E) High wave energy, low littoral drift; F) high wave energy, strong littoral drift.

by Fisher *et al.,* (1969; see also Gallo-way, 1975), who proposed a subdivision into river-, wave- and tide-dominated types (these are the three end members or "norms" referred to above). Wright *et al.,* (1974) elaborated this classicifica-tion, showing that various combinations of the three main processes could form six principal delta types (Fig. 2). Useful summaries of this work are provided by Coleman (1981) and Coleman and Wright (1975), and it is discussed later in this paper. An excellent general sum-mary of deltaic sedimentation is given by Elliot (1978).

The only major development in delta studies during the last ten years has been the increasing recognition of the importance of syndepositional deforma-tion on delta front surfaces, particularly in river-dominated deltas. Slumps, slides and growth faults are pervasive in many modern and ancient deltas, and have a major effect on subsurface stra-tigraphy and lithofacies distributions (Coleman *et al.,* 1983; Winker and Edwards, 1983).

Most of the major developments in the understanding of deltas are attrib-uted to Gulf Coast geologists, particu-larly the staff of the Coastal Studies Institute at Louisiana State University and the Bureau of Economic Geology at the University of Texas. The pre-eminence of this group is remarkable, and is mainly a reflection of the pro-found importance of modern and

ancient Gulf Coast deltas to the econ-omy of that region (petroleum, coal and uranium production, environmental geology). However, it has tended to bias geologists everywhere towards interpre-tations based on Gulf Coast models, particularly that of the Mississippi delta, although these are not everywhere appropriate and, to some extent, may even be unique.

Delta facies models seem now to have reached a mature phase of devel-opment, in contrast to those for other environments, particularly models of continental margin sedimentation and shelf sedimentation (Walker, "Shelf and Shallow Marine Sands", this volume), which are still undergoing rapid evolu-tion. However, considerable work is needed to test the models by careful documentation of the ancient record. This is especially necessary for wave- and tide-influenced deltas, of which few well-described ancient examples exist.

DELTA FORMATION AND CLASSIFICATION
The distribution, orientation and inter-nal geometry of deltaic deposits is con-trolled by a variety of factors, including climate, water discharge, sediment load, river-mouth processes, waves, tides, currents, winds, shelf width and slope, and the tectonics and geometry of the receiving basin (Wright *et al.,* 1974). In a brief paper such as this it is impossible to describe fully the inter-relationships

between all these variables, but several generalizations are possible, such as those on which the principal classifica-tion of deltas are based (Figs. 1 and 2; discussed below).

Variations in Sediment Input
Climate, water discharge (rate and vari-ability) and sediment load (quantity and grain-size) are to some extent inter-related. In humid, tropical regions pre-cipitation normally is high relative to evapotranspiration; runoff tends to be high and steady. The predominance of chemical over mechanical weathering leads to high dissolved-load sediment yields. These factors give rise to rela-tively stable, meandering channel patterns.

In arctic or arid conditions precipita-tion is erratic, vegetation is sparse, and braided channel patterns with large bed-loads tend to occur (Coleman, 1981, and Coleman and Wright, 1975 provide a more complete discussion of this topic).

These distinctions are most easily recognized in the fluvial delta plain dep-osits by the geometry and grain size of the distributary channel fill units (see "Coarse Alluvial Deposits", and "Sandy Fluvial Systems", this volume). How-ever, where the delta is not significantly modified by processes there will be dif-ferences in the structure of the delta as a whole, as discussed below.

Variations in River-Mouth Flow Behaviour
When a sediment-laden river enters a body of standing water one of three types of flow dispersal may occur, depending on the density differences between the river water and that of the lake or sea into which it flows. Variations in temperature, salinity and sediment load can cause such differences in density.

A) Inflow More Dense. This is a com-mon occurrence where sediment-laden streams enter fresh-water lakes (e.g., glacier-fed streams in Alpine regions). A narrow, arcuate zone of active deltaic progradation containing the coarse bed-load may occur along the shore.
The delta which forms contains the dis-tinct, steeply-dipping forests of the clas-sical Gilbertian delta. The finer sediment fraction may be dispersed offshore as density interflows or underflows, form-ing repeated graded units.

B) Inflow Equally Dense. This is also a common occurrence in fresh-water deltas, and may also develop at the mouths of rivers entering brackish back-barrier lagoons. Sediment is dispersed radially and competency is lost rapidly. The bulk of the sediment is deposited on a Gilbertian delta.

C) Inflow Less Dense. Most marine deltas are formed under these conditions because freshwater is less dense than seawater, unless it is unusually cold or sediment laden. Lacustrine deltas formed at the mouths of suspended-load rivers are also of this type. The river effluent tends to form a discrete plume floating on the surface of the sea. The suspended sediment load is widely dispersed, resulting in a large active delta-front area, typically dipping at 1° or less, and contrasting with the 10 to 20° dip of typical Gilbertian deltas.

Marine waters beneath the effluent jet form a "salt-wedge", which may extend for tens of kilometres upstream, particularly during high tide. Marine faunas can thus be found well inland – a possible source of confusion in the study of ancient deltaic deposits.

These patterns can be radically modified by tide or current activity, as described below.

Variations in Transport Pattern on the Delta

The type of energy conditions that exist in the sea at the river mouth are of fundamental importance in controlling depositional environments and the geometry of the resulting sediments. In fact the most useful classification of delta types is one based on the relative strengths of fluvial and marine processes (Fig. 1), as shown by Fisher *et al.* (1969), Coleman (1981), Galloway (1975) and Coleman and Wright (1975). Interrelationships between these processes form the main basis for recognizing three deltaic "norms".

A) River-Dominated Deltas. If waves, tidal currents and longshore currents are weak, rapid seaward progradation takes place, and a variety of characteristic, fluvially dominated depositional environments develops. At the mouth of each distributary subaqueous levees may form where the competence of the effluent jet is reduced by friction with the static sea water at the margins of the flow (Fig. 3). The main sediment load is

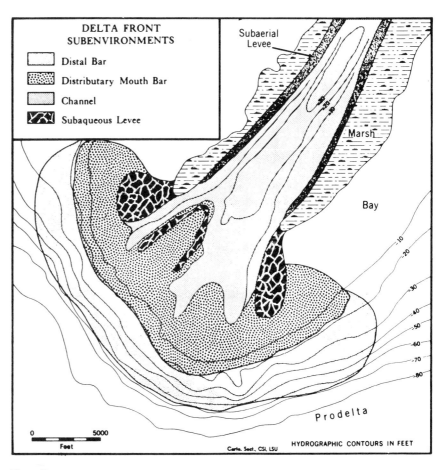

Figure 3
Subenvironments at a distributary mouth in a river-dominated, birdsfoot-type delta, South Pass, Mississippi delta. Progradation sea- *ward leads to the development of elongate sand bodies called "bar-finger" or "shoestring" sands (Coleman and Gagliano, 1965).*

deposited in a distributary mouth bar, which becomes finer grained toward the sea. The proximal mouth bar region is characterized by scour channels and by temporary bars and islands with abundant crossbedding, resulting from variations in flow conditions (changes in river discharge, tidal effects).

In the case of mixed- or suspended-load distributary channels, which are relatively stable in position, and in the absence of significant wave- or tide-induced scour, sedimentation gradually extends the mouths seaward. The resulting lithofacies assemblage, of which the mouth bar sand is the most important, tends to be oriented at a high angle to the coastline (basin margin), as in Figure 2A, a fact that can be of considerable importance in the understanding of an ancient deltaic deposit. "Bar-finger" or "shoestring" sands are a typical component of such a deltaic assemblage. The modern Mississippi delta is the best modern example of this

pattern, showing the distinctive "birdsfoot" shape in plan view (Figs. 3 and 4).

Between the distributaries are interdistributary bays, which commonly are areas of low energy, muddy sedimentation and abundant organic activity. Shell beds and bioturbation are common. These bays eventually fill with sediment and become marshes. One of the most important ways in which this occurs is by the development of crevasse splays, which occurs in the following manner.

As progradation proceeds the river slope is flattened and flow becomes less competent. At this stage a breach in the subaerial levee may occur upstream during a period of high discharge. Such a breach is termed a crevasse. The shorter route it offers to the sea via an interdistributary bay generally is the cause of a major flow diversion, and a subdelta (crevasse-splay) deposit may develop rapidly. Eventually the crevasse may become a major distributary and the process is repeated.

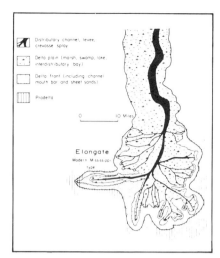

Figure 4
A birdsfoot-type river-dominated delta; the modern Mississippi delta (Fisher et al., 1969).

Where delta distributaries are of the unstable, low sinuosity (braided) type, with shifting courses and numerous bars and islands, a different type of delta may develop. The outline tends to be lobate, and mouth bars merge laterally into a sheet sand. Crevasse splays may be absent, but sediment is distributed throughout the delta by distributary switching (avulsion), a process analogous to that of crevassing. The radiating pattern of distributaries is similar to that of alluvial fans, and the term fan-delta is commonly used to describe them (Fig. 5). Pebbly sands and gravels are common to dominant components of the delta plain and delta front environment. Good descriptions of modern fan delta sedimentation have been given by McGowen (1970), Galloway (1976), and Wescott and Ethridge (1980).

At present, fan deltas tend to occur in arctic or arid environments, where the abundance of coarse bedload and the variable river discharge favour unstable braided distributary networks. Fan deltas were probably the dominant type of river-dominated delta in pre-Devonian time because, until the advent of land vegetation, which tends to store rainfall and regulate runoff, braided channel networks were probably the main fluvial style.

B) Wave-Dominated Deltas. On most coastlines waves rework shoreline sediments and account for local distinctive facies. However, the contrasts between the minor wave activity in areas such as

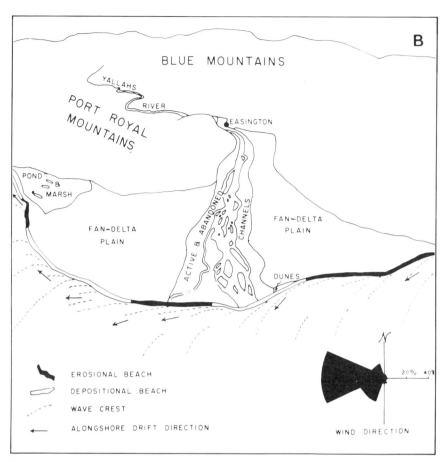

Figure 5
Interpretive sketch map of the modern Yallahs fan delta, Jamaica, drawn from an   *oblique air photo (Wescott and Ethridge, 1980).*

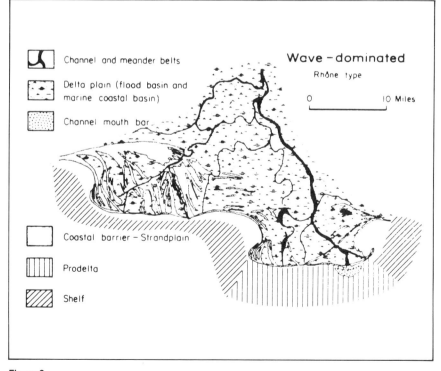

Figure 6
A wave-dominated delta; the modern Rhône delta (Fisher et al., 1969).

the Gulf Coast, and the wave-dominated coastlines of much of the Atlantic and Pacific oceans, are dramatic. Coleman and Wright (1975) suggested that it takes a whole year of wave activity on the Mississippi delta to equal ten hours of wave energy expenditure on the São Francisco delta, Brazil.

In a wave-influenced delta (e.g., Figs. 2C, 2D, 6), mouth bar deposits are continually reworked into a series of curved beach ridges. If the winds are predominantly onshore, they may redistribute much of the beach sand as an eolian dune field capping the delta plain.

The geometry of the delta front beach complex depends largely on the nature of shoreline circulation patterns. An oblique angle of wave attack may develop a powerful longshore drift current, in which case the entire delta may become asymmetrical and skewed downcurrent (Fig. 2F). Beaches grow laterally and fill interdistributary bays by the develoment of curved spits, as in the modern Rhône delta (Fig. 6). Whether or not this longshore drift occurs, individual sand bodies tend to be oriented more or less parallel to the coastline in marked distinction to that of other delta types. The facies characteristics and mature petrography of these shoreline sand bodies are distinctive, as discussed elsewhere in this volume.

C) Tide-Dominated Deltas. Where the tidal range is high the reversing flow that occurs in the distributary channels during flood and ebb may become the principal source of sediment dispersal energy. Within and seaward of the distributary mouths the sediment may be reworked into a series of parallel, linear or digitate ridges parallel to the direction of tidal currents and separated from each other by linear scour channels (Fig. 7). The ridge-and-channel morphology, with a trend perpendicular to shoreline, is one of the most characteristic features of the tide-dominated delta, and may be readily detected by careful lithofacies mapping (Figs. 2B and 2C). The subaerial part of the delta consists largely of tidal flats comprising mainly fine-grained deposits. Distributaries may contain well sorted sands deposited under conditions of reversing flow, and large quantities of clay and silt will tend to be flushed into the delta marsh by overbank flooding during high tides.

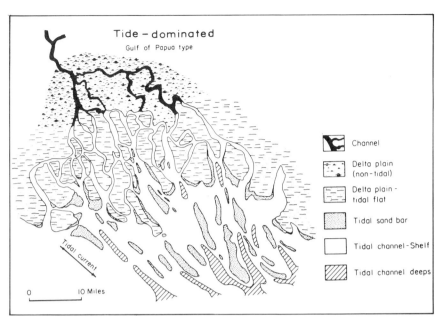

Figure 7
A tide-dominated delta; the modern Ganges-Brahmaputra delta (Fisher et al., 1969).

As in the case of wave-dominated deltas, tidal currents may completely rework the deposits and redistribute them away from the river mouth. In such a case it may be difficult to recognize the deposits as deltaic. Many ancient beach or shallow marine deposits, with evidence of wave or tidal reworking, may have been misidentified as a result. The large volume of the deposit, or the presence of a landward facies change into a thick fluvial sequence, may be the only clues to a deltaic interpretation.

Syndepositional Deformation
Rapid sedimentation on deltas leads to gravitational instabilities and the generation of a variety of small to medium scale structures as a result of loading or slope failure (Fig. 8; see Coleman et al., 1983). Such structures are likely to be more common on river-dominated deltas, where the rate of seaward growth tends to be more rapid. The most important of these structures are growth faults, formed by sediment loading and episodic failure on the seaward side of the fault plane. Sedimentary units

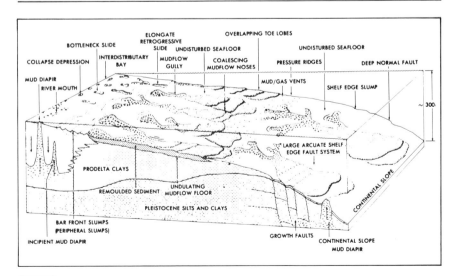

Figure 8
Schematic block diagram showing the various types of delta front to prodelta sediment *instabilities off the modern Mississippi delta (Coleman et al., 1983).*

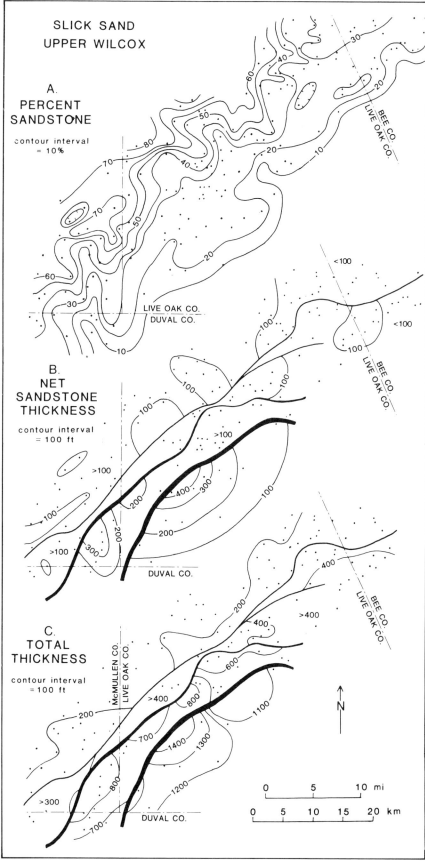

Figure 9
Lithofacies maps of an interval in the Wilcox Sand (Eocene), Gulf Coast. See text for discussion (Winker and Edwards, 1983).

thicken across the fault as a result of syndepositional movement. This occurs commonly particularly during deposition of denser sediment such as sand, and can result in the development of significantly thickened strike-parallel wedges of sandstone in the section (Fig. 9). These wedges could be misinterpreted as wave-modified sand bodies similar to those in Figures 2C and 2D, unless independent evidence or structure (e.g., seismic data) was available (Winker and Edwards, 1983).

The delta-front surface may be unstable because of sedimentary oversteepening and under-compaction. Slumps and slides commonly are the result, generating slide scars, large slide blocks, slump structures and convolute bedding. Diapiric intrusion of prodeltaic mud (or evaporite) into overlying deltaic facies is caused by rapid sediment loading. Growth of the diapirs tends to be long-lived, and they frequently rise to the surface to form sea-floor mounds, or even islands.

DELTAIC CYCLES
Scruton (1960) was one of the first to point out that the growth of a delta is cyclic. The process has now been described many times (e.g., Fisher *et al.*, 1969; Coleman and Wright, 1975; Elliot, 1978). There are two phases.

A) Progradational Phase. Active seaward progradation causes prodelta muds to be overlain by delta front silts and sands, and these in turn by distributary mouth deposits, mainly sands (and gravels, if present), and finally by topset delta marsh sediments, including fluvial facies and peats, mud, or eolian dunes, depending on local climate and sediment supply (Fig. 10).

B) Abandonment Phase. A delta lobe is eventually abandoned if crevassing generates a shorter route to the sea. The topmost beds are then attacked by wave and current activity and may be completely reworked. Compaction and/or subsidence may allow a local marine transgression to occur. The result typically is a thin to moderately thick unit of sands or clays containing a marine fauna, abundant bioturbation and possibly, glauconite. There may be abundant evidence of wave and tide reworking in the form of distinctive assemblages of sedimentary structures.

Lobe switching is probably more common in river-dominated deltas, resulting in a more frequent initiation of new progradional cycles. The overall mechanism probably is similar to wave-dominated deltas (e.g., the Rhône), but may not occur on tide-dominated deltas. Large-scale alternation between the two phases may reflect regional regression-transgression cycles caused by tectonism or eustatic sea level changes. An example is discussed below.

The complete delta cycle (sometimes termed a megacycle) may be about 50 to 150 m (or more) in thickness, but it may contain or pass laterally into numerous smaller cycles representing the progradation of individual distributaries or crevasse splays. As shown by Coleman and Gagliano (1964) and Elliott (1974) these can range from approximately 2 to 14 m in thickness. As in the case of the larger scale cycles they tend to coarsen upward, as described below.

The manner in which cyclic deltaic

Figure 10

Development of the "clinoform"; depositional surface of the delta front and prodelta: the
progradational phase of delta growth (Scruton, 1960).

sequences are superimposed upon each other depends on the relative rates of sedimentation, subsidence (including

compaction) and lobe switching. If the rates of sedimentation and subsidence are in approximate balance a delta will

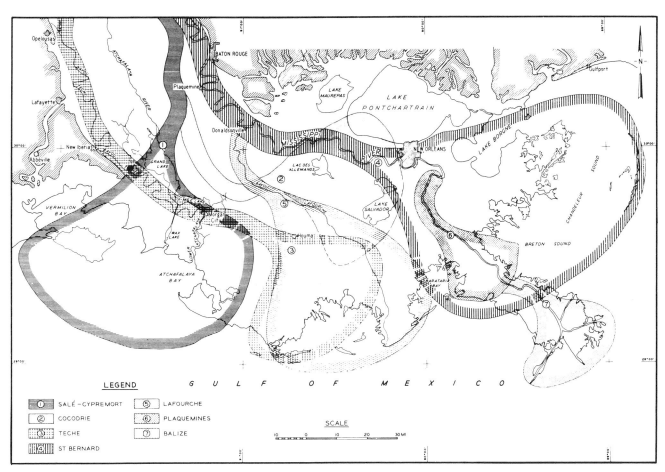

Figure 11

The seven partially overlapping lobes of the Mississippi delta which have developed dur-
ing the last 5000 years (Kolb and Van Lopik, 1966). Sedimentation is now active again in
the area of lobe 1 (Roberts et al., 1980) as well as on the main modern lobe (#7).

tend to build vertically; if subsidence is slower the delta will prograde seaward. As each part of the depositional basin becomes filled, successive progradational events will move laterally (Curtis, 1970, p. 293-297). This is demonstrated dramatically by the Mississippi delta. Here both subsidence and sedimentation have been rapid since the Pleistocene, but the enormous sediment supply has resulted in the development of a suite of seven separate but partially overlapping lobes at the mouth of the Mississippi during the last 5000 years (Fig. 11). The most recent lobe is itself in the process of forming several subdeltas, by similar processes of crevasse splay and distributary switching.

Given a broad shelf or a generally shallow basin a delta may continue to prograde basinward for many kilometres. The depositional surfaces representing each time horizon (Fig. 10) define gently-dipping, wedge-shaped stratigraphic units termed clinoforms. These are very distinctive on regional seismic cross-sections (Fig. 12, Brazos Delta; see Brown and Fisher, 1977; Winker and Edwards, 1983). In strike sections these same units show a large scale mounded or hummocky pattern, recording the lateral switching or offsetting of individual delta lobes.

RECOGNIZING ANCIENT DELTAS

Deltas contain no single distinctive lithofacies but consist of assemblages of lithofacies, each of which can occur in a variety of other environments. It is, necessary, therefore, to identify ancient deltas by a series of steps, eliminating other possibilities and using distinguishing characteristics of facies type, bed geometry and type of cyclic succession to focus in gradually on the correct delta model. This process is complicated by the existence of three end-member "norms", and by the fact that most natural modern and ancient deltas probably are combinations of all three, with added local complications of basin geometry and basin tectonics to be unravelled. In addition, very few good examples of ancient wave- and tide-dominated deltas are available for use as analogues.

The most useful overall indicator of a major deltaic deposit is the presence of a thick wedge or lobe of nonmarine to shallow marine lacustrine sediment, passing basinward into finer grained, deeper water facies, and landward into an entirely nonmarine (usually fluvial) facies (although the latter may have been removed by uplift and erosion of the basin margin). To detect such a deposit requires careful stratigraphic

correlation and the application of lithofacies mapping techniques.

Attempts to correlate deltaic units must be carried out with care because the presence of numerous lateral facies changes can be the cause of many mistakes. Cant ("Subsurface Facies Analysis", this volume) describes the methods of subsurface correlation using geophysical logs, and Figure 12 (Southwest Pass) is an example of correlation of a Recent sand unit in the Mississippi delta. Note the typical coarsening-upward profile, and the interpretation of a locally thickened sand wedge in terms of growth fault. Figure 12 (Brazos Delta) is an example of the clinoform seismic facies so commonly recorded from deltaic deposits. This example is of a modern delta, in which the relationship of the dipping depositional surface to the clinoform stratigraphy is quite obvious (see Fig. 10). A word of caution is required, however, because clinoform reflections can be generated in other environments (alluvial fans, submarine fans, continental slopes, reef talus wedges) and so are not always reliable as a primary facies indicator of a deltaic environment.

If a network of well correlated surface or subsurface sections can be developed, the deltas can be delineated

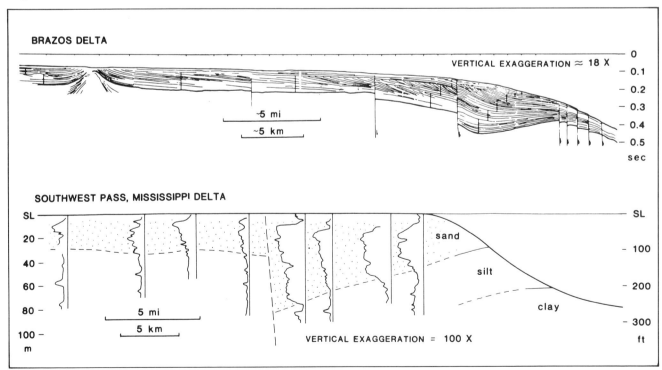

Figure 12
Seismic facies of the modern Brazos River delta (Winker and Edwards, 1983); and sub- *surface correlation of a deltaic sand-silt unit, in Southwest Pass, Mississippi delta, showing characteristic geophysical log profile of* *coarsening-upward cycles, and recognition of a growth fault.*

113

using lithofacies mapping techniques.
Various parameters may be used,
including sand/shale ratio, total sand
thickness, or sand thickness expressed
as a per cent of a total section. The
results may show important differences.
For example, the same interval of
Eocene sand on the Gulf Coast is
mapped in three ways in Figure 9. Map
A shows the characteristic lobate pattern of river-dominated deltas, with sand
content diminishing distally toward the
southeast. Maps B and C show a very
different pattern. Lobes of thick sand
are present, oriented parallel to strike,
but are interpreted here in terms of
locally increased subsidence and sedimentation rates along growth faults.
The strike-parallel pattern of sand
bodies could be confused with that of a
wave-influenced delta (see Fig. 2C) if
the researcher was not aware of the
growth faults. Because the entire thickness of section increases across growth
faults, maps of sand percentage (Fig.
9A) may not reveal the effects of syndepositional faulting. However, if allow-
ance is made for these possibilities the
outline of local deltaic depocentres
revealed by lithofacies mapping techniques may yield useful clues about
delta type. For example, Figure 13
shows a map of total porous section
(mainly sandstone) in a member of the
Toad Grayling Formation (Triassic) of
northwest Alberta (Miall, 1976a). The
shapes of the lobes and fingers of thick
sandstone can be compared to idealized diagrams such as Figure 2. The
subcrop of the Toad Grayling beneath
the Jurassic is known to be approximately parallel to regional shoreline.
The sandstone trends are more or less
perpendicular to this shoreline, and
have the shape of birdsfoot and lobate
river-dominated deltas. Other excellent
examples of such maps have been published by Busch (1971) and Wermund
and Jenkins (1970).

Interpretations can be refined by
detailed examination of vertical sections, using the characteristics of the
three end-member delta types as
"norms" and as guides for interpretation. For example, they may show the
repeated coarsening-upward cycles
characteristic of wave- and river-
dominated deltas (Fig. 12, Southwest
Pass). Cores and outcrops may reveal
distinctive assemblages of lithofacies
and sedimentary structures, and

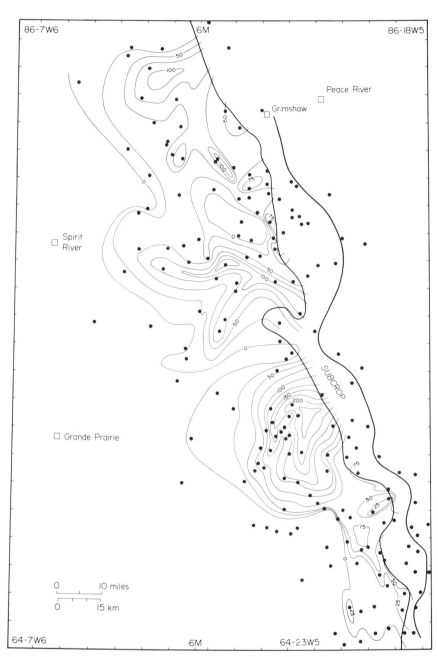

Figure 13
*Lobate and birdsfoot deltas in a member of
the Triassic Toad-Grayling Formation,*
*northwest Alberta. Contours show the distri-
bution of net porous section, in feet (Miall,
1976a).*

paleocurrent analysis may be employed
(if suitable outcrops are available) in
order to map dispersal patterns. Using
these data the effects of fluvial and
marine currents can be assessed and
suitable comparisons with the appropriate deltaic norms (Figs. 1 and 2) can
be suggested, and compared with the
results of lithofacies mapping.

Figure 14 illustrates two outcrop pro-
files through the Bokkeveld Group
(Early Devonian) of Cape Province,
South Africa (Tankard and Barwis,

1982). The generalized section on the
left illustrates repeated coarsening
upward megacycles, while the detailed,
interpreted section shows some of the
subenvironments that can be recognized within individual megacycles.
Smaller scale cycles up to 20 m thick
record the progradation of mouth bars
and some of the barrier and tidal sands
produced by marine reworking. The
lower 105 m of the detailed section is a
typical product of river-dominated delta
progradation, with a coarsening-

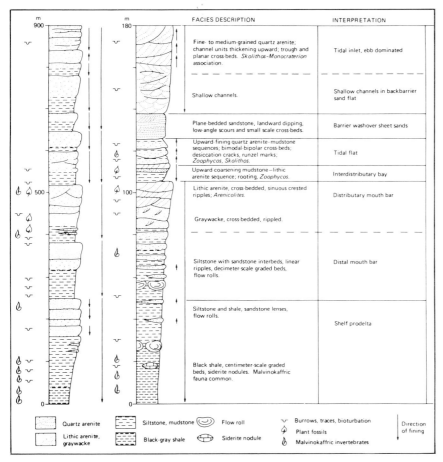

FACIES DESCRIPTION	INTERPRETATION
Fine- to medium-grained quartz arenite; channel units thickening upward; trough and planar cross-beds. *Skolithos–Monocraterion* association.	Tidal inlet, ebb dominated
Shallow channels.	Shallow channels in backbarrier sand flat
Plane-bedded sandstone, landward dipping, low-angle scours and small scale cross-beds.	Barrier washover sheet sands
Upward-fining quartz arenite-mudstone sequences; bimodal-bipolar cross-beds; desiccation cracks, runzel marks; *Zoophycos, Skolithos.*	Tidal flat
Upward-coarsening mudstone-lithic arenite sequence; rooting, *Zoophycos.*	Interdistributary bay
Lithic arenite, cross-bedded, sinuous crested ripples; *Arenicolites.*	Distributary mouth bar
Graywacke, cross-bedded, rippled.	
Siltstone with sandstone interbeds, linear ripples, decimeter-scale graded beds, flow rolls.	Distal mouth bar
Siltstone and shale, sandstone lenses, flow rolls.	Shelf prodelta
Black shale, centimeter-scale graded beds, siderite nodules. Malvinokaffric fauna common.	

Legend:
- Quartz arenite
- Lithic arenite, graywacke
- Siltstone, mudstone
- Black-gray shale
- Flow roll
- Siderite nodule
- Burrows, traces, bioturbation
- Plant fossils
- Malvinokaffric invertebrates
- Direction of fining

Figure 14
Stratigraphic section through the Bokkeveld Group, Cape Province, South Africa (left)
and detailed lithofacies and interpretation of an idealized cyclic sequence (Tankard and Barwis, 1982).

upward succession of shales, siltstones and thin sands representing the build up of the prodelta to distal mouth bar sediments. The sequence is capped by scoured and crossbedded lithic arenites of the proximal mouth bar.

The progradational facies are overlain here by quartz arenites up to 70 m thick showing evidence of wave and tide reworking of the Bokkeveld deltas. Facies and structures are similar to those occurring in other wave- and tide-influenced coastlines (see "Barrier Island and Associated Strand Plain Systems", this volume) but their thickness and associations here suggest a deltaic origin. Barriers and washover sheets are indicated by flat to gently dipping planar sand sheets with a seaward oriented foreshore dip or with the landward dip of washover fans. Tidal inlet and associated delta deposits show polymodal, but commonly ebb-dominated paleocurrent patterns in medium scale crossbedding. Each facies contains a distinct

ichnofacies (see "Trace Fossil Facies Models", this volume). The Bokkeveld deltas are interpreted as "wave-influenced" deltas, the lower part of each megacycle shows a predominant fluvial influence, while the reworked marine facies indicate strong wave activity and a moderate tidal influence. This alternation is probably the result of subsidence or sea level change periodically altering the subtle balance between fluvial and marine influences. Another similar example was described by Vos (1981b).

Examples of ancient tidally-influenced deltas have been described by Clemmensen (1976), Eriksson (1979), Verdier *et al.,* (1980) and Rahmani (1982). For example, Eriksson (1979) documented the presence of flood-dominated elongate sand shoals oriented perpendicular to the shoreline, and proposed a model of a non-barred estuary for part of the Archean Moodies Group of South Africa. Figure 15 illus-

trates a local facies model developed for the modern Niger River by Allen (1970). This river shows elements of all three deltaic end members or "norms", including well-developed beach ridges and active tidal channels undergoing vigorous reversing flow. The lithofacies characteristics shown in the circles around the block diagram illustrate the characteristic coarsening upward nature of the deposit, with distinctive beach-accretion sets and herringbone cross-bedding attesting to the strong marine influence.

Numerous examples of ancient river-dominated deltas have been described. Selected examples are listed in the bibliography. The presence of lobate or finer-shaped deltaic trends, radial paleocurrent patterns, and the characteristic lithofacies assemblages of shoe string sands, interdistributary bays, crevasse splays and mouth bars, are the main criteria for recognizing this type of delta. A Tertiary example is shown in Figure 16 exhibiting, in this case, most of the characteristic features of the river-dominated deltaic "norm".

Increasing attention is being paid to the fan-delta model, particularly by sedimentologists studying pre-Devonian (pre-vegetation) deltas. Another common paleogeographic environment in which fan deltas are found is at the mouths of short, steep rivers carrying abundant bedload. Fan deltas typically lack interdistributary bays and crevasse splays. They show a highly scoured and channelized transition between the coarse, commonly conglomeratic, delta plain and delta front deposits and the finer grained prodelta facies. Selected examples are listed in the bibliography.

CONCLUSIONS
The delta of the Mississippi is still pre-eminent in the minds of many geologists, for the historical and economic reasons described at the beginning of this paper. However, analyses of ancient deltas are becoming increasingly sophisticated, and the Mississippi is no longer the model automatically used in interpretations of the ancient record.

The next development in the interpretation of ancient deltas may be to interpret the alternations of progradational and abandonment phases in terms of regional changes in relative sea level, and to relate dispersal patterns to

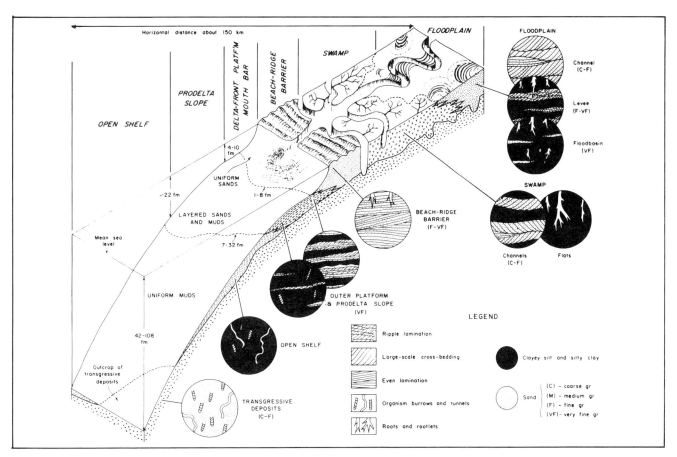

Figure 15
Block diagram model of the modern Niger delta (Allen, 1970).

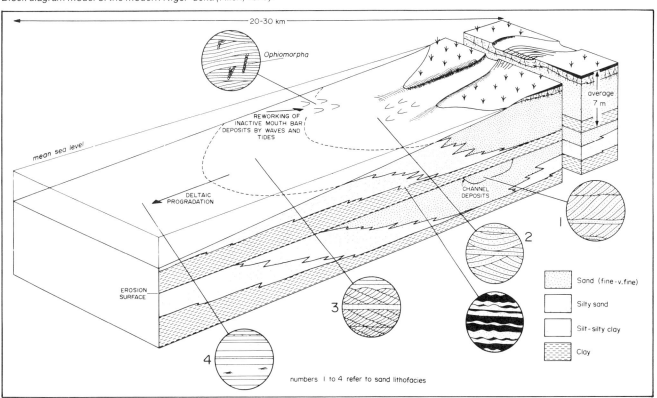

Figure 16
Block diagram model of the Eureka Sound

Formation (Tertiary), Banks Island, Arctic Canada, showing interpretation of coarsen-

ing upward cycles in terms of distributary mouth bar sands (Miall, 1976b).

tectonic setting and structural grain. As suggested by Miall (1981) some useful information about local plate tectonic history may emerge from this type of analysis.

REFERENCES AND ADDITIONAL READINGS

PRIMARY REFERENCE LIST

Coleman, J.M., 1981. Deltas, processes of deposition and models for exploration. Minneapolis, Burgess Publishing Company, 2nd. Ed., 124 p.
A useful summary of the worldwide researches by the Coastal Studies Institute.

Coleman, J.M. and Wright, L.D., 1975. Modern river deltas: variability of processes and sand bodies. In Broussard, M.L., ed., Deltas, models for exploration. Houston Geological Society, p. 99-150.
Discussion of geomorphology and sedimentary processes of the six major delta types.

Eliott, T., 1978. Deltas. In Reading, H.G., ed., Sedimentary environments and facies. Oxford, Blackwell Scientific Publications, p. 97-142.
The best up to date study of modern deltas and ancient examples.

Fisher, W.L., Brown, L.F., Jr., Scott, A.J., and McGowen, J.H., 1969. Delta systems in the exploration for oil and gas. Texas Bureau of Economic Geology, 78 p.
Modern and ancient deltas are described and classified. The abundant illustrations are particulary useful.

Galloway, W.E., 1975. Process framework for describing the morphologic and stratigraphic evolution of deltaic depositional systems. In Broussard, M.L. ed., Deltas, models for exploration. Houston Geological Society, p. 87-98.
Establishes the by-now widely accepted tripartite classification of deltaic end members or "norms".

Le Blanc, R.J., ed., 1976a. Modern deltas. American Association of Petroleum Geologists, Reprint Series No. 18, 205 p.

Le Blanc, R.J., ed., 1976b. Ancient deltas. American Association of Petroleum Geologists, Reprint Series No. 19, 226 p.
Two collections of historically important and interesting papers.

IMPORTANT STUDIES OF MODERN DELTAS

Allen, J.R.L., 1970. Sediments of the modern Niger delta: a summary and review. In Morgan, J.P. ed., Deltaic sedimentation – modern and ancient. Society of Economic Paleontologists and Mineralogists, Special Publication 15, p. 138-151.

Bates, C.C., 1953. Rational theory of delta tion. American Association of Petroleum Geologists, Bulletin, v. 37, p. 2119-2162.
The first description of flow dispersal patterns at river-mouths.

Coleman, J.M. and Gagliano, S.M., 1964. Cyclic sedimentation in the Mississippi River deltaic plain. Gulf Coast Association of Geological Societies, Transactions, v. 14, p. 67-80.

Coleman, J.M. and Gagliano, S.M., 1965. Sedimentary structures: Mississippi River deltaic plain. In Middleton, G.V., ed., Primary sedimentary structures and their hydrodynamic interpretation. Society of Economic Paleontologists and Mineralogists, Special Publication 12, p. 133-148.
These two Coleman and Gagliano papers are important contributions on sediments and sedimentary processes in a river-dominated delta.

Coleman, J.M., Prior, D.B., and Lindsay, J.F., 1983. Deltaic influences of shelf edge instability processes. In Stanley, D.J., and Moore, G.T., eds., The shelfbreak; critical interface on continental margins. Society of Economic Paleontologists and Mineralogists, Special Publication 33, p. 121-137.
This promises to become a standard paper on the subject, based on many year's work on the Mississippi Delta.

Frazier, D.E., 1967. Recent deltaic deposits of the Mississippi River: their development and chronology. Gulf Coast Association of Geological Societies, Transactions, v. 17, p. 287-315.
A classic study of this birdsfoot delta.

Galloway, W.E., 1976. Sediments and stratigraphic framework of the Copper River fan-delta, Alaska. Journal of Sedimentary Petrology, v. 46, p. 726-737.
Brief description of environments and sedimentary processes.

Kolb, C.R. and van Lopik, J.R., 1966. Depositional environments of the Mississippi River deltaic plain – southeastern Louisiana. In Shirley, M.E., ed., Deltas. Houston Geological Society, p. 17-62.
Documents the development of the modern Mississippi delta as a series of overlapping lobes.

McGowen, J.H., 1970 Gum Hollow fan delta, Nueces Bay, Texas. Texas Bureau of Economic Geology, Report of Investigations 69, 91p.
Probably the first thorough study of a modern fan delta.

Oomkens, E., 1970. Depositional sequences and sand distribution in the post-glacial Rhône Delta complex. In Morgan, J.P., ed., Deltaic sedimentation – modern and ancient. Society of Economic Paleontologists and Mineralogists, Special Publication 15, p. 198-212.

Oomkens, E., 1974. Lithofacies relations in the Late Quaternary Niger Delta complex. Sedimentology, v. 21, p. 195-222.

Roberts, H.H., Adams, R.D., and Cunningham, R.H.W., 1980. Evolution of sand-dominant subaerial phase, Atchafalaya Delta. American Association of Petroleum Geologists, Bulletin, v. 364 p. 264-279.

Scruton, 1960. Delta building and the deltaic sequence. In Shepard, F.P., Phleger, F.B., and van Andel, T.H., eds., Recent sediments, northwest Gulf of Mexico. American Association of Petroleum Geologists, p. 82-102.
Recognition of the delta cycle, and what we now term the "clinoform" stratigraphy of deltaic accumulations.

Van Andel, Tj. H., 1967. The Orinoco Delta. Journal of Sedimentary Petrology, v. 37, p. 297-310

Wescott, W.A. and Ethridge, F.G., 1980. Fan-delta sedimentology and tectonic setting – Yallahs fan delta, southeast Jamaica. American Association of Petroleum Geologists, Bulletin, v. 64, p. 374-399.
Erection of a fan-delta depositional systems model.

Wright, L.D., Coleman, J.M., and Erickson, M.W., 1974. Analysis of major river systems and their deltas: morphologic and process comparisons. Baton Rouge, Louisiana, Coastal Studies Institute, Louisiana State University, Technical Report No. 156.
A study of 34 modern alluvial-deltaic systems using multivariate statistical techniques.

SELECTED EXAMPLES OF ANCIENT DELTAS

A) River-Dominated Deltas

Busch, D.A., 1971. Genetic units in delta prospecting. American Association of Petroleum Geologists, Bulletin, v. 55, p. 1137-1154.
Classic example of dendritic shoestring sands.

Collinson, J.D. and Banks, N.L., 1975. The Haslingden Flags (Namurian G_1) of southeast Lancashire; bar-finger sands in the Pennine Basin. Proceedings of the Yorkshire Geological Society, v. 40, p. 431-458.
Bar finger and distributary mouth deposits.

Dixon, J., 1981. Sedimentology of the Eocene Taglu Delta, Beaufort-Mackenzie Basin: example of a river-dominant delta. Geological Survey of Canada, Paper 80-11, 11p.

Edwards, M.B., 1981. Upper Wilcox Rosita delta system of South Texas: growth-faulted shelf-edge deltas. American Association of Petroleum Geologists, Bulletin, v. 65, p. 54-73.

Elliott, T., 1975. The sedimentary history of a delta lobe from a Yoredale (Carboniferous) cyclothem. Proceedings of the Yorkshire Geological Society, v. 40, p. 505-536.
A river-dominated delta, with progradational and abandonment phases.

Fisher, W.L. and McGowen, J.H., 1967. Depositional systems in the Wilcox Group of Texas and their relationship to occurrence of oil and gas. Gulf Coast Association of Geological Societies, Transactions, v. 17, p. 105-125.
A classic subsurface study.

Horne, J.C., Ferm, J.C., Caruccio, F.T., and Baganz, B.P., 1978. Depositional models in coal exploration and mine planning in Appalachian region. American Association of Petroleum Geologists, Bulletin, v. 62, p. 2379-2411.
Use of detailed outcrop studies to construct local facies models. Many good detailed maps and block diagrams of Carboniferous river-dominated deltas.

McCabe, P.J., 1977. Deep distributary channels and giant bedforms in the Upper Carboniferous of the Central Pennines, northern England. Sedimentology, v. 24, p. 271-290.
Giant bar deposits in distributary channels.

Miall, A.D., 1976a. The Triassic sediments of Sturgeon Lake South and adjacent areas. In Lerand, M., ed., The sedimentology of selected clastic oil and gas reservoirs in Alberta, Canadian Society of Petroleum Geologists, p. 25-43.
Subsurface study of river-dominated deltas.

Miall, A.D., 1976b. Sedimentary structures and paleocurrents in a Tertiary deltaic succession, Northern Banks Basin, Arctic Canada. Canadian Journal of Earth Sciences, v. 13, p. 1422-1432.
Facies analysis of a river-dominated delta system. Gross geometry of delta lobes can be outlined from scattered outcrop data.

Wermund, E.G. and Jenkins, W.A., Jr., 1970. Recognition of deltas by fitting trend surfaces to Upper Pennsylvanian sandstones in North-Central Texas. In Morgan, J.P., ed., Deltaic sedimentation – modern and ancient. Society of Economic Paleontologists and Mineralogists, Special Publication 15, p. 256-269.
Use of trend surface analysis to map a distributary sand complex in a major delta.

B) Fan Deltas

Dixon, J., 1979. The Lower Cretaceous Atkinson Point Formation (new name) on the Tuktoyaktuk Peninsula, N.W.T., a coastal fan-delta to marine sequence. Bulletin of Canadian Petroleum Geology, v. 27, p. 163-182.
Subsurface study of a small conglomeratic fan delta.

Dutton, S.P., 1982. Pennsylvanian fan-delta and carbonate deposition, Mobeetie Field, Texas Panhandle. American Association of Petroleum Geologists, Bulletin, v. 66, p. 389-407.

Flores, R.M., 1975. Short-headed stream delta: model for Pennsylvanian Haymond Formation, west Texas. American Association of Petroleum Geologists, Bulletin, v. 59, p. 2288-2301.
A coarse-grained, lobate delta.

Sykes, R.M., and Brand, R.P., 1976. Fan-delta sedimentation: an example from the Late Jurassic-Early Cretaceous of Milne Land, central East Greenland. Geologie en Mijnbouw, v. 55, p. 195-203.

Vos, R.G., 1981a. Sedimentology of an Ordovician fan delta complex, western Libya. Sedimentary Geology, v. 29, p. 153-170.

Wescott, W.A., and Ethridge, F.G., 1983. Eocene fan delta-submarine deposition in the Wagwater trough, east-central Jamaica. Sedimentology, v. 30, p. 235-248.

C) Wave-Influenced Deltas

Hubert, J.F., Butera, J.G., and Rice, R.F., 1972. Sedimentology of Upper Cretaceous Cody-Parkman delta, southwestern Powder River Basin, Wyoming. Geological Society of America, Bulletin, v. 83, p. 1649-1670.
A wave-dominated delta. Detailed paleocurrent studies, including the measurement and interpretation or oriented pillow structures.

Tankard, A.J. and Barwis, J.H., 1982. Wave-dominated deltaic sedimentation in the Devonian Bokkeveld Basin of South Africa. Journal of Sedimentary Petrology, v. 52, p. 959-974.
Alternation of river- and wave-influenced sequences, reflecting repeated transgression and regression.

Vos, R.G., 1981b. Deltaic sedimentation in the Devonian of Western Libya. Sedimentary Geology, v. 29, p. 67-88.
Alternation of river- and wave-influenced sequences.

D) Tide-Influenced Deltas

Clemmensen, L.B., 1976. Tidally influenced deltaic sequences from the Kap Stewart Formation (Rhaetic-Liassic), Scoresby Land, East Greenland. Bulletin of the Geological Society of Denmark, v. 25, p. 1-13.

Erkisson, K.A., 1979. Marginal marine depositional processes from the Archean Moo-dies Group, Barberton Mountain Land, South Africa: evidence and significance. Precambrian Research, v. 8, p. 153-182.
Probably the world's oldest well-described deltaic deposit.

Rahmani, R.A., 1982. Facies relationships and paleoenvironments of a Late Cretaceous tide-dominated delta, Drumheller, Alberta. In Walker R.G., ed., Clastic units of the Front Ranges, Foothills and Plains in the area between Field, B.C. and Drumheller, Alberta. International Association of Sedimentologists, 11th International Congress on Sedimentology (Hamilton, Canada), Excursion 21A, Guidebook, p. 31-60.

Verdier, A.D., Oki, T., and Atik, S., 1980. Geology of the Handil Field (East Kalimantan, Indonesia). In Halbouty, M., ed., Giant oil and gas fields of the decade 1968-1978. American Association of Petroleum Geologists, Memoir 30, p. 399-421.
Comparison of modern tide-dominated delta with ancient oil producing deltaic sediments.

OTHER REFERENCES CITED IN TEXT

Barrell, J., 1912. Criteria for the recognition of ancient delta deposits. Geological Society of America, Bulletin, v. 23, p. 377-446.
Classic paper dealing with the Catskill "delta".

Broussard, M.L., ed., 1975. Deltas, models for exploration. Houston Geological Society, 555 p.
Papers on process variability and delta classification by Galloway and by Coleman and Wright and a historical survey by LeBlanc are the most useful contributions.

Brown, L.F., Jr. and Fisher, W.L., 1977. Seismic stratigraphic interpretation of depositional systems: examples from Brazilian rift and pull-apart basisn. In Payton, C.E., ed., Seismic stratigraphy – applications to hydrocarbon exploration. American Association of Petroleum Geologists, Memoir 26, p. 213-248.
Many examples of deltas and related facies as observed in seismic records. Good discussion of seismic facies.

Curtis, D.M., 1970. Miocene deltaic sedimentation, Louisiana Gulf Coast. In Morgan, J.P., ed., Deltaic sedimentation – modern and ancient. Society of Economic Paleontologists and Mineralogists, Special Publication 15, p. 293-308.

Elliott, T., 1974. Interdistributary bay sequences and their genesis. Sedimentology, v. 21, p. 611-622.
A series of vertical profiles for recognizing some of the minor subenvironments in river-dominated deltas.

Miall, A.D., 1981. Alluvial sedimentary basins: tectonic setting and basin architecture. *In* Miall, A.D., ed., Sedimentation and tectonics in alluvial basins. Geological Association of Canada, Special Paper 23, p. 1-33. Discussion of nine basin-fill architectural models and their relationship to plate tectonic setting.

Morgan, J.P., ed., 1970. Deltaic sedimentation – modern and ancient. Society of Economic Paleontologists and Mineralogists, Special Publication 15. A somewhat mixed bag of papers, but including much data unavailable elsewhere.

Shepard, F.P., Phleger, F.B., and van Andel, T.H., eds., 1960. Recent sediments, Northwest Gulf of Mexico, 1951-1958. American Association of Petroleum Geologists, 394 p.

Shirley, M.L. and Ragsdale, J.A., eds., 1966. Deltas in their geologic framework. Houston Geological Society, 251 p. Now rather dated, but containing much useful information.

Winker, C.D. and Edwards, M.B., 1983. Unstable progradational clastic shelf margins. *In* Stanley, D.J., and Moore, G.T., eds., The shelfbreak: critical interface on continental margins. Society of Economic Paleontologists and Mineralogists, Special Publication 33, p. 139-157. An excellent up to date paper on the extensional deformation (including growth faulting) associated with major deltas, based on a wealth of subsurface data.

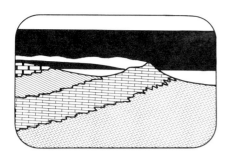

Barrier-Island and Associated Strand-Plain Systems

G.E. REINSON
*Consulting Geologist
180 Cornwall Dr., N.W.
Calgary, Alberta T2K 1V2*

INTRODUCTION

Depositional Setting
Wave-dominated sandy shorelines in interdeltaic and non-deltaic coastal regions are characterized by elongate, shore-parallel sand deposits. These can occur as a single mainland-attached beach, a broader beach-ridge strand plain consisting of multiple parallel beach ridges and intervening swale zones or as barrier islands partially- or wholly-separated from the mainland by a lagoon, estuary or marsh (Fig. 1). Barrier islands are transitional in character to strand plains. For example, barrier islands can consist of a single active barrier beach (transgressive barrier, Fig. 1d), or a series of parallel beach ridges and swales situated behind the active beach shoreline (regressive or progradational barrier, Fig. 1c). The regressive barrier is similar to the classical beach-ridge strand plain (Fig. 1b), but the latter is much wider and connected to the mainland, lacking extensive enclosed lagoonal or tidal inlet - channel environments. Because of the close genetic relationship of prograding barriers and strand plains, it is apparent that certain of the facies sequences encountered in barrier-island deposits will also be applicable to strand plains.

This review paper concentrates on barrier-island systems and related strand-plain deposits. Deltas, estuaries, tidal flats, and chenier plains are other coastal depositional environments that can occur associated with, or in proximity to, strand plains and barrier-island settings. Deltas are reviewed elsewhere in this volume, and the reader is also referred to excellent reviews by Elliott (1978) who covers the broad spectrum of non-deltaic clastic shorelines, and Heward (1981), who discusses all wave-dominated clastic shoreline deposits. Estuarine and tidal-flat deposits are covered by both Scholle and Spearing (1982) and Davis (1983).

There are three major geomorphic elements in a barrier-island system (Fig. 2): 1) the sandy barrier-island chain itself, 2) the enclosed body of water behind it (lagoon or estuary) and, 3) the channels which cut through the barrier and connect the lagoon to the open sea (tidal inlets). This tripartite geomorphic framework clearly demonstrates that barrier-island systems are composites of three major clastic depositional environments: 1) the subtidal to sub-aerial barrier-beach complex, 2) the back-barrier region or subtidal-intertidal lagoon, and 3) the subtidal-intertidal delta and inlet-channel complex (Fig. 3). In strand-plain settings the subaerial barrier-beach complex would be the dominant depositional environment, whereas in baymouth-barrier systems, subtidal lagoonal-estuarine and tidal delta-channel environments would be most prevalent. Thus the barrier-island and related strand-plain system should be viewed as a composite depositional

Figure 1
Generalized diagram illustrating the morphological relationship between beaches, strand plains and barrier islands.

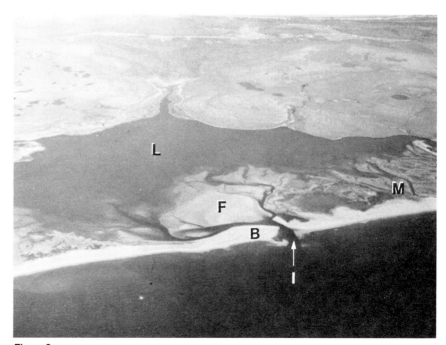

Figure 2
Oblique aerial view of a small barrier-island system on the northeast coast of New Brunswick, showing the linear barrier-beach (B), the tidal inlet (I) through the barrier, and the lagoon (L) behind the barrier. Note the flood-tidal delta (F) and the back-barrier marsh (M) developed on abandoned delta deposits. Photo taken in September, 1980.

120

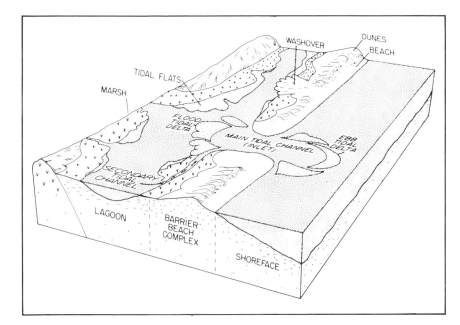

Figure 3
Block diagram illustrating the various subenvironments in a barrier-island system.

system, with specific systems displaying a combination of the three environments, within the broad spectrum of depositional settings ranging from barrier island (Fig. 1d) to strand plain (Fig. 1b).

The notion that the barrier-island system can be a composite depositional system, and not just a prograding barrier-beach complex, was not fully appreciated by geologists until very recently. This lack of appreciation is evident in most of the pre-1970 literature where there was an overwhelming preference for the use of just one barrier-island model (prograding Galveston Island model) for interpreting ancient rocks. Indeed, Heward (1981) considers that the barrier-island depositional model, in general, has been overused as an ancient analog. Possibly, this is a reflection of the dependence on the prograding barrier-beach model, which has been heretofore adopted as "the" norm. If one recognizes the barrier-beach, lagoon, and tidal channel – delta scenario, it should be obvious that a single model for such a complex system is completely unrealistic. Fortunately, within the last 15 years there has been a renaissance in the interpretation of ancient barrier-island sequences. This has come about largely through the investigations of modern barrier-island systems by numerous workers including M.O. Hayes and J.C. Kraft (Hayes

and Kana, 1976; Kraft, 1971, 1978; Leatherman, 1979). Because of these modern studies we are now recognizing that the prograding barrier-beach sequence (i.e., Galveston Island) is just one of at least three distinct stratigraphic models.

Basis for Models
The objective of this review is an attempt to synthesize the various facies sequences encountered in barrier-island systems into three "end-member" sequences, or depositional models, for use in interpreting ancient rocks. Our ideas on ancient barrier-island deposits in the geological record, and for that matter on most wave-dominated clastic shoreline deposits, stem from the study of modern systems. Consequently the review draws heavily on examples of modern deposits to develop the "end-member" models. There are drawbacks to the models (discussed later), because any distillation of a complex depositional system into three basic models can lead to oversimplification. However, the purpose of facies analysis in sedimentology is to simplify, in order to "distinguish the forest from the trees", so to speak. The models are meant to be used as a comparative tool to guide our interpretations of specific ancient sequences, and as a predictive tool for projecting three-dimensional rock body geometries, and geometric relationships

of different lithofacies. This is particularly important where we only have access to limited data, such as in isolated vertical outcrops, or in the subsurface where specific borehole-obtained facies sequences are two-dimensional.

ORIGIN AND OCCURRENCE
Theories regarding the origin of barrier islands have been reviewed at length in the recent geological literature (Schwartz, 1973; Swift, 1975; Wanless, 1976; Field and Duane, 1976; Halsey, 1979). The question of origin is controversial but there are three main hypotheses: 1) the building-up of submarine bars; 2) spit progradation parallel to the coast and segmentation by inlets; and 3) submergence of coastal beach ridges. The controversy remains largely unresolved because most of the evidence pertaining to origin has usually been destroyed by subsequent modification. Extensive modification and evolution of modern barrier islands has been occurring since the early Holocene through a combination of processes including inlet cut and fill, washover deposition, and longshore transport (Field and Duane, 1976). These processes have been enhanced by the progressive landward retreat of the barrier islands in response to the Holocene transgression (Swift, 1975).

Swift (1975) and Field and Duane (1976) consider that barrier formation by offshore bar emergence is insignificant compared to the other two mechanisms. Swift (1975) favors submergence of mainland beach ridges as the most important mode of formation. Considering the trend of sea level rise throughout the Holocene, it is certainly the most feasible mechanism for explaining the evolution, if not the initial origin, of most of the extensive barrier-island regions existing today. However, spit progradation parallel to the coast cannot be completely dismissed as a significant mode of origin, because it is also readily observed to be initiating, as well as modifying, barriers at the present time. Many extensive barrier-island chains of the present day probably have had a composite mode of origin, by both spit progradation and coastal submergence. Variations in sediment supply and wave climate could easily induce periodic spit progradation in specific localities while submergence of coastal ridges was occurring on a more regional scale.

Barrier islands and strand plains are more prevalent in coastal settings which have the following characteristics: 1) a low-gradient continental shelf adjacent to a low-relief coastal plain, 2) an abundant sediment supply, and 3) moderate to low tidal ranges (Glaeser, 1978). Both the shelf and the coastal plain are composed of unconsolidated sediments, which are the material source for the building of barrier islands by nearshore processes. Glaeser noted that only ten per cent of the world's barrier islands are present along coastlines where tidal ranges exceed three metres. However, it was Hayes (1975, 1979) who focused attention on the importance of tidal range in controlling the occurrence and morphology of barrier-island and related strand-plain systems. Hayes observed not only that barrier islands were rare on macrotidal coastlines (greater than 4 m tidal range), but that there were geomorphological differences between barrier islands of microtidal regions (less than 2 m tidal range) and those of mesotidal regions (2 to 4 m tidal range). In general microtidal barrier islands are long and linear with extensive storm washover features (Fig. 4), and tidal inlets and deltas are of relatively minor importance. Mesotidal barrier islands are short and stunted, and characterized by large tidal inlets and deltas. Microtidal barriers are overwashed frequently by storm waves because of the lack of large enough tidal inlets to allow storm surges to flow past the barrier, rather than overtopping it. According to Hayes, microtidal barrier islands can be considered to be wave dominated as opposed to mesotidal barriers which are affected by both wave and current processes.

DEPOSITIONAL ENVIRONMENTS AND LITHOFACIES

The three main environments of a barrier-island system (barrier beach, lagoon, tidal channel – delta complex) are made up of a number of subenvironments (Fig. 3), each of which is characterized by distinct lithofacies. Facies of the barrier-beach and channel-delta environments are mainly sand and gravel, whereas the lagoonal (back-barrier) deposits can consist of both mud and sand. Barrier-beach deposits are elongate bodies which parallel the strandline and enclose finer-grained

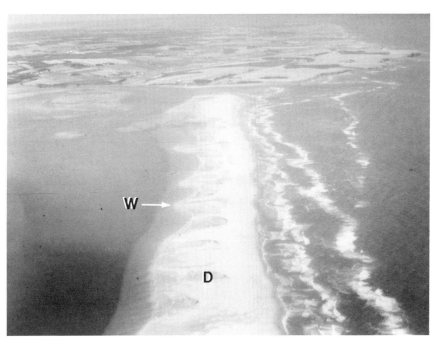

Figure 4
Oblique aerial photo of the barrier beach at Cavendish, Prince Edward Island, Canada, illustrating lobate washover fan deposits (W) extending into the lagoon. The dune ridge (D) is dissected by many washover channels.
Note the occurrence of a dual bar system (delineated by the zones of breaking waves) in the nearshore zone. This is a microtidal area, with a tidal range of about 0.7 m. Photo taken in September, 1980.

deposits of the lagoon. Tidal-channel and delta sand deposits, on the other hand, are generally oriented perpendicular or oblique to the barrier complex, and can extend into the lagoon and seaward into the nearshore zone. The transition between lagoon deposits and barrier and channel-delta deposits occurs in the overlapping subenvironments of the back-barrier tidal flats, marsh, washover fans and flood-tidal deltas.

The lateral and vertical extent and the occurrence of specific facies with a barrier-island system is dependent upon tidal range and the relative importance of tidal-current versus wave-generated processes, as discussed previously. For example, tidal-flat deposits will not be an important facies in microtidal environments because of the limited tidal range, whereas they may be extensive in mesotidal environments. Similarly, tidal channel and delta deposits are likely to be more prevalent in mesotidal than in microtidal environments because of the stronger tidal currents generated by the larger tidal range. The following discussion covers all the depositional environments and corresponding deposits of barrier-island

systems and beach-ridge strand plains. It should be remembered that all facies will not necessarily be present in every barrier-island deposit, and that the strand-plain system will be dominated by facies of the barrier-beach complex (e.g., Curray *et al.,* 1969).

Barrier Beach and Related Facies
The depositional subenvironments of a barrier-beach complex include: 1) the subtidal zone or *shoreface,* 2) the intertidal zone or *beach (foreshore),* 3) the subaerial zone or *back shore - dune* landward of the beachface and, 4) the supratidal to subaerial wave- and wind-formed *washover* flats which extend across the barrier into the lagoon (Figs. 3 and 5). Shoreface deposits are discussed with the barrier-beach complex because they form the foundation for the barrier and also are a major source of sediment for barrier-island accretion.

Shoreface Deposits. The shoreface environment is defined as the area seaward of the barrier from low tide mark to a depth of about 10 to 20 m (Fig. 5). The lower limits of the shoreface correspond to fairweather wave base, that is, the position at which normal waves begin to

122

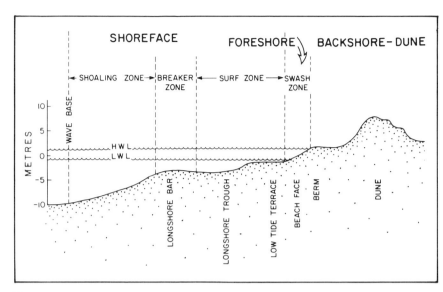

Figure 5
Generalized profile of the barrier beach and shoreface environments.

affect the sea bed. Hence the shoreface is an environment in which depositional processes are governed by wave energy. The amount of wave energy dissipated on the bottom decreases with increased water depth, and this inverse relationship governs the range of textures and sedimentary structures observed in shoreface deposits.

The shoreface is usually divided into three interrelated zones whose boundaries are not oftern sharply-defined. These zones are termed 'lower', 'middle' and 'upper' in some studies, and 'transi-

tional', 'lower' and 'upper' in others. The former division, adhered to in this review, was generally utilized until very recently, in studies of both modern and ancient deposits. For examples of the recent trends, compare the zonal divisions of Howard (1972) with those of Howard and Reineck (1981), and the interpretation of the Galveston borehole sequence in Figure 12 with that of McCubbin (1982, Fig. 22). This inconsistency in terminology may reflect the findings of some recent studies, which suggest that the shoreface environment

and resultant deposits can be much more variable than realized previously (this is discussed further in a later section).

Lower shoreface deposits occur seaward of the break in the shoreface slope at the toe of the barrier-island sediment prism. Under normal conditions, the lower shoreface is a relatively low-energy transitional zone, where waves begin to affect the bottom, but where offshore shelf or basinal depositional processes also occur. This is reflected in the sediments which consist generally of very fine to fine-grained sands with intercalated layers of silt and sandy mud. Physical sedimentary structures include mainly planar laminated beds, which are often almost completely obliterated by bioturbation. Trace-fossil assemblages are abundant in lower shoreface sediments (see "Trace Fossil Facies Models", this volume; Howard, 1972).

Middle shoreface deposits extend over the zone of shoaling and breaking waves. This zone is subjected to high wave energy relative to the lower shoreface and is characterized generally by one or more longshore bars (Fig. 4). The occurrence of longshore bars is related to a low-gradient shoreface and abundant sediment supply (Davis, 1978); both these conditions favor the landward movement and build-up of linear sand bars by shoaling and breaking waves.

Middle shoreface deposits can be highly variable in terms of sedimentary structures and textures, depending on whether nearshore bars are present or absent (Hunter *et al.*, 1979). Generally fine- to medium-grained, clean sands predominate, with minor amounts of silt and shell layers. Depositional structures include low-angle wedge-shaped sets of planar laminae, but ripple laminae and trough cross laminae are common (Campbell, 1971; Howard, 1972; Land, 1972). Middle shoreface deposits may be extensively bioturbated (Fig. 6), especially in the lower parts, but the biogenic structures are generally less diverse than in deposits of the lower shoreface (see "Trace Fossil Facies Models", this volume; and Howard, 1972). The model proposed by Davidson-Arnott and Greenwood (1976) illustrates the complexity of sedimentary structures that can occur in a barred nearshore zone (Fig. 7). Vertical

Figure 6
Alternating laminated-to-burrowed (Ophiomorpha) beds in lower to middle shoreface

deposits of the Upper Cretaceous Blood Reserve Sandstone, southern Alberta (photo courtesy of Monti Lerand).

rock sequences of such deposits could display interbedded sets of landward dipping ripple cross lamination, seaward dipping low-angle plane bedding, subhorizontal plane laminations and both landward- and seaward-dipping trough cross-bedded sets.

The shoreface environment is subjected to extreme modification by storm processes because effective wave base can be lowered dramatically by larger than normal, storm-generated waves. Under such conditions high amplitude waves can scour the bottom, suspending and then redepositing the sediment farther seaward as the storm wanes. Storm-generated deposits in modern shoreface settings have been documented by Hayes (1967), Reineck and Singh (1972), Kumar and Sanders (1976), Howard and Reineck (1981), and Nelson (1982). It is now thought that storm-related deposits may constitute much of the ancient record of inner shelf to middle shoreface environments. Hummocky cross-stratified sandstones, considered to form under the influence of storm waves (see "Shelf and Shallow Marine Sands", this volume), have been documented in many ancient deposits. They can occur as thick amalgamated, truncated laminar bedsets, in alternating beds with truncated and bioturbated zones, or in thin interbedded association with fine-grained sediments (e.g., Howard, 1972; Goldring and Bridges, 1973; McCubbin, 1982; Leckie and Walker, 1982).

Upper shoreface sediments are closely associated with foreshore deposits, because they are situated in the high energy surf zone just seaward of the beachface and landward of the breaker zone (Fig. 5). Consequently they have been grouped with foreshore facies in some rock studies (e.g., Davies et al., 1971), but have been considered to represent the shoreface-foreshore transition zone in others (Howard, 1982). The complex hydraulic environment of the surf zone, with shore-normal currents generated by plunging waves superimposed on shore-parallel wave-driven currents, gives rise to the complex sequence of multidirecitonal sedimentary structures and variable sediment textures characteristic of these deposits. Textures range from fine sand to gravel, and biogenic structures are common but not abundant. The predominant upper shoreface deposi-

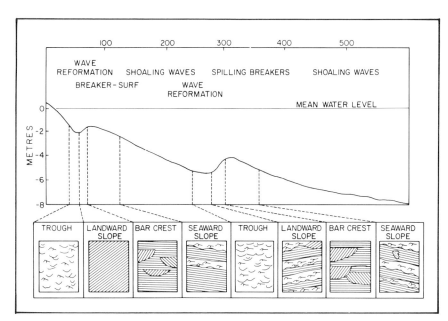

Figure 7
Model of nearshore bars in Kouchibouguac Bay, New Brunswick, Canada, illustrating characteristic sedimentary structures and wave transformation zones (from Davidson-Arnott and Greenwood, 1976).

tional structures are multidirectional trough cross-bed sets (15 to 45 cm thick) (Fig. 8), but low-angle bidirectional planar cross-bedded sets and subhorizontal plane beds may also be present. The trough cross-beds are thought to indicate the multidirectional current flow in the surf zone (Clifton et al., 1971; Carter, 1978). Predominantly bidirectional trough cross-beds oriented parallel to depositional strike are common in upper shoreface deposits, and may be indicative of deposition under strong longshore current conditions.

The effects of storm activity or seasonal changes in wave energy, are reflected in the beach-nearshore profile, and also can be recorded in the resultant deposits. For example, the ridge and runnel sequence depicted in Figure 9 may result when storm waves erode the beachface, removing sediment to the shoreface. The sediment is returned to the beach during the post-storm recovery, in the form of a ridge and runnel (bar and trough), which develops on the low tide terrace just seaward of the foreshore (Davis et al., 1972; Owens and Frobel, 1977). The ridge migrates shoreward eventually welding onto the beachface and creating a distinctive sequence of upper shoreface - foreshore deposits.

Foreshore Deposits. The foreshore environment is confined to the intertidal

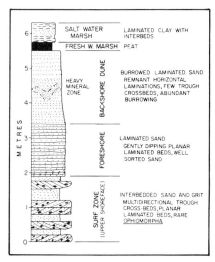

Figure 8
Generalized barrier sequence in the Upper Tertiary Cohansey Sand of New Jersey (modified from Carter, 1978).

zone, which is usually marked by a sharp change in slope, both at the base and at the top of the beachface (Fig. 5). The foreshore is the zone of wave swash, the surge of water caused by incoming plunging breakers in the surf zone. Swash runup occurs with each wave surge and backwash runoff between each surge. The swash-backwash mechanism is mainly responsible for the distinct subparallel to low-angle, seaward-dipping, planar laminations which occur as wedge-shaped sets in most beach deposits.

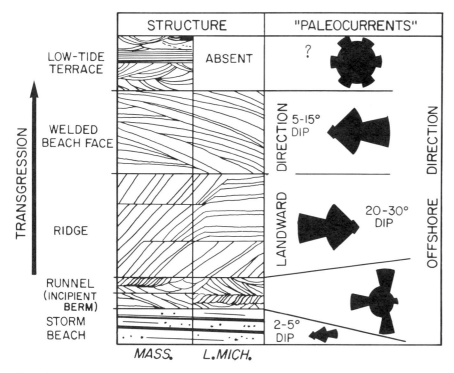

Figure 9

Transgressive sequence formed by the landward migration of ridge-and-runnel during beach constructional phase. Vertical sequence would be about 1 m thick (from

Davis et al., 1972). Note the similarity between the Massachusetts and Lake Michigan sequences, both occurring as the result of post-storm recovery.

Figure 10

Horizontal, parallel-laminated fine-grained sandstone beds of the beach (foreshore) facies, Blood Reserve Sandstone, southern

Alberta. Bedding-plane partings are from 10 to 20 cm apart (photo courtesy of Monti Lerand).

The boundaries between sets are generally not truncated, but rather mark the changing slope of the prograding beachface during the accretionary phase. Examples of foreshore deposits in the rock record include those illustrated in Figures 8 and 10, and those proposed by Campbell (1971), Howard (1982), Davies *et al.* (1971), Land (1972), Hamblin and Walker (1979), and Cotter (1983).

Backshore-Dune Deposits. The backshore-dune environment is characterized by subaerial, predominantly wind-generated depositional processes. The backshore seaward of the dunes is a flat-lying to landward-sloping area called the berm; the seaward limit, called the berm crest, is well defined by the marked change in slope at the top of the beachface (Fig. 5). Sediment is transported to the berm crest by high spring tides or storms and is distributed over the backshore area by winds and washover (discussed below). Subhorizontal to landward-dipping plane beds characterize the backshore (Fig. 11) and may be interbedded or overlain by small to medium-scale trough cross-beds of incipient dune origin. Trough cross-stratified sets, up to 2 m in thickness, are characteristic of dune deposits, but planar cross-stratified sets are also common. The trough cross-strata may be multidirectional in orientation and bounded by curved bedding surfaces (Campbell, 1971). Dune beds are commonly extensively disturbed by root growth (Figs. 11 and 12) and may contain small paleosol horizons and isolated organic debris. Other biogenic structures such as decapod burrows may also occur in backshore-foredune deposits (Fig. 8).

Washover Deposits. Washover deposits result when wind-generated storm surges overtop and cut through barriers, creating lobate or sheet deposits of sand which extend into the lagoon (Figs. 3 and 4). These washover flats then provide corridors for transferring wind-transported sand across the foredune belt to form back-barrier sand flats (Fig. 11). This mechanism increases the width of the barrier, providing environments favorable for stabilization by marsh growth.

Modern studies of washover deposits indicate that there are two dominant

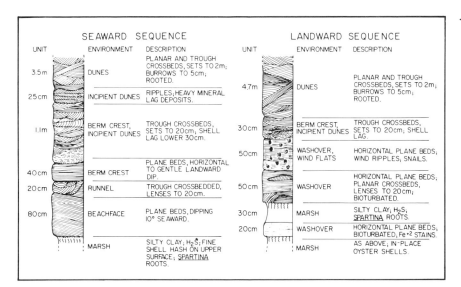

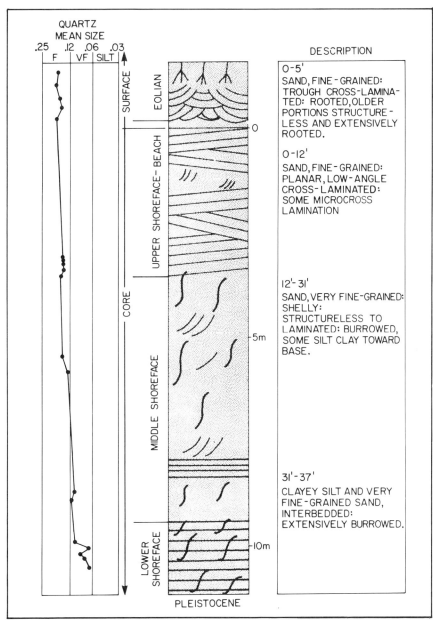

sedimentary structures, subhorizontal (planar) stratification, and small to medium-scale delta foreset strata where the washover detritus protrudes into the lagoon (Fig. 13). Textural and heavy mineral laminations and graded bedding can also occur (Andrews, 1970; Schwartz, 1982) depending on the nature of the source material. Textures may range from fine sand to gravel, but generally fine- to medium-grained sand forms the bulk of washover deposits. Washover deposits are generally thin, ranging from a few centimetres to two metres for each overwash event. In plan, they form elongate, semi-circular, sheet-like or tabular bodies a few hundred metres in width and oriented normal to the shoreline (Fig. 4). Coalescing washover fans can be in the order of kilometres in width, creating extensive washover flats which cover large tracts of the barrier.

Recent studies on modern barrier-island systems have illustrated that washover deposits form a significant portion of barrier sand bodies, especially in microtidal regions. Under transgressing conditions washover is one of the main processes by which the barrier island migrates landward, and scouring associated with washover is probably one of the main mechanisms responsible for the initiation of new tidal inlets. It is likely that washover deposits are more prevalent in ancient barrier sequences than has been recognized to date. Examples of ancient washover deposits include those documented by Bridges (1976), Horne and Ferm (1978), Hobday and Tankard (1978), and Hobday and Jackson (1979).

Tidal Channel (Inlet) and Tidal-Delta Facies

Tidal channel and tidal-delta sand bodies are intricately associated facies both with respect to their close proximity to one another, and with regard to

126

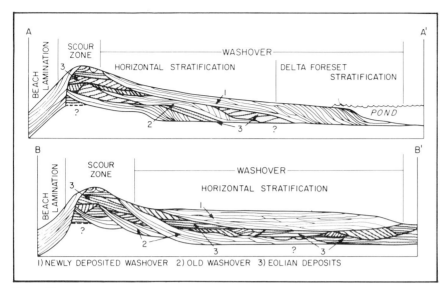

Figure 13

Schematic cross-sections through two washover fans showing sequences of sedimentary structures. A "transgressive" situation is depicted. The sedimentary structures represent the upper few metres or less of the sand-body.

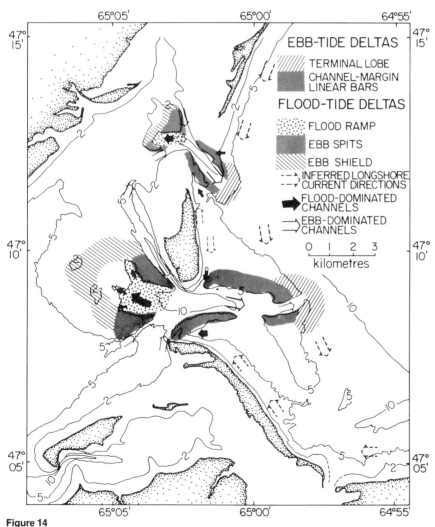

Figure 14

Morphology of tidal deltas and inferred tidal- and longshore-current patterns at the mouth of the Miramichi estuary, New Brunswick (from Reinson, 1977).

their internal sedimentary structures and textures. This is because their formation is governed primarily by tidal-current processes directed normal or oblique to the sand barrier. The *ebb-tidal delta,* the sand accumulation formed seaward of the barrier by ebb-tidal currents, is affected by longshore and wave-generated currents, whereas the *flood-tidal delta,* the sand body deposited landward of the barrier by flood-tidal currents, is little influenced by wave and wind-generated processes (Figs. 3 and 14).

There are two types of tidal-channel environments, the main channels, or tidal inlets connecting the lagoon to the ocean, and the secondary channels located adjacent to the tidal deltas and back barrier lagoon margins. Secondary tidal channels are sometimes so closely related to the formation of tidal delta complexes that the resultant facies are difficult to differentiate. Tidal channel and tidal delta deposits are separated here mainly for ease in discussion. However, this separation serves also to emphasize the fact that channel facies can occur independent of tidal deltas, whereas the occurrence of tidal delta facies is dependent on the presence of tidal channels.

Tidal Channel Deposits. Tidal channel deposits form mainly by lateral migration, as in a meander bend in a river. The best known and most important channel deposits are tidal-inlet fill sequences, which result from the shore-parallel migration of tidal inlets (Fig. 15). The direction and rate of inlet-channel migration is controlled by the magnitude of net longshore sediment supply. Barrier extension occurs by spit accretion on the updrift side of an inlet, with a corresponding erosion of the downdrift channel margin (Fig. 16). The shifting of the main inlet through a barrier causes the tidal channels both landward and seaward of the barrier, and the tidal deltas, to shift position also. The sand body that is deposited by inlet migration will be elongated parallel to the barrier island, having a length equal to the distance the inlet has migrated (Fig. 16). The thickness of the inlet lithosome will be equal to the depth of the inlet, if no subsequent erosion of the upper boundary occurs during deposition of dune, beach and washover deposits of the overlying accreting barrier.

The studies of Land (1972), Kumar and Sanders (1974), Hubbard and Barwis (1976), Barwis and Makurath (1978), Carter (1978), and Hayes (1980), indicate that channel-fill sequences resulting from barrier-inlet (or tidal channel) migration have the following general characteristics: 1) an erosional base often marked by a coarse lag deposit; 2) a deep channel facies consisting of bidirectional large-scale planar and/or medium-scale trough cross-beds; 3) a shallow channel facies consisting of bidirectional small to medium-scale trough cross-beds and/or plane-beds and "washed out" ripple laminae; and 4) a fining-upward textural trend and a thinning upward of cross-bed set thickness. The difference in size, orientation and type of sedimentary structures in the deep channel and shallow channel deposits generally reflects an increase in current-flow conditions in the shallow channel relative to the deep-channel environment.

The modern inlet-fill sequence (Fig. 15) described by Kumar and Sanders (1974) has a deep channel facies characterized by ebb-oriented planar cross-laminae; this reflects the predominance of sand-wave bedforms deposited under lower flow regime conditions in an ebb-current dominated environment. The overlying shallow channel facies is characterized by plane-parallel laminae and "washed-out" ripple laminae, reflecting plane bed depositon under "transitional" or upper flow regime conditions.

The studies of Barwis and Makurath (1978) and Land (1972) serve as comparative rock analogs to the Fire Island Inlet deposits (Fig. 15). The Silurian inlet sequence of Barwis and Makurath consists of a channel lag deposit overlain by 4.1 m of bidirectional trough and planar cross-bedded, medium-grained sandstone, with set thickness averaging 15 cm. The cross-bed orientations reflect deposition under tidal-current transport reversals along an axis oblique to the paleostrand. This deep channel facies is overlain gradationally by a fine-grained sandstone unit (1.8 m thick) dominated by bidirectional trough cross-bed sets averaging 2.5 cm in thickness, and "washed-out" ripples. The tidal channel sequence described by Land (1972) averages 8 m in thickness and consists of bimodal to polymodal trough cross-bed sets (ranging from 10 cm to 90 cm

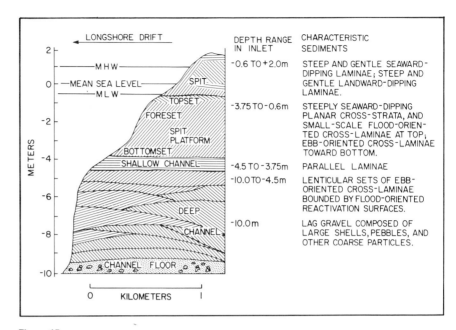

Figure 15
Vertical sequence of sedimentary structures formed by the migration of Fire Island Inlet, *New York (modified from Kumar and Sanders, 1974).*

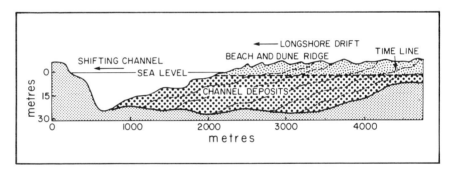

Figure 16
Generalized cross-section parallel to shoreline illustrating the development of a barrier- *inlet sand body by lateral inlet migration (modified from Hoyt and Henry, 1965).*

in thickness) in the lower 5 to 6 m, and subparallel beds in the upper 2 to 3 m.

The hypothetical tidal-inlet sequences proposed by Hayes (1980), and by Hubbard and Barwis (1976), based on their study of mesotidal inlets of South Carolina, differ slightly from the Kumar and Sanders model (Fig. 15) with regard to the vertical sequence of sedimentary structures. However, the inference of sequential deposition under increasing flow conditions is still evident. Their inlet sequence is as follows: 1) a basal lag or disconformable bottom; 2) a deep channel deposit consisting of bidirectional large-scale planar cross-beds that have a slight seaward dominance, interlayered with bidirectional medium-scale trough cross-beds; and 3) a shallow

channel deposit consisting predominantly of small to medium-scale bidirectional trough cross-beds. The planar cross-beds are suggestive of sand-wave deposition under ebb-dominant channel flow, whereas the trough cross-beds record deposition as megaripples under stronger currents and alternating reversals of flow directions.

Rock sequences similar to the hypothetical inlet sequences of Hayes (1980) and Hubbard and Barwis (1976) are illustrated in Figures 17 and 18. Carter (1978) interprets the sequence in Figure 17 as a back-barrier tidal channel deposit, because the presence of the interbedded sand and clay facies seems to preclude an inlet-fill origin. This example illustrates the similarity between

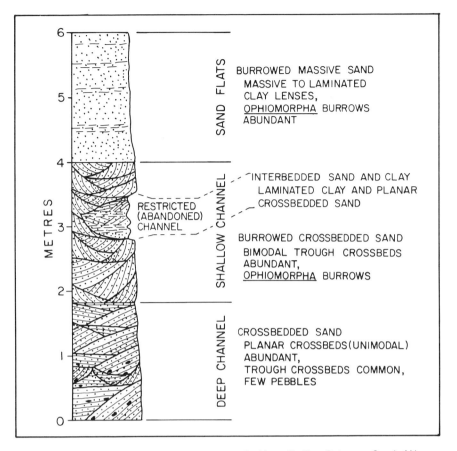

Figure 17
Generalized barrier-protected sequence in the Upper Tertiary Cohansey Sand of New Jersey (modified from Carter, 1978).

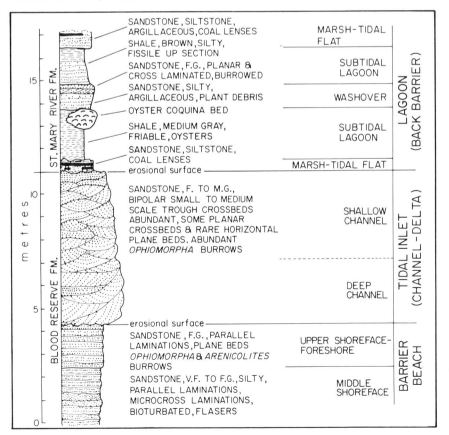

back-barrier tidal channel deposits and tidal inlet deposits, and also points to a similar mode of origin; that of lateral channel migration concomitant with barrier-inlet migration. The tidal channel sequence in Figure 17 could also be interpreted as part of a flood-tidal delta complex, and the reasons for this alternate hypothesis will become evident in the following discussion on tidal delta deposits.

Tidal Delta Deposits. Hayes (1975) recognized from his work in New England and Alaska, that tidal deltas display a common morphological pattern governed by segregated zones of ebb and flood flow. This recognition prompted him to propose generalized models for both ebb- and flood-tidal delta deposition. Subsequent studies by Hayes and co-workers (Hayes and Kana, 1976) and others (Reinson, 1977; Armon, 1980), indicate that the models are generally applicable elsewhere, in both microtidal and mesotidal regions. Tidal deltas can occur in a variety of forms (from linear shoals to complex channel-shoal systems) depending on tidal range, wave climate, and sediment supply, but the basic morphological pattern as illustrated in Figure 14 is generally clearly evident.

The typical morphology of a flood-tidal delta, that of a seaward-opening parabola bounded by marginal channels, is related to the segregation of tidal-current flow paths during ebb and flood phases. This flow segregation results from the time-velocity asymmetry of the tidal currents; that is, maximum flood and ebb flows occur near high water and low water respectively. Maximum flood flow traverses through the flood ramp and over the shoal, whereas maximum ebb flow is diverted around the shoal because of the drop in water level. This flow segregation gives rise to a distinct pattern of bedform distribution (Boothroyd and Hubbard, 1975; Hubbard and Barwis, 1976; Reinson, 1979), with predominantly flood-oriented sand waves covering the flood ramp and centre of the shoal, bidirectional megaripples on the ebb-

◄ **Figure 18**
Composite stratigraphic section of the Upper Cretaceous Blood Reserve - St. Mary River Formations, southern Alberta (modified from Young and Reinson, 1975).

shield and ebb spits, and ebb-oriented sand waves in the adjacent channels.

The deposits resulting from flood-tidal delta formation will be characterized by a varied sequence of planar cross-beds and trough cross-beds. The preponderance of one bedform over the other, and their orientation and position in vertical sequence, will depend on the locality at which the sequence is located within the tidal-delta complex. Hubbard and Barwis (1976) proposed a lithologic sequence for a flood-tidal delta as follows: 1) basal bidirectional cross-strata (megaripples), which represent early phases of deposition; 2) interbedded seaward-oriented trough cross-strata (megaripples) and landward-oriented planar cross-beds (sand waves), which represent deposition prior to ebb-shield development; and 3) landward-oriented planar cross-strata with upward-decreasing set thickness (sand waves), which represent deposition on the flood ramp. Deposits adjacent to this sequence would be characterized by bi-directional trough cross-strata (mega-ripples), representing ebb-shield and ebb-spit deposition. The total thickness of such a sequence would be in the order of 10 m. Hayes (1980) proposed a stratigraphic sequence for a regressive flood-tidal delta situation (Fig. 19). This sequence is dominated by planar bidirectional cross-strata.

The morphology of ebb-tidal deltas is controlled largely by tidal-current segregation during different phases of the tidal cycle, but the interaction of waves with tidal currents is also important in the formation of ebb deltas. This interaction is reflected in the complex bedform distribution, which consists of ebb-oriented sand waves or megaripples in the main ebb-channel, with flood-oriented sand waves or megaripples in the marginal flood channels (Fig. 14). Channel-margin, linear bars and swash bars (areas of intense wave and current interaction) are characterized by multi-directional megaripples and plane beds. As in flood deltas, the vertical sequences resulting from ebb-delta formation would exhibit extreme variations in sedimentary structures from one locality to another, within a specific ebb-delta deposit. Ebb-delta deposits are so dependent on inlet conditions and wave climate that it is impossible to characterize them in a specific sequence. Perhaps the major

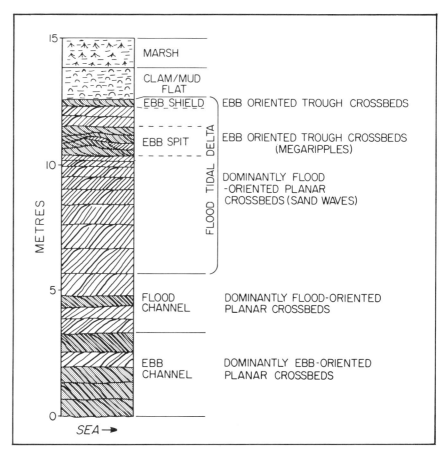

Figure 19
Hypothetical regressive sequence for a *mesotidal flood-tidal delta complex (modified from Hayes, 1980).*

difference between ebb-tidal delta deposits and flood-delta deposits is the occurrence of multi-directional cross beds in ebb delta sequences, as opposed to the predominantly flood-oriented or bidirectional cross-beds of flood-tidal delta sequences.

As mentioned earlier, flood- and ebb-delta deposits have textures and sedimentary structures similar to inlet fill sequences, and therefore the identification of delta sand bodies in the rock record may depend largely on their geometry and stratigraphic position relative to surrounding facies. In modern barrier systems, tidal inlet - delta associated deposits are intergral parts of barrier-island sand bodies. By analogy such deposits should be expected to occur in ancient barrier sequences, yet they have been little recognized up until very recently. The studies of Barwis and Makurath (1978), Horne and Ferm (1978), Hobday and Tankard (1978) and Land (1972) amply illustrate the importance of channel-delta deposits in ancient barrier sequences, and also lead

one to suspect that such deposits have been misinterpreted in many rock sequences in the past.

Lagoonal (Back Barrier) Facies
Lagoonal sequences generally consist of interbedded and interfingering sandstone, shale, silstone and coal facies characteristic of a number of overlapping subenvironments (Figs. 18 and 10). Sand facies include *washover* sheet deposits and sheet and channel-fill deposits of *flood-tidal delta* origin. Fine-grained facies include those of the *subaqueous lagoon* and the *tidal flats,* which are situated adjacent to the barrier or on the landward side of the lagoon abutting the hinterland marsh and swamp flatland (Fig. 3). Organic deposits of coal and peat record *marsh* and *swamp* environments, and usually are very thin, having formed on sand and mud flats of the logoonal margin, and on emergent washover flats. Abandoned or mature flood-tidal deltas can also become stabilized by marsh vegetation. This situation and that of the vege-

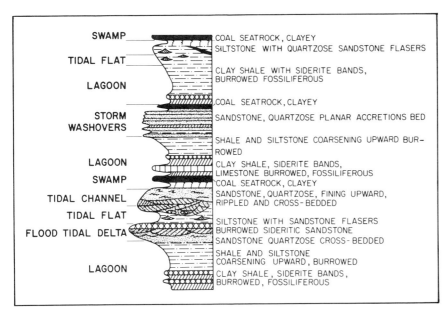

Figure 20
Generalized lagoonal sequence through back-barrier deposits in the Carboniferous of eastern Kentucky and southern West Virginia. Such sequences range from 7.5 to 24 m thick (from Horne and Ferm, 1978).

Figure 21
Photo showing the sharp contrast between the clean sandstones of the Upper Cretaceous Blood Reserve Formation and the overlying finer-grained lagoonal deposits of the St. Mary River Formation, southern Alberta.

tated washover flat can lead to the presence of very thin coal lenses overlying organic-rich sheet sandstones in the rock record (Fig. 20). Subaqueous shale and siltsone facies are often characterized by brackish water macroinvertebrate shells, and in Cretaceous lagoonal deposits, coquinid oyster beds up to 1 m thick are common (Fig. 18; and Land, 1972). Disseminated carbonaceous material, imprints of plant remains, and root and reed fragments are common in some shale beds, indicating the interfingering of proximal marsh and subaqueous lagoonal environments.

The topic of tidal flats cannot be given justice here, but some mention is made of these deposits because they do occur in the barrier-island setting. The extent of tidal flat environments in a barrier-island system is a function of tidal range, the greater the tidal range, the more extensive are the flats. In mesotidal barrier systems, we may expect to find sequences similar to the classical tidal flat deposits described by Van Straaten (1961), Evans (1965), Reineck and Singh (1980) and Klein (1977). The low tidal flats would be characterized by fine- to medium-grained, ripple-laminated sand, the mid flats by interbedded sand and mud containing flasers and lenticular layers, and the high tidal flats by layered mud. The high tidal flats would be succeeded landward (and upwards in a prograding situation) by salt marsh. In most microtidal and mesotidal barrier-island systems the tidal-flat sequence described above is attenuated because of the limiting conditions of tidal range.

Lagoonal or back-barrier sequences present a marked contrast to the predominantly clean sandstone sequences of the barrier-beach and inlet-delta environments (Fig. 21). Although the sandstone deposits interfinger with the fine-grained lagoonal deposits in the back-barrier marsh, tidal flat, washover, and flood-tidal environments, this lateral facies change from sandstone to siltstone and shale is still relatively abrupt.

TRANSGRESSION, REGRESSION, AND PRESERVATION OF FACIES

The preservation of specific barrier facies is dependent upon a number of factors including sea-level fluctuations, sediment supply, inlet conditions (migrating or stable) and wave climate. The most important condition, dependent largely on sea-level fluctuations, is the nature of the shoreline in terms of transgression or regression. The concepts of transgression and regression as used by geologists usually refer to the overlapping of deeper water deposits over more landward or shallower water deposits (transgressive sequence), or shallow water deposits over more marine or deep water facies (regressive). The terms "transgression" and "regression" are also used to imply the process of migration of the shoreline of a water body, in a landward direction (transgression), or in a seaward direction (regression) (Curray, 1964). Generally, transgressive and regressive barrier-shoreline migrations produce corresponding simple transgressive and regressive overlapping sequences (Figs. 22 and 23), but this is not always the case. This is because shoreline migrational trends can be "regional" or they can be "local". Regional transgressive shoreline trends can be caused by relative sea-level rise such as is now occurring on the Atlantic coast of the United States, or they can occur by shoreline erosion under relatively stable sea level conditions, in areas where sediment supply is cut off and wave attack is intensified (Kraft, 1978).

There is some controversy as to the preservation potential of barrier-island and related deposits during marine transgressions. Klein (1974) suggests that transgressive sequences have a low preservation potential relative to regressive sequences. However, Kraft (1971) contends that the possibility exists for a complete transgressive sequence to be preserved, and that the relative rate of sea-level rise will govern the amount of preservation. The variation in barrier-island behavior with variable rate of sea level rise is exemplified by the two contrasting hypotheses discussed by Sanders and Kumar (1975), and Rampino and Sanders (1980). The first hypothesis, that of "shoreface retreat" (Fig. 24A,B), involves relatively slow and continuous sea-level rise with the barrier shoreline migrating landward, leading to complete or almost complete destruction of back-barrier sediments by exposure to erosion and wave reworking on the shoreface. The preserved record would include only a thin transgressive "lag" buried by nearshore marine sediments. The contrasting view, "stepwise retreat" (Figs. 24C,D), involves a relatively rapid rise in sea level, with the barrier essentially drowning in place. The wave zone does not pass continuously across the area submerged, but rather oversteps landward to form a new barrier shoreline on the inner side of the lagoon. In this scenario, an almost entire transgressive sequence would be preserved on the inner shelf (Rampino and Sanders, 1980).

Dominantly transgressive shorelines can have "local" regressive segments within them. Such situations are caused by short-term temporal variations in depositional conditions along the barrier-island strandline. Longshore sediment supply, local wave climate, and number and location of tidal inlets

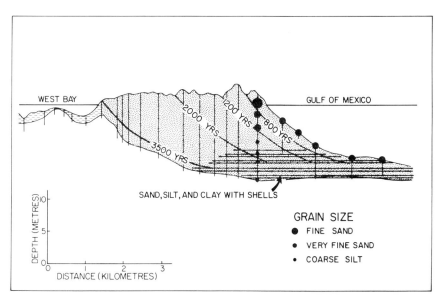

Figure 22
Cross-section of the prograding Galveston barrier island (from Bernard et al., 1962).

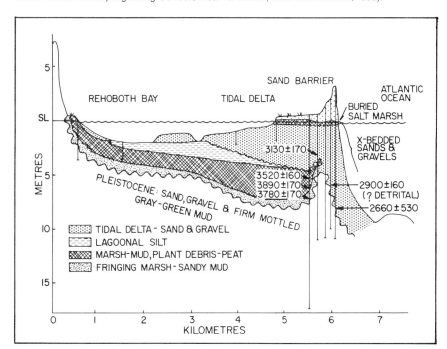

Figure 23
Cross-section of the Delaware barrier coast in the vicinity of a tidal delta, showing the

transgressive nature of the Holocene sequence (modified from Kraft, 1971, Fig. 16).

are some of the conditions which can change significantly and can affect both progradational and erosional trends in near juxtaposition. This is illustrated by the beach sequences in Figure 11, the landward sequence being transgressive and the seaward sequence progradational or regressive. The Holocene studies of Kraft *et al.* (1978) also indicate that both transgressive and regressive shoreline trends could be inferred by

two different vertical sequences in proximity. Given the presence of "local" regressive sequences in Holocene deposits, the possibility exists for their preservation in the rock record under conditions of rapid sea level rise. If such isolated stratigraphic sequences were encountered in the rock record they could be wrongly interpreted as being representative of the regional paleogeographic submergent or emergent

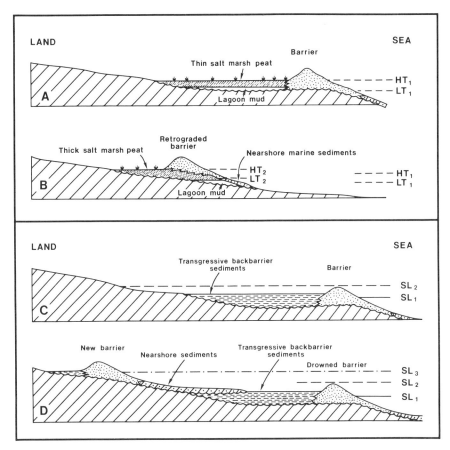

Figure 24
Diagrammatic sketch showing the two contrasting hypotheses regarding the behavior of barrier islands during a marine transgression. A and B - Barrier retreat by shoreface
erosion under slow but continuous sea level rise. C and D - Stepwise retreat of the shoreline involves a rapid rise in sea level, with the barrier essentially "drowning" in-place (from Rampino and Sanders, 1980).

conditions.

Certain facies have a higher potential for preservation than others because of their vertical position with respect to the intertidal zone (i.e., subtidal, intertidal), and their lateral position relative to the wave-dominated open coast or to a migratory inlet. Tidal-inlet channel facies will probably have the highest preservation potential of all the sand facies because, depending on the depth of the inlet, they may extend well below low tide level, their basal portion thus being protected from shoreface erosion during transgressive conditions. In addition they would be protected by the overlying beach-dune facies (Fig. 16). Flood-tidal delta deposits would have a high preservation potential as well because they are situated in the back-barrier protected region (for the most part in the subtidal zone), and under migrating inlet conditions could form relict sand shoals disconnected permanently from the tidal-current conduit

(Fig. 25). The distal portions of washover deposits, where they interfinger with fine-grained lagoonal facies, would have a high preservation potential, as would most of the lagoonal facies which are relatively protected by the seaward barrier. These deposits would be the last "to go" under intense shoreline retreat. Ebb-tidal delta deposits would have a low preservation potential under both migrating inlet conditions and transgression, because of exposure to reworking by longshore currents and onshore wave processes.

Regardless of potential for preservation, given the right combination of sediment supply, inlet stability, wave climate and sea-level fluctuations, any one of the barrier-island facies could be preserved in barrier-island stratigraphic sequences; we should be prepared to encounter all of them in the rock record.

STRATIGRAPHIC MODELS
From the examples of modern, and

some ancient sequences it is obvious that there cannot be just one generalized facies model for barrier-island deposits. If we apply the facies model criteria of Walker ("General Introduction", this volume), three "end-member" models for barrier-island stratigraphic sequences can be recognized; the regressive (prograding) model, the transgressive model, and the migrating barrier-inlet model (Fig. 26).

Regressive Model
The distillation of the generalized regressive facies model has come from modern examples, particularly the Galveston Island model (Fig. 22). As mentioned previously, prior to 1970 this example was the "one and only" model accepted for use in interpreting ancient sequences. Such a situation arose because the study of Bernard *et al.* (1962) was one of the first to present a detailed stratigraphic model for a barrier-island system. Some of the early literature depicted other stratigraphic models (e.g., Hoyt, 1967 for transgressive barriers, and Hoyt and Henry, 1965, for migrating inlet barriers), but these were largely ignored in the wave of enthusiasm for the Galveston model. Galveston Island should be recognized for what it is, a good example of the regressive facies model. It is not adequate as a "norm", because it does not include the essential characteristics displayed by most modern middle and upper shoreface deposits (Figs. 7 and 9).

The regressive facies model in Figure 26 serves as a norm for interpreting ancient regressive barrier sequences only. It is a gradational-based, coarsening-upwards sequence, dominated by shoreface, foreshore and backshore-dune facies of the barrier-beach complex.

Ancient examples which contribute to the regressive model include the outcrop occurrences documented by Campbell (1971), Howard (1972), Ryer (1977), McCubbin (1982), Lerand (1983), Rahmani (1983), and Tavener-Smith (1982). Subsurface examples include: the Lower Cretaceous Muddy Sandstone (Davies *et al.,* 1971), the Cretaceous La Ventana Sandstone and Upper Almond Formation of New Mexico and Wyoming respectively (McCubbin, 1982), the Lower Cretaceous Kamik Formation of the Mackenzie Delta

Figure 25

Schematic map and cross-sections illustrating how an inlet-delta sand body bounded by disconformities could be formed under conditions of inlet migration and concomitant shoreface erosion. The occurrence and shape of the sand body, and the nature of the enclosing sediments, vary with position in the barrier-island complex. (The heavy and light dashed lines on the map delineate former positions of the subaerial barrier.)

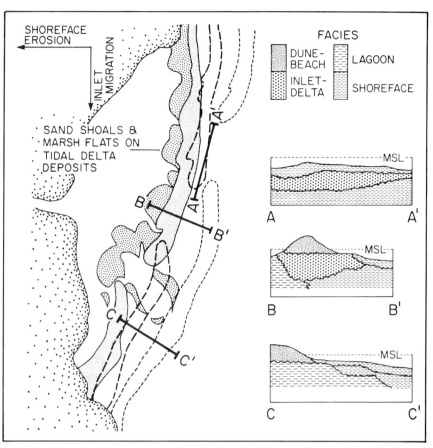

(Dixon, 1982), the Lower Cretaceous Glauconitic Sandstone of southern Alberta (Tilley and Longstaffe, 1984), and the Jurassic Borden Island Formation of the Canadian Arctic (Douglas and Oliver, 1979; see also Reinson, 1975). Some of these subsurface studies depict the coarsening upward, funnel-shaped, mechanical log response considered to be indicative of a prograding shoreline sequence (see "Subsurface Facies Analysis", this volume).

It is noteworthy that many ancient documented examples of prograding barrier – strand plain sequences are shown to be associated with deltas, either in interdeltaic positions, or in superposition but alternating with episodes of deltaic progradation. The primary requisite for development of prograding sequences is an abundance of sediment supply, and deltaic and interdeltaic coastal settings provide this.

Transgressive Model

The distillation of the generalized "end-member" sequence for the transgressive facies model comes also from modern examples, such as that depicted in Figure 23. This facies model is more complicated than the regressive model in terms of interbedding of facies and alternating lithologies. It is characterized by subtidal and intertidal back-barrier facies and does not show a fining-upwards or coarsening-upwards trend. The contact between some facies may be sharp or erosional. Many ancient sequences will deviate substantially from the normative model, because the facies stacking in transgressive sequences is quite variable,

Figure 26

The three "end-member" facies models of ▶ barrier island stratigraphic sequences (a standard 10-metre unit is shown, but thickness could range up to a few tens of metres).

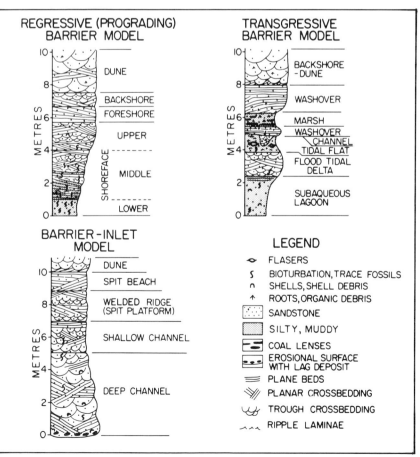

due to the rapid response of depositional environments to change in sediment supply and inlet conditions in transgressive situations.

One of the main differences between the regressive model and the transgressive model lies in the relationship with lagoonal facies. In the regressive sequence lagoonal deposits will overlie the sand facies, whereas in the transgressive model lagoonal facies underlie, or are incorporated within the lower to middle portions of the sequence (Fig. 26).

Well documented ancient examples of transgressive sequences are few, but include those of Bridges (1976), Hobday and Tankard (1978), Hobday and Jackson (1979), and Franks (1980). Cotter (1983) describes alternating partial sequences within the Tuscarora Formation and attributes their origin to rapid shifts in sea level caused possibly by tectonic or eustatic events. McCubbin (1982, p. 273-275) describes stacked prograding shoreline sand bodies separated by lagoonal deposits in the La Ventana Sandstone, and attributes this stacking to progradation during stillstands in an overall transgression. After progradation, McCubbin considers that the shoreline 'jumped' landward with little erosion of shoreline – back barrier facies. It is difficult to comprehend the absence of at least partially transgressive sequences (similar to the facies model) in the rock record during an overall transgressive event such as described by McCubbin. Franks (1980), describes an "unusually complete" transgressive sequence in the Early Cretaceous Kiowa Formation of Kansas. Franks considers this record of a marine transgression to be an important exception to the dominant concept, that transgression of barrier-islands involves continuous shoreface erosion concomitant with steady shoreline retreat (see Figs. 24A,B), leaving only a thin sheet sand or a disconformity as a record of the transgressive event. Franks invokes the concept of transgression accompanied by vertical growth, eventual submergence, and stepwise landward shift of the barriers (see Figs. 24C,D) to account for the high preservation of the transgressive sequence. The stepwise retreat process has not often been used for interpretation of ancient shorelines, leading one to wonder whether it has been overlooked in favour of the hereto-

fore overemphasis of the regressive or prograding shoreline model.

There is no simple pattern of mechanical-log response that could be considered characteristic of a subsurface transgressive shoreline deposit, because the variability of lithologies and contacts within such a sequence is so high. Cant ("Subsurface Facies Analysis", this volume, Fig. 11) illustrates a generalized log response for transgressive sheet sands, but a subsurface sequence such as described by Franks (1980) could more closely resemble the funnel-shaped curve without a strong overall coarsening-upward trend.

Barrier-Inlet Model
The distillation of the barrier-inlet model derives from well-documented modern and ancient examples (Figs. 15,16,18) including the studies of Hayes (1980), Barwis and Makurath (1978) and Land (1972). The barrier-inlet facies model is a fining-upwards sequence with a thinning-upwards trend in cross-bed set thickness (Fig. 26). It is characterized by an erosional base and dominated by sand facies of tidal-channel and marginal spit – beach environments.

More inlet-fill sequences are now being recognized in the rock record (Dixon, 1982; McCubbin, 1982, Fig. 43; Tavener-Smith, 1982; Lerand, 1983; Rahmani, 1983), as important subfacies of overall beach strand and barrier-island related rock bodies. The barrier-inlet sequence is difficult to determine in the subsurface from mechanical logs alone, but one might expect to encounter an abrupt-based, bell-shaped curve for the SP or gamma ray response, such as illustrated by Cant ("Subsurface Facies Analysis", this volume, Fig. 11). Such a response is characteristic of a fluvial point bar, ("Sandy Fluvial Systems", this volume) with which the barrier-inlet model has some similarities (Fig. 26).

Hybrid Models
Transgressive, regressive, and barrier-inlet depositional conditions can occur in combination to produce mixed sequences which have affinities with more than one "end-member" norm.

The so-called vertical build-up barrier of Padre Island is really a combination of the regressive and transgressive models, with the landward side of the barrier migrating into the lagoon by

washover deposition, and the seaward side prograding outwards by beach-ridge accretion (Hayes, 1976; Dickinson et al., 1972). Matagorda Island, situated near Galveston Island, has been shown by Wilkinson (1975) to have formed during both a transgressive phase and a subsequent regressive phase. Vertical sequences from the landward side of the Padre and Matagorda barriers are comparable to the transgressive model, whereas sequences from the seaward side are comparable to the regressive model.

Possible examples of a combined regressive and barrier-inlet model are illustrated in Figure 18, and in McCubbin (1982) for the Cretaceous Gallup Sandstone. The top of the channel sequence in Figure 18 is truncated by the overlying lagoonal deposits, and only the lower part of the barrier-inlet "end-member" model is preserved. In the McCubbin example, the inlet fill passes upward from channel to tidal delta to lagoonal marsh, and is interpreted as recording seaward migration of an inlet-channel in an overall progradational barrier-island setting. The barrier-inlet "end-member" model (Fig. 26) may in itself be considered in part regressive because of the progradation of beach and dune facies over deeper-water channel deposits.

Perhaps the most complicated hybrid sequence that could occur is the situation of transgression concomitant with, or just after, barrier-inlet migration. Barwis and Makurath (1978) discuss the stratigraphic implications of such a setting in some detail. Basically, if transgression is occurring largely by shoreface erosion, and the migrating inlet is deep enough to produce an inlet deposit whose base is substantially below the foreshore-shoreface boundary, an inlet-delta sand body, bounded above and below by disconformities, could occur (Fig. 25). In vertical sequence such a deposit would be comparable to the lower part of the barrier-inlet "end-member" model, with an erosional surface similar to the basal lag, situated at the top. Kumar and Sanders (1970) consider that this dual migration setting could be the origin of many linear sand bodies on the inner shelf. They further suggest that submergence of migrating barrier-inlet shorelines may account for some of the basal transgressive sands in the geological record, the sands being of inlet-fill as opposed to barrier-beach or offshore bar origin.

Many of the ancient examples previously cited already indicate an appreciation of the existence of hybrid models or mixed facies sequences; thus it appears that the main purpose for proposing "end-member facies models" is being served.

LIMITATIONS TO MODELS

There are drawbacks and limitations inherent in every model, because a model, by definition, is a proposed standard (derived from an existing data base), against which deviations from the norm are to be compared and interpreted. The validity of the proposed standard depends on the quality and extent of the data base from which it was formulated. The models proposed here represent complete or idealized sequences, hence the term "end-members". In the rock record, individually complete standard sequences are rarely encountered due, for example, to lateral variation in facies sequence (McCubbin, 1982), or to the occurrence of complicated and hybrid, cyclic transgressive-regressive events (e.g., Ryer, 1977; Cotter, 1983).

The perceived drawbacks to the models relate primarily to the regressive end-member. The regressive model contains shoreface facies as primary elements (Fig. 26). Recent articles on both modern and ancient shoreface deposits (Hunter *et al.*, 1979; Howard and Reineck, 1981; Leckie and Walker, 1982; McCubbin, 1982) indicate that the shoreface environment may be too complicated to distill into one model. As mentioned earlier, there are inconsistencies between workers in the application of shoreface terminology, and even in the assignment of facies to specific shoreface zones, particularly near the shoreface-offshore boundary. Perhaps there is room for submodels which differentiate barred versus non-barred, high-wave energy versus low-wave energy, and storm-dominated versus normal shoreface settings. The above sets of shoreface environments however, are all interrelated to a degree, and other factors such as sediment supply and nearshore slope gradient will have a bearing on near-

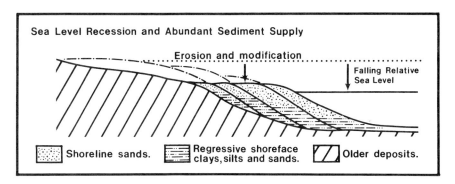

Figure 27
Diagrammatic cross-section of shoreline behaviour under conditions of sea-level recession combined with an abundant sediment supply (after Heward (1981), modified from Vail et al., 1977). The top of the sand deposit would be truncated by subaerial and fluvial erosion, and the base could also be disconformable if wave base exceeds water depth.

shore morphology (barred or non-barred), and inshore wave climate or storm-generated effects. Development of additional models is problematical because the sedimentological and hydrodynamic criteria needed for submodel distillation are not yet clearly differentiated. At present, additonal work is required to fill our gaps in knowledge of nearshore depositional systems (Hunter *et al.*, 1979). Only then will we be able to assess what type of additional models are needed. We must guard against the generation of too many models, because the model concept then becomes redundant, and we are back to 'square 1', that of a large number of separate, unrelated individual sequences.

A second reservation about the regressive model is not really a drawback to the model itself, or its contained facies elements, but to its limitation in application. This limitation can be explained by the example of two conditions of regressive shoreline behaviour illustrated in Figures 22 and 27. The first condition, regression due primarily to excess sediment supply (Fig. 22), is the current popular mode by which ancient prograding sequences are perceived to form, and this is the general basis for the proposed regressive model (Fig. 26). A minor drawback to the model, which should be noted, is that if progradation proceeds into water shallower than wave base, fine-grained lower shoreface-transitional deposits may be absent and the sequence will be sharply-based (Heward, 1981). The model, however, is still valid because

this situation would represent an incomplete sequence compared to the norm, and would relate to lateral variations in facies, discussed above. The second condition (Fig. 27), that of relative sea level drop and abundant sediment supply, may not be adequately addressed by the propsed regressive model. The presence of coarsening-upward or sharply-based sequences will depend on water-depth to wave-base ratio also, but the tops of such deposits may be extensively modified and truncated (Heward, 1981). It is suggested that under regressive conditions of Figure 27, sharply-based deposits rather than gradationally-based deposits may be the normative situation, and further, this mechanism may be responsible for some of the extensive, apparently wave-dominated, progradational shore-attached sheet and lenticular sands encountered in the rock record. Clearly, the regressive model, as a comparative or predictive tool, would not be directly applicable to this situation.

The mechanism of formation of some extensive, thick, shore-attached sandstones, as products of asymmetrical transgressive-progradational cycles, has been documented thoroughly by Cant (1984), Clifton (1981) and Ryer (1977). Such studies do not affect the validity of the facies models, for the facies models form the basis on which individual sequences can be identified within the overall clastic deposit. However, the foregoing discussion serves to emphasize that the application of facies models to many shore-attached wedge and sheet

136

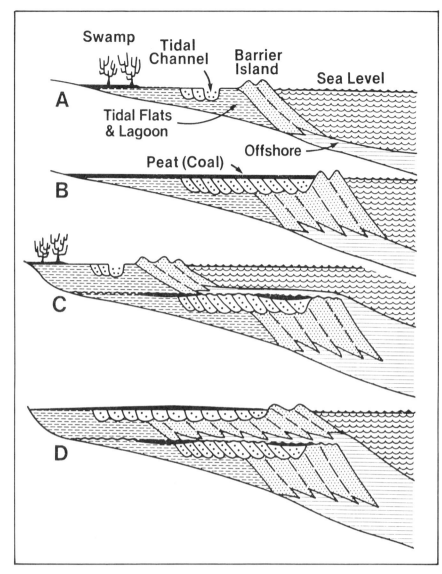

Figure 28
Interpretive diagram depicting the mode of formation of the barrier-island succession within the Horesehoe Canyon Fm., Drumheller, Alberta. A) Establishment of a mesotidal barrier complex. B) Progradation of the barrier complex. C) Sudden in-place drowning of the barrier and the establishment of a younger barrier complex inland from the previous one. D) Seaward progradation of the younger barrier-island complex over the older complex (from Rahmani, 1983).

sandstones is yet to be fully and adequately addressed.

SUMMARY
Prior to the 1970s, the prograding Galveston Island depositional model was in the forefront in the minds of most geologists, as the "one and only" facies model for use in interpreting ancient barrier-island sequences. Studies conducted within the last 15 years on modern and ancient barrier-island deposits indicate that the "regressive facies model" cannot be applied to a number of barrier-island

sequences, and therefore the use of one normative model is unrealistic. Three generalized facies models or "end-member" norms can be recognized, the regressive barrier model, the transgressive barrier model, and the barrier-inlet model (Fig. 26). Most sequences can be explained through comparative analysis with individual "end-member" models, or combinations of them, and this is emphasized by the recent studies of Horne and Ferm (1978), Barwis and Makurath (1978), Tavener-Smith (1982), Rahmani (1983) (Fig. 28) and others.

ACKNOWLEDGEMENTS
I thank R.G. Walker for reviewing my preliminary manuscript for the second edition of this volume. Douglas Cant and Barbara Tilley provided me with preprint copies of their respective papers relevant to this review. Monti Lerand supplied the photographs for Figures 6 and 10, and Lynn Green and Denise Chaulk typed the preliminary and final manuscripts, respectively.

REFERENCES

ESSENTIAL READING LIST

Davis, R.A. Jr., ed., 1979. Coastal sedimentary environments. New York, Springer-Verlag, 420 p.
Contains excellent review chapters on modern beach deposits by R.A. Davis and Holocene coastal stratigraphic sequences by J.C. Kraft.

Elliott, T., 1978. Clastic shorelines. *In* Reading, H.G., ed., Sedimentary environments and facies. Oxford, Blackwell, p. 143-177.
Excellent general systhesis of non-deltaic shoreline deposits including barrier-islands, strand plains, estuaries, and tidal flats.

Hayes, M.O., and Kana T.W., eds., 1976. Terrigenous clastic depositional environments: some modern examples. University of South Carolina, Technical Report No. 11-CRD, 315 p.
This field course guidebook is a must for geologists who wish to become aware of the latest thinking on the evolution of barrier-island deposits. Contains an excellent summary on transitional-coastal depositional environments by Hayes, an extensive bibliography on barrier-island and related environments, and some other useful papers on South Carolina barrier-island environments.

Heward, A.P., 1981. A review of wave-dominated clastic shoreline deposits. Earth-Science Reviews, v. 17, p. 223-276.
Excellent review of clastic shoreline deposits including deltas, with a comprehensive reference list of both modern and ancient studies.

McCubbin, D.G., 1982. Barrier-island and strand-plain facies. *In* Scholle, P.A., and Spearing, D.R., eds., Sandstone depositional environments. American Association of Petroleum Geologists, Memoir 31, p. 247-280.
A review similar to this paper, but containing outstanding color illustrations, also contains some well-documented ancient shoreline examples, particularly subsurface reservoirs.

Schwartz, M.L., ed., 1973. Barrier islands. Stroudsburg, PA., Dowden, Hutchinson and Ross, 451 p.
A reprint collection of the classical historical and contemporary papers dealing with the origin and geomorphic development of barrier-island shorelines.

Swift, D.J.P., 1975. Barrier island genesis: evidence from the Middle Atlantic Shelf of North America. Sedimentary Geology, v. 14, p. 1-43.
This paper discusses the origin and evolution of barrier islands, within the context of the east-coast setting of the United States.

STUDIES OF HOLOCENE DEPOSITS

Andrews, P.B., 1970. Facies and genesis of a hurricane-washover fan, St. Joseph Island, Central Texas coast. Texas Bureau of Economic Geology, Report of Investigation No. 67, 147 p.
Thorough study of a modern washover fan deposit.

Bernard, H.A., Leblanc, R.J., and Major, C.F., 1962. Recent and Pleistocene geology of southeast Texas: In Rainwater, E.H., and Zingula, R.P., eds., Geology of the Gulf Coast and Central Texas and guidebook of excursions. Houston Geological Society - Geological Society of America Annual Meeting, 1962, Houston, Texas, p. 175-205.
Documentation of the oft-cited (and illustrated) prograding Galveston barrier-island model. The material in this original paper is more accessible in the following summary article. Bernard, H.A., and Leb-land, R.J., 1965. Resume of the Quaternary geology of the northwestern Gulf of Mexico Province. In Wright, H.E., Jr., and Frey, D.G., eds., The Quaternary of the United States. Princeton, N.J., Princeton University Press, p. 137-185.

Boothroyd, J.C., and Hubbard, D.K., 1975. Genesis of bedforms in mesotidal estuaries. In Cronin, L.E., ed., Estuarine research, v. 2, Geology and engineering. New York, Academic Press, p. 167-182.
Illustrates the patterns of bedform development and distribution on tidal deltas in some New England estuaries.

Clifton, H.E., Hunter, R.E., and Phillips, R.L., 1971. Depositional structures and processes in the non-barred high energy nearshore. Journal of Sedimentary Petrology, v. 41, p. 651-670.
Presents a sequence of bedforms for the upper shoreface-foreshore in a modern high-energy shoreline setting.

Curray, J.R., Emmel, F.J., and Crampton, P.J.S., 1969. Holocene history of a strand plain, lagoonal coast, Nayarit, Mexico. In Castanares, A.A., and Phleger, F.B., eds., Costal lagoons, a symposium. Universidad Nacional Autonoma de Mexico, p. 63-100.
This benchmark paper contains the classical example of a modern beach strand plain, the one so often cited and illustrated in other papers.

Davidson-Arnott, R.G.D. and Greenwood, B., 1976. Facies relationships in a barred coast, Kouchibouguac Bay, New Brunswick, Canada. In Davis, R.J., Jr., ed., Beach and nearshore sedimentation. Society of Economic Paleontologists and Mineralogists, Special Publication No. 24, p. 149-168.
Excellent study of the internal structures and facies in longshore bars of the shoreface environment.

Davis, R.A. Jr., Fox, W.T., Hayes, M.O., and Boothroyd, J.C. 1972. Comparison of ridge-and-runnel systems in tidal and nontidal environments. Journal of Sedimentary Petrology, v. 32, p. 413-421.
Documents the vertical sequence that results when bars migrate shoreward and weld onto the beachface. This sequence of sedimentary structures is far more complicated than the usual seaward dipping beach laminated deposit.

Dickinson, K.A., Berryhill, H.L. Jr., and Holmes, C.W., 1972. Criteria for recognizing ancient barrier coastlines. In Rigby, J.K., and Hamblin, W.K., eds., Recognition of ancient sedimentary environments. Society of Economic Paleontologists and Mineralogists, Special Publication No. 16, p. 192-214.
Would be more properly titled "Holocene barrier-island environments of the Gulf of Mexico, with some ancient examples."

Hayes, M.O., 1975. Morphology of sand accumulations in estuaries. In Cronin, L.E., ed., Estuarine Research, v. 2, Geology and Engineering. New York, Academic Press, p. 3-22.
Outlines morphological models for flood and ebb-tidal deltas, and presents observations on the differences between microtidal and mesotidal barrier-island coastlines.

Howard, J.D., and Reineck, H.E., 1981. Depositional facies of high-energy beach-to-offshore sequence: comparison with low-energy sequence. American Association of Petroleum Geologists, Bulletin, v. 65, p. 807-830.
A significant study in that it illustrates the variability of shoreface deposits, by way of comparison of cored sequences obtained from contrasting modern beach-to-offshore settings.

Hunter, R.E., Clifton, H.E., and Phillips, R.L., 1979. Depositional processes, sedimentary structures, and predicted vertical sequences in barred nearshore systems, northern Oregon coast. Journal of Sedimentary Petrology, v. 49, p. 711-726.
Excellent study showing the variation in nearshore deposits between a barred versus a non-barred system, also presents a vertical sequence for each system.

Kraft, J.C., 1971. Sedimentary facies patterns and geologic history of a Holocene marine transgression. Geological Society of America, Bulletin, v. 82, p. 2131-2158.
Discussion and documentation of the stratigraphy and facies distribution of a modern transgressive barrier-island system.

Kraft, J.C., Allen, E.A., and Maurmeyer, E.M., 1978. The geological and paleogeomorphological evolution of a spit system and its associated coastal environments. Cape Henlopen spit, Delaware. Journal of Sedimentary Petrology, v. 48, p. 211-226.
Documentation of vertical sedimentary sequences in a Holocene spit complex, with examples of both "regressive" and "transgressive" sequences occurring in the same region.

Kumar, N., and Sanders, J.E. 1974. Inlet sequence: a vertical succession of sedimentary structures and textures created by the lateral migration of tidal inlets. Sedimentology, v. 21, p. 491-532
An excellent study of an inlet sequence and development of an inlet-fill model.

Kumar, N. and Sanders, J.E., 1976. Characteristics of shoreface storm deposits, modern and ancient examples. Journal of Sedimentary Petrology, v. 46, p. 145-162.
Emphasizes the possible significance of storm deposits in the geogical record, by illustration of modern examples.

Leatherman, S.P., ed., 1979. Barrier islands - from the Gulf of St. Lawrence to the Gulf of Mexico. New York, Academic Press, 325 p.
A compendium of papers on modern barrier-island studies; the two most significant papers are those of M.O. Hayes (cited later in this bibliography), and S.B. McCann, who provides an excellent review of modern barrier islands in the southern Gulf of St. Lawrence.

Nelson, C.H., 1982. Modern shallow-water graded sand layers from storm surges, Bering Shelf: a mimic of Bouma sequences and turbidite systems. Journal of Sedimentary Petrology, v. 52, p. 537-546.
An interesting documentation of graded sand beds allegedly formed from rapidly waning storm-surge-associated currents, in a very shallow epicontinental setting; the graded sands extend some 100 km offshore from the deltaic shoreline.

Owens, E.H., 1977. Temporal variations in beach and nearshore dynamics. Journal of Sedimentary Petrology, v. 47, p. 168-190.
Detailed study of the sedimentary processes operative on the opposite-facing

barrier beaches of the Magdalen Islands, Gulf of St. Lawrence.

Rampino, M.R. and Sanders, J.E., 1980. Holocene transgression in south-central Long Island, New York. Journal of Sedimentary Petrology, v. 50, p. 1063-1080.
Presents interpretive stratigraphic sections of transgressive barrier-island deposits on Long Island; the extensive preservation of transgressive sequences on the inner shelf is interpreted as resulting from in-place "drowning" of barriers and stepwise retreat of the shoreline to landward.

Reineck. H.E. and Singh, I.B., 1972. Genesis of laminated sand and graded rhythmites in storm-sand layers of shelf mud. Sedimentology, v. 18, p. 123-128.
Gives an explanation for the origin of planar laminated sand units (devoid of ripple laminae) in lower shoreface deposits.

Reinson, G.E., 1977. Tidal current control of submarine morphology at the mouth of the Miramichi estuary, New Brunswick. Canadian Journal of Earth Sciences, v. 14, p. 2524-2532.
Documentation of extensive flood- and ebb-tidal deltaic deposits associated with a barrier system situated at the mouth of a large estuarine bay, in a microtidal coastal setting.

Roy, P.S., Thom, B.G., and Wright, L.D., 1980. Holocene sequences on an embayed high-energy coast: an evolutionary model. Sedimentary Geology, v. 21, p. 1-19.
This article categorizes and summarizes the types of estuarine and barrier deposits occurring on the New South Wales coast of Australia. There are some excellent examples of barrier-island systems on this coastline.

Schwartz, R.K., 1982. Bedforms and stratification characteristics of some modern small-scale washover sand bodies. Sedimentology, v. 29, p. 835-850.
Detailed study of the stratigraphy, morphology, and internal geometry of some modern barrier-island washover deposits.

STUDIES OF ANCIENT DEPOSITS

Barwis, J.H. and Makurath, J.H., 1978. Recognition of ancient tidal inlet sequences: an example from the Upper Silurian Keyser Limestone in Virginia. Sedimentology, v. 25, p. 61-82.
Excellent documentation of an ancient tidal inlet-fill deposit. Also contains succinct reviews of modern tidal inlet studies and of published studies on ancient barrier deposits which appear to have tidal-inlet affinities.

Bridges, P.H., 1976. Lower Silurian transgressive barrier-island deposits, southwest Wales. Sedimentology, v. 23, p. 347-362.
Sandstone-mudstone sequences are interpreted as transgressive barrier-island deposits. The case for transgressive sequences is well documented.

Campbell, C.V., 1971. Depositional model – Upper Cretaceous Gallup beach shoreline, Ship Rock area, Northwestern New Mexico. Journal of Sedimentary Petrology, v. 41, p. 395-409.
Contains detailed descriptions of the geometry and sedimentary structures of Cretaceous barrier-beach facies.

Cant, D.J., 1984. Development of shoreline-shelf sand bodies in a Cretaceous epeiric sea deposit. Journal of Sedimentary Petrology, in press.
Interprets the development of a shoreline-attached clastic wedge, some 350 m thick, as a composite of eight transgressive-regressive cycles. Each progradational sequence is sharp-based, and is interpreted to contain shoreface-beach deposits overlain by backswamp-lagoon sediments.

Carter, C.H., 1978. A regressive barrier and barrier-protected deposit: depositional environment and geographic setting of the Late Tertiary Cohansey Sand. Journal of Sedimentary Petrology, v. 48, p. 933-950.
Includes ancient sequences interpreted as containing surf-zone deposits and tidal channel deposits.

Clifton, H.E., 1981. Progradational sequences in Miocene shoreline deposits, sotheastern Caliente Range, California. Journal of Sedimentary Petrology, v. 51, p. 165-184.
Some 50 individual progradational sequences are recognized within a thick (1000 - 2500 m) Miocene succession. Individual sequences rest on a thin gravel deposit (interpreted as transgressive lag) above an erosional surface. The typical sequence contains a coarse-grained cross-bedded sandstone facies (underlying the beach foreshore facies) thought to be indicative of a bar - rip channel - surf zone assemblage.

Cotter, E., 1975. Late Cretaceous sedimentation in a low-energy coastal zone. The Ferron Sandstone of Utah. Journal of Sedimentary Petrology, v. 45, p. 669-685.
Interpretation of shoreface and tidal inlet deposits, with a short review of papers in which ancient tidal inlet deposits have been inferred.

Cotter, E., 1983. Shelf, paralic, and fluvial environments and eustatic sea-level fluctuations in the origin of the Tuscarora Formation (Lower Silurian) of central Pennsylvania. Journal of Sedimentary Petrology, v. 53, p. 25-49.
Interesting study of a Silurian succession interpreted to consist of alternating sequences of braided-fluvial, beachstrand, and shallow-shelf facies.

Davies, D.K., and Ethridge, F.G., 1971. The Claiborne Group of Central Texas: a record of Middle Eocene marine and coastal plain deposition. Gulf Coast Association of Geological Societies, Transactions, v. 21, p. 115-124.
Presents a regressive barrier-island sequence that contains (from the base up) middle shoreface, tidal channel, washover, subaqueous lagoon, and tidal flat deposits.

Davies, D.K., Ethridge, F.G., and Berg, R.R., 1971. Recognition of barrier environments. American Association of Petroleum Geologists, Bulletin, v. 55, p. 550-565.
Comparative study of the Galveston barrier model with Cretaceous and Jurassic sandstone deposits, illustrates the use of the modern analogue in interpretation of ancient barrier-island deposits, and presents a model for barrier-island sedimentation. An excellent paper, but we must remember that the model presented is only one type of barrier island, the Galveston type. There are others.

Dixon, J., 1982. Sedimentology of the Neocomian Parsons Group in the subsurface of the Mackenzie Delta area, Arctic Canada. Bulletin of Canadian Petroleum Geology, v. 30, p. 9-28.
Stacked barrier-island sequences, including associated tidal-channel, and lagoonal deposits, are interpreted from core examination, supplemented by mechanical logs.

Douglas, T.R., and Oliver, T.A., 1979. Environments of deposition of the Borden Island gas zone in the subsurface of the Sabine Peninsula area, Melville Island, Arctic Archipelago. Bulletin of Canadian Petroleum Geology, v. 27, p. 273-313.
Examination of cores and mechanical logs indicates the occurrence of cyclic sandstone-siltstone sequences interpreted as prograding beach shoreline deposits.

Franks, P.C., 1980. Models of marine transgression - example from Lower Cretaceous fluvial and paralic deposits, north-central Kansas. Geology, v. 8, p. 56-61.
Describes the occurrence of a well-preserved, thick transgressive sequence; this sequence is interpreted to have resulted from barrier 'drowning' and stepwise landward shift of the shoreline.

Hamblin, A.P., and Walker, R.G., 1979. Storm-dominated shallow marine deposits: the Fernie-Kootenay (Jurassic) transition, southern Rocky Mountains. Canadian Journal of Earth Sciences, v. 16, p. 1673-1689.
Describes the occurrence of a relatively thick (34 m) parallel-laminated sandstone sequence interpreted as beach deposits; the depositional setting may be similar to the classical beach strand-plain situation, with the 34 m thick deposit not having originated entirely in the intertidal zone.

Hobday, D.K., and Horne, J.C., 1977. Tidally influenced barrier-island and estuarine sedimentation in the Upper Carboniferous of southern West Virginia. Sedimentary Geology, v. 18, p. 97-122.
Interpretation of Upper Carboniferous sandstone units as barrier-island deposits, with the recognition of tidal-delta, tidal-channel and washover facies.

Hobday, D.K., and Tankard, A.J., 1978. Transgressive-barrier and shallow-shelf interpretation of the lower Paleozoic Peninsula Formation, South Africa. Geological Society of America, Bulletin, v. 89, p. 1733-1744.
Interprets the occurrence of a transgressive-barrier sequence containing washover deposits and small-scale back-barrier tidal channels, overlain by large-scale channel deposits of migrating tidal-inlet origin.

Hobday, D.K., and Jackson, M.P.A., 1979. Transgressive shore zone sedimentation and syndepositional deformation in the Pleistocene of Zululand, South Africa. Journal of Sedimentary Petrology, v. 49, p. 145-158.
Documentation of a Pleistocene transgressive sequence consisting, from base to top, of lagoonal sandy clays, back-barrier peat and bioturbated sand, overwash sands, and eolian deposits.

Horne, J.C., and Ferm, J.S., 1978. Carboniferous depositional environments: eastern Kentucky and southern West Virginia. Department of Geology, University of South Carolina, 151 p.
This excellent field guidebook summarizes the studies of Horne, Ferm and co-workers on the regional stratigraphy and paleoenvironmental interpretation of Carboniferous deltaic and barrier-island deposits of southeastern United States. Contains numerous outcrop illustrations and environmental reconstructions of various barrier-island facies and synthesizes these into a composite depositional framework. Some of this material has been published in the following paper. Horne, J.C., Frem, J.C., Caruccio, F.T., and Baganz, B.P., 1978. Depositional models in coal exploration and mine planning in Appalachian region. American Association of Petroleum Geologists, Bulletin, v. 62, p. 2379-2411.

Howard, J.D., 1972. Trace fossils as criteria for recognizing shorelines in stratigraphic record. In Rigby, J.K., and Hamblin, W.K., eds., Recognition of ancient sedimentary environments. Society of Economic Palaeontologists and Mineralogists, Special Publication No. 16, p. 215-225.
This article attempts to demonstrate the usefulness of trace fossils for interpreting ancient-barrier-island environments, and succeeds admirably.

Land, C.B. Jr., 1972. Stratigraphy of Fox Hills Sandstone and associated formations, Rock Springs uplift and Wamsutter arch area, Sweetwater County, Wyoming: a shoreline-estuary sandstone model for the Late Cretaceous. Quarterly Journal of Colorado School of Mines, v. 67, no. 2, 69 p.
Well-documented sedimentological and stratigraphic study of Upper Cretaceous tidal-channel, barrier-beach, and lagoonal deposits.

Leckie, D.A., and Walker, R.G., 1982. Storm- and tide-dominated shorelines in Cretaceous Moosebar-Lower Gates interval - outcrop equivalents of deep basin gas trap in Western Canada. American Association of Petroleum Geologists, Bulletin, v. 66, p. 138-157.
This study interprets the occurrence of storm-dominated structures on the shoreface. The structures are termed 'swaley cross stratification', a variant of hummocky cross-stratification.

Lerand, M., 1983. The sedimentology of the Blood Reserve Sandstone in southern Alberta. Canadian Society of Petroleum Geologists, Field Trip Guidebook, 55 p.
This guidebook expands on the work of Young and Reinson (1975) by providing a more thorough documentaiton, at three different localities, of the prograding barrier-beach shoreline and lagoonal deposits of the Blood Reserve – St. Mary River succession.

Rahmani, R.A., 1983. Facies relationships and paleoenvironments of a Late Cretaceous tide-dominated delta, Drumheller, Alberta. Canadian Society of Petroleum Geologists, Mesozoic of Middle North America Conference, May, 1983, Field Trip Guidebook, 36 p. plus figures.
An interesting and well-illustrated, environmental study of an Upper Cretaceous succession interpreted to contain a mesotidal barrier-island system in proximity to an estuarine embayment.

Ryer, T.A., 1977. Patterns of Cretaceous shallow-marine sedimentation, Coalville and Rockport areas, Utah. Geological Society of America Bulletin, v. 88, p. 177-188.
A thick section of Cretaceous strata, comprising a number of progradational nearshore-shoreline sequences bounded above and below by disconformities, is interpreted to represent asymmetrical progradational-transgressive cycles of marine sedimentation. Each progradation is thought to be succeeded by transgressive shoreface erosion, resulting in a disconformity or ravinement deposit.

Tavener-Smith, R., 1982. Prograding coastal facies associations in the Vryheid Formation (Permian) at Effingham Quarries near Durban, South Africa. Sedimentary Geology, v. 32, p. 111-140.
Excellent outcrop study that proposes a depositional model which encompasses all the subenvironments and resultant facies of a barrier-island system.

Tilley, B., and Longstaffe, F.J., 1984. Controls on hydrocarbon accumulation in the Glauconitic Sandstone, Suffield heavy oil sands, southern Alberta. American Association of Petroluem Geologists, Bulletin, in press.
Detailed subsurface core and mechanical log study of a thick, heavy oil-bearing sand body. The sand body is interpreted to be representative of a progradational barrier-island system. The beach-shoreface sequence is unusually thick (45 m); this magnitude of thickness is attributed to local variations in subsidence rates caused by underlying fault movements during sand deposition.

OTHER REFERENCES CITED IN TEXT

Armon, J.W., 1980. Changeability in small flood tidal deltas and its effects, the Malpeque barrier system, Prince Edward Island. In McCann, S.B., ed., The Coastline of Canada: Geological Survey of Canada, Paper 8-10, p. 41-50.

Barwis, J.H., 1978. Stratigraphy of Kiawah Island beach ridges. Southeastern Geology, v. 19, p. 111-122.

Curray, J.R., 1964. Transgressions and regressions. In Miller, R.C., ed., Papers in marine geology - Shepard commemorative volume. New York, MacMillan and Company, p. 175-203.

Davis, R.J. Jr., 1983. Depositional systems - a genetic approach to sedimentary geology. Englewood Cliffs, New Jersey, Prentice-Hall Inc., 669 p.

Evans, G., 1965. Intertidal flat sediments and their environments of deposition in the Wash. Quarterly Journal of the Geological Society of London, v. 121, p. 209-245.

Field, M.E. and Duane, D.B., 1976. Post-Pleistocene history of the United States inner continental shelf. Significance to origin of barrier islands. Geological Society of America, Bulletin, v. 87, p. 691-702.

Glaeser, J.D., 1978. Global distribution of barrier islands in terms of tectonic setting. Journal of Geology, v. 86, p. 283-297.

Goldring, R., and Bridges, P., 1973. Sublittoral sheet sandstones. Journal of Sedimentary Petrology, v. 43, p. 736-747.

Halsey, S.D., 1979. Nexus: New model of barrier island development. *In* Leatherman, S.P., ed., Barrier islands - from the Gulf of St. Lawrence to the Gulf of Mexico. New York, Academic Press, p. 185-210.

Hayes, M.O., 1967. Hurricanes as geological agents: case studies of Hurricanes Carla, 1961; and Cindy, 1963. Texas Bureau of Economic Geology, Report of Investigation No. 61, 56 p.

Hayes, M.O., 1979. Barrier-island morphology as a function of tidal and wave regime. *In* Leatherman, S.P., ed., Barrier-islands -from the Gulf of St. Lawrence to the Gulf of Mexico, New York, Academic Press, p. 1-28.

Hayes, M.O., 1980. General morphology and sediment patterns in tidal inlets. Sedimentary Geology, v. 26, p. 139-156

Hoyt, J.H., 1967. Barrier island formation. Geological Society of America, Bulletin, v. 78, p. 1125-1136.

Hoyt, J.H., and Henry, V.J., Jr., 1965. Significance of inlet sedimentation in the recognition of ancient barrier islands. Wyoming Geological Association, 19th field Conference Guidebook, p. 190-194.

Hubbard, D.K., and Barwis, J.H., 1976. Discussion of tidal inlet sand deposits: examples from the South Carolina Coast. *In* Hayes, M.O., and Kana, T.W., eds., Terrigenous clastic depositional environments: Some modern examples. American Assoication of Petroleum Geologists, Field Course, University of South Carolina, Technical Report No. 11 -CRD, p. II 128 – II 142.

Klein, G. de V., 1974. Estimating water depths from analysis of barrier island and deltaic sedimentary sequences. Geology, v. 2, p. 409-412.

Klein, G. de V., 1977. Clastic tidal facies. Champaign, Illinois, Continuing Education Publication Company, 149 p.

Kraft, J.C., 1978. Coastal stratigraphic sequences. *In* Davis, R.A., Jr., ed., Coastal sedimentary environments. New York, Springer-Verlag, p. 361-384.

Kumar, N., and Sanders, J.E., 1970. Are basal transgressive sands chiefly inlet-filling sands. Maritime Sediments, v. 6, p. 12-14.

Owens, E.H., and Frobel, D., 1977. Ridge and runnel systems in the Magdalen Islands, Quebec. Journal of Sedimentary Petrology, v. 47, p. 191-198.

Reineck, H.E., and Singh, I.B., 1980. Depositional sedimentary environments with reference to terrigenous clasics. Berlin, Springer-Verlag, 549 p.

Reinson, G.E., 1975. Lithofacies analysis of cores from the Borden Island Formation. Drake Point, Melville Island. Geological Survey of Canada, Report of Activities 75-1, Part B, p. 297-301.

Reinson, G.E., 1979. Longitudinal and transverse bedforms on a large tidal delta, Gulf of St. Lawrence, Canada. Marine Geology v. 31, p. 279-296.

Sanders, J.E., and Kumar, N., 1975. Evidence of shoreface retreat and in-place "drowning" during Holocene submergence of barriers, shelf off Fire Island, New York. Geological Society of America, Bulletin, v. 86, p. 65-76.

Scholle, P.A., and Spearing, D., eds. 1982. Sandstone depositional environments. American Association of Petroleum Geologists, Memoir 31, 410 p.

Vail, P.R., Mitchum, R.M., and Thompson, S., 1977. Seismic stratigraphy and global changes of sea level, part 3: relative changes of sea level form coastal onlap. *In* Payton, C.E., ed., Seismic stratigraphy - applications to hydrocarbon exploration. American Association of Petroleum Geologists, Memoir 26, p.63-81.

Van Straaten, L.M.J.U., 1961. Sedimentation in tidal flat areas. Journal of the Alberta Society of Petroleum Geologists, v. 9, p. 204-226.

Wanless, H.R., 1976. Intracoastal sedimentation. *In* Stanley, D.J., and Swift, D.J.P., eds., Marine sediment transport and environmental management. New York, John Wiley and Sons, p. 221-240.

Wilkinson, B.J., 1975. Matagorda Island Texas: the evolution of a Gulf Coast barrier complex. Geolgoical Society of America, Bulletin, v. 86, p. 959-967.

Young, F.G., and Reinson, G.E., 1975. Sedimentology of Blood Reserve and adjacent formations (Upper Cretaceous), St. Mary River, Southern Alberta. *In* Shawa, M.S., ed., Guidebook to selected sedimentary environments in southwestern Alberta, Canada. Canadian Society of Petroleum Geologists, Field Conference, p. 10-20.

Shelf and Shallow Marine Sands

ROGER G. WALKER
Department of Geology
McMaster University
Hamilton, Ontario L8S 4M1

INTRODUCTION

Of all the major clastic environments discussed in this volume, the shallow marine systems are probably the most complex, due in part to the interaction of many different processes, and in part to the effects of the Holocene rise of sea level on Recent shelf sediments. Research is very active in both ancient and modern shallow marine systems, and many of the ideas in this paper have been developed from promising but not yet fully worked out lines of research. Thus the reader is warned that ideas are in a particularly active state of flux, and that no neatly-packaged facies models have been developed yet. I will use the terms shelf and shallow marine interchangeably, ignoring the structural implications of the correct use of the term shelf.

HISTORY OF SHELF/SHALLOW MARINE STUDIES

One of the earlier ideas about the shelf concerned the grain size distribution. Johnson (1919) coined the term "graded shelf", implying a progressive decrease in grain size from coarse at the shoreline to very fine at the shelf edge. In 1932, Shepard commented that "many geologists have stated that marine sediments vary from coarse to fine as the distance from the shore and depth of water increase. Such gradation seems so reasonable in view of our knowledge of waves and currents that what is practically a geologic axiom has come into existence" (Shepard, 1932, p. 1017-1018). Shepard's point, however, was that the idea of a graded shelf was

incorrect, and that sediment deposited during low stands of sea level by fluvial or glacial processes could be inundated by a rise of sea level without significant reworking. Such sediment was later termed "relict". Shepard (1932, p. 1038) concluded that "the most outstanding feature of the sediments on the Continental Shelves is the general scarcity of outward decreasing gradation of texture … the broad shelves have for the most part a patchy arrangement of sediment without any apparent relation to either the shoreline or the other edge of the shelf".

The idea of "relict" sediments was most recently re-stated by Emery (1968). However, shortly afterward it was suggested by Swift *et al.* (1971) that during a rise of sea level, the older sediment could be partly or completely reworked and brought into partial or complete dynamic equilibrium with shelf processes – such sediments were termed "palimpsest". In the same paper, Swift *et al.* (1971, p. 324) first emphasized the different types of shelf currents, identifying: 1) intruding ocean currents, 2) tidal currents, 3) meteorological (storm) currents, and 4) density currents as the four main types. This classification, along with subsequent work, has suggested a division of shallow marine/shelf systems into three main types (Swift *et al.*, in press): 1) tide dominated (17% of the world's shelves), 2) storm dominated (80%), and 3) shelves dominated by intruding ocean currents (3%).

History of Tide-Dominated-Shelf Studies

In these systems, large sand waves or megaripples are the characteristic and dominant bedforms. These were recognized by Van Veen (1935) and Hulsemann (1955) in the southern North Sea, but the important modern studies appeared in the early 1960s; Jordan (1962; Georges Bank, Atlantic Shelf of USA), Stride (1963; British Coast), Reineck (1963; southern North Sea) and Off (1963; various localities). More recently, work done by Houbolt (1968) and McCave (1971) in the southern North Sea has led to the definition of tidal sand waves (up to about 7 m high) and tidal sand ridges (up to 40 m high). At about the same time, Klein (1970) described similar features in the Bay of Fundy.

Although many ancient nearshore tidal sandstones (tidal channels, tidal flats) had been described by the mid 1970s, there were remarkably few descriptions of open marine tidally-dominated sandstones. Only one or two are considered in the compilation of examples edited by Ginsburg (1975). In transgressive situations, sandwave complexes may be built and maintained by tidal currents, as discussed by Nio (1976), but there remain few examples of open marine ancient tidal sandstones.

History of Storm-Dominated-Shelf Studies.

The beginning of the present emphasis on storms can be traced to Hayes (1967), who discussed the effect of Hurricanes Carla and Cindy on the Texas coast and shelf. He suggested that during Hurricane Carla a density current had been generated which spread eroded sand from the barrier island across the shelf as a graded bed. This idea has been in the forefront of thought for 15 years, although there are now significant modifications. In the early 1970s, there were several storm interpretations of ancient rocks, for example by Ball (1971, Westphalia Limestone of US Midwest), and Hobday and Reading (1972, various stratigraphic units). However, the most important event was the description of "hummocky cross stratification" (HCS) by Harms (in Harms *et al.*, 1975), and its interpretation as a storm-formed sedimentary structure. Hummocky cross stratification has been used in the interpretation of ancient sandstones since 1979 (e.g., Hamblin and Walker, 1979; Bourgeois, 1980; plus over 100 other examples, Duke, in press), and is currently the topic of extensive discussion and research. Also, during the last 10 years, there have been very important contributions from marine geologists and oceanographers concerning storm-generated flows on shelves (e.g., Swift *et al.*, in press). However, the geological record gives a very different viewpoint on storms from that of marine geologists, a problem discussed by Swift (1984) and Walker (1984a), and considered again below.

It follows from these brief historical reviews that storm-dominated, tide-dominated, and ocean-current-dominated shelves should be consi-

142

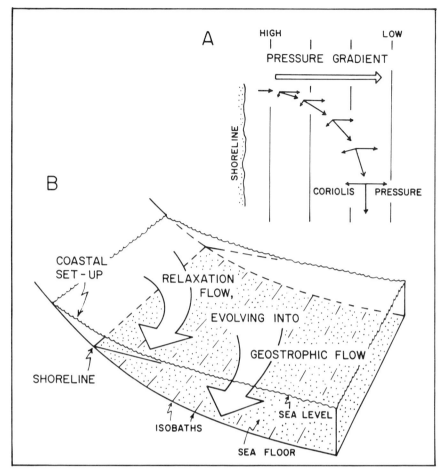

Figure 1
Coastal set-up ("storm surge") creates a seaward pressure gradient. Bottom water flows seaward as a result, but is deflected to the right (northern hemisphere) by Coriolis force to form a geostrophic flow parallel to isobaths. The relaxation, or seaward-directed flow is too transient to be measured, and neither sketch is to scale. After Swift et al. (in press) and Strahler (1963).

dered separately, although many interpretations of shelf sediments propose combinations of processes.

STORM DOMINATED SHELVES –
THE OCEANOGRAPHIC VIEWPOINT
The oceanographer or marine geologist approaches the storm-dominated shelf in a very different manner from that of a land-based geologist, and acquires very different types of data. I will first present the oceanographer's view of shelf processes, and then the marine geologist's view of recent sediment accumulations. Finally, I will consider the land-based geologist's viewpoint, and see to what extent these various approaches converge toward a general model(s) for storm dominated shelves. I will begin by examining storm processes under the general headings of wind-forced currents, relaxation (storm-surge-ebb) currents, and turbidity currents.

Wind-forced currents are generated as the wind blows across the water surface, gradually entraining deeper and deeper ocean layers, until the moving water column may move sediment on the bed. In the simplest case (Fig. 1), the wind forces water onshore, creating an elevation of the water surface and hence a seaward pressure gradient. Water particles experience the pressure force, but also a Coriolis force, and the initial seaward flow will be deflected to the right (in the northern Hemisphere) and will evolve into a geostrophic flow moving parallel to isobaths. D.J.P. Swift (pers. commun., 1983) has suggested that the geostrophic discharge may be 2000 to 3000 times as great as the "relaxation" (seaward oriented) discharge for a 2-day storm. In general, Swift et al. (in press) note that "on a north-south, east facing coast in the northern hemisphere, a wind from

either the northeast or northwest quadrant will cause set-up. Similarly, a wind from either the southeast or southwest quadrant will cause set-down". Resulting flows are shown in Figure 2.

There is now some data on the magnitude of such flows close to the bed. Measurements by Swift and colleagues (see Swift et al., 1979; Swift and Field, 1981) have shown near bottom flow velocites of up to about 60 cm/sec on the Atlantic Shelf in depths of 10 to 20 m (Fig. 3) – velocities of several tens of cm/sec occur several times per year as a result of northeasterly storms. These flows generate current ripples and megaripples, and the megaripples may appear in the geological record as medium scale, angle-of-repose cross bedding. The flows also deposit abundant graded beds, as observed in vibracores (Swift, pers. commun., 1984).

More catastropic storm flows have been monitored in the Gulf of Mexico. Tropical Storm Delia (Sept. 3-5, 1973; Forristall et al., 1977) was monitored on a drilling platform 50 km offshore from Galveston Island, in about 21 m of water (Fig. 4). Alongshore flows reached nearly 2 m/sec and seaward-directed flows were between 50 and 75 cm/sec. The peak storm surge of 2 m at Galveston Island did not occur until 30 hours after storm landfall, whereas the maximum alongshore velocity occurred some 38 hours before peak storm surge. This suggests that the alongshore flow was due directly to wind stress, not to storm surge ebb. The geological effects of these flows can only be guessed, but the alongshore velocities suggest effective sand transport, and the creation of ripples, sinuous crested dunes and possible upper plane bed during the 30 or so hours of gradually increasing flows (Fig. 4). In wind-forced flows where the entire water column is moving, flow depths may be much too great for the formation of upper plane bed, although fine grain sizes (fine, very fine sand) even in deep flows favour upper flat bed rather than sinuous crested dunes. The stability fields of the various bed forms have been given by Southard (in Harms et al., 1982), although there is little data for flows several metres deep. As the Tropical Storm Delia velocities decreased again during the following 18 hours (Fig. 4), the plane bed would have been reworked into dunes (if the sand were coarser than the middle of the fine

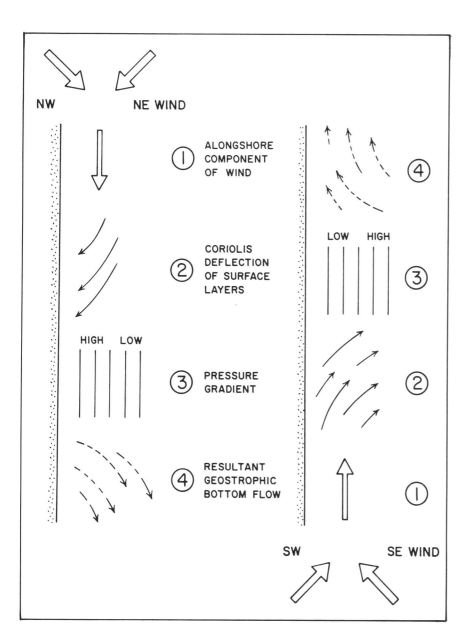

Figure 2
An east-facing coastline trends roughly N-S. Winds from the NW and NE will have a southward, alongshore component. This will entrain surface waters, which are deflected to the right (northern hemisphere), resulting in coastal set-up. Ebb of bottom waters, with Coriolis deflection, will produce a south-flowing geostrophic current. Similarly, winds from the SW or SE wil produce coastal set-down, and the resulting pressure gradient will produce a north-flowing geostrophic current. Note, importantly, that this step-wise analysis is presented only to clarify the processes. It is not observed in the field – what is measured is only the resultant geostrophic flow.

Figure 3
Sediment concentration, wave energy, and flow velocity measured at the 10 m isobath, almost 2 km off Tobay Beach, Long Island, New York. Note storm of October 20-22, and the very gentle, reversing tidal currents of October 22-29th. Data recorded once per second for an eight minute burst, once an hour. From Swift and Field, 1981.

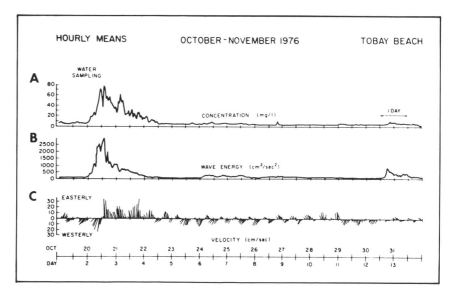

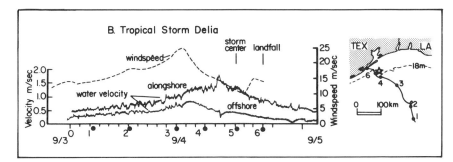

Figure 4
Windspeed, offshore and alongshore current velocities during Tropical Storm Delia, 3-5 September, 1973. Data recorded at site of *drilling platform 50 km offshore of Galveston Island, Texas, in a depth of 21 m. From Forristall et al., 1977.*

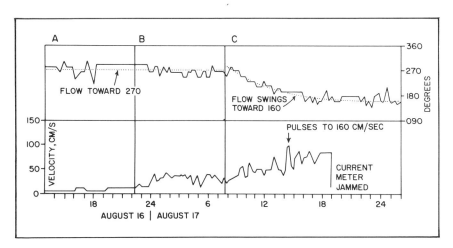

Figure 5
Current speed and directions during Hurricane Camille, 16-18 August, 1969. Recording site was 360 m offshore of the panhandle of *Florida, in a depth of 6.3 m, about 160 km east of the path of the eye of the hurricane. Phases A, B and C discussed in text. From Murray, 1970.*

sand range), and the dunes subsequently reworked into current ripples. The net result may therefore be an increment of sand transport, but no preservation of sedimentary structures other than ripple cross lamination.

Wind and current velocities were measured during Hurricane Camille (Aug. 16-18, 1969; Murray, 1970) using instruments installed in 6.3 m of water, 360 m offshore of the Florida coast. This location was about 160 km east of the path of the eye of the hurricane. During phase B (Murray, 1980; Fig. 5) flows gradually intensified, and were directed alongshore (toward 270°) – the wind was blowing from the east (080°). Murray's explanation for this flow was "that the longshore current generated in the surf zone set in motion by lateral friction the water beyond the outer bar" (1970, p. 4580). During phase C (Fig. 5), the flows intensified to about 1 m/sec, with pulses to 1.6 m/sec. The wind gradually

changed from blowing from the east (080°) to blowing from the south (180°), and the bottom flow changed from 270° to 160° (offshore). The onshore wind piled water up against the shoreline, the resulting offshore (160°) flow can be ascribed to the seaward pressure gradient. This flow may have veered westward (to the right) due to Coriolis forces as it moved further offshore beyond the recording instruments. These storm flows effected an increment of sediment transport, but although dunes (and possibly upper flat beds) were formed locally, they were probably reworked into ripples during waning storm flows. Thus the effects of both Delia and Camille might be undetectable in the geological record of shelf deposits.

Relaxation (storm surge ebb) currents were emphasized by Hayes (1967), and have been subsequently invoked in many geological interpreta-

tions. Storm surges, or set-ups are unusually high water elevations due to storm winds blowing water onshore (Fig. 1). As coastal water levels rise, there is a bottom return flow which is normally a geostrophic flow (Figs. 1 and 2). In major storms, particularly hurricanes, the storm surge may reach maximum elevations of 6 to 7 metres, but these heights are only maintained for up to about five hours.

It has been assumed by geologists that the seaward flow driven by this hydraulic head, and the final ebbing of the head itself, would create a bottom current capable of transporting sand seaward below fairweather wave base. This was first suggested by Hayes (1967), who observed a graded bed on the Texas Shelf off Padre Island following Hurricane Carla in 1961. Hayes suggested that Carla had created a 7 m storm surge, which ebbed seaward as a "density current" (i.e., a *turbidity* current, because the density would have been due to suspended sediment), depositing the graded bed. However, the 7 m surge was at Matagorda Bay, about 185 km to the northeast, not at Padre Island (Hayes, 1967, Fig. 5; Morton, 1981). It now appears that the Carla graded bed was deposited by a geostrophic flow moving southward along the Texas coast, and not directly from a seaward moving storm surge ebb.

A second interpretation of recent marine sediments as storm surge ebb deposits was published by Nelson (1982). On the Bering Shelf off the Yukon River Delta, there are graded sand and silt layers with an idealized sequence of sedimentary structures including "basal parallel-laminated medium to fine sand (S_b), a centre section of the sand layer with cross and convolute lamination (S_c), commonly containing laminated beds of epiclastic plant fragments (S_d), and an upper mud cap (S_e), that is absent in many places" (Nelson, 1981, p. 539). Nelson also comments that "because of the similarity to the vertical sequence of structures defined by Bouma (1962) for graded turbidite beds, I have chosen to designate shelf structures by sustituting the T of Bouma's T_{a-e} designation with a capital S, signifying shallow water, graded storm-sand beds". The beds can be traced for some 100 km from the Yukon Delta, but no single bed can unambiguously be correlated with a known

145

storm surge ebb. Nelson (1982, p. 541) considers three mechanisms for formation of the layers – the "sudden high river discharge at the time of spring break up . . . wind forced currents and storm surge ebb-flow currents", and comments that "both [wind forced currents and storm-surge ebb-flow currents] appear to be responsible on the basis of limited oceanographic data". He does not discuss the obvious possibility that the "S_{b-e}" beds were actually deposited by turbidity currents. In view of the geological evidence for shelf/shallow marine turbidity currents discussed below, I suggest this is a more likely possibility for Nelson's beds than appealing to 100 km of bedload transport driven by "storm-surge ebb-flows". Swift (pers. commun., 1984) disagrees, and suggests incremental movement of the sand and silt by a geostrophic wind-forced flows. The sharp-based Bouma-like beds would therefore represent the *final* incremental flow.

Many of the ideas presented in this section, and the previous section on wind-forced currents, are presently (Spring of 1984) at the forefront of current research, and are controversial. This is at least partly due to the different types of data handled by geologists and oceanographers. I would suggest the following tentative conclusions:

1) for small coastal set-ups of a metre or two, the relaxation flow (Fig. 1) is deflected by Coriolis forces and evolves into a geostrophic flow. Sand is transported mostly parallel to isobaths, rather than directly seaward. This conclusion is based on extensive measurements during minor (annual) storms (Swift *et al.*, in press).

2) for major coastal set-ups of several metres (5 to 7 m range), there is little oceanographic data on the distances of seaward or alongshore movement of the surge ebb current. Geologists have deduced from the paleocurrent patterns of sharp-based sandstones that sand *can* be transported directly seaward, and introduced suddenly into normally quiet depositional environments. Examples are discussed below. In many cases, they have appealed to "storm surge ebb" currents, perhaps of magnitudes not yet observed and documented by oceanographers.

3) the geological record contains some evidence that the sharp-based sandstones have been introduced by turbidity currents. Possible generating mechanisms are discussed later. If a turbidity current were generated, it would

then be driven downslope by gravity, rather than being driven by a combination of pressure and Coriolis forces and therefore evolving into a geostrophic flow parallel to isobaths. The turbidity current possibility is considered below.

Turbidity currents are discussed in detail in a separate paper ("Turbidites and Associated Coarse Clastic Deposits") in this volume. It is emphasized that they are simply a special case of a density current, where the excess density of the flow is due to suspended sediment (rather than elevated salinities or lower temperatures). The turbidity current mechanism can operate in flumes and lakes, in shallow seas and on the continental shelf, and in deep ocean basins. For beds to be *recognized* as turbidites, they must retain the sedimentary structures imposed by the turbidity current, and this normally requires deposition below *storm* wave base.

Turbidity currents have not been directly observed on modern shelves. The gradient of the shelf averages 0° 07', or 0.002 (Shepard, 1963, p. 257), but this is probably no obstacle to turbidity current flow, because in the deep oceans they are known to travel hundreds of km across abyssal plains

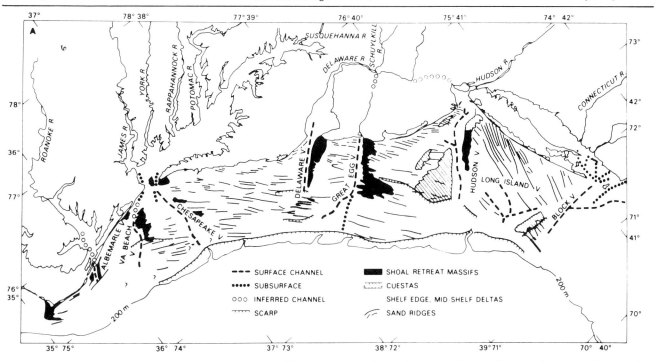

Figure 6.
Major morphologhical features of the Middle Atlantic Bight. Note relationship of shoal

retreat massifs to present estuaries (and capes – e.g., Cape Hatteras, lower left corner of diagram). Note consistent 22° angle

between linear sand ridges and the shoreline. From Johnson, 1978, after Swift et al., 1973.

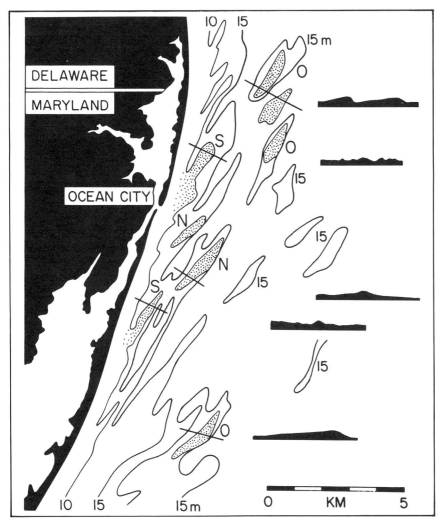

Figure 7
Bathymetry of the Assateague ridge field, offshore Maryland, U.S.A. Note typical shoreface (S), nearshore (N), and offshore (0) ridges, with typical bathymetric cross sec- *tions. The bathymetric cross sections are not to the same scale as the map of the ridges. Redrawn from Swift and Field (1981). Isobaths in metres.*

with gradients of 1:1500 or less. Before travelling such distances, they have accelerated to high velocities on the continental slope. Such long transport distances would not be expected on the shelf. Here the problem is more one of *flow generation,* and *preservation of the deposit.* Because the "evidence" for shelf turbidity currents is mostly inference from the geological record, I will re-evalue turbidity currents after examining geological storm deposits.

STORM DOMINATED SHELVES – RECENT SEDIMENTS
The most extensive studies of recent shelf sediments are probably those of Swift and colleagues on the Atlantic shelf between Nantucket and South

Carolina. Three scales of sand body can be identified:

1) shoal retreat massifs
2) linear sand ridges
3) ripple, megaripple and sandwave bedforms.

Shoal retreat massifs (Fig. 6) formed on the Atlantic shelf during the Holocene rise of sea level. Coastal depocentres were progressively transgressed, leaving a shore-perpendicular sand body on the shelf. Swift *et al.* (1972) identified *cape* retreat massifs, and *estuarine* retreat massifs (Fig. 6). Swift and co-workers have never been specific about the dimensions of shoal retreat massifs, but the Cape retreat massifs of the Carolina coast (Swift,

1975, Fig. 4) average about 10 km wide, 30 km long perpendicular to the coast, and about 2 m thick. Locally, however, relief may be up to 20 m, as on Diamond Shoals. The estuarine retreat massifs off the Middle Atlantic Bight (Fig. 6) average about 17 km wide and 45 km long perpendicular to shoreline (Swift, 1975, Fig. 3); thickness of the Delaware massif is about 15 m.

Linear sand ridges (Fig. 7) are superimposed on the shoal retreat massifs, but also occur in the areas between retreat massifs. They are up to about 10 m high, 2 to 3 km wide, and have spacings of about 2 to 6.5 km. They are up to a few tens of km long, and make an average angle of 22° (Fig. 6) with the shoreline trend. Maximum slopes are a few degrees or less. They are recognized on the Atlantic Shelf from the Gulf of Maine to South Carolina, and have also been studied on the shelf off Argentina (Parker *et al.,* 1982) and in the southern North Sea (Swift *et al.,* 1978). The most detailed study is that of Swift and Field (1981), in the Delaware-Maryland sector of the Middle Atlantic Bight. Here, they recognize systematic morphological changes from *shoreface* ridges through *nearshore* ridges to *offshore* ridges (Fig. 7), which are summarized in Table 1. The shoreface ridges can be traced into water as shallow as 3 m before they lose their identity.

Swift and Field (1981, p. 480) concluded that "the sand ridges of the Maryland coast begin as bodies of sand extracted from the littoral drift and stored in the upper shoreface by hydrodynamic processes acting during storm events". Their original suggestion for the oblique orientation of the ridges with respect to the shoreline was a combination of erosional retreat of the upper shoreface combined with higher sediment transport rates closer to shoreline. Swift (pers. commun., 1984; and Figueiredo *et al.,* 1981; Parker *et al.,* 1982) now suggests that the stability model of Huthnance (1982) might be more appropriate (Fig. 8). In this model, formulated mathematically for tidally dominated ridges in the North Sea, slight original topographic elements tend to grow upward, at a rate proportional to their spacing and orientation with respect to prevailing currents. Parker *et al.* (1982) note that "in Huthnance's scheme, an oblique orientation

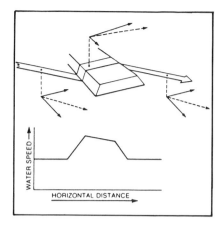

Figure 8
Huthnance model of flow-oblique sand ridge formation, from Parker et al., *1982. As flow moves obliquely up the ridge flank, the cross-ridge component accelerates due to decreasing cross-sectional area. Over the crest, the along-ridge component of velocity is reduced due to frictional drag. The cross-ridge component decreases to its original value.*

Table 1

Dimensions of shoreface, nearshore and offshore linear sand ridges

Ridges, General Parameter	Extreme low	Extreme high	Typical
Relief (m)	3.0	12.1	6.1 - 9.1
Length (km)	3.7	18.5	8.3 - 13.9
Width (km)	0.9	2.8	1.4 - 2.3
Spacing (km)	1.5	11.1	4.5 - 6.5
Angle to coast (°)	10	40	15 - 35
Max. slopes (°)	0.2	7.0	0.75 - 2.0

Comparison, Shoreface, Nearshore and Offshore Ridges Parameter	Shoreface ridges	Nearshore ridges	Offshore ridges
Mean slope	1.5°	1.0°	0.5°
Steepest slope	2.5°	2.0°	7.0°
Landward:seaward slope	1:1	1:2	1:5
Length:width	9:1	6:1	3:1

with respect to flow is essential because ridges parallel to flow can have no sand carried to their tops . . . ridges normal to flow must experience an acceleration across the crests in order to satisfy continuity, hence cannot deposit sand there . . . when flow is oblique with respect to the ridge crest, the cross-ridge component of flow must similarly accelerate. However, the along ridge components experience frictional retardation and the ensuing deceleration over the crestal area result in sand deposition". In essence, the alongshore geostrophic flows will favour the growth of those irregularities originally oriented obliquely to the shoreline; a rigourous mathematical treatment is given by Huthnance (1982).

As the transgression continues, the shoreface ridges begin to respond to deepening water, and evolve into nearshore ridges. The high frequency component of flow due to wave orbital motion is less important than wind-forced southward moving geostrophic flow, and hence unidirectional flow bedforms (especially sand waves) can form. Mud is deposited in the troughs between linear sand ridges. Over a period of time there is a tendency for erosion on the landward side, and deposition of fine sand on the seaward side, giving a net seaward lateral accretion. In even deeper water, the ridges

become more asymmetrical, and adopt "some of the characteristics of flow-transverse bedforms" (Swift and Field, 1981, p. 480). Textural gradients associated with the ridges are preserved as far as 20 km from the beach, suggesting that these *offshore* ridges are still responding to flows – they are not relict.

If ridges of this type are formed by erosional retreat of the shoreface during transgression, we might expect to find them in transgressive situations in the geological record. They will tend to have sharp bases resting on a transgressive lag of coarse material. There are many linear sand bodies in the Cretaceous Western Interior Seaway, but they mostly grade downward into offshore bioturbated marine mudstones. I will show later that none of them has been interpreted in terms of erosional shoreface retreat as described by Swift and colleagues.

Ripples, Megaripples and Sandwaves are the smallest of the three types of sand bodies recognized on the Atlantic Shelf. *Ripples* occur from shoreline to shelf edge, and are current formed (asymmetrical) during peak storm flows. They are probably reworked to symmetrical wave ripples as the flow wanes (Swift *et al.*, 1979). The *megaripples* have low crestal continuity, and a spacing of 1 to 40 m. They form on the

inner shelf during storm months (November to March) and may cover up to 15% of the area of the inner shelf in patches several km in diameter. They are modified or erased during the quiet summer months, with formation of rounded crests and slopes well below angle-of-repose. Swift *et al.* (1979, p. 401) suggest that this is due to the "ploughing and bulldozing action of benthic animals", although they have recently suggested (Swift *et al.*, 1983) that other rounded megaripples may be the bedform that gives rise to hummocky cross stratification (discussed below). Swift (pers. commun., 1984) notes that both degraded sharp-crested megaripples and true hummocky megaripples are present on the shelf. The *sandwaves* have spacings greater than 40 m, and heights normally less than 1 m. Swift *et al.* (1979, p. 401) note that "the virtual restriction of Middle Atlantic Bight sandwave fields to the inner shelf (<30 m depth) is probably a consequence of the greater frequency with which wind stresses are transmitted to the seafloor in this shallow region". Significantly, "portions of the downcurrent slopes of these sandwaves [are] frequently at the angle of repose" (Swift *et al.*, 1979, p. 401). Large sandwaves, up to about 7 m high "occur where the shelf cross-sectional area is constricted at Kitty Hawk, and on the cape exten-

Table 2

Recurrance intervals for preserved storm emplaced sharp based sandstones

Stratigraphic Unit	Author	Calculated Recurrance Interval, Years
"Passage Beds" (U. Jurassic) Alberta	Hamblin and Walker, 1979	3200
Devonian, Germany	Goldring and Langenstrassen, 1979	400 to 2000
Ordovician, Norway	Brenchley *et al.*, 1979	10000 to 15000
Triassic, Germany	Aigner, 1982	2500 to 5000, or 5000 to 10000
Ordovician, Virginia, USA	Kreisa, 1981	1200 to 3100

Approximate average 5000 years

sion shoals (Diamond Shoals, Frying Pan Shoals)" (Swift, pers. commun., 1984). These sandwaves are built by storm, not tidal currents.

In conclusion it would appear that the linear sand ridges form in the upper shoreface by a combination of oscillatory and unidirectional flow. Thus the internal structure should consist largely of current and wave ripples, and medium scale angle-of-repose cross bedding. Swift (pers. commun., 1984) comments that in vibracores, the most common primary structure after bioturbation is horizontal lamination. During deepening (transgression), ripples, megaripples and sandwaves may form on the flanks and in the troughs of the

sand ridges, again forming wave ripples, angle-of-repose cross bedding (from sandwaves), and bioturbated low angle stratification (from megaripples). Continued transgression may allow the burial of the ridges by mud, and hence the preservation of their sedimentary structures and gross morphology in the geological record.

STORM DOMINATED SHELVES - THE GEOLOGICAL VIEWPOINT

The geologist's view of storm deposits is very different from that of marine geologists and oceanographers. This is probably due to the fact that many of the beds in the geological record represent the "thousand year event"

(Table 2), and hence were deposited by processes which may not have been observed or monitored by marine geologists. In most shallow seas, we can identify two main areas of deposition. The first is a *shoreface zone* (Fig. 9) characterized by abundant day-to-day sand transport above fairweather water base. The depth of fairweather wave base varies, but normally lies in the 5 to 15 m range (Walker, 1984a). Below fairweather wave base there is the *normally quiet shallow shelf* (Fig. 9), commonly a site of quiet deposition of mud with extensive bioturbation by organisms that graze and mine the substrate (the *Cruziana,* and particularly the *Zoophycos* ichnofacies of Frey and Pemberton ("Trace Fossil Facies Models", this volume). It is of fundamental importance that sand cannot normally cross the interface between shoreface and open shelf, and that only storm-dominated processes can transport sand below fairweather wave base.

The first clue to the storm origin of some beds is therefore the occurrence of sandstones (and/or conglomerates) interbedded with bioturbated mudstones of the *Cruziana* or *Zoophycos* ichnofacies. Such sandstones commonly have sharp and/or erosive bases, and average 5 to 100 cm in thickness (Fig. 10). The tops of the beds may grade up into mudstone, or more commonly, the top contact is disrupted by bioturbation. In this interbedded sand-

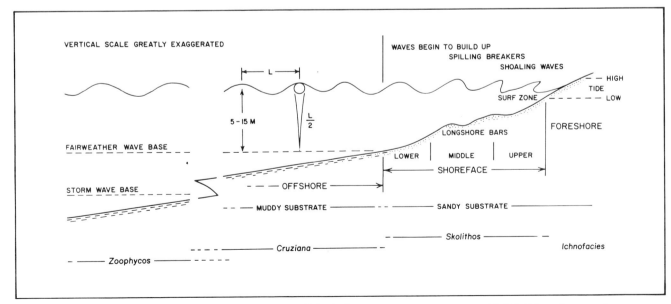

Figure 9

Offshore profile locating foreshore, shoreface and offshore, as well as fairweather wave base and ichnofacies occurrences. Note fairweather waves of wavelength L cannot agitate the bed at depths greater than roughly L/2. Fairweather wave base commonly lies at about 5-15 m depths.

stone/bioturbated mudstone facies, current ripple cross lamination and medium scale angle-of-repose cross bedding tend to be rare or absent, and the characteristic sedimentary structure is hummocky cross stratification (Fig. 11).

Hummocky Cross Stratification (HCS). The structure is shown in the block diagram of Figure 11, and in outcrop form the Cardium Formation (U. Cretaceous) at Seebe, Alberta (Fig. 10). The stratification consists of curving laminations, both convex-up (hummocks) and concave-up (swales), with maximum dips of about 12 to 15°. The laminations commonly intersect at low angles as the hummocks and swales migrate on the sea floor during aggradation. Laminae may thicken toward the centres of swales, but toward the tops of individual beds, hummocks and swales tend to lose their topography, flatten out, and pass into a thin veneer of small symmetrical oscillation ripples. The hummocky cross stratification looks the same regardless of the orientation of a vertical cross section through it; wavelengths are commonly of the order of 1 to 5 m, and heights are a few tens of centimetres. Full geometric descriptions have been given by Walker (1982), Dott and Bourgeois (1982, 1983) and Walker *et al.* (1983).

The term "hummocky cross stratification" was created by Harms (in Harms *et al.,* 1975), and there are now more than 100 stratigraphic units known to contain the structure (Duke, in press). Harms suggested its formation by "strong surges of varying direction that are generated by relatively large storm waves of a rough sea", and most workers now agree that storm waves acting below fairweather wave base are one of the main agents forming hummocky cross stratification. The interpretation of wave action *below fairweather wave base* is based on the nature of the interbedded bioturbated mudstones, and the fact that in the interbedded HCS sandstone/-bioturbated mudstone facies (Fig. 10), medium scale angle-of-repose cross bedding is rare to absent. This implies that either grain size is consistently too fine for the formation of medium scale cross bedding, or that there has been no fairweather reworking of the storm-formed hummocky cross stratification, hence suggesting original formation

Figure 10
Sharp-based hummocky cross stratified sandstones interbedded with bioturbated *mudstones. Base of Cardium Formation at Seebe, Alberta. Hummocks (H) and swales (S) are arrowed.*

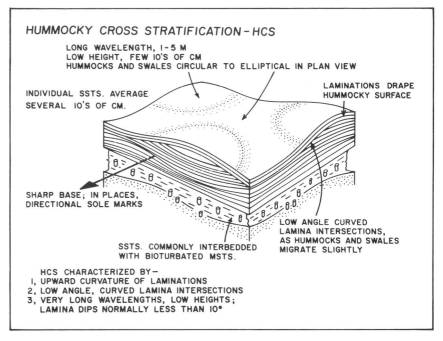

Figure 11
Block diagram of hummocky cross stratification, showing its typical occurrence in the *interbedded HCS sandstone/bioturbated mudstone facies. From Walker, 1982.*

above storm wave base but below fairweather wave base. The most recent discussions of the mechanics of HCS formation are by Dott and Bourgeois (1983), Walker *et al.* (1983) and Swift *et al.* (1983) - these latter workers suggest a combination of waning storm-generated unidirectional flows with superimposed oscillatory storm wave action.

Hummocky cross stratification has been recognized in Precambrian to Pleistocene deposits, in all parts of the world. It seems to be most commonly

developed in fine to very fine sands, but also occurs in very coarse sand and granule gravels (Walker *et al.,* 1983, Fig. 4). It is common in the Cretaceous Western Interior Seaway of North America, particularly in the Gallup Sandstone (Harms *et al.,* 1975), the Cardium Formation (Wright and Walker, 1981; Walker, 1983b) and in parts of the Viking Formation. Hummocky cross stratification can be recognized in cores by the low angle lamina dips, the low angle lamina intersections, and the occasionally visible gentle curvature of the lami-

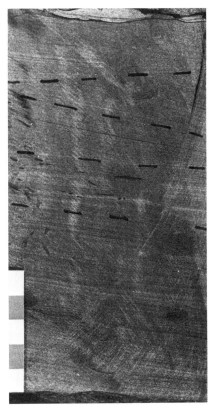

Figure 12
Core showing low angle lamination, with subtle low angle changes in dips of lamination, interpreted as hummocky cross stratification. Scale in cm. Base of sandstone rests sharply on bioturbated mudstone. Cardium Formation, well 4-22-35-8W5 between Caroline and Ricinus fields, southern Alberta, depth 8799 ft (2682 m).

Figure 13
Core showing low angle lamination, with convex-up and concave-up curvature, and subtle low angle changes in dips of laminae. This is apparently not ripple cross lamination, nor angle-of-repose cross bedding, nor upper plane bed – it is interpreted as hummocky cross stratification. Nikanassin Formation, well 7-5-69-9W6. Elmworth Field, central Alberta; 8263 ft (2519 m). Core is about 7 cm wide.

nae (Figs. 12 and 13). The structure appears the same which ever way the core is viewed; part of the identification is on negative grounds, that the structure (Figs. 12 and 13) is neither ripple cross lamination, angle-of-repose cross bedding, nor plane lamination. In a context of bioturbated mudstones, hummocky cross stratification is the most likely alternative.

Emplacement of Hummocky Cross Stratified Sandstones

The identification of hummocky cross stratification as a storm formed structure below fairweather wave base is generally agreed upon, but there are still fundamental problems concerning *how* the sand was first transported to its depositional site before the hummocky cross stratification was formed. There appear to be three main possibilities:
1) wind-forced currents
2) relaxation (storm surge ebb) currents
3) turbidity currents

1) *Wind-Forced Currents.* As reviewed above, wind forced currents commonly achieve speeds of several tens of cm/sec on the Atlantic Shelf, with measured speeds of up to 2 m/sec as a result of hurricane winds. There is little doubt that these flows effectively transport sand below fairweather wave base, and it seems reasonable that superimposed oscillatory wave currents could form hummocky cross stratification. This method of sand transport is here termed *incremental,* in as much as the sand may not have moved to the final depositional site in one sudden flow. It is the incremental addition of sand transported during many storm events that finally creates the deposit. There are no examples of hummocky cross stratification in the literature which are *demonstrably* incremental. If there were, one might also expect to find evidence of geostrophic (parallel to isobaths) dispersal patterns, and some preserved ripple cross lamination or medium scale cross bedding, made by flows which moved sand but without superimposed storm waves to make hummocky cross stratification. Beds would probably tend to be relatively thin. Most workers agree that sharp-based sandstones similar to those in Figure 10 are single depositional events. They could represent the *last* of a series of incremental sand

movements, or they may have been emplaced more catastrophically by one of the processes discussed below.

2) *Relaxation (Storm Surge Ebb) Currents.* This has been a popular geological interpretation of hummocky cross stratified beds, and the interpretation is based upon Hayes' (1967) study of hurricanes Carla and Cindy. As discussed above, Hayes' interpretation may be incorrect. Also, Swift *et al.* (in press) have emphasized that the "relaxation" (or seaward-directed) part of a storm surge ebb (Fig. 1) will be minor compared with the geostrophic flow parallel to isobaths. The geological record does not contribute solid evidence concerning seaward-directed bottom flows generated by storm surge ebb, so I will turn to a third mechanism, and then return to the problem of storm surges and their evolution into flows.

3) *Turbidity Currents.* There are two or three geological situations which strongly suggest that sharp based hummocky cross stratified sandstones have been initially transported seaward by turbidity currents.

a) Fernie-Kootenay (U. Jurassic) transition, Alberta (Hamblin and Walker, 1979). A composite stratigraphic section is shown in Figure 14. The lower part consists of classical turbidites mostly with Bouma BC sequences, and abundant sole marks indicating flow toward NNW (Fig. 14). There is a short transition zone where turbidites and hummocky cross stratified sandstones are interbedded (60 m level, Fig. 14), and then the upper part of the section is dominated by sharp-based hummocky cross stratified sandstones (Fig. 15). These have sole marks oriented in an identical direction to those of the turbidites (Fig. 14). The turbidity currents flowed down the paleoslope, driven by gravity acting on the density difference between the flow and the ambient sea water. The flows that emplaced the sharp-based hummocky cross stratified sandstones followed the same paleoslope, and it seems reasonable to suggest that they were also turbidity currents. This paleocurrent relationship would *not* be expected if the turbidity currents flowed downslope perpendicular to isobaths, and the hummocky cross stratified beds were emplaced incrementally by geostrophic flows *parallel* to isobaths.

Instead of Bouma sequences, the beds contain hummocky cross stratification, suggesting that they were deposited from turbidity currents *above* storm wave base, where the storm waves suppressed the Bouma divisions and formed hummocky cross stratification instead. This sequence is very well exposed in a continuous section just east of the traffic circle at Banff, Alberta.

b) Wapiabi-Chungo (U. Cretaceous) transition, southern Alberta (Walker and Hunter, 1982, p. 61-71). Sections at Trap Creek, and particularly in the Highwood River, southern Alberta, show sequences similar to the Fernie-Kootenay transition, namely classical turbidites with Bouma divisions passing upward into sharp-based hummocky cross stratified sandstones. There is not much paleocurrent data in the Trap Creek – Highwood River area, but the same transition at Lundbreck Falls (Bullock, 1981) shows northward flow both for the classical turbidites and for the hummocky cross stratified sandstones (Fig. 16). I deduce that the hummocky cross stratified beds were emplaced by flows responding to paleoslope dip orientation (as for the Fernie-Kootenay transition), making them much more likely to be turbidity currents than wind-forced geostrophic flows paralleling isobaths.

c) Cardium Formation (U. Cretaceous), Ricinus Field, Alberta (Walker, 1984b). In the subsurface, dispersal of Cardium sand appears to be southeastward (Fig. 17). In Caroline and Garrington fields, sandstones with preserved sedimentary structures only show hummocky cross stratification. The sandstone at Ricinus clearly channels into the "A sand" at Caroline and Garrington (Walker, 1983a; Fig. 18). In some Ricinus cores, the sandstones are thick and structureless, but in others graded bedding (Fig. 19) and Bouma BC sequences are common. Beds are sharp based, and commonly contain ripped up mud clasts. Rarely, the complete Bouma ABC sequence is present (Fig. 20). In view of the fact that the Ricinus channel (about 45 km long, 4 to 5 km wide before palinspastic reconstruction, and 20 to 40 m deep) lies at least 100, and probably 140 to 200 km offshore (Fig. 17), and in view of the fact

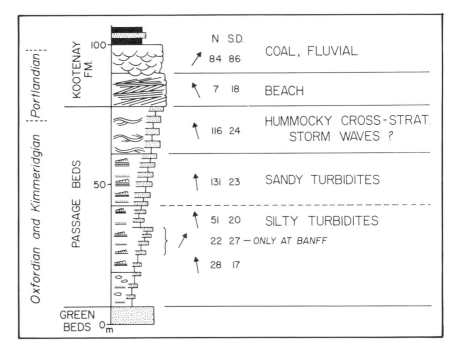

Figure 14
Generalized stratigraphic sequence for the Upper Jurassic "Passage Beds", Crowsnest Pass to Banff area, Alberta. Arrows show paleoflow vector means, N = sample size, SD = standard deviation. Turbidites show Bouma sequences, and form a thickening upward sequence at Banff. Note the same paleoflow directions for HCS beds and tubidites. The part of the section labelled "beach" may have to be reinterpreted due to highway construction and new exposures (1983) near Banff. Modified from Hamblin and Walker, 1979.

Figure 15
Hummocky cross stratified sandstone bed, intebedded with bioturbated mudstones, from the U. Jurassic "Passage Beds" at Banff, Alberta. The section is overturned, and the photo is shown with BEDDING UPSIDE DOWN. B = base of bed, H = hummock and G = gradational top of bed into mudstone.

that it contains graded beds, and Bouma BC and ABC sequences within the fill, it seems reasonable to conclude 1) that the fill was deposited by turbidity currents, and 2) that the channel itself was probably cut by turbidity currents. Because the A and B sands at Caroline and Garrington also lie similar distances offshore and have similar inferred dispersal directions, it seems reasonable to propose turbidity current emplacement of these sands, but with storm wave modification during deposition, to form hummocky cross stratification.

152

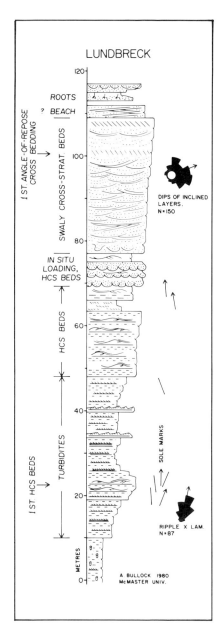

Figure 16

Measured section from Lundbreck Falls, Alberta, of the transition from Hanson (Santonian) to Chungo (Campanian) Members of Wapiabi Formation. Note similar northward paleoflow direction in turbidites and HCS sandstones, and overall progradational nature of the sequence. After Bullock, 1981.

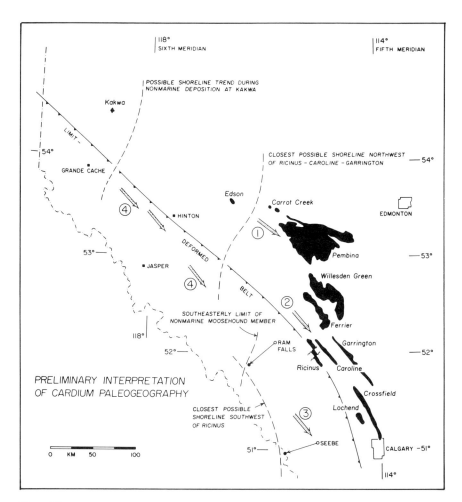

Figure 17

Preliminary interpretation of Cardium (Turonian) dispersal patterns, southern Alberta. Major Cardium fields shown black. 1) Southeast-oriented trends within Pembina field; 2) southeast trend of channel at Ricinus field; 3) southeastward paleoflow docu- *mented in outcrops between Seebe and Ram Falls; 4) southeastward paleoflow in more northerly Cardium outcrops. Arrows at Seebe and Ram Falls show palinspastically reconstructed positions (black circles). From Walker, 1983b.*

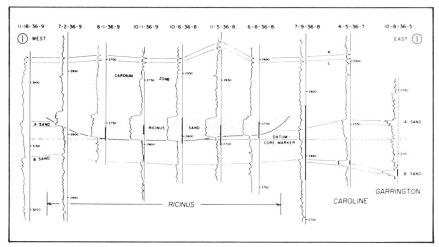

Figure 18

West to east cross section of Cardium sand (Turonian) in northern part of Ricinus field (Fig. 17). All logs are gamma rays – note the "cleaner upward" profiles for the A and B *sands at Caroline and Garrington fields (Fig. 17), and the very blocky profile for the Ricinus channel sand. Datum is a core marker, cut out by the channel. From Walker, 1983a.*

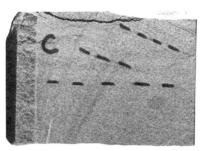

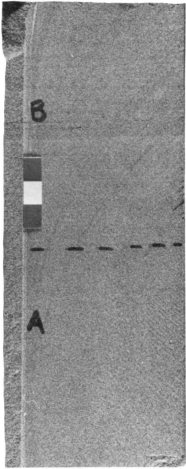

Figure 19
Graded beds from Cardium Formation (Turonian), Ricinus field, Alberta, well 3-29-34-8W5, 9384 ft (2860 m). Scale in cm. Dip is due to structural deformation within the field.

Figure 20
Complete Bouma ABC sequence from a Cardium sandstone in Ricinus field, Alberta, well 10-3-34-8W5, 8685 ft (2647 m). This bed (as well as the graded beds of Fig. 19) is interpreted as a turbidite. Scale in cm.

density for offshore gravity flow, rather than alongshore geostrophic flow (Fig. 1). In the revised version (Fig. 21), it is proposed that storms produce cyclic wave-loading of rapidly-deposited fine sediment, which in turn causes liquefaction of the substrate. As this liquefied sediment flows downslope, the combination of flow acceleration and expulsion of pore fluid may be sufficient to suspend fine and very fine sand, and generate a turbidity current. There is an extensive literature on the effects of storm waves on the substrate, liquefaction, and sediment slumping. Readers are referred to the volume edited by Saxov and Nieuwenhuis (1982).

One of the most dramatic examples of substrate liquefaction occurred offshore of South Pass, Mississippi Delta, during Hurricane Camille in 1969, where Shell Oil Company's South Pass 70 Platform B overturned and sank (Sterling and Strohbeck, 1975; Bea and Audibert, 1980). Substrate borings before and after the accident showed a significant loss of cohesive shear strength in the upper 80 feet (24 m) of sediment. An area of at least 6.7×10^6 m² showed loss of sediment to depths averaging about one metre– this sediment flowed, and subsequently piled up in adjacent areas, raising the sea floor. Although a turbidity current does not appear to have been generated here, a slightly steeper deltaic slope than that of the Mississippi might have led to a moving liquefied sediment mass that could have accelerated to become a turbidity current (see Morgenstern, 1967). A slump of South Pass Block 70 size (roughly 6.7×10^7 m³) could have formed a deposit averaging 20 cm thick and covering an area of 33.5 km². In the Cretaceous Western Interior Seaway, uplift of the Cordillera would give rapid sediment supply and relatively steep basin margins– perhaps the ingredients needed for storm wave loading to be effective in generating turbidity currents.

STORM-DOMINATED SHELVES– SYNTHESIS AND MODELS
It is presently impossible to synthesize observations from oceanography, marine geology, and the geological record into a single model. Two main "associations of features" are perhaps emerging: 1) an association of bioturbated mudstones with sharp based hummocky cross stratified sandstones

There is no space here to review the geological evidence for turbidity currents in very great detail, but the facts presented appear compelling. We are forced to ask the question, "is the geological evidence for turbidity currents so strong that we must hypothesize a generating mechanism, or must we re-evaluate the geological evidence because studies of modern storm-dominated shorelines rule out the pos-sibility of turbidity current generation?" I suggest that the geological evidence steers us toward some form of turbidity current generation at the shoreline, and this is summarized in Figure 21.

This model is a development of that presented in the first edition of Facies Models. In the earlier version, it was difficult to envisage how large volumes of sand could be suspended at the shoreline. This is necessary to give sufficient

154

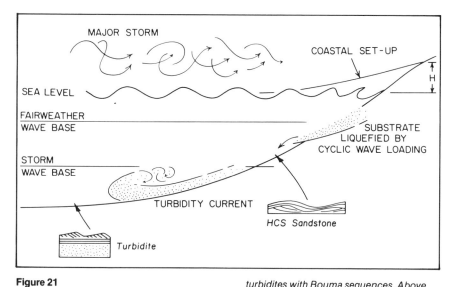

Figure 21
Storm winds create coastal set up, and cyclic loading of the substate by storm waves may liquefy the substrate. The liquefied sediment may flow and accelerate basinward, transforming into a turbidity current with all of the sediment in suspension. Deposition from this flow below storm wave base would result in turbidites with Bouma sequences. Above storm wave base, waves feeling the bottom would rework the turbidity current deposits into hummocky cross stratification. HCS could also form above fairweather wave base, but would probably be reworked into other sedimentary structures by the fair-weather processes See text for details.

10-100 cm thick (Figs. 10 and 15), and 2) an association of various scales of cross-bedding in sharp based linear sand ridges a few km wide, several km long, and 3 to 12 m thick (Figs. 6 and 7; Table 1). There are no descriptions of shorefaced-detached, storm-maintained ridges (Fig. 7) in the geological record.

It is puzzling that the better known features of marine geology– the storm-maintained ridges– are not known in the geological record, whereas the abundant HCS sandstone/bioturbated mudstone facies of the geological record (Figs. 10 and 15) is almost unknown in recent sediment studies. The HCS sandstone/bioturbated mudstone facies functions as a model of limited scale, in a similar way to the Bouma sequence for turbidites (see "General Introduction", and "Turbidites and Associated Coarse Clastic Deposits", this volume). It is a point of reference (a "norm"– see especially Dott and Bourgeois, 1982 and Walker *et al.,* 1983), a guide to observations, and a basis for interpretation (Dott and Bourgeois, 1982). In its characteristic position in vertical facies sequences (Figs. 14 and 16), the HCS sandstone/bioturbated mudstone facies functions as a predictor of facies above and below.

TIDE-DOMINATED SHELVES: TIDAL CURRENTS AND RECENT SEDIMENTS

Tides are generated by the gravitational attraction of the moon and the sun, interacting with the rotation of the earth (Coriolis force) and the geometry of ocean basins. The resulting tides may be *semidiurnal* (two high and two low tides per day), *diurnal* (one high and one low per day) or *mixed.* A good non-technical discussion of tidal current generation is given by Fox (1983), and a more technical account is presented by Howarth (1982).

Enclosed basins, or basins with small connections to open oceans, tend to have very low tidal ranges. Open seas (or enclosed seas with large connections to open seas) have higher tidal ranges, the range partly depending on the resonant oscillation period of the basin, which in turn depends upon configuration and depth. In tidal seas such as the North Sea, a progressive tidal wave moves parallel to the shoreline, circling an *amphidromic point* of zero tidal range (Fig. 22). At any one point, the tidal flow can be expressed as a vector showing magnitude and direction. These vectors can be enclosed in an ellipse ("tidal ellipse") which shows the change of magnitude and direction dur-

ing one tidal cycle. In more open parts of the North Sea, the tidal ellipses locally approach circles, but in restricted areas, the ellipses are strongly elongated (Fig. 23). Here the velocities are for a height of 1 m above the bed, and they indicate that off Lowestoft, for example, flows are oriented strongly northward at about 1 m/sec for about half the tidal cyle, and strongly southward at the same velocity for the other half of the cycle.

By contrast, the Atlantic Shelf of North America has a low tidal range except in enclosed areas such as the Gulf of Maine and the Bay of Fundy, and on shallow banks such as Georges Bank. Near-bottom tidal currents measured by Swift *et al.* (1979; Fig. 3) off Tobay Beach (Long Island) in 10 m water depths barely reach 18 cm/sec, which is the threshold velocity for sediment movement in this area. It is noticeable that flow strengths are asymmetrical (Fig. 3) – this is a common pattern and results in unidirectional sediment movement even in areas of bi-directional tidal flows. The asymmetry may be one of magnitude and/or duration, or ebb and flood currents may follow different paths – this is particularly the case where bottom flows are strongly influenced by large sand waves or tidal sand ridges.

Sand Bodies in the North Sea
The origin of sand around the British Coast and in the North Sea is largely from the unmixing of pre-Holocene deposits during and after the Holocene transgression. Transport paths have been documented by Stride (1963) and Johnson *et al.* (1982). In Figure 24, it can be seen that sand is dispersing from the English Channel northeastward into the southern North Sea, and the down-transport path shows a progressive change from bare rock with gravel lag, through sand ribbons and scattered dunes into the main tidal sand wave accumulation. The sand waves off the Rhine-Meuse Estuary (McCave, 1971) cover an area of about 15000 km², and are up to 7 m high (Fig. 25), with most of the steep sides facing northeast. The echo-sounder profiles show smaller megaripples on the backs of the sand waves but the vertical scale is grossly exaggerated – the "steep"faces have dips of only 5 to 6°. Angle-of-repose slip faces develop only in areas where there

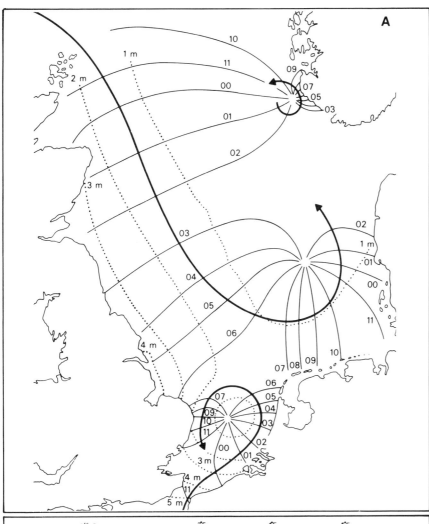

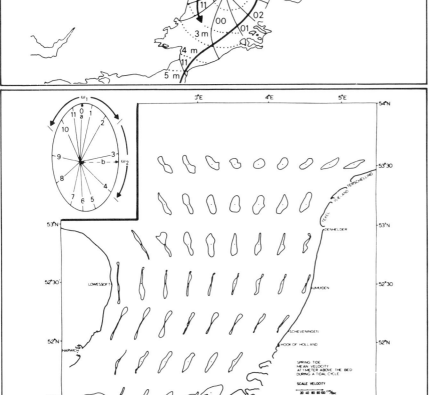

Figure 22
Amphidromic tidal system in the North Sea, showing amphidromic points of zero tidal range, and tidal co-range lines (dotted) showing increasing range from amphidromic points. Continuous co-tidal lines show times of high water in "lunar hours". From Johnson, 1978, after Houbolt, 1968.

Figure 23
North Sea tidal current ellipses for computed velocities 1 m above bed. Note extreme elongation of ellipses due to flow constriction in southern North Sea, with northward and southward velocities of about 1 m/sec off Lowestoft. Inset – example of a tidal current ellipse with complex time-velocity asymmetry. Here, velocity a > velocity b and ω_1 (roughly northward flows) occupy 4.5 hours, and ω_2 (roughly eastward flows) occupy the other 1.5 hours of half the tidal cycle. From Johnson, 1978 and McCave, 1971 – original data source the Deutshces Hydrographisches Institut, 1963.

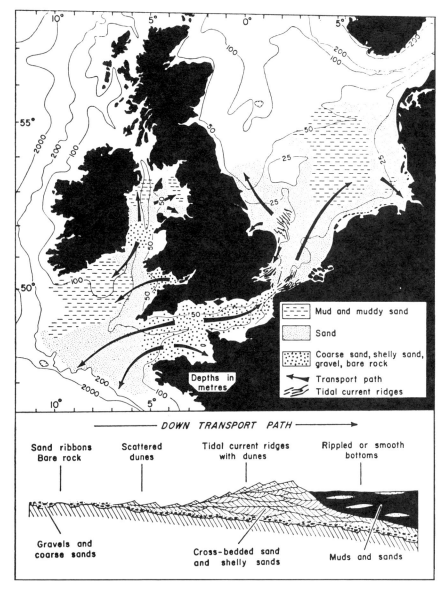

Figure 24
Dispersal of sand around the British coast, with sketch showing typical changes observed in a downcurrent direction, from bare rock and sand ribbons, through scattered dunes into tidal current ridges and sandwave complexes. These grade finally into muds, with or without sand patches. From Allen, 1970, after Stride, 1963.

is a strong time-asymmetry of tidal flows (Allen, 1980; see Fig. 32 and discussion below). The internal structure of these low angle sand waves may therefore consist of sets of cross bedding perhaps up to a metre or so in thickness (a little less than the height of the megaripples), with bounding surfaces dipping downstream at 5 to 6° reflecting the dip of the "steep" face and the migration of megaripples down that face (Fig. 26).

Large tidal sand ridges up to 40 m high have been described by Houbolt (1968) off the Norfolk coast of Britain

(Figs. 27 and 28). The ridges are "linear sand ridges" in the sense of Swift *et al.* (1973), and together they make up a shoal retreat massif (Swift, 1975, p. 128-9; Fig. 27). The area occupied by sand ridges is about 5000 km². There is no doubt that the ridges are presently being maintained by tidal flows (Houbolt, 1968), and they appear to have formed by shoreline detachment during the Holocene transgression (Swift, 1975, p. 126-128). Crests are in 10 to 20 m of water, and the ridges are about 5 km wide and up to 60 km long (Fig. 27). The "steep" side faces seaward, and

dips at about 5 to 6° (Fig. 28). The internal reflectors were at one time mistakenly interpreted as angle-of-repose cross bedding, but presumably represent older positions of the "steep" face, implying a gradual seaward migration of the ridges. Houbolt (1968, p. 252) recognized that the sand "actually seems to go round the ridge" in what is now termed a "racetrack"pattern, and details of sediment transport and sand wave migration around the northern end of Haisborough Sand (Fig. 27) have been published by McCave and Langhorne (1982).

Sand Bodies on Georges Bank
Tidal sand ridges, sand waves, and megaripples are known from areas other than the North Sea. Nantucket Shoals (Mann *et al.*, 1981) and Georges Bank (Twichell, 1983) are good examples. On Georges Bank the sand ridges and sand waves cover an area of about 20000 km². They overlie the Holocene transgressive surface, and could have formed in the present tidal regime. Twichell (1983) describes the ridges as occurring in depths less than 60 m. They are 10 to 35 m high, 15 to 90 km long, and have wavelengths of 15 km. The "steep" (about 4°) side faces southwest. Superimposed sand waves also occur in depths less than 60 m; they are 1 to 15 m high with wavelengths of 50 to 100 m. Smaller megaripples have heights mostly less than 1 m, and wavelengths of 1 to 15 m.

In general, the sand ridges and sand waves line up with the long axes of the tidal current ellipses, indicating a tidal control. Sand wave migration "is oblique to the ridges and in opposite direction on the two sides of the ridges [indicating] that the ridges themselves may be active bed forms" (Twichell, 1983, p. 707). Although Twichell does not discuss lee face angles for the sand waves, measurements from his Figure 4A indicates "steep" slopes of about 1.4°. His Figure 4B indicates slopes of about 10°.

Stratification Produced by Tidal Sand Ridges and Sand Waves
The large tidal sand ridges and sand waves have not been cored systematically. The only studies that document the internal structure of these features are those of Reineck (1963; Fig. 29) and Houbolt (1968). From these two studies,

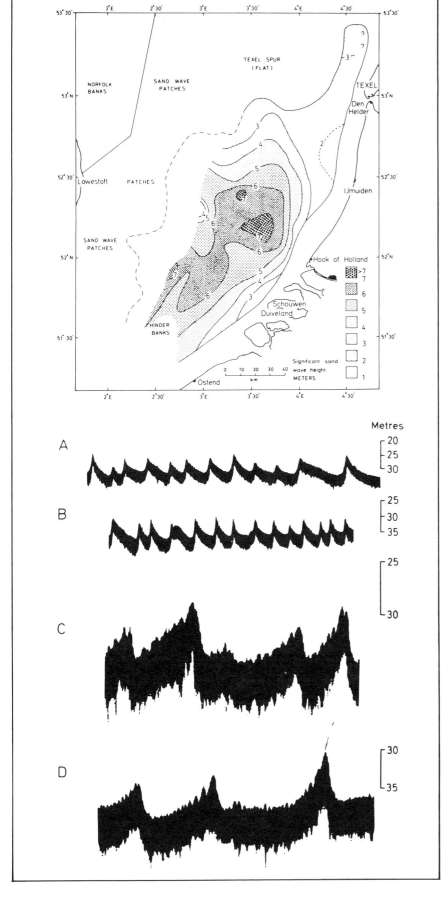

157

and the work on sand wave and sand ridge morphology by McCave (1971) and Twichell (1983), we can argue that the internal structure might be characterized by low angle surfaces (the 5 to 6° "steep" faces) with smaller sets of cross bedding dipping down or up those low angle "master bedding surfaces" (Figs. 26, 29, 30, 31 and 32). Allen (1980) formalized this into a series of sand wave classes, suggesting that the controlling factors would be "(1) the tidal time-velocity pattern, (2) water depth, and (3) bed-material calibre" (Allen, 1980, p. 303). The six classes are shown in Figure 32. Classes 1 and 2 represent fluctuating unidirectional flows. Class 3 has a significant still-stand period between critical ebb and flood velocities for sand movement U_{CR}, during which time the foreset may begin to be bioturbated (Fig. 33). Class 4 shows major reactivation surfaces (E_2 denotes second order bedding surfaces), and classes 5 and 6 show almost symmetrical ebb and flood currents.

With Allen's model in mind, and recognizing its basis in theory and in observation of modern sand waves, we may proceed to look at the geological record.

TIDE-DOMINATED SHELVES – ANCIENT SEDIMENTS

Although there are several good examples of ancient tidal flat and tidal channel environments (see Ginsburg, 1975, and Reinson, this volume), there are remarkably few examples of open shelf tidal deposits. Of the latter, there are perhaps two categories – first, the very thick (100s or 1000s of m) cross bedded quartzites typical of the late Precambrian and Early Cambrian craton margins, and second, thin transgressive sandstones (a few 10s of metres). In some cases the cross bedding is abundant and/or ubiquitous but flow directions may be almost unidirectional, making a specifically tidal interpretation hard to establish. Many illustrations are given in a recent review by Walker (1984c).

Figure 25

Sand wave heights, averaged over the period Aug. 1968 to May 1969. The echo sounder profiles show sand wave topography. Lengths of lines are: A) 3800 m; B) 2800 m; C) 900 m; and D) 1200 m. The vertical scale is grossly exaggerated, and calculated dips of lee faces from these data give 5 to 6°. From McCave, 1971.

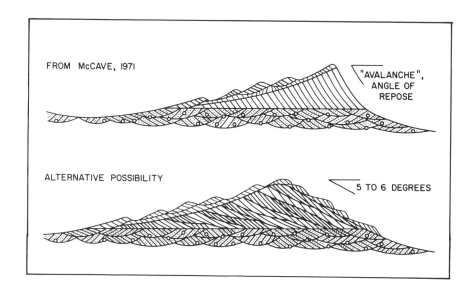

FROM McCAVE, 1971

"AVALANCHE", ANGLE OF REPOSE

ALTERNATIVE POSSIBILITY

5 TO 6 DEGREES

Figure 26

The upper model, from McCave 1971, shows the inferred internal geometry of the sand waves. However, it must be emphasized that most of the sand waves have lee faces in the 5 to 6° range (Fig. 25), and angle-of-repose cross bedding would not be predicted. This diagram has been reproduced by Brenner (1980), Stride et al., (1982) and Galloway and Hobday (1983), with no comment concerning the style of cross bedding that would result when the exaggerated echo sounder profiles are reduced to real scale. I have made a guess (lower diagram), which shows megaripples moving down the lee (5 to 6°) side, forming compound cross stratification similar to that of Figures 31 and 32.

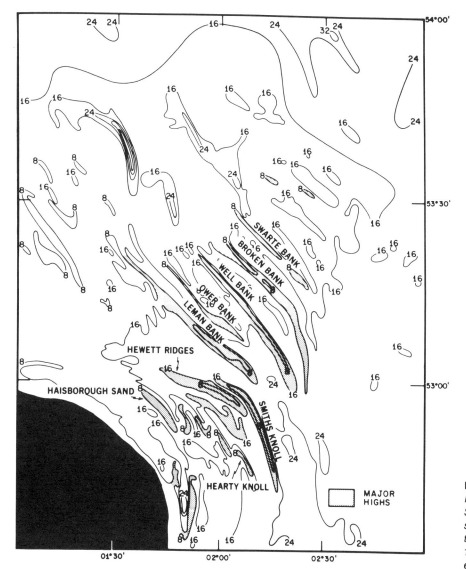

Figure 27

Map of sand ridges in the North Sea, from Swift (1975) after Houbolt (1968). The sparker profiles show that the ridges are up to 35-40 m high, and their crests are in about 10 to 15 m of water. "Steep" sides face northeast, but dip at only about 5° (see Fig. 28).

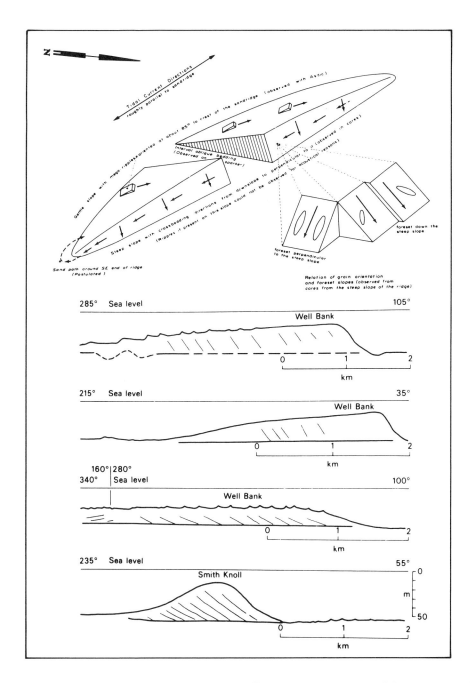

Figure 28
North Sea sand ridge as sketched by Hou-bolt (1968). Lower diagram shows sparker profiles of Well Bank (see Fig. 27), with great vertical exaggeration. Dips of the internal reflectors and the "steep" faces average about 5 to 6°.

Figure 29
Internal structure of giant ripples from the outer Jade, German Bight, southern North Sea. Note "steep" face is on lee side; diagram has 10 x vertical exaggeration. In the outer Jade, the sand wave heights vary from 1.7 to 5.5 m. The internal structure is inferred from box coring studies of the uppermost parts of the sand waves. After Reineck, 1963.

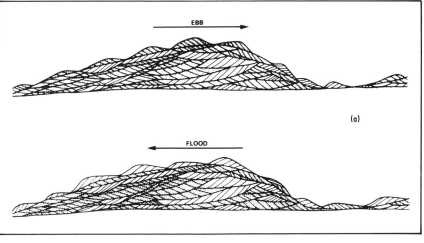

Figure 30
Large sandwave in the Lower Greensand (L. Cretaceous) near Leighton Buzzard, England. Main set is about 5 m thick, but is trun- cated by thinner, horizontally-bounded sets at the top.

Figure 31
Compound cross bedding in the Lower Greensand (L. Cretaceous) at Leighton Buz- zard, England. Regional bedding is horizon- tal – note the 5° dipping boundary surfaces of the cross bed sets. Bob Dalrymple is attempting to cope with field conditions.

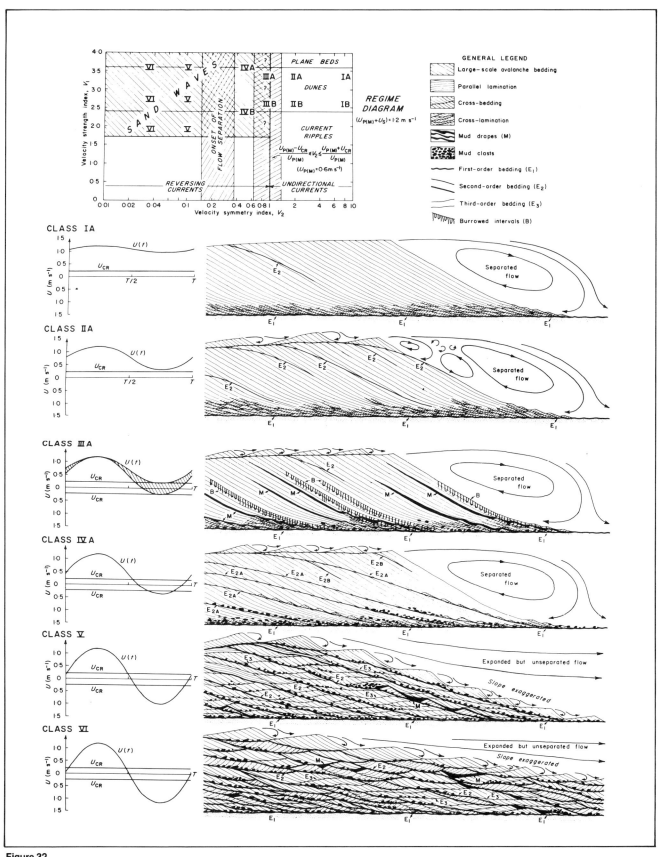

Figure 32

Regime diagram, and predicted categories of sand wave and dune internal structure. Note that the six classes are defined by the

time/velocity asymmetry (or symmetry). Classes I to IV have large foresets (commonly with reactivation surfaces, E_2) and

flow separation, but classes V and VI have much lower slopes on the "steep" side, and no flow separation. From Allen, 1980.

162

Figure 33
*Detail of large foresets shown in Figure 30.
Note extensive mottling (bioturbation) of the*

*darker foresets, and compare this figure and
Figure 30 with Allen's class III in Figure 32.*

Precambrian – Lower Cambrian Quartzites

The most detailed example of a thick
Precambrian tidal quartzite is that of
Anderton (1976) from the Jura Quartzite
(Dalradian) of Scotland. The unit is
about 5 km thick, and can be divided
into a coarse facies and a fine facies.
The coarse facies consists of various
cross bedded sandstones, with sets
from a few cm to 4.5 m thick. Locally,
bimodal-bipolar paleoflow directions
were observed, leading to an interpretation of the coarse cross bedded facies
as various tidal sand wave deposits. The
fine facies consist of interbedded mudstones and sharp-based sandstones
with parallel lamination and ripple cross
lamination. Beds over 10 cm thick
"show a sequence of structures similar
to that found in some turbidites" (Anderton, 1976, p. 441 – the structure sequences referred to in Anderton's Fig. 12 are
ABCE, BCE and CE in Bouma's (1962)
terminology). However, Anderton (1976,
p. 445) notes that the facies " could have
been deposited by density currents",
and later suggests "tidally-dispersed,
storm generated suspension clouds".
The possibility of finding turbidites
associated with shelf deposits has been
discussed earlier in this paper. One
important point to emerge from Anderton's paper is that the various facies
"alternate in vertical succession in an
apparently random manner" (p. 447).

The Gog Quartzite (Lower Cambrian)
of the Southern Rocky Mountains of
B.C. and Alberta is up to about 3 km
thick, and in the section along the
Trans-Canada Highway in the Kicking
Horse Pass (Hein, 1982), there is
abundant cross bedding in sets up to
almost 1 m thick. Paleocurrent patterns
are complex, with some bimodal patterns suggesting tidally-influenced dune
and bar systems. However, as with the
Jura Quartzite, Hein has documented
many other facies (some of which suggest a storm influence). It would appear
that in general the thick quartzites have
many depositional influences. Finally,
Hein's (1982, p. 129-130) measured sections show no evidence of cyclicity or
preferred facies sequence.

In another late Precambrian example
from north Norway, Levell (1980) has
documented the occurrence of simple
and compound sets of cross bedding.
The compound sets are made up of
downcurrent-dipping bounding surfaces, with angle-of-repose cross bedding between the bounding surfaces.
Levell (1980, p. 545) comments that "the
compound cross bedding, in which
each small-scale set is separated from
its neighbours by a convex-upward surface could represent either a large bedform with megaripples superimposed
on its lee face ... or a large bedform with
extremely closely spaced, periodic,
reactivation surfaces formed by reworking of a single angle-of-repose lee face".
Levell's sketches and photographs

closely resemble the model of Allen
(Fig. 32, classes IIA and IVA). However,
Levell notes that paleoflow directions
are consistently eastward, and within
his preferred tidal interpretation, suggests, 1) a regional transport dominance (as in the southern North Sea),
2) a local transport dominance (mutually evasive ebb and flood flows), and 3)
a preservation factor that favours the
lateral migration of large subtidal sand
bodies.

Transgressive Sandwave Complexes
The general occurrence of sandwave
complexes in transgressive situations
was noted by Nio (1976) and Nio and
Siegenthaler (1978), quoting particularly the Roda complex (lower Eocene,
Spain) and the Lower Greensand
(Lower Cretaceous, southern England).
In the Roda, there are angle-of-repose
cross bed sets up to 20 m thick; Nio's
present interpretation is that these
sandwaves are estuarine, and hence I
can no longer use this example in a discussion of tidal shelf deposits. The
Lower Greensand has been described
breifly by Narayan (1971), de Raaf and
Boersma (1971) and Bridges (1982). It is
in an overall transgressive situation, and
contains individual cross bed sets up to
4 or 5 m thick. There is evidence that
smaller bedforms migrated both up and
down low angle (1 to 5°) dipping surfaces (Figs. 30 and 31), in a manner
illustrative of Allen's (1980) model (Fig.
32, classes IIA and IIIA). Paleoflow
directions are essentially unidirectional,
to the south in the Woburn area
(Schwarzacher, 1953) and to the southeast in the Weald (Narayan, 1971;
Bridges, 1982, p. 183-7). In commenting
on earlier work, Bridges only notes that
"a tidal interpretation is indeed attractive", but there are apparently no definitive criteria.

**TIDE-DOMINATED SHELVES –
SYNTHESIS AND MODELS**
Ancient and recent examples suggest
that tide-dominated shelves are characterized by sand waves and sand ridges.
Most of these tend to have asymmetrical
profiles, commonly with "steep" faces
inclined at 10° or less. Consequently,
the internal structure is characterized by
gently dipping master bedding surfaces
(commonly reactivation surfaces), with
angle-of-repose cross bedding formed
by migration of megaripples on the
master bedding surfaces. The range of

possible structures is summarized well by Allen's model (Fig. 32).

The relatively thin transgressive sandwave complexes pose no major problems of sediment supply – it is essentially sediment reworked during transgression, as in the modern North Sea. The very thick late Precambrian/ Cambrian quartzites pose two problems – first, how was the sediment transported from the shoreline out onto the shelf, and second, how did supply and subsidence remain so closely matched. If supply had lagged, we might expect deepening and mud deposition. If supply had exceeded subsidence we might expect shallowing and shoreline progradation. However, shorelines have rarely been recognized in these thick quartzites.

Finally, tidal shelf examples in the geological record tend to show dominantly unimodal paleoflow directions, as opposed to the common bimodal-bipolar patterns of very nearshore (barrier-associated) deposits. Levell (1980) addresses this problem, suggesting either regional transport dominance (southern North Sea), local transport dominance, or preservation over the long term *only* of master bedding surfaces inclined in one direction.

LONG, NARROW SHALLOW MARINE SAND BODIES

These are common in the Jurassic and Cretaceous of the Western Interior Seaway (Fig. 34). Details are given in Table 3, but it should be emphasized that linear bodies of several distinct origins may be tabulated here, and "average" dimensions should be interpreted with care. One point that they all have in common is a progressively coarsening-upward sequence, with marine mudstones passing up into bioturbated siltstones and thence into various types of cross bedded or hummocky cross stratified sandstones. Sand body orientation tends to be sub-parallel or somewhat oblique to regional shorelines, and where there is evidence of contemporaneous shorelines, the sand bodies appear to have formed many tens of km offshore (Table 3).

The Cardium examples in Table 3 probably do not belong – it has been shown that Garrington and Caroline are long, narrow zones of production within *sheet* sandstones (Walker, 1983a), and that Ricinus is probably a channel cut and filled by turbidity currents (Walker, 1984b). However, average dimensions change only slightly if these three examples are deleted.

It will be noted in Table 3 that there are several "kitchen sink" interpretations – loose combinations of storms, tidal currents and oceanic circulations. However, it is also clear that almost all authors envisage storms as a major sand transporting process, recognizing that the sands in the lower part of the coarsening-upward sequences have to be transported long distances offshore into muddy environments. The fact of gradational bases for the sand bodies is a major reason why few of the authors strongly favour tidal currents, because the modern linear sand ridges and sand waves both rest at least in part unconformably on transgressive surfaces with gravel lags. It is commonly not stated whether sand transport is incremental or from relaxation (storm surge ebb) or turbidity currents, but in many cases it appears that the authors envisage a somewhat steady movement of sand parallel to isobaths, with special events sculpting this sand into distinct ridges. Thus there is some apparent opinion in favour of incremental dispersal parallel to isobaths, probably by storm-generated geostrophic flows (Fig. 34).

The suggestions of tidal modification are based on the presence of cross bedding in the upper parts of sand

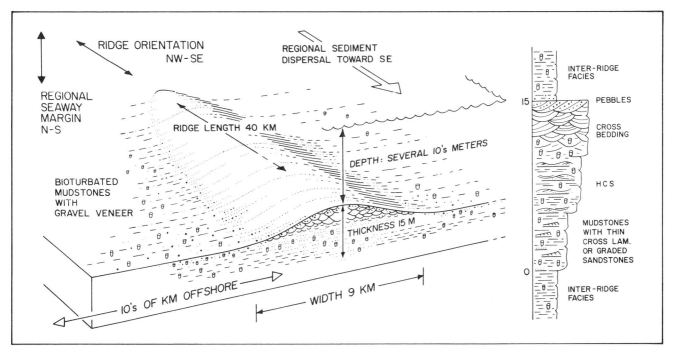

Figure 34
Diagrammtic summary of the main features of linear sand bars from the Cretaceous Western Interior Seaway. Data from Table 3.

Table 3

Dimensions of shallow marine sand bodies, western North America

Formation	Thickness of sand body (m)	Length (km)	Width (km)	Author	Interpretation, with (page references). Distance offshore quoted where possible.
Shannon, Upper ss.	15	50	30	Spearing, 1976	"storm system, superimposed on oceanic or tidal currents" (70). 100 km offshore.
Lower ss.	21	100	50		
Shannon	20	17.6	2.4	Seeling, 1978	"ancient hydraulic environment . . . was analogous in some important respects to those present day environments with prominent currents off the east coast of the United States and in the southern part of the North Sea" (133). 120 km offshore.
Sussex	12	40	1.6	Berg, 1975	"storm surge, density currents or other phenomena" (2109). 200 km from shoreline.
Sussex	c.30	c.50	up to 10	Brenner, 1978	"influenced by tidal and storm generated currents . . . neap and spring tides . . . intense storms" (195-7).
Sussex	12.2	45	1.6	Hobson et al., 1982	"storm related and other marine currents" (697). > 160 km from shoreline.
Oxfordian ss.	c.15	>5	0.2 to 2	Brenner and Davies, 1974	"storms played a major role" (425). "Storm driven currents, normal tidal currents and regional circulation currents" (427).
Duffy Mountain	27	50+	8 - 16	Boyles and Scott, 1982	"fairweather shelf currents formed sand waves along the bar crest . . . transported sand . . . onto the back bar". "Interaction of fairweather and storm sediment transport" (505). At least 16 km offshore.
Semilla ss. Holy Ghost bar	21	20+	15	La Fon, 1981	"tidal origin doubtful" (720). "Sandstone bars were deposited by periodic storm events" (720), "storms, possibly augmented by weak tidal currents" (720).
Bernalillito Arroyo bar	12	?20	?8		
Frontier	13	10.4 - 12	3.2	Winn et al., 1983	"storm generated shelf sand ridges . . . tides and permanent marine currents apparently were not important in transporting sand" (41).
Cardium Crossfield	6	96	1.6-2.8	Berven, 1966	"offshore bars . . . waves and nearshore currents" (208). sheet sand emplaced by turbidity currents but modified by storms (Walker, 1983a). At least 100, probably 140-200 km offshore.
Garrington	c.5	71	6	Walker, 1983a, b	
Caroline	c.5	48	5.4		
Ricinus	18	45	5	Walker, 1983a, b	turbidites in channel, channel probably cut by turbidity currents (see Walker, 1984b). At least 100, probably 140-200 km offshore.
Carrot Creek	13.4	c.7	c.2.5	Swagor et al., 1976	"pebbles were driven dominantly by storms across a shallow shelf" (94).
Viking Dodsland-Hoosier	8	up to 80	c.10	Evans, 1970	"Offshore environment affected by tidal currents" (484).
Gilby	c.2.5	30	3.3	Koldijk, 1976	"cannot be explained by normal marine conditions (76) . . . ephemeral currents, e.g. during severe storms" (77).
Joffre	9.5	40	1.6-3	Reinson et al., 1983	"frequent storm events . . . tectonically induced strong density currents. Strong bottom traction currents (tidal current streams) redistributed the detritus" (104).
AVERAGE	14.0	43.5	9.0		
AVERAGE	14.9	41.4	9.7	(without Garrington, Caroline and Ricinus)	

bodies, which in places has apparently bimodal directions (Spearing, 1976, p. 76.) However, it is clear from the work of Swift and colleagues discussed earlier (Swift *et al.,* 1979) that megaripples up to about 1 m high can form as a response to storm flows, and can migrate and produce cross bedding. Thus the hard evidence for tidal flows is lacking. Seeling (1978) compares the Shannon morphologically with linear sand ridges of both the Atlantic Shelf (storm dominated) and the North Sea (tidally dominated), but does not preferentially suggest a tidal interpretation. In those examples where there is paleo-flow evidence (Spearing, 1976; Brenner, 1978; Hobson *et al.,* 1982; Brenner and Davies, 1974; Boyles and Scott, 1982; Walker, 1983), dispersal is consistently south or southeastward. The only exception is apparently the Semilla Sandstone, where La Fon (1981, p. 719) reports trough cross beds that "generally dip northwest, paralleling the direction of elongation of the bar, although some sets dip southeast". Northwest and westerly flows, without supporting data, are also shown in La Fon's Figure 3.

In most of the examples in Table 3, there is little or no evidence of any relationship between the linear ridges and regional transgression. The major exception is the Sussex example in the interpretation of Hobson *et al.* (1982). Thus it is not possible to compare the ancient ridges with Swift's shoreface-attached ridges that become detached during transgression. Not only is the context wrong with respect to transgression; the ancient linear ridges coarsen upward from offshore marine mudstone, which would *not* be predicted for Swift's shoreface-attached ridges. The major problem, therefore, is not so much how the sand disperses southward down the seaway, but how these processes (incremental movement of sand by storms?) concentrate the sand into isolated bars and ridges that coarsen upward. If the flows were oblique to the crests of the linear ridges, Huthnance's (1982) stability model might apply (Fig. 8). Rate of ridge growth would then be a function of ridge/current obliquity, mean depth, a drag coefficient and the ridge spacing (see Figueiredo *et al.,* 1981, p. 188).

SHELVES DOMINATED BY INTRUDING OCEAN CURRENTS

This type makes up only about 3% of modern shelves, and the best example is that of Flemming (1978, 1980) from the southeastern shelf of South Africa (Fig. 35). Here, the intruding ocean current is the Agulhas Current of the Indian Ocean. The sand waves made by this current occur in 40 to 60 m of water, some 4 to 8 km offshore. They have been observed on side-scan sonar, and occur in continuous fields up to 20 km long and 10 km wide. Heights are variable, but the maximum is about 17 m. The largest sand waves have wavelengths of about 700 m and lee faces in excess of 25° (Flemming, pers. commun., 1979). Hence these sand waves might be expected to form angle-of-repose cross bedding in sets many metres thick.

The Agulhas Current is not contributing new sediment to the shelf, and hence the coarse lags (heavy stipple, Fig. 35) sand ribbons and sand waves (Fig. 35) represent the reworking of older sediment. It is unlikely in this situation (or in other situations where transgressed older sediments are reworked by intruding ocean currents) that a stratigraphic thickness of more than a few metres will build up, and this situation is probably rare in the geological record. I know of no ancient example that has been convincingly interpreted by this mechanism, although it may be a possibility for some transgressive sand wave complexes with consistent unidirectional flow (as described above).

CONCLUSIONS

The shelf is one of the most complex depositional environments because of the interaction of three different major processes – ocean currents, storm-generated currents and tidal currents. In some cases, modern and ancient studies converge toward the beginnings of a coherent model (as for tidal sand bodies). In other cases, there seem to be no modern equivalent of deposits seen in the geological record, particularly the gradationally-based linear sand ridges of the Western Interior Seaway. In yet other cases, the geological record suggests processes which have not been observed on modern shelves; here, I am referring particularly to the interbedded HCS sandstone/biotur-

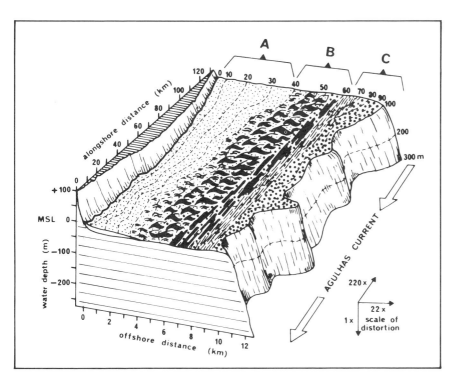

Figure 35.
Sandwaves, as observed on side scan sonar, on the shelf edge off the southeastern tip of Africa. The sand waves are driven by the Agulhas Current, which is a major Indian Ocean circulation that spills up onto the shelf. Stipple indicates coarse lag, black streaks indicate sand ribbons. Individual sand wave fields are up to 20 km long and 10 km wide. Sand waves are up to 17 m high, with angle-of-repose (25°) lee faces. From Flemming, 1980.

bated mudstone facies with evidence that some of the beds were emplaced by turbidity currents.

On the other hand, there are well defined modern processes and deposits that have yet to be firmly identified in the geological record. For example there are no specific geological interpretations of incremental sand movement by storm-generated geostrophic flows (although this may be one way in which the linear sand ridges of the Western Interior Seaway were formed). Also, there are no examples of transgressive, shoreface-detached linear sand ridges similar to those described by Swift and colleagues.

These problems contribute to the present lively debate concerning shelf sands and sandstones, but really powerful models will not emerge until there is a closer synthesis of ancient and modern examples.

ACKNOWLEDGEMENTS

I am indebted to Don Swift for his careful and detailed review of this manuscript. Many of the ideas herein are new, and in a state of flux, and there is still considerable disagreement on interpretive matters. In marshalling a big body of literature into simplified facies models, any errors of interpretation which have crept in are mine. I also thank Bill Duke and Don Keith for their comments. The work has been supported by Strategic and Operating Grants from the Natural Sciences and Engineering Research Council of Canada.

REFERENCES

The references are presented in alphabetical order. For the newcomer to the subject, the most useful general reviews are in the SEPM Short Course Notes by Tillman, Swift and Walker (1984). At a more technical level, the compilation of papers edited by Tillman and Siemers (1984) is a very useful source of ideas and additional references. Most of the citations to hummocky cross stratification are given by Duke (in press), and citations to tidal processes and deposits are given by Allen (1980).

Aigner, T., 1982. Calcareous tempestites: storm-dominated stratification in Upper Muschelkalk limestones (Middle Trias, S.W. Germany). *In* Einsele, G. and Seilacher, A., eds., Cyclic and event stratification. New York, Springer, p. 180-198.

Allen, J.R.L., 1970. Physical processes of sedimentation. New York, American Elsevier, 248 p.

Allen, J.R.L., 1980. Sand waves: a model of origin and internal structures. Sedimentary Geology, v. 26, p. 281-328.
A documentation of field examples, and development of a theoretical model for sand waves. The model for stratification is based largely on the symmetry of flow (or lack of it) over the sand waves.

Anderton, R., 1976. Tidal shelf sedimentation: an example from the Scottish Dalradian. Sedimentology, v. 23, p. 429-458.
One of the most detailed descriptions and interpretations of tidal facies in a very thick Precambrian quartzite.

Ball, S.M., 1971. The Westphalia Limestone of the Northern Midcontinent: a possible ancient storm deposit. Journal of Sedimentary Petrology, v. 41, p. 217-232.
Description of transported foraminifera, with interesting calculations of volume of material moved. One of the earliest modern storm interpretations.

Bea, R.G., and Audibert, J.M.E., 1980. Offshore platforms and pipelines in Mississippi River delta. American Society of Civil Engineers, Proceedings; Journal of the Geotechnical Engineering Division, v. 106 (G.T. 8), p. 853-869.
A review of the effect of substrate conditions and substrate disturbance on platform and pipeline structures.

Berg, R.R., 1975. Depositional environment of Upper Cretaceous Sussex Sandstone, House Creek Field, Wyoming. American Association of Petroleum Geologists, Bulletin, v. 59, p. 2099-2110.

Berven, R.J., 1966. Cardium sandstone bodies, Crossfield-Garrington area, Alberta. Bulletin of Canadian Petroleum Geology, v. 14, p. 208-240.

Bouma, A.H., 1962. Sedimentology of some flysch deposits. Amsterdam, Elsevier, 168 p.
The famous "Bouma sequence" for turbidites is established in this book.

Bourgeois, J., 1980. A transgressive shelf sequence exhibiting hummocky stratification: the Cape Sebastian Sandstone (Upper Cretaceous), southwestern Oregon. Journal of Sedimentary Petrology, v. 50, p. 681-702.
This is probably the best documented case of HCS in an overall *transgressive* situation.

Boyles, J.M., and Scott, A.D., 1982. A model for migrating shelf-bar sandstones in Upper Mancos Shale (Campanian), northwestern Colorado. American Association of Petroleum Geologists, Bulletin, v. 66, p. 491-508.

Elongate bars; sand source believed to be trangressed littoral deposits. Bars migrated by fairweather and storm processes.

Brenchley, P.J., Newall, G., and Stanistreet, I.G., 1979. A storm surge origin for sandstone beds in an epicontinental platform sequence, Ordovician, Norway. Sedimentary Geology, v. 22, p. 185-217.

Brenner, R.L., 1978. Sussex Sandstone of Wyoming – example of Cretaceous offshore sedimentation. American Association of Petroleum Geologists, Bulletin, v. 62, p. 181-200.
Outcrop and subsurface study which suggests ridge formation by storm and tidal currents, with ridge breaching by storms, the channels thus formed being subsequently used by tidal currents to form tidal deltas.

Brenner, R.L., 1980. Construction of process-response models for ancient epicontinental seaway depositional systems using partial analogs. American Association of Petroleum Geologists, Bulletin, v. 64, p. 1223-1244.
A comparison of modern shelves with ancient epicontinental situations.

Brenner, R. L., and Davies, D.K., 1974. Oxfordan sedimentation in Western Interior United States. American Association of Petroleum Geologists, Bulletin, v. 58, p. 407-428.
Outcrop study of various marine coarsening-upward sequences. Marine bars believed to result from interplay of storms, tidal currents and regional circulation.

Bridges, P.H., 1982. Ancient offshore tidal deposits. *In* Stride, A.H., ed., Offshore tidal sands. London, Chapman and Hall, p. 172-192.
The most recent review of offshore tidal sands. Emphasizes the Lower Greensand and Western Interior Seaway (quoting several coarsening-upward sequences which may not be tidally dominated).

Bullock, A., 1981. Sedimentation of the Wapiabi-Belly River transition (Upper Cretaceous) at Lundbreck Falls, Alberta. B.Sc. Thesis, McMaster University, Hamilton, Canada, 94 p.
Documentation of HCS sandstones overlying turbidites, both facies having identical northward-directed paleoflows.

de Raaf, J.F.M., and Boersma, J.R., 1971. Tidal deposits and their sedimentary structures. Geologie en Mijnbouw, v. 50, p. 479-504.
Briefly discusses seven examples, including the Lower Greensand. Good photos.

Dott, R.H. Jr., and Bourgeois, J., 1982. Hummocky stratification: significance of its variable bedding sequences. Bulletin of the

Geological Society of America, v. 93, p. 663-680.

Duke, W.L., in press. Hummocky cross stratification, tropical hurricanes and intense winter storms. Sedimentology.
A documentation of 105 occurrences of HCS, with interpretation of the origin of HCS from hurricanes or intense winter storms.

Emery, K.O., 1968. Relict sediments on continental shelves of world. American Association of Petroleum Geologists, Bulletin, v. 52, p. 445-464.
This is the most recent statement of the "relict" idea – see Swift, Stanley and Curray, 1971 for modifications of relict sediments.

Evans, W.E., 1970. Imbricate linear sandstone bodies in Doosland-Hoosier area of Southwestern Saskatchewan, Canada. American Association of Petroleum Geologists, Bulletin, v. 54. p. 469-486.

Figueiredo, A.G., Swift, D.J.P., Stubblefield, W.L., and Clark, T.L., 1981. Sand ridges on the inner Atlantic Shelf of North America: morphometric comparisons with the Huthnance stability model. Geo-Marine Letters, v. 1, p. 187-191.
Points out the possibility that Huthnance's model for tidal current ridges might be modified to apply to storm maintained ridges.

Flemming, B.W., 1978. Underwater sand dunes along the southeast African continental margin – observations and implications. Marine Geology, v. 26, p. 177-198.
Side scan sonar pictures of sand waves, now being driven by the Agulhas current spilling up onto the Continental Shelf. This, along with Flemming (1980) is the best study of ocean current spillup on a shelf.

Flemming, B.W., 1980. Sand transport and bedform patterns on the Continental Shelf between Durban and Port Elizabeth (southeast Africa continental margin). Sedimentary Geology, v. 26, p. 179-205.
Follow up on Flemming (1978).

Forristall, G.Z., Hamilton, R.C., and Cardone, V.J., 1977. Continental Shelf currents in Tropical Storm Delia: observations and theory. Journal of Physical Oceanography, v. 87, p. 532-546.
Presentation of flow data resulting from a major Tropical Storm.

Fox, W.T., 1983. At the sea's edge,. Prentice Hall, Englewood Cliffs, N.J., 317 p.
Chapter 4, Tides (p. 93-124) is an excellent, non-technical discussion of tides, tide generating forces, and tidal currents.

Galloway, W.E., and Hobday, D.K., 1983. Terrigenous clastic depositional systems. New York, Springer-Verlag, 423 p.
Chapter 7, p. 143-165, gives an overview of terrigenous shelf systems.

Ginsburg, R.N., ed., 1975. Tidal deposits. New York, Springer-Verlag, 428 p.
A compilation of examples of modern and ancient clastic and carbonate tidal facies. The clastic examples (p. 5-195) consist of a series of short papers written in a standard format – a very useful standardized compilation of data.

Goldring, R., and Bridges, P., 1973. Sublittoral sheet sandstoes. Journal of Sedimentary Petrology, v. 43, p. 736-747.
Excellent description of what is now termed hummocky cross stratification, with comments on its facies associations and processes of formation. Still a very useful paper; originally it was some 5-6 years ahead of its time.

Goldring, R., and Langenstrassen, F., 1979. Open shelf and nearshore clastic facies in the Devonian. Special Papers in Paleontology, v. 23, p. 81-97.

Hamblin, A.P., and Walker, R.G., 1979. Storm dominated shallow marine deposits: the Fernie-Kootenay (Jurassic) transition, southern Rocky Mountains. Canadian Journal of Earth Sciences, v. 16 p. 1673-1690.
One of the first Journal papers to use HCS in the interpretation of an ancient sandstone. Established same paleoflow direction for HCS beds and classical turbidites below, hence introducing the possibility of sand transport by turbidity currents to emplace the HCS beds.

Harms, J.C., Southard, J.B., Spearing, D.R., and Walker, R.G.. 1975. Depositional environments as interpreted from primary sedimentary structures and stratification sequences. Society of Economic Paleontologists and Mineralogists, Short Course 2, 161 p.
In these notes, Harms introduced the term "hummocky cross stratification", described the deposits, and suggested a storm wave origin. Historically, an extremely important contribution.

Harms, J.C., Southard, J.B., and Walker, R.G., 1982. Structures and sequences in clastic rocks. Society of Economic Paleontologists and Mineralogists, Short Course 9.
This volume is an update of SEPM Short Course 2, with an excellent section on flow, bed configurations, and stratification.

Hayes, M.O., 1967. Hurricanes as geological agents: case studies of Hurricanes Carla, 1961, and Cindy, 1963. Texas Bureau of Economic Geology, Report of Investigations No. 61, 54 p.
A classic paper which first emphasized storm surge ebb currents, and their ability to transport sediment onto the shelf and deposit graded beds. The paper has been very influential but some of Hayes' interpretations have recently been modified by Morton (1981). Nevertheless, it remains an important publication.

Hein, F.J., 1982. Slope to shelf transition: Precambrian Miette Group to Lower Cambrian Gog Group, Kicking Horse Pass/Spiral Tunnels, B.C. and Alberta. In Walker, R.G., ed., Clastic units of the Front Ranges, Foothills and Plains in the area between Field, B.C. and Drumheller, Alberta. International Association of Sedimentologists, 11th International Congress on Sedimentology (Hamilton, Canada). Guidebook to Excursion 21A, p. 117-136.
Measured sections and basic descriptions of the Gog Quartzite at Spiral Tunnels. Includes a basic facies classification and paleocurrent data.

Hobday, D.K., and Reading, H.G., 1972. Fairweather versus storm processes in shallow marine sand bar sequences in the late Precambrian of Finnmark, North Norway. Journal of Sedimentary Petrology, v. 41, p. 318-324.
Interpretation of major low angle dipping surfaces suggested alternations of storm and fairweather processes.

Hobson, J.P. Jr., Fowler, M.L., and Beaumont, E.A., 1982. Depositional and statistical exploration models, Upper Cretaceous offshore sandstone complex, Sussex Member, House Creek Field, Wyoming. American Association of Petroleum Geologists, Bulletin, v. 66, p. 689-707.
One of the few papers on the Western Interior Seaway to propose a transgressive origin for the sand bodies.

Houbolt, J.J.H.C., 1968. Recent sediments in the southern bight of the North Sea. Geologie en Mijnbouw, v. 47, p. 245-273.
Pioneering and classic account of tidal sand ridges off the British Coast. Internal structures demonstrated by Sparker surveys, and round-and-round sand movement first proposed for linear ridges.

Howarth, M.J., 1982. Tidal currents of the Continental Shelf. In Stride, A.H., ed., Offshore tidal sands. London, Chapman and Hall, p. 10-26.
Review of tidal processes on the world's shelves.

Hulsemann, J., 1955. Grossrippeln and Schragschichtungs Gefuge in Nordsee Watt und in der Molasse. Senckenbergiana Lethaea, v. 36, p. 359-388.
A discussion of "sandwaves" in the North Sea, mostly relatively small bedforms.

Huthnance, J.M., 1982. On one mechanism forming linear sand banks. Esturarine, Coastal, Shelf Science. v. 14, p. 79-99.
A mathematical treatment of sand bar growth and spacing.

168

Johnson, D.W., 1919. Shore processes and shoreline development. New York, Wiley, 584 p. (reprinted 1965, New York, Hafner Pub. Co.).
Introduced the idea of a graded shelf.

Johnson, M.A., Kenyon, N.H., Belderson, R.H. and Stride, A.H., 1982. Sand transport. In Stride, A.H., ed., Offshore tidal sands. London, Chapman and Hall, p. 58-94.
Very useful review of sand transport by tidal currents, with particular reference to the area around Britain and the southern North Sea.

Jordan, G.F., 1962. Large submarine sand waves. Science, v. 136, p. 839-848.
First major discussion of sand waves on the North American Atlantic Shelf, from the Gulf of Maine.

Klein, G. deV, 1970. Depositional and dispersal dynamics of intertidal sand bars. Journal of Sedimentary Petrology, v. 40, p. 1095-1127.
A thorough study of currents, bedforms, internal structures and sand dispersal for sand bars in the Bay of Fundy. Klein's data re-emphasized Houbolt's (1968) round-and-round "racetrack" model.

Kreisa, R.D., 1981. Storm-generated sedimentary structures in subtidal marine facies with examples from the middle and upper Ordovician of southwestern Virginia. Journal of Sedimentary Petrology, v. 51, p. 823-848.

Koldijk, W.S., 1976. Gilby Viking B: a storm deposit. In Lerand, M.M., ed., The sedimentology of selected clastic oil and gas reservoirs in Alberta. Canadian Society of Petroleum Geologists, p. 62-77.

La Fon, N.A., 1981. Offshore bar deposits of Semilla Sandstone Member of Mancos Shale (Upper Cretaceous), San Juan Basin, New Mexico. American Association of Petroleum Geologists, Bulletin, v. 65, p. 706-721.
Outcrop study of two bars which originally formed 50-80 km offshore. Storms more likely than tidal currents.

Levell, B.K., 1980. A late Precambrian tidal shelf deposit, the lower Sandfjord Formation, Finnmark, North Norway. Sedimentology, v. 27, p. 539-557.
Good facies descriptions of a thick Precambrian tidal quartzite with depositional summary relating the facies paleogeographically.

Mann, R.G., Swift, D.J.P., and Perry, R., 1981. Size classes of flow-transverse bedforms in a subtidal environment, Nantucket Shoals, North American Atlantic shelf. Geo-Marine Letters, v. 1, p. 39-43.

McCave, I.N., 1971. Sand waves in the North Sea off the coast of Holland. Marine Geology, v. 10, p. 199-225.

Excellent description of sandwaves up to 7 m high. Although the model of Figure 26 suggests large angle-of-repose cross bedding, the angles shown by echo sounding do not exceed 6 degrees.

McCave, I.N., and Langhorne, D.N., 1982. Sand waves and sediment transport around the end of a tidal sand bank. Sedimentology, v. 29, p. 95-110.
Detailed documentation of the orientation of smaller bedforms around the northern end of Haisborough Sand off the Norfolk Coast. Data suggests sand recirculation around the end of the sand bank.

Morgenstern, N.R., 1967. Submarine slumping and the initiation of turbidity currents. In Richards, A.F., ed., Marine geotechnique. Urbana, University of Illinois Press, p. 189-220.
This is still one of the best discussions of the initiation of turbidity currents.

Morton, R.A., 1981. Formation of storm deposits by wind-forced currents in the Gulf of Mexico and the North Sea. In Nio, S.D. et al., eds., Holocene marine sedimentation in the North Sea Basin. International Association of Sedimentologists, Special Publication 5, p. 385-396.
Emphasizes the importance of wind forced currents rather than storm-surge-ebb currents for the Carla graded bed (Hayes, 1967).

Murray, S.P., 1970. Bottom currents near the coast during Hurricane Camille. Journal of Geophysical Research, v. 75, p. 4579-4582.
Brief presentation of flow data resulting from Hurricane Camille.

Narayan, J., 1971. Sedimentary structures in the Lower Greensand of the Weald, England and Bas-Boulonnais, France. Sedimentary Geology, v. 6, p. 73-109.

Nelson, C.H., 1982. Modern shallow water graded sand layers from storm surges, Bering Shelf: a mimic of Bouma sequences and turbidite systems. Journal of Sedimentary Petrology, v. 52, p. 537-545.
Describes graded beds with Bouma sequences on the Bering Shelf, but does not discuss a turbidity current origin. Hypothesizes a storm-surge-ebb origin.

Nio, S.D., 1976. Marine transgressions as a factor in the formation of sandwave complexes. Geologie en Mijnbouw, v. 55, p. 18-40.
Discusses large sandwaves in three ancient examples. The origin of some of these sandwave complexes is still controversial, but Nio's data is valuable.

Nio, S.D., and Siegenthaler, J.C., 1978. A lower Eocene estuarine-shelf complex in the Isabena Valley. State University of Utrecht, Sedimentology Group Report no. 18, p. 1-44.

Good descriptions and diagrams - a follow up to Nio, 1976.

Off, T., 1963. Rythmic linear sand bodies caused by tidal currents. American Association of Petroleum Geologists, Bulletin, v. 47, p. 324-341.
Off discusses the influence of tidal currents on linear ridges defined by bathymetric charts. There is no field data and little in the way of hydrodynamic data, but he pointed out the occurence of topographically similar features in many parts of the world.

Parker, G., Lanfredi, N.W., and Swift, D.J.P., 1982. Seafloor response to flow in a southern hemisphere sandridge field: Argentine inner shelf. Sedimentary Geology, v. 33, p. 195-216.
Description and interpretation of linear sand ridges on the Argentine shelf.

Reineck, H.E., 1963. Sedimentgefuge in Bereich der sudlichen Nordsee. Abhandlungen der Senckenbergischen Naturforschen des Gesellschaft, no. 505, 138 p.
Discussion of recent sediments and sandwaves in the southern North Sea.

Reinson, G.E. Foscolos, A.E., and Powell, T.G., 1983. Comparison of Viking sand stone sequences, Joffre and Caroline Fields. In McLean, J.R. and Reinson, G.E., eds., Sedimentology of selected Mesozoic clastic sequences. Canadian Society of Petroleum Geologists, p. 101-117.

Saxov, S., and Nieuwenhuis, J.K., eds., 1982. Marine slides and other mass movements. New York, Plenum Press, 353 p.
A collection of papers devoted to the topics named in the book title.

Seeling, A., 1978. The Shannon Sandstone, a further look at the environment of deposition at Heldt Draw Field, Wyoming. Mountain Geologist, v. 15, p. 133-144.
Compares the linear sand ridges with those in the North Sea and on the Atlantic Shelf. Does not suggest whether the main influence was tidal or storm.

Shepard, F.P., 1932. Sediments on the Continental Shelves. Geological Society of America, Bulletin, v. 43, p. 1017-1039.
Introduced the concept of relict sediments.

Shepard, F.P., 1963. Submarine geology. New York, Harper and Row, 557 p.

Spearing, D.R., 1976. Upper Cretaceous Shannon Sandstone: an offshore shallow marine sand body. Wyoming Geological Association, 28th Annual Field Conference, Guidebook, p. 65-72.
Brief description of facies and paleocurrent patterns, with interpretation in terms of tidal, storm and oceanic currents.

Strahler, A., 1963. The earth sceinces. New York, Harper and Row, 681 p.

Stride, A.H., 1963. Current-swept sea floors near the southern half of Great Britain. Quarterly Journal of the Geological Society of London, v. 119, p. 175-199.
Important and influential paper on the unmixing of older sediments inundated by the Holocene rise of sea level, and the dispersal of sand by tidal currents to form sand ribbons and sand waves.

Stride, A.H., Belderson, R.H., Kenyon, N.H.,and Johnson, M.A., 1982. Offshore tidal deposits: sand sheet and sand bank facies. In Stride, A.H., ed., Offshore tidal sands. London, Chapman and Hall, p. 95-125.
Excellent discussion of the origin and possible internal structure of large tidal sand bodies.

Swagor, N.S., Oliver, T.A., and Johnson, B.A., 1976. Carrot Creek Field, central Alberta. In Lerand, M.M., ed., The sedimentology of selected clastic oil and gas reservoirs in Alberta. Canadian Society of Petroluem Geologists, p. 78-95

Swift, D.J.P., 1975. Tidal sand ridges and shoal retreat massifs. Marine Geology, v. 18, p. 105-134.
Full discussion with many examples of the origin of these features – a classic paper.

Swift, D.J.P., 1984. Fluid and sediment dynamics on continental shelves. In Tillman, R.W. et al., eds., Shelf sands and sand-stone reservoirs. Society of Economic Paleontologists and Mineralogists, Short Course.
A review of storm and tidal currents on the shelf, and fluid and sediment dynamics on the shoreface.

Swift, D.J.P., Tillman, R.W., Siemers, C.T., and Rine, J., in press. Fluid and sediment dynamics on a modern shelf: implications for models of ancient shelf sedimentation. Sedimentology.
A thorough review of processes on the modern Atlantic shelf. Careful reading of this paper will highlight for the reader the differing viewpoint of geologists and marine geologists.

Swift, D.J., Duane, D.B., and McKinney, T.F., 1973. Ridge and swale topography of the Middle Atlantic Bight, North America: secular response to the Holocene hydraulic regime. Marine Geology, v. 15, p. 227-247.
Suggests that the ridge and swale topography of the Middle Atlantic Bight develops at the shoreline, and that growing ridges become detached during transgression. Paper contains examples and develops general mechanisms for ridge formation.

Swift, D.J.P., and Field, M.E., 1981. Evolution of a classic sand ridge field: Maryland sec-tor, North American inner shelf. Sedimentology, v. 28, p. 461-481.
This is probably the best and most detailed study of the evolution of a field of linear sand ridges.

Swift, D.J.P., Figueiredo, A.G., Freeland, G.L., and Oertel, G.F., 1983. Hummocky cross stratification and megaripples: a geological double standard. Journal of Sedimentary Petrology, v. 53, p. 1295-1317.
A discussion of HCS, flows on the shelf and the possibility that HCS forms from combined flows. Rounded "hummocky" megaripples might be the modern HCS bedform.

Swift, D.J.P., Freeland, G.L., and Young, R.A., 1979. Time and space distribution of megaripples and associated bedforms, Middle Atlantic Bight, North American Atlantic Shelf. Sedimentology, v. 26, p. 389-406.
Best available discussion of the smaller bedforms on the Atlantic shelf.

Swift, D.J.P., Parker, G., Lanfredi, N.W., Perillo, G., and Figge, K. 1978. Shoreface connected sand ridges on American and Eurpean shelves: a comparison. Estuarine and Coastal Marine Science, v. 7, p. 257-273.
A useful comparison of data most of which had been previously published separately.

Swift, D.J.W., Stanley, D.J., and Curray, J.R., 1971. Relict sediments on continental shelves: a reconsideration. Journal of Geology, v. 79, p. 322-346.
This paper introduces the idea or reworking sediments during the Holocene marine transgression; historically, it ushers in modern ideas on dynamic equilibrium on shelves.

Tillman, R.W., Swift, D.J.P., and Walker, R.G., 1984. Shelf sands and sandstone reservoirs. Society of Economic Paleontologists and Mineralogists, Short Course Notes, San Antonio, May 1984, variously paginated.
At time of writing, only a preliminary version of these notes exists. A published version should be available from SEPM in the fall of 1984. The volume contains much new research integrated into a series of review articles. An excellent source of current information.

Tillman, R.W. and Siemers, C.T., eds., 1984. Siliciclastic shelf sediments. Society of Economic Paleontologists and Mineralogists, Special Publication 34, 268 p.
This volume contains an excellent group of research contributions, hot off the press in May 1984.

Twichell, D.C., 1983. Bedform distribution and inferred sand transport on Georges Bank, United States Atlantic Continental Shelf. Sedimentology, v. 30, p. 695-710.
Excellent side scan sonar and echo sounding data for sand waves, sand ridges and megaripples, with inferences about sediment movement.

Van Veen, J., 1935. Sandwaves in the southern North Sea. Hydrographic Reviews, v. 12, p. 21-29.

Walker, R.G., 1982. Hummocky and swaley cross stratification. In Walker, R.G., ed., Clastic units of the Front Ranges, Foothills and Plains in the area between Field, B.C. and Drumheller, Alberta. International Association of Sedimentologists, 11th International Congress on Sedimentology (Hamilton, Canada), Guidebook to Excursion 21A, p. 22-30.
Full description of the geometry of HCS and SCS, and how these structures differ from angle-of-repose cross bedding.

Walker, R.G., 1983a. Cardium Formation 2. Sand body geometry and stratigraphy in Garrington-Caroline-Ricinus area, Alberta — the "ragged blanket" model. Bulletin of Canadian Petroleum Geology, v. 31, p. 14-26

Walker, R.G., 1983b. Cardium Formation 3. Sedimentology and stratigraphy in the Garrington-Caroline area. Bulletin of Canadian Petroleum Geology, v. 31, p. 213-230.
Description of coarsening upward sequences, with details of the various facies, in the Cardium "A" and "B" sands. Describes HCS in cores.

Walker, R.G., 1984a. Geological evidence for storm transportation and deposition on ancient shelves. In Tillman, R.W. et al., eds., Shelf sands and sandstone reservoirs. Society of Economic Paleontologists and Short Course, San Antonio, TX., p. 1-58.
These notes review in more detail than this paper the geological evidence for storms on shelves.

Walker, R.G., 1984b. Upper Cretaceous (Turonian) Cardium Formation, southern Foothills and Plains, Alberta. In Tillman, R.W. et al., eds., Shelf sands and sand-stone reservoirs. Society of Economic Paleontologists and Mineralogists, Short Course, San Antonio, TX., p. 1-44.
Review of Cardium facies, depositional processes and environments in surface and subsurface. Ricinus field is interpreted as a channel which was both cut and filled by turbidity currents.

Walker, R.G., 1984c. Ancient examples of tidal sand bodies formed in open, shallow seas. In Tillman, R.W. et al., eds., Shelf sands and sandstone reservoirs. Society of Economic Paleontologists and Mineralogists, Short Course, San Antonio, TX., p. 1-34.
Review of many examples of ancient tidal sand bodies — a useful collection of illustrations.

Walker, R.G., Duke, W.L., and Leckie, D.A., 1983. Hummocky stratification: significance of its variable bedding sequences: discussion. Bulletin of the Geological Society of America, v. 94, p. 1245-1249.
Discussion of Dott and Bourgeois (1982), modifying their internal structure sequence and commenting further on the mode of formation HCS.

Walker, R.G., and Hunter, D.F., 1982. Transition, Wapiabi to Belly River Formation at Trap Creek, Alberta. *In* Walker, R.G., ed., Clastic units of the Front Ranges, Foothills and Plains in the area between Field, B.C. and Drumheller, Alberta. International Association of Sedimentologists, 11th International Congress on Sedimentology (Hamilton, Canada), Guidebook to Excursion 21A, p. 61-71.
Basic descriptions of the Trap Creek and Highwood River sections.
No interpretations.

Winn, R.D. Jr., Stonecipher, S.A., and Bishop, M.G., 1983. Depositional environments and diagenesis of offshore sand ridges, Frontier Formation, Spearhead Ranch Field, Wyoming. Mountain Geologist, v. 20, p. 41-58.
Subsurface study of storm-generated ridges with HCS in coarsening-upward sequences.

Wright, M.E., and Walker, R.G., 1981. Cardium Formation (U. Cretaceous) at Seebe, Alberta – storm transported sandstones and conglomerates in shallow marine depositional environments below fair-weather wave base. Canadian Journal of Earth Sciences, v. 18, p. 795-809.
Description of the classic outcrop at Seebe, and calculations pertaining to the mode and rate of gravel emplacement into the Cardium basin.

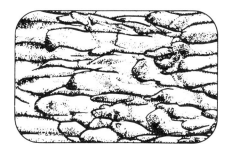

Turbidites and Associated Coarse Clastic Deposits

ROGER G. WALKER
Department of Geology
McMaster University
Hamilton, Ontario L8S 4M1

INTRODUCTION

The turbidity current concept is both simple and elegant. Each turbidite is the result of a single, short-lived event, and once deposited it is extremely unlikely to be reworked by other currents. The concept is elegant because it suggests that the deposition of thousands of graded sandstone beds, alternating with shales, is the result of a series of similar events. It can safely be stated that no similar volume of clastic rock can be interpreted so simply.

This review is presented in six parts, following closely the philosophy of facies models outlined in the "General Introduction" to this volume;

1) Introduction to turbidity currents and turbidites.
2) The variety of turbidites in the geologic record (the model as descriptor).
3) Turbidites in modern oceans (model as descriptor).
4) Combination of ancient and modern examples (to distill a model).
5) Use of the model (the model as predictor).
6) Feedback – facies sequences refining existing models and defining new ones.

TURBIDITY CURRENTS AND TURBIDITES

Density currents flow downslope on the ocean floor, being driven by gravity acting on the density difference between

Figure 1
Experimental turbidity current in a flume at Caltech. Water depth is 28 cm. Note characteristic shape of the head of the current, and eddies behind the head. Sediment is thrown out of the main flow by these eddies - the main flow is only about half of the height of the head.

the current and the surrounding sea water. The density could be due to colder temperatures, higher salinities, or suspended sediment in the current. When the density is due to suspended sediment, the flow is termed a *turbidity current* (Fig. 1). A *turbidite* is defined as the deposit of a turbidity current.

The concept of turbidity currents was introduced to the geological profession in 1950. At that time, nobody had observed a modern turbidity current in the ocean, yet the evidence for turbidity currents had become overwhelming. The concept accounted for graded sandstone beds that lacked evidence of shallow water reworking, and it accounted for transported shallow water foraminifera in the sandstones, yet with bathyal or abyssal foraminifera in the interbedded shales. Low density currents were known in lakes and reservoirs, and they appeared to be competent to transport sediment fairly long distances. Many of these different kinds of evidence were pulled together by Kuenen and Migliorini (1950) when they published experimental and field observations in a now classic paper on "Turbidity currents as a cause of graded bedding". A full review of why and how the concept was established in geology was published by Walker (1973).

It is now known that turbidity currents operate on vast scales. In 1935, a slump removed 480 m of breakwater at the mouth of the Magdalena River in Colombia. The slump cut a channel 10 m deep through a bar, evolved into a

turbidity current, and several hours later broke a submarine telegraph cable 24 km from the river mouth in 1400 m water depth (Heezen, 1956; Menard, 1964, p. 197). Surveys of the sea floor before and after the slump indicate that the minimum volume of sediment lost was 3×10^8 m³. This is an unimaginably large volume of sediment – it would require 2.14 million standard 50-foot box cars to transport this sediment by railroad. The resulting train would be 35,000 km long. However, the largest turbidite known makes the Magdalena flow seem small. The "black shell" turbidite, named for the distinctive corroded shells that it contains, covers an area about 500 km long and 200 km wide on the Hatteras Abyssal Plain off the eastern margin of North America. Its volume has been estimated at over 100 km³ (Elmore *et al.*, 1979), about 333 times that of the Magdalena flow.

Relatively little is known about flow velocities. The classic data comes from the 1929 earthquake near the Grand Banks of Newfoundland, which triggered a flow that broke a sequence of submarine cables. Recently recalculated velocities of the head of the flow (Uchupi and Austin, 1979) give 20.3 m/sec at the cable broken 183 minutes after the quake, 14.4 m/sec (541 minute break), 12.8 m/sec (618 minute break), and 11.4 m/sec at the 797 (13 hours 17 minutes) minute break. At a velocity of 11.4 m/sec, the current could suspend by fluid turbulence alone low concentrations of quartz pebbles up to about 3

172

cm in diameter.

The Grand Banks flow appears to
have travelled several hundred kilometres across the essentially flat Sohm
Abyssal Plain. Similarly, the "black
shell" flow must have travelled at least
500 to 600 km along the Hatteras Abyssal Plain.

Turbidity currents can be triggered by
earthquakes (as in the Grand Banks), by
rivers in flood (as in the Congo, Heezen
et al., 1964) and by spontaneous failure
of rapidly deposited piles of sediment,
commonly with relatively fine grain
sizes and high pore pressures (the
Magdalena flows [Heezen, 1956;
Menard, 1964] seem to have been of this
type). It has been suggested recently
that cyclic wave loading by major
storms can liquefy enough sediment
near the shoreline to generate turbidity
currents; see, for example, "Shelf and
Shallow Marine Sands" in this volume.

Turbidity currents must be considered commonplace in modern seas
and oceans. Their deposits are likely to
be extensive and volumetrically important. To preserve the sedimentary structures made by the turbidity currents
(i.e., to be able to *recognize* the beds as
turbidites), deposition must take place
below effective wave base. It has been
suggested that turbidites have been
deposited in some epeiric seas (see
"Shelf and Shallow Marine Sands", in
this volume), as well as in the more tra-
ditional "deep water" turbidite habitat of
submarine fans and basin plains.

TURBIDITES IN THE GEOLOGIC
RECORD

After its introduction in 1950, the turbidity current concept was applied to rocks
of many different ages, in many different places. Emphasis was laid upon
describing a vast and new assemblage
of sedimentary structures, and using
those structures to interpret paleocurrent directions. In the absence of a turbidite facies model, there was no norm
with which to compare individual
examples, no framework for organizing
observations, no logical basis for prediction in new situations, and no basis for a
consistent hydrodynamic interpretation.
Yet gradually during the years 1950-
1960, a relatively small but consistent
set of sedimentary features began to be
associated with turbidites. These are
considered in the following list, and can
now be taken as a set of descriptors for

Figure 2
*Monotonous interbedding of thin, sharp-
based sandstones and mudstones. No sea-*
floor topography (channels, levees) visible.
*Stratigraphic top to right. Devonian, Cape
Liptrap, South Australia.*

classical turbidites:
1) Sandstones and shales are
monotonously interbedded
through many tens or hundreds of
metres of stratigraphic sections
(Fig. 2). Beds tend to have flat tops
and bottoms, with no scouring and
channelling on a scale greater
than a few centimetres.
2) Sandstone beds have sharp,
abrupt bases, and tend to grade
upward into finer sand, silt and
mud. Much of the mud was
brought into the basin by the turbidity current (it contains a shallow water transported faunal
assemblage), but the uppermost
very fine clay may contain a bathyal or abyssal benthonic fauna
and hence represent slow hemipelagic deposition between turbidity
current events.
3) On the undersurface (sole) of the

sandstones there are abundant
markings, now classified into three
types; *tool* marks carved into the
underlying mud by rigid objects
(sticks, stones) in the turbidity current; *scour* marks cut into the
underlying muds by fluid scour;
and *organic* markings representing trails and burrows filled in by
the turbidity current. Tool and
scour marks give accurate indications of local paleoflow directions,
and by now, many thousands have
been measured to reconstruct
paleoflow patterns in hundreds of
turbidite basins.
4) Within the sandstone beds, combinations of parallel lamination
(Fig. 3), ripple cross lamination
(Fig. 3), climbing ripple cross lamination, convolute lamination and
graded bedding (Fig. 3) have been
noted by many authors. An ideal,

Figure 3
Complete Bouma sequence, beginning with a graded division A, overlain by parallel laminated division B and cross-laminated division C. Divisions D and E (see Fig. 4) broke off this specimen, which is from the Cote Frechette road cut, Levis Formation (Cambrian), Québec.

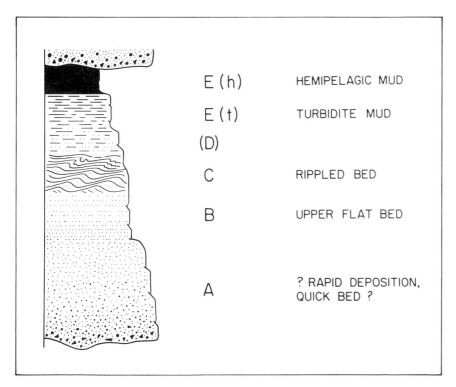

E (h)   HEMIPELAGIC MUD

E (t)   TURBIDITE MUD

(D)

C   RIPPLED BED

B   UPPER FLAT BED

A   ? RAPID DEPOSITION, QUICK BED ?

Figure 4
Five divisions of the Bouma sequence: A) massive or graded; B) sandy parallel laminations; C) rippled and/or convoluted; D) delicate parallel interlaminations of silt and mud; E(t)) mud introduced by the turbidity current and E(h)) the hemipelagic background mud of the basin. See text for details.

or generalized sequence was proposed by Arnold Bouma in 1962, and the Bouma sequence (Figs. 3 and 4) can be regarded as an excellent facies model for *classical* turbidites (see "General Introduction", especially Fig. 9).

THE BOUMA SEQUENCE AS A FACIES MODEL

On a small scale, the Bouma sequence has functioned so well as a facies model that I will digress briefly to illustrate some of the ideas developed in the introductory paper to this volume. First, the Bouma sequence has been distilled from a vast number of examples – literally thousands of individual beds. It can therefore be regarded as a homogeneous model of great generality. It functions well as a *norm* (Fig. 4), or point of comparison, and hence helps to explain those turbidites without the full sequence (Walker, 1967). For example, without a norm we would not know that BDE turbidites were any more or less common than ABCDE turbidites. The *norm* establishes a general point of reference. The model has acted well as a *guide* for further observations, making one aware both of the features presented by any one bed, and of features embodied in the model that might be missing in any specific bed.

The model has acted well as a *predictor*. For example, if an outcrop shows beds that begin only with Bouma's division C, the model predicts that these were deposited from slower turbidity currents, perhaps in a more distal geographic setting than beds which begin with Bouma's division A (Fig. 5; Walker, 1967). Alternatively, groups of beds beginning with division C might be proximal levee deposits, laterally adjacent to beds beginning with division A in a nearby channel.

Finally, the model has acted as a general basis for hydrodynamic interpretations. Before the Bouma sequence, varied interpretations were offered for individual beds or groups of beds. The Bouma sequence suggests a single coherent interpretation (Fig. 4), with division A suggesting very rapid settling of grains from suspension, possible in such quantities and at such a rate that water is rapidly expelled upward, and momentarily the grain/water mixture becomes fluidized. Fluidization would

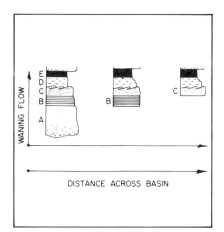

Figure 5
The ABCDE sequence in one individual turbidite suggests waning flow at the depositional site. Using the Bouma sequence as a predictor, we could suggest that groups of beds beginning with division B, and with division C, must represent deposition from progressively slower currents. Waning flow in the lateral sense can be correlated with distance flowed across the basin. There are limitations to this prediction – see text.

destroy any possible sedimentary structures except graded bedding. The second phase of deposition involves traction of grains on the bed, with division B representing the "upper plane bed" of experimental work (Harms *et al.*, 1982), and division C representing a rippled bedform. The upper flat bed passes directly into a rippled bed (with no formation of dunes) if the grain size is finer than about 0.15 mm (Southard, in Harms *et al.*, 1982, Figs. 2 to 5), as it is in many turbidites. If there is a high rate of deposition from suspension during rippling, climbing ripple cross lamination will form. Finally, as the flow dies away, turbidity current mud will blanket the bed (division (D) and E(t)), followed by hemipelagic mud E(h) (Fig. 4).

GENERAL TURBIDITE FACIES CLASSIFICATIONS

The above discussion was concerned with *classical turbidites,* those which consist of monotonous alternations of sandstones and shales, parallel bedded without significant scouring or channelling, and where all the beds can reasonably be described using the Bouma sequence.

It is interesting that the turbidite system was the first in which a universal facies scheme was proposed, by Mutti

and Ricci Lucchi (1972). A universal scheme for fluvial deposits has recently been introduced and is discussed by Rust and Koster ("Coarse Alluvial Deposits", this volume). The Mutti and Ricci Lucchi scheme has been modified over the years (Mutti and Ricci Lucchi, 1975; Mutti, 1979), and is a more detailed scheme than is required here. I will use the simpler scheme introduced by Walker (1978), namely:

1) classical turbidites (discussed above),
2) massive sandstones,
3) pebbly sandstones,
4) conglomerates,
5) slumps, slides, debris flows and other exotic facies.

Both descriptive schemes serve their purposes well, and both can be related to deposition on various parts of submarine fans, as discussed below.

MASSIVE SANDSTONES

This facies consists of thick sandstones with thin (or absent) interbedded shales (Fig. 6). Individual sandstone beds range in thickness from about 50 cm to many metres, and the only Bouma division normally present is division A. A typical sequence of beds would be measured as A.A.A.A. using the Bouma model. However, I would consider this to be a mis-application of the Bouma model, because it is characteristically a five-part model being applied to beds that charateristically only contain one part. The functions of the model as norm, guide, predictor, and basis for interpretation are all seriously weakened to the point of uselessness if the beds only show an A.A.A.A. sequence.

The massive sandstones are commonly not so parallel sided as the classical turbidites; channelling is more common, and one flow may cut down and weld onto the previous one ("amalgamation") giving rise to a series of multiple sandstone beds.

The one common sedimentary structure found in the massive sandstones is termed "dish" structure, and is indicative of abundant fluid escape during deposition of the sandstone (Lowe, 1975). It indicates rapid deposition of a large amount of sand from a "fluidized flow" (akin to a flowing quicksand). This does not imply that the massive sandstone facies was transported all the way from source into the basin by a fluidized flow. However, it does imply that a turbidity

Figure 6
Massive sandstone facies: the Upper Eocene Annot Sandstone, southern France. About 180 m of section can be seen in the photograph. Note thickness of individual sandstone beds, and absence of mudstone interbeds.

current, which normally maintains its sand load in suspension by fluid turbulence, can pass through a stage of fluidized flow during the final few seconds or minutes of flow immediately preceding deposition. The massive sandstone facies is prominent in the Cambrian Charny Formation around Québec City and Lévis, and dish structures in massive sandstones are common in the Cambro-Ordovician Cap Enragé Formation (Hein, 1982) near Rimouski, Québec. Massive sandstones are also well represented in many of the Cretaceous and Tertiary turbidite sequences of California and Oregon (e.g., Link and Nilsen, 1980; Link *et al.*, 1981; Nilsen and Abbott, 1981; Link and Welton, 1982; Chan and Dott, 1983).

PEBBLY SANDSTONES

The pebbly sandstone facies cannot be described using the Bouma model, nor does it have much in common with the massive sandstone facies. Pebbly sandstones tend to be well graded (Fig. 7),

Figure 7
Graded bed of pebbly sandstone, followed abruptly by a second bed without a mudstone interbed. St. Damase Formation (Orodvician) near Kamouraska, Québec.

Figure 8
Pebbly sandstone facies showing medium scale cross bedding. In isolation, this photograph could easily be confused with one of fluvial gravels. In fact, it is from the Cambro-Ordovician Cap Enragé Formation, and the cross beds are interbedded with classical turbidites and graded pebbly sandstones.

and stratification is fairly abundant. It can either be a rather coarse, crude, horizontal stratification, or a well developed cross bedding of the trough, or planar-tabular type (Fig. 8). Imbrication of individual pebbles within the bed is common. At present, there is no "Bouma-like" model for the internal structures of pebbly sandstones; the sequence of structures, and their abundance and thickness has not yet been distilled into a general model. Models based on the characteristics of the Cap Enragé Formation have been proposed by Hein (1982). Pebbly sandstone beds are commonly channelled and laterally discontinuous, and interbedded shales are rare.

It is clear that with abundant channelling, and the presence of cross bedding in pebbly sandstones, this facies could easily be confused with a coarse fluvial facies (see "Coarse Alluvial Deposits", this volume). The differences are subtle and can be misleading to sedimentologists – the safest way to approach the

interpretation of pebbly sandstones is to examine their context. If associated with, or interbedded with classical turbidites, the pebbly sandstone interpretation would be clear. Similarly, if associated with non-marine shales, root traces, caliche-like nodules, mud cracks, and other indicators of flood plain environments, the interpretation would also be clear. This facies highlights the fact that environmental interpretations cannot be based upon a "checklist" of features: the relative abundance and type of features, in their stratigraphic context, must always be the basis of interpretation.

Pebbly sandstones are particularly well exposed in the Cambro-Ordovician Cap Enragé Formation (Hein, 1982) at St. Simon (near Rimouski, Québec), where grading, stratification and cross bedding are prominent. The facies is also abundant in the Cambrian St. Damase Formation near Kamouraska, Québec, and in the Cambrian St. Roch Formation at L'Islet Wharf (near St-

Jean-Port-Joli, Québec) (Walker, 1979). Many examples exist in the Cretaceous and Tertiary turbidite sequences of California and Oregon (e.g., Nilsen and Abbott, 1981).

CONGLOMERATES
Although volumetrically less abundant than classical turbidites, conglomerates are an important facies in deep water environments. They are abundant in California and Oregon (e.g., Walker, 1977; Nilsen and Abbott, 1981), and are particularly well exposed at many localities in the Gaspé Peninsula (Davies and Walker, 1974; Hendry, 1978; Johnson and Walker, 1979; Hein, 1982). Sedimentologists have tended to ignore conglomerates, probably because without a facies model, there has been no framework to guide observations, and hence the feeling of "not being quite sure what to measure in the field". I have proposed some generalized "Bouma-like" models for conglomerates (Walker, 1975a), but because the models are based upon

176

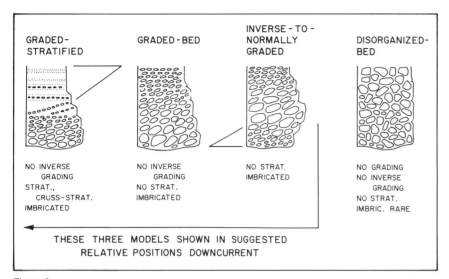

Figure 9

Four models for resedimented (deep water) conglomerates, shown in their inferred

downcurrent relative positions. See text for details.

Figure 10

Normally-graded and stratified conglomerate, Cambro-Ordovician Cap Enragé Formation, Bic, Québec. Basal conglomerate rests

on slates, and grades up into stratified conglomerate, very coarse sandstone with crude "dish structure", and finally into massive structureless sandstone.

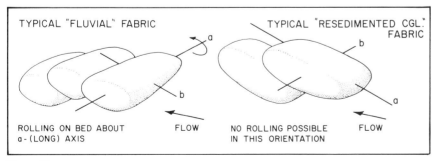

Figure 11

Contrast between a fabric produced by clast rolling (a-axis transverse), and a fabric characteristic of resedimented conglomerates (a-axis parallel to flow and dipping upstream).

The a-axis-parallel fabric is incompatible with clast rolling, and is believed to form by clasts colliding in the flow, whilst dispersed above the bed.

fewer than thirty studies, they lack the universality and authority of the Bouma model for classical turbidites. The paper (Walker, 1975a) discusses the models, their relationships, and how they were established. In Figure 9, it can be seen that the descriptors include the type of grading (normal [Fig. 10] or inverse), stratification (Fig. 10), and fabric; in different combinations they give rise to three models which are probably intergradational, and a fourth (disorganized-bed) characterized only by the absence of descriptors.

One of the most important features of conglomerates is the type of fabric they possess. In fluvial situations, where pebbles and cobbles are rolled on the bed, the long (a-) axis is usually transverse to flow directions, and the intermediate (b-) axis dips upstream, characterizing the imbrication. However, for most conglomerates associated with turbidites, the fabric is quite different: the long axis is parallel to flow, and also dips upstream to define the imbrication (Fig. 11). This fabric is interpreted as indicating no bedload rolling of clasts. The only two reasonable alternatives involve mass movements (debris flows), or dispersion of the clasts in a fluid above the bed. Mass movements in which clasts are not free to move relative to each other do not produce abundant graded bedding, stratification, and cross-stratification, so I suggest the clasts were supported above the bed in a turbulent flow, The support mechanism may have been partly fluid turbulence, and partly clast collisions. Upon deposition, the clasts immediately stopped moving (no rolling), and the fabric was "frozen" into the deposit.

In the absence of experimental work on cobbles and boulders, the interpretation of the conglomerate models must be based largely on theory. I suggest a downcurrent trend from the inverse-to-normally-graded model, into the graded-stratified model. This trend does not necessarily exist in any one bed: rather, deposition from a particular current in one of the three downstream positions in Figure 9 will be of the type indicated in the figure.

Clast supported conglomerates are abundant in the Ordovician Grosses Roches Formation (Hendry, 1978) and Cambro-Ordovician Cap Enragé Formation (Hein, 1982; Hein and Walker, 1982), Gaspé Peninsula, Québec, and also make up part of the Cambrian St. Roch Formation east of Rivière-du-Loup, Québec. They are abundant in California and Oregon (Walker, 1977 and in press; Nilsen and Abbott, 1981).

SLUMPS, SLIDES, DEBRIS FLOWS AND EXOTIC FACIES

This facies includes a diverse group of rocks which are generally poorly to unstratified, which are commonly poorly sorted (blocks and boulders in a fine grained matrix), and which may show evidence of sedimentary deformation.

The debris flow deposits have clasts supported in a muddy matrix – they may show basal inverse grading and preferred clast alignment. Because the larger clasts in a debris flow are maintained above the bed by the strength of the matrix, the deposit commonly has large blocks projecting up above the top of the bed, or even resting almost entirely on top of the bed. The deposit shows no internal evidence of slumping.

By contrast, other exotic facies commonly show evidence of slumping, and represent the mixing of sediment within the depositional basin by post-depositional slumping. The deposits can range all the way from very cohesive slumps involving many beds, to very watery slumps generated by the deposition of coarse sediment on top of wet, poorly consolidated clays. The latter process gives rise to the classical pebbly mudstones (Crowell, 1957; Howell and Joyce, 1981).

Inasmuch as subaqueous debris flows, and slumps, require greater slopes than classical turbidity currents, the chaotic facies is most abundant at the foot of the slope into the basin. Very few examples have been described in Canada. Large scale slumps are known in Upper Ordovician turbidites in northeastern Newfoundland (Helwig, 1970), and pebbly mudstones are known in several units in western Newfoundland (Stevens, 1970). The best described debris flows are Devonian reef-margin examples adjacent to the Ancient Wall, Miette and Southesk-Cairn reef complexes in Alberta (Cook et al., 1972; Srivastava et al., 1972). Elsewhere, slumps have been described from the Tortonian of northwestern Italy (Clari and Ghibaudo, 1979), the Plio-Pleistocene of northern California (Piper et al., 1976) and the Miocene of

New Zealand (Gregory, 1969).

TURBIDITES IN MODERN OCEANS

Effective facies models must combine data from ancient and recent sediments, and hence it is necessary to review briefly what is known about turbidites in modern oceans. The main depositional environments are submarine fans (which may coalesce laterally to build up the Continental Rise) and basin plains. By far the greatest volume of modern turbidites occur in the submarine fans.

Many different submarine fans have now been described, and general models that try to summarize this work have been presented by Normark (1970, 1978). In his 1970 paper ("Growth patterns of deep-sea fans"), Normark proposed a general model, widely accepted by the profession, that was built essentially on data from only two California

Borderland fans, La Jolla and San Lucas. The model consisted of three parts – a leveed valley on the upper fan, a mid-fan built up of suprafan lobes that periodically switched position, and a flat lower fan without channels. Many more examples were incorporated in Normark's (1978) later statement of the model (Fig. 12).

The most detailed study of the evolution of a small fan is that of Normark et al. (1979) and Piper and Normark (1983) for Navy Fan, California Borderlands. Based on precision echo sounding, seismic reflection profiling and side scan sonar, a three-dimensional physiographic map of Navy Fan was produced, showing the surface and subsurface locations of six suprafan lobes. By studying the way in which these lobes overlap, an evolutionary sequence was determined (Fig. 13).

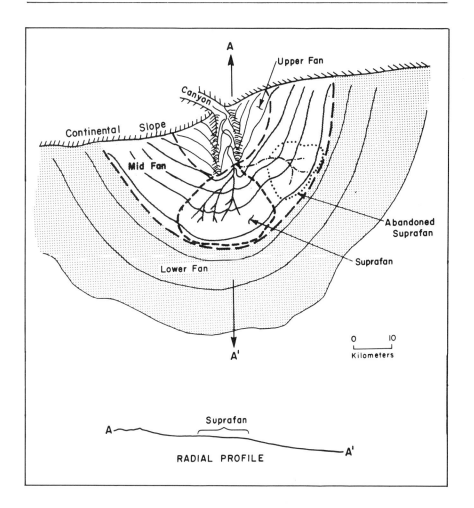

Figure 12
Submarine fan model of Normark (1978), based on several studies of modern fans.

This model for fan growth emphasizes active and abandoned depositional lobes termed suprafans.

178

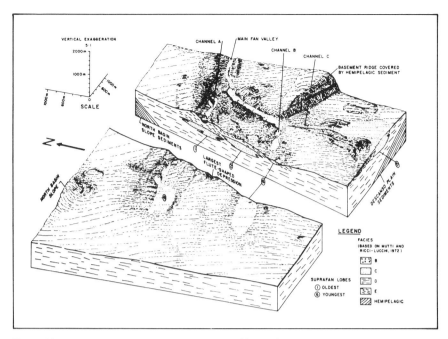

Figure 13
Block diagram of Navy Fan, California, based on seismic reflection profiling. Note suprafan lobes at ends of channels, with lobe 6 at the end of channel B being the youngest. From

Normark et al. (1979) – these authors discuss in detail the pattern of channel and lobe switching. This fan strongly supports the ideas embodied in Normark's fan model (Fig. 12).

The upper fan has a single leveed channel that is about 400 m wide, but decreases in depth from 50 to 15 m over a length of 8 km. Only distributary channel B (Fig. 13) is presently continuous with the upper fan leveed channel. The pattern of channel switching suggests that as one lobe grows, and its feeder channel aggrades (or backfills), it eventually initiates a levee break and turbidity currents are diverted to a lower part of the mid-fan surface to begin construction of a new lobe. Thus on Navy Fan, the mid-fan is built up of a series of individual lobes formed by distinct jumps in the positions of distributary channels (not gradual lateral channel migration). The implication is that when lobe 5 (say) is active, lobes 1,2 and 4 receive only fine grained muds spilled over the distributary channel margins. In other words, when one suprafan lobe is active, other lobes and their former distributary channels are being blanketed by mud. This process is important in forming stratigraphic traps over potential suprafan oil and gas reservoirs. The geometry of individual beds, and their mode of deposition, has been studied in detail by Piper and Normark (1983).

Although Navy Fan has been studied

in the most detail, Normark's (1978) later model was based particularly on Astoria, Monterey, Amazon and Bengal Fans (large fans built on oceanic crust), and Redondo, La Jolla, Navy and San Lucas Fans from the California Borderland. Since 1978, there have been detailed studies of Laurentian Fan (Uchupi and Austin, 1979; Stow, 1981; Piper and Normark, 1982; Normark et al., 1983), Mozambique Fan (Kolla et al., 1980), Amazon Cone (Damuth and Embley, 1981; Damuth et al., 1983a, 1983b), Zodiac Fan (Aleutian Abyssal Plain, Stevenson et al., 1983), Magdalena Fan (Colombia; Kolla et al., 1984) and La Jolla Fan (Graham and Bachman, 1983).
These studies cannot easily be combined with Normark's (1978) model. For example, the Amazon Cone appears to have three huge "slump/debris flow complexes" which cover areas of 32,500 km², 28,850 km² and 21,200 km² (Damuth and Embley, 1981, p. 633-637). The thicknesses are less than 75 m, 10 to 50 m and up to 50 m, respectively. It is not clear how these complexes formed on the very low slopes of the fan. Also on Amazon Cone are a series of channel-levee complexes, with amazingly sinuous channel patterns (Damuth

et al., 1983a) which cannot be related to present concepts of turbidity current flow.

Remarkably little is known about the ages and thicknesses of major submarine fans. Few have been penetrated completely during the Deep Sea Drilling Program. Many appear "to have built out substantially since Miocene time, and especially during Pleistocene time" (Kelts and Arthur, 1981). Thicknesses range from about 300 m (margin of Astoria Fan) to well over 10 km (Bengal Fan). Rates of deposition can be incredibly high; at DSDP site 222 on the Indus Cone, sediment was deposited at 600 m/m.y. in the late Miocene, 135 to 350 m/m.y. in the Pliocene, and at less than 50 m/m.y. in the Quaternary (Whitmarsh et al., 1974).

Fan sediments tend to pass distally into basin plain deposits. Here, the turbidites tend to be very extensive and continuous (Pilkey et al., 1980), with more abundant and thicker sands close to points of entry onto the basin plains. Thicknesses on modern abyssal plains tend to be only a few hundred metres (Horn et al., 1972). These few generalities constitute the essence of a "model" for abyssal, or basin plains.

The problem of coring deep sea facies, particularly the sands, and preserving long (several metres) sections with sedimentary structures, makes the comparison of modern and ancient turbidite facies rather difficult. Modern fan studies have contributed data on fan morphology on a rather large scale, whereas most studies of ancient rocks have been of a smaller scale. Studies such as those by Normark et al. (1979) and Damuth et al. (1983a, 1983b) are beginning to show the fine topographic details of modern fans – the problems of comparison are addressed below.

GENERAL FAN MODELS: COMPARISON OF ANCIENT AND RECENT SEDIMENTS
Interpretations of ancient sediments as fan deposits began in the early 1960s (Sullwold, 1960; Walker, 1966), but became more common as more modern fans were studied (Normark, 1970). Emiliano Mutti and his colleagues in Italy contributed extremely influential work (especially Mutti and Ricci Lucchi, 1972; Mutti and Ghibaudo, 1972), proposing a fan model based upon ancient rocks in Italy. This model was so similar

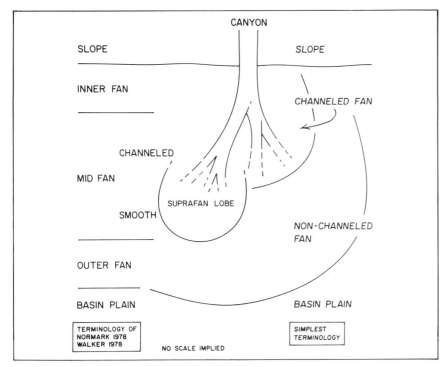

Figure 14

Simplified fan model. On the right is the simplest possible terminology, showing the absolute basics of almost all ancient and modern fans. On the left is a terminology which, although a little more complex, *embodies the salient characteristics of Normark's model (Fig. 12) for modern fans along with the characteristics proposed by Mutti and colleagues for many inferred ancient fans.*

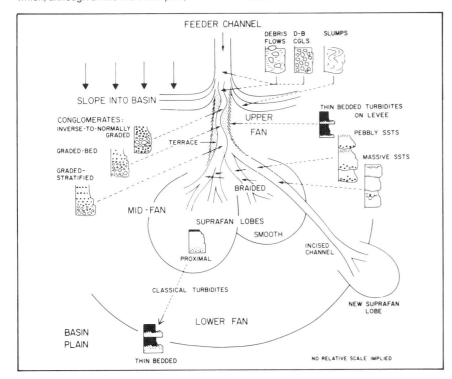

Figure 15

Fan model proposed by Walker (1978). Note that it incorporates features (terraces, inner fan meandering channel, levees, etc.) which although common, may not occur on all fans. Facies defined in ancient rocks are *shown in their inferred positions on the fan. An incised channel is also shown, indicating a phase of downcutting, fan extension, and new lobe development (as in the modern La Jolla Fan of California).*

to that of Normark's for modern fans that modern and ancient studies were distilled together to form the first modern-ancient integrated model (Walker and Mutti, 1973). As more work has been done, this model has evolved and diversified (see Walker, 1980, p. 1101-7), and I use the sketch in Figure 14 as a starting point. In the simplest possible terminology, almost all modern fans can be subdivided into a *channelled* fan, a *smooth* fan, and a *basin plain*. Many modern fans can be described by the terminology on the left (Fig. 14):

1) an inner (or upper) fan with a single channel
2) a mid fan, consisting of shallower branching channels which feed a depositional lobe (the "suprafan" of Normark, 1978)
3) a topographically smooth outer (lower) fan, which grades into
4) a basin plain.

Details can be added to this scheme; for example, the inner fan channels on some fans have prominent levees, and a flat aggradational floor with a smaller thalweg. This is typical of the inner fan channel of La Jolla Fan, where the main channel is 1 to 2 km wide, and about 140 m deep. The incised channel meanders within the main channel, and is about 200 to 300 m wide and 20 m deep. An example of a more complex fan model is given in Figure 15.

Currently, variations on this simple statement of the model (Fig. 14) include fans with prominent channel deposits but apparently no lobes, fans with abundant lobe deposits but fewer channels, and coalesced inner fan deposits that consist largely of channel-levee complexes. Because there are only one or two examples of each of these, it is probably premature to suggest many different fan *models*. It is important to understand how the existing general model(s) can be adapted to account for these new situations.

FACIES AND FAN MORPHOLOGY

Mutti and Ricci Lucchi (1972) assigned their turbidite facies to three associations – slope, fan, and basin plain. The schemes in Figures 14 and 15 are developed from this. The data base for the diagrams is a blend of ancient rock characteristics (especially grain size and observed frequency of channelling associated with the facies) and mor-

phology of modern fans. The weakest
part of the model is the relative lack of
core data from modern fans.

Classical turbidites are spectacularly
parallel bedded and unchannellized in
the field, and hence are assigned to
smooth fan environments – smooth
outer parts of suprafan lobes, lower fan,
and basin plain (Fig. 15). Beds change
from being relatively coarse, thick-
bedded and beginning with Bouma's
division A to beds that are finer, thinner
bedded, and beginning with divisions B
and/or C with increasing distance from
the ends of the distributary channels.

Massive and *pebbly sandstones* are
commonly channellized in the field, and
hence are assigned to channellized fan
environments (Fig. 15). The finer facies
occur in the distributary channels, and
coarse facies occur higher on the fan
surface, toward the inner fan channel.

Conglomerates, if supplied to the
basin, tend to occur in the inner fan
channel, or as a lag in some of the distributary channels (Fig. 15).

Major complications occur in the
inner fan channel-levee complexes,
where thin bedded classical turbidites
(beginning with Bouma's division B or
C) may occur on channel margins or
levees, or in the basins behind the
levees. Local facies changes may also
involve finer beds on the terraces and
coarser beds plugging the incised inner
fan channel.

In general, these facies assignments
are accepted by most workers, and they
allow the development of specific facies
sequences that seem to be characteristic of particular fan environments.

FACIES SEQUENCES
Sequences are basically related to lobe
progradation and aggradation, and to
channel filling. The formative ideas are
those of Mutti and Ghibaudo (1972),
and it is now fair to state that:
1) most fan interpretations are based
   on facies sequences;
2) facies sequences are being used
   to modify fan models; and
3) some alleged facies sequences
   exist only in the eye of the
   beholder!
In depositional lobes, the marginal
facies will tend to be thinner bedded
than those near the apex of the lobe;
consequently, if the lobe progrades it
will produce a *thickening-upward
sequence* (Fig. 16). As well as

Figure 16
*Ordovician Cloridorme Formation, Québec,
showing beds slightly overturned with strati-
graphic top to left. Note prominent* *thickening-upward sequence (arrowed), with
abrupt return to thin-bedded turbidites and
mudstones at the top.*

Figure 17
*Cambrian St. Roch Formation near St. Jean-
Port-Joli, Québec. Note prominent thinning-
upward sequence (arrowed) which begins* *with a massive sandstone facies (compare
with Fig. 18), and is interpreted as a chan-
nel fill.*

thickening-upward, the sequence may
also become coarser grained upward,
and beds that begin with Bouma's division C and B will tend to be replaced
upward by beds beginning with division
A. Thickening-upward sequences are
very common in the geological record –
prograding lobe fringes may form
sequences only a few metres thick
composed of relatively thin bedded turbidites, whereas an entire lobe may
form a sequence typically a few tens of
metres in thickness.

By contrast, *thinning-upward*

sequences (Fig. 17) were interpreted by
Mutti and Ghibaudo (1972) to represent
gradual channel filling and abandonment. Thinning-upward sequences tend
to be a few metres to about 50 m thick,
and in those cases where a channel
morphology can be observed in the
field, the lower beds of the fill are commonly pebbly or massive sandstones,
rather than classical turbidites. Many
channels on modern fans are deeper
than 50 m, especially on the inner fan,
but systematic thinning-upward
sequences more than 50 m thick are

Figure 18
Thinning-upward sequence (arrowed) in the Paleocene turbidites at Shelter Cove, Point San Pedro, Calfiornia. The spectacular continuity of the turbidites, and absence of a massive sandstone facies suggest that this sequence is not necessarily a channel fill. It

may result from lateral lobe switching, with the thicker beds at the lobe centre, and the thinner beds representing lobe fringe. Alternatively, the turbidites may be interchannel, the thinning-upward sequence representing channel migration away from this area.

Figure 19
Thinning-upward sequence (arrowed) from turbidites, via a soft sediment slump (small arrows show way up) into mudstones. Stratigraphic top to right; Cretaceous tubidites at Wheeler Gorge, California. Compare this sequence with those in Figures 17 and 18. It

probably represents neither channel filling nor lobe switching – its context, and especially the slumping, suggests deposition on a levee. The thinning-upward may reflect migration of the main turbidite channel away from the levee. See Walker (in press).

levee crest) is indicated to be about 60 m (Heritier *et al.,* 1979, Fig. 13).

The association of *thinning-upward sequences* with *channel filling* has become a standard part of the fan model, but it is becoming apparent that some thinning-upward sequences, especially those composed only of relatively thin-bedded classical turbidites, imply other processes. For example, the sequence shown in Figure 18 exhibits convincing thinning-upward, but the thin-bedded classical turbidites and smooth sea floor do not suggest channelling. The sequence could indicate gradual lateral lobe shifting, from a lobe centre to lobe fringe environment. Similarly, the sequence in Figure 19 also shows thinning-upward, but the soft-sediment slumping and thin-bedded turbidites could indicate deposition on the back of an inner fan levee, the sequence being due to gradual migration of the channel away from the depositional area.

If an entire fan complex were to prograde, an idealized sequence predicted by the fan model as its various lobe and channel sequences build up would be similar to that shown in Figure 20, which is largely self-explanatory. One of the most useful aspects of thickening- and thinning-upward sequences is that they can be recognized in sub-surface well logs. In Figure 21, I show one possible interpretation of an SP and resistivity log (see "Subsurface Facies Analysis", this volume) from Devonian turbidites in Pennsylvania. Again, the comparison of Figures 20 and 21 is obvious, and shows how the fan model can be used as a basis for interpretation. Many other examples are given by Walker (1978), and by Tillman and Ali (1982) who have compiled a very useful series of turbidite papers into a reprint volume of the American Association of Petroleum Geologists.

FEEDBACK: THE EVOLUTION OF FAN MODELS
In the first paper of this volume, it was emphasized that models are formed by the "distillation" of many local examples. It follows that as new examples are studied, there is more input, or feedback, into the model, and hence the possibility for the model to evolve. Currently, fan models are evolving as the result of more studies of ancient rocks, and better studies of modern fans.

uncommon in the geological record. This suggests that deeper turbidite channels fill in a more complex way than the shallower ones. For example, well logs from the Miocene Rosedale Channel of California (Martin, 1963, Figs. 5, 6 and 7) indicate several packets of sand alternating with finer grained sediments in a channel fill up to about

400 m thick. There is certainly no suggestion of an overall fining-upward sequence. Similarly, channel-levee complexes in the Paleocene Frigg Fan of the North Sea (Heritier *et al.,* 1979, Figs. 9, 10, 12, and 13) may be 200 m or more in thickness, but are apparently compound, and not single channel fills. Relief on any single channel (floor to

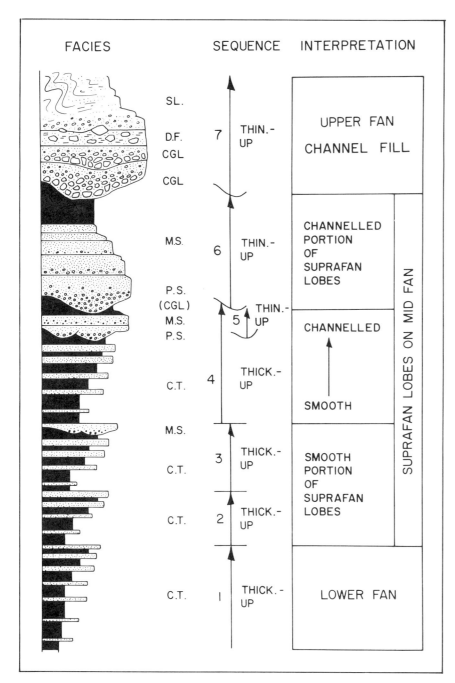

FACIES   SEQUENCE   INTERPRETATION

Figure 20

Generalized hypothetical sequence produced during over-all fan progradation. CT = classical turbidites; MS = massive sandstones; PS = pebbly sandstones; CGL = conglomerate; DF = debris flow; SL = slump. Sequences shown by arrows are THIN.-UP (thinning upward) or THICK.-UP (thickening upward).

The input from ancient rocks comes particularly from work on facies sequences. I mentioned earlier that some of these sequences perhaps exist only in the eye of the beholder – this is illustrated in Figure 22, and the general problem has been addressed by Hiscott (1981). One modification of the general fan model of Figure 14 is the "fan of low transport efficiency" (Mutti, 1979), in which most of the sand is deposited in channel complexes rather than on lobes. The evidence comes both from observations of channel contacts in the field, and from the abundance of thinning-upward sequences observed in units such as the Eocene Tyee Formation of Oregon (Chan and Dott, 1983) and The Rocks Sandstone of California (Link and Nilsen, 1980). A measured section of The Rocks is shown in Figure 23, where the thinning and fining-upward sequences are shown. Note that sequences average about 10 m in thickness; they mostly have erosional bases, and involve individual sandstone beds up to 7.5 m thick.

In using this example to modify existing models, note that two levels of interpretation are involved – first, the existence of the sequences themselves is an interpretation (and some of the sequences involve very few beds, and/or unconvincing thickness trends, Fig. 23), and second, it is an interpretation to suggest that the sequences necessarily involve channel filling. However, in view of the bed thickness and erosional bases, the latter interpretation seems reasonable and convincing.

A second modification of the basic fan model of Figure 14 is the recognition of channel-levee complexes, rather than a single channel with a levee. Channel-levee complexes exist on modern fans such as the Amazon (Damuth *et al.*, 1983a, 1983b), Indus, Laurentian (Stow, 1981) and Crati (Colella *et al.*, 1981), and are possibly present in ancient examples such as the Paleocene-Lower Eocene Frigg Fan (North Sea; Heritier *et al.*, 1979).

A channel-levee complex is essentially a central channel with fine grained sediment wedges on either side. The wedges stand up above the general topography of the basin floor, but gradually lose their relief away from the channel and merge with the basin floor. Most active levees appear to be constructed by spill-over from turbidity currents using the channel. Dimensions are extremely variable – on the Amazon Cone, mid-fan channel-levee complexes are up to 500 m thick and 25 km wide and those on the Laurentian Fan are a little thinner and perhaps a little wider (Stow, 1981). On a much smaller scale, the upper fan channel-levee complex on Crati Fan (Southern Italy; Colella *et al.*, 1981) is a total of 5 km wide, and is built up from at least 3 channels a little over 10 m deep.

Channel-levee complexes differ from fans of low efficiency, in that the latter are sand-rich, whereas the bulk of the channel-levee complex is relatively fine-grained. In the Amazon example, channels appear to switch abruptly by avul-

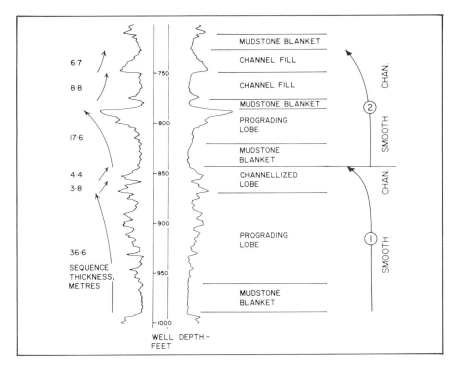

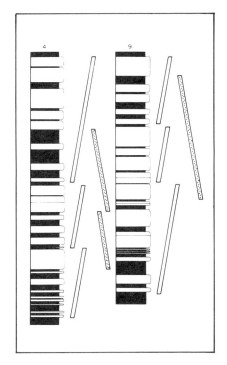

Figure 21
SP and resistivity logs from a turbidite formation in Pennsylvania. I have interpreted the shapes of the SP/resistivity trends as channel fill ("bell-shaped") or lobe progradation ("funnel-shaped"), with some mudstone

blankets in between. Note that two overall lobe-to-channel sequences can be defined (see Fig. 20), the lower one having a greater proportion of lobe deposits (smooth fan surface), the upper one having a greater proportion of channel deposits.

Figure 22
Some sequences in turbidites are "in the eye of the beholder". This diagram is from Mutti and Ghibaudo (1972) and shows part of their Figure 15 from the Miocene Arenarie di San Salvatore. Open bars show "negative megasequences", that is, thickening-upward sequences as proposed by Mutti and Ghibaudo. However, I have added some extra bars, stippled, which propose positive megasequences, or thinning-upward sequences. The reader should decide which sequences are preferable, remembering that one implies lobe fringe progradation, the other implies channel filling on a different part of a fan.

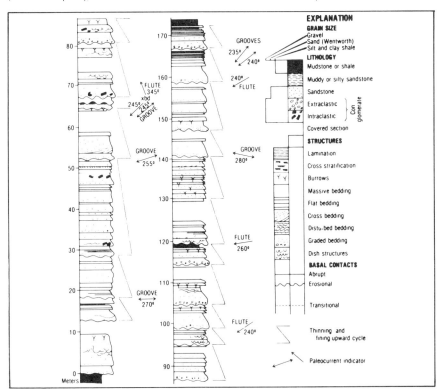

Figure 23
Measured section of The Rocks Sandstone (Eocene) in the Santa Lucia Range, California. Note the "thinning- and fining-upward cycles"; some are based on very few beds, or

only show very weakly the proposed trends. Others seen well established with erosional (or channelled) bases. From Link and Nilsen, 1980.

sion (Damuth et al., 1983a, 1983b), but in other fans (possibly the Indus is a good example) the channel appears to migrate progressively laterally, eroding into its older levee deposits as the whole system aggrades.

In the geological record the only well described candidate for a channel-levee complex is Frigg Fan in the Paleocene-Lower Eocene section of the North Sea (Heritier et al., 1979). The fan is composed of four radiating sandy fingers apparently without well defined depositional lobes at the end. The topographically highest fingers are 2 to 4 km wide, and about 600 m thick. Within the fingers, there are interbedded channel turbidites, sandy levee deposits, and back-levee or interchannel shales. A second possible candidate is an Upper Cretaceous conglomerate channel complex at Wheeler Gorge, California (Walker, 1975b and in press), where the conglomerates are overlain by several thinning-upward sequences of thin-bedded turbidites with abundant slump features. The vertical succession of conglomerates to thin-bedded turbidites with slumps suggests the migration of conglomerate-filled channels away from the area, with the slumped thin-bedded turbidites representing back-levee deposits of (? nearby) higher conglomerate-filled channels.

LIMITATIONS OF FAN MODELS
In 1976, when the "turbidite facies model" first appeared in Geoscience Canada, it was one of the better defined models. Many published studies in the last eight years have described systems that vary considerably from that model (low efficiency fans, channel-levee complexes), and descriptions of modern fans show variations from the summary model of Normark (1978). I believe that it is definitely premature to propose several different types of fan models - the data base for each proposed type is too scanty. It seems better to regard the "basic fan model" (Fig. 14 is but one example) as a norm, hence identifying, say, low efficiency fans as different from the norm. It is thus a fixed point for the comparison of many different fans, and can be modified to suppress the depositional lobes, and emphasize the channels, or channel-levee complexes, as appropriate. Once modified, it should still be possible to use the model in a predictive way, understanding how the modification of the model will affect channel and lobe distributions, sand body geometry, etc.

As presented, the fan model seems to be a useful framework for the investigation of small to medium scale ancient fans, with single points of input (single feeder channels) into the basin. The model loses much of its power if two separate fans overlap, because facies sequences may no longer be controlled by single processes (e.g., lobe progradation), but may be the result of irregular interbedding of beds from multiple sources.

The fan model may also lose some power when applied to long (hundreds of km) narrow "exogeosynclinal" troughs in which the paleoflow pattern is dominantly parallel to tectonic strike. Examples of turbidites in such troughs

include the Middle Ordovician Cloridorme Formation (Gaspé Peninsula) and its time equivalent in the Central Appalachians, the Martinsburg Formation. The deposits consist dominantly of classical turbidites hundreds of metres thick, but showing no consistent proximal to distal change along the length of the trough in the downflow direction. It is commonly suggested that turbidity currents flowed downslope toward the trough axis, perhaps constructing fans at the trough margin. However, at the trough axis the flows turned and continued to flow parallel to the trough axis. The marginal fans were presumably destroyed by subsequent tectonics, and the absence of consistent proximal to distal changes along the trough axis is probably due to input from a whole series of fans along the trough margin. Thus any consistent changes developing from one source would be masked by input from adjacent sources up and down the trough. At present, there is no facies model that acts as a good predictor in this type of turbidite basin.

Even in short narrow elongate troughs, the fan models (Figs. 14 and 15) may be inapplicable. Hsu et al. (1980) have criticized the use of fan models in the Ventura Basin (California), and instead, they have emphasized the data for longitudinal flow along the axis of the basin. It follows that "the presence of most reservoir-sand beds [is] in the deepest part of the trough, not in a canyon or a fan environment on the basin flank" (Hsu et al., 1980, p. 1050). This work combined with studies of small, tectonically active modern basins in the California Borderlands (e.g., Normark et al., 1979; Field and Edwards, 1980; Underwood et al., 1980; Graham and Bachman, 1983) emphasizes that basin geometry may greatly modify the way in which fans build into basins, adding another limitation to the use of fan facies relationships as predictors.

Recently, studies emphasizing facies and thickness sequences have been made of part of the Middle Ordovician Cloridorme Formation of Québec (Beeden, 1983). It was shown that thickening-upward sequences of classical turbidites (mostly relatively thin bedded) were present, and could be interpreted in terms of prograding lobe-fringe environments. In the same Middle Ordovician elongate trough between the rising Taconic Orogen and the

craton, Belt and Bussieres (1981) have also described submarine fan facies (see their Fig. 8) in the area northeast of Québec City. Thus it may be that further studies of long narrow basins using techniques such as thickness sequence analysis will reveal more evidence of submarine fan environments.

REFERENCES
SOURCES OF INFORMATION
For a general background on some of the current arguments concerning ancient and modern fan models, the introductory papers in the reprint volume edited by Tillman and Ali (1982) are the best source. These papers include Walker (1978), Normark (1970, 1978), Nilsen (1980; a discussion of the earlier papers) and replies by Walker (1980) and Normark (1980). Another useful review is that of Howell and Normark (1982). For other aspects of models, consult the annotations of the general papers (below). As well as a general heading, I have subdivided the references into modern sediments and ancient rocks. Consult the annotations for details.

GENERAL PAPERS: MODELS
Bouma, A.H., 1962. Sedimentology of some flysch deposits. Amsterdam, Elsevier, 168 p.
This book contains a lot of useful but local data. It does, however, establish the classic Bouma sequence, and lays out some ideas on how the sequence might change laterally.

Harms, J.C., Southard, J.B., and Walker, R.G., 1982. Structures and sequences clastic rocks. Society of Economic Paleontologists and Mineralogists, Short Course 9, variously paginated.
The introductory sections on flow, bed forms and stratification lay out the basis for interpreting sedimentary structures.

Hiscott, R.N., 1981. Deep sea fan deposits in the Macigno Formation (Middle-Upper Oliogocene) of the Gordana Valley, Northern Appennines, Italy: Discussion. Journal of Sedimentary Petrology, v. 51, p. 1015-1021.
A very lucid discussion of the problems of identifying sequences in turbidites.

Howell, D.G., and Normark, W.R., 1982. Sedimentology of submarine fans. In Scholle, P.A., and Spearing, D.R., eds., Sandstone depositional environments. American Association of Petroleum Geologists, Memoir 31, p. 365-404.
A very useful review of all important aspects of fans, with many colour illustrations. The next paper to consult after reading this one.

Kelts, K., and Arthur, M.A., 1981. Turbidites

after ten years of deep-sea drilling - wringing out the mop? *In* Warme, J.E., Douglas, R.G., and Winterer, E.L., eds., The deep sea drilling project: a decade of progress. Society of Economic Paleontologists and Mineralogists, Special Publication 32, p. 91-127.
This is the only coherent source of information on the DSDP findings with respect to turbidites and submarine fans. It forms an invaluable entry into the vast library of DSDP reports. Read Walker (1973) to understand the significance of the title.

Kuenen, P.H., and Migliorini, C., 1950. Turbidity currents as a cause of graded bedding. Journal of Geology, v. 58, p. 91-127.
This paper established the turbidite concept, and is one of the most important papers in sedimentology this century. Required reading, not only for historical reasons.

Lowe, D.R., 1975. Water escape structures in coarse grained sediments. Sedimentology, v. 22, p. 157-204.
A thorough and very abundantly illustrated discussion of these structures, which are common in many turbidite facies.

Menard, H.W., 1964. Marine geology of the Pacific. New York, McGraw Hill, 271 p.
Chapter 9 on turbidity currents is still a useful review, and contains important quantitative data.

Mutti, E., 1979. Turbidites et cones sous-marins profonds. *In* Homewood, P., ed., Sedimentation detritique (fluviatile, littorale et marine). Institut de Geologie de l'University de Fribourg, Short Course 1979, p. 353-419.
Excellent review (in French) of submarine fan facies, facies sequences and facies models. Full discussion of channel mouth bars and by-passing, and introduces the idea of fans of "low and high transport efficiency". Required reading - a different point of view from Walker (1978).

Mutti, E., and Ghibaudo, G., 1972. Un esempio di torbiditi di conoide sottomarina esterna: le Arenarie di San Salvatore (Formazione di Bobbio, Miocene) nell'Appennino de Piacenza. Memorie dell'Accademia delle Scienze di Torino, Classe di Scienze Fisiche, Matematiche e Naturali, Series 4, No. 16, 40 p.
As well as describing the facies, this paper emphasizes facies sequences, and for the first time compares turbidite fining-up sequences with delta channels, and coarsening-up sequences with prograding deltaic lobes. Suggests a fan model with lobes at the ends of channels (see Mutti and Ricci Lucchi, 1972, below).

Mutti, E. and Ricci Lucchi, F., 1972. Le torbiditi dell'Appennino settentrionale: introduzione all'analisi di facies. Memorie dell Societa Geologica Italiana, v. 11, p. 161-199. An extremely important and influential paper that established a widely-used facies classification, grouped the facies into associations, and related the associations to fan depositional environments. Did not discuss sequences in as much detail as Mutti and Ghibaudo (1972), above, and proposed a fan model with channels but no lobes.
REQUIRED READING - fortunately, there is an English translation by T.H. Nilsen, 1978. Turbidites of the northern Appennines: introduction to facies analysis. International Geology Review, v. 20, p. 125-166.

Mutti, E., and Ricci Lucchi, F., 1975. Examples of turbidite facies and facies associations from selected formations of the northern Appennines. Nice, France, 9th International Congress of Sedimentology, Guidebook to Field Trip A 11 (Mutti, E., *et al.*, eds.), 120 p.

Nilsen, T.H., 1980. Modern and ancient submarine fans: discussion of papers by R.G. Walker and W.R. Normark. American Association of Petroleum Geologists, Bulletin, v. 64, p. 1094-1101.
Discussion of Walker (1978) and Normark (1978). An important paper which establishes many of the current topics of research and disagreement.

Normark, W.R., 1970. Growth patterns of deep sea fans. American Association of Petroleum Geologists, Bulletin, v. 54, p. 2170-2195.
This is the first generalization about fan morphology and growth patterns, now superceded by Normark, 1978.

Normark, W.R., 1978. Fan-valleys, channels and depositional lobes on modern submarine fans: characters for the recognition of sandy turbidite environments. American Association of Petroluem Geologists, Bulletin, v. 61, p. 912-931.
Summary of growth patterns of many modern fans, and still the best general summary. See discussion by Nilsen (1980) and Normark's reply (1980).

Normark, W.R., 1980. Modern and ancient submarine fans: reply. American Association of Petroleum Geologists, Bulletin, v. 64, p. 1108-1112.
Here, Normark replies to the discussion of his 1978 paper by Nilsen (above).

Tillman, R.W., and Ali, S.A., 1982. Deep water canyons, fans and facies: models for stratigraphic trap exploration. American Association of Petroleum Geologists, Reprint Series 26, 596 p.
A very useful collection of papers from the AAPG Bulletin. Pages 1-100 usefully group the papers by Walker and Normark, with Nilsen's discussion and authors' replies.

Walker, R.G., 1967. Turbidite sedimentary structures and their relationship to proximal and distal depositional environments. Journal of Sedimentary Petrology, v. 37, p. 25-43.
Uses the Bouma sequence as starting point for an investigation of turbidite variablility. The proximal/distal ideas show how the sequence can be used as a predictor, but being "pre-fan", the predictions are now out of date.

Walker, R.G., 1973. Mopping-up the turbidite mess. *In* Ginsburg, R.N., ed., Evolving concepts in sedimentology. Baltimore, The John Hopkins University Press, p. 1-37.
A philosophical history of the turbidite concept, based on the ideas of Thomas H. Kuhn. Read the paper to understand the title!

Walker, R.G., 1975a. Generalized facies models for resedimented conglomerates of turbidite association. Geological Society of America, Bulletin, v. 86, p. 737-748.
Established four "Bouma-like" sequences for conglomerates - the scheme has been little-modified during the last 10 years but still has a rather slim data base.

Walker, R.G., 1978. Deep water sandstone facies and ancient submarine fans: models for exploration for stratigraphic traps. American Association of Petroleum Geologists, Bulletin, v. 62, p. 932-966.
Review of facies, facies sequences and facies models. A very useful source of references, and ideas current to 1978. There is now a greater variety of modern fans and ancient rock studies that need to be blended or distilled into a general model.

Walker, R.G., 1980. Modern and ancient submarine fans: reply. American Association of Petroleum Geologists, v. 64, p. 1101-1108.
Reply to Nilsen's (1980) discussion of Walker (1978).

Walker, R.G. and Mutti, E., 1973. Turbidite facies and facies associations. *In* Middleton, G.V., and Bouma, A.H. eds., Turbidites and deep water sedimentation. Pacific Section, Society of Economic Paleontologists and Mineralogists, Short Course (Anaheim, 1973), p. 119-157.
This is the first attempt to blend modern fan studies (Normark, 1970) and ancient rock studies (Mutti and Ricci Lucchi, 1972) into a combined recent/ancient fan model. The evolution of this model has been discussed by Walker (1980).

RECENT SEDIMENTS

Colella, A., *et al.*, 1981. The Crati submarine fan, Ionian Sea. A preliminary report. International Association of Sedimentologists, Second European Meeting, Bologna, Abstracts, p. 34-39
Brief description of a complex of channels

and levees, passing basinward into elongate lobes and interlobe areas.

Damuth, J.E., and Embley, R.W., 1981. Mass-transport processes on Amazon Cone: Western Equatorial Atlantic. American Association of Petroleum Geologists, Bulletin, v. 65, p. 629-643.
General description of the Amazon Cone, emphasizing three huge slump/debris flow deposits.

Damuth, J.E. et al., 1983a. Distributary channel meandering and bifurcation patterns on the Amazon deep sea fan as revealed by long-range side-scan sonar (GLORIA). Geology, v. 11, p. 94-98.
Beautiful and amazing side-scan sonar pictures of extremely sinuous channels within channel-levee complexes.

Damuth, J.E., et al., 1983b. Age relationship of distributary channels on Amazon deep sea fan: implications for fan growth pattern. Geology, v. 11, p. 470-473.
Detailed description of the evolution of western and eastern channel-levee complexes.

Elmore, R.D., Pilkey, O.H., Cleary, W.J., and Curran, H.A., 1979. Black Shell turbidite, Hatteras abyssal plain, western Atlantic Ocean. Geological Society of America, Bulletin, v. 90, p 1165-1176.
Detailed description of the world's largest known turbidite, and its relationship to other Hatteras abyssal plain sediments.

Field, M.E., and Edwards, B.D., 1980. Slopes of the southern California continental borderland: a regime of mass transport. In Field, M.E., et al., eds., Quaternary depositional environments of the Pacific coast. Pacific Coast Paleogeography Symposium 4, Los Angeles, Pacific Section, Society of Economic Paleontologists and Mineralogists, p. 169-184.
Shows the influence of basin topography on the way in which basins are filled.

Graham, S.A. and Bachman, S.B., 1983. Structural controls on submarine fan geometry and internal architecture: upper La Jolla Fan system, offshore southern California. American Association of Petroleum Geologists, Bulletin, v. 676, p. 83-96.
Shows the La Jolla Fan feeder channels (Newport, La Jolla, Loma) and the structural control of their evolution. Channel-levee complexes are well developed in the Newport system.

Heezen, B.C., 1956. Corrientes de turbidez del Rio Magdalena. Societa Geografica de Colombia, Boll., v. 52-2, p. 135-143.
This paper, quoted by Menard (1964), is apparently the data source for the Magdalena turbidity current of 1935. See Menard (1964) and Kolla et al. (1984).

Heezen, B.C., Menzies, R.J., Schneider, E.D., Ewing, W.M., and Granelli, N.C.L., 1964. Congo submarine canyon. American Association of Petroleum Geologists, Bulletin, v. 48, p. 1126-1149.
An important paper that establishes a direct relationship between turbidity current generation (cable breaking) and the behaviour of the Congo river – specifically months of high discharge and years when the river is establishing a new path through its estuarine sand bars. The paper is reprinted in Tillman and Ali (1982).

Horn, D.R., Ewing, J.I., and Ewing, M., 1972. Graded bed sequences emplaced by turbidity currents north of 20°N in the Pacific, Atlantic and Mediterranean. Sedimentology, v. 18, p. 247-275.
Describes abyssal plains, their sediments and sediment thicknesses, and points of input into the basins.

Kolla, V., Buffler, R.T., and Ladd, J.W., 1984. Seismic stratigraphy and sedimentation of Magdalena Fan, southern Colombia Basin, Caribbean Sea. American Association of Petroleum Geologists, Bulletin, v. 68, p. 316-332.
Establishes six seismic sequences, and models channellized and overbank turbidity current flow (upper fan) and unchannelized flow (down fan). A possible modern example of a "high efficiency" fan (see Mutti, 1979).

Kolla, V., Kostecki, J.A., Henderson, L., and Hess, L., 1980. Morphology and Quaternary sedimentation of the Mozambique Fan and environs, southwestern Indian Ocean. Sedimentology, v. 27, p. 357-378.
General description of Mozambique Fan.

Normark, W.R., Piper, D.J.W., and Hess, G.R., 1979. Distributary channels, sand lobes and mesotopography of Navy submarine fan, California Borderlands, with applications to ancient fan sediments. Sedimentology, v. 26, p. 749-774.
Establishes in detail the pattern of lobe/channel switching and sediment distribution. Contributes an important data base to fan models of the Normark type.

Normark, W.R., Piper, D.J.W., and Stow, D.A.V., 1983. Quaternary development of channels, levees and lobes on middle Laurentian Fan. American Association of Petroleum Geologists, Bulletin, v. 67, p. 1400-1409.
Establishes a pattern of channel switching and levee growth.

Pilkey, O.H., Locker, S.D., and Cleary, W.J., 1980. Comparison of sand-layer geometry on flat floors of 10 modern depositional basins. American Association of Petroleum Geologists, Bulletin, v. 64, p. 841-856.
Important and useful comparison of turbidite geometries on Atlantic and Caribbean abyssal plains (plus Santa Monica basin).

Piper, D.J.W., and Normark, W.R., 1982. Acoustic interpretation of Quaternary sedimentation and erosion on the channelled upper Laurentian fan, Atlantic margin of Canada. Canadian Journal of Earth Sciences, v. 19, p. 1974-1984.
Shows that previously suggested large slumps are in fact absent, but establishes a channel switching pattern.

Piper, D.J.W., and Normark, W.R., 1983. Turbidite depositional patterns and flow characteristics, Navy submarine fan, California Borderlands. Sedimentology, v. 30, p. 681-694.
Correlates beds on the fan, and introduces the concept of "flow stripping", whereby most of a flow can overtop a levee at a channel bend.

Stevenson, A.J., Scholl, D.W., and Vallier, T.L., 1983. Tectonic and geologic implications of the Zodiac Fan, Aleutian Abyssal Plain, northeast Pacific. Geological Society of America, Bulletin, v. 94, p. 259-273.
A large fan that differs from many others in that the channels continue essentially to the margins of the fan. Well developed channel-levee complexes.

Stow, D.A.V., 1981. Laurentian Fan: morphology, sediments, processes and growth patterns. American Association of Petroleum Geologists, Bulletin, v. 65, p. 375-393.
A good general description and discussion of all of the above topics.

Uchupi, E., and Austin, J.A., 1979. The stratigraphy and structure of the Laurentian Cone region. Canadian Journal of Earth Sciences, v. 16, p. 1726-1752.
Seismic reflection profiling shows two fan megasequences. Re-survey of the fan gives better definition of channel patterns, and allowed re-calculation of Grand Bands turbidity current velocities.

Underwood, M.B., Bachman, S.B., and Schweller, W.J., 1980. Sedimentary processes and facies associations within trench and trench-slope settings. In Field, M.E., et al., eds., Quaternary depositional environments of the Pacific Coast. Pacific Coast Paleogeography Symposium 4. Los Angeles, Pacific Section, Society of Economic Paleontologists and Mineralogists, p. 211-229.
Describes and models the tectonic control of turbidite facies and channels in trench settings.

Whitmarsh, R.B., et al., 1974. Initial reports of the Deep Sea Drilling Project, Volume 23. Washington, D.C., U.S. Government Printing Office, p. 211-289.
Documents DSDP Site 222, with comments on rates of sedimentation for this site (on the western margin of the Indus Cone).

ANCIENT ROCKS

Beeden, D.R., 1983. Sedimentology of some turbidites and related rocks from the Cloridorme Group, Ordovician, Québec. Hamilton, Ontario, McMaster University, M.Sc. Thesis, 256 p.
Documents sequences in turbidites, the turbidites occurring in a long narrow trough with all paleocurrent directions parallel to regional strike. Possible submarine fan facies in a long narrow trough.

Belt, E.S. and Bussieres, L., 1981. Upper Middle Ordovician submarine fans and associated facies, northeast of Québec City. Canadian Journal of Earth Sciences, v. 18, p. 981-994.
Documents submarine fans in a very long narrow basin between the Taconic Orogen and the Craton. Possibly a similar situation to that of Beeden (1983).

Chan, M.A. and Dott, R.H. Jr., 1983. Shelf and deep sea sedimentation in Eocene forearc basin, western Oregon – fan or non-fan? American Association of Petroleum Geologists, Bulletin, v. 67, p. 2100-2116.
Proposes a sand-rich (or "poorly efficient") fan interpretation for the Eocene Tyee Formation.

Clari, P. and Ghibaudo, G., 1979. Multiple slump scars in the Tortonian type area (Piedmont Basin, northwestern Italy). Sedimentology, v. 26, p. 719-730.
Excellent documentation of large slump scars, interpreted to have formed near the shelf-slope break.

Cook, H.E., McDaniel, P.N., Mountjoy, E., and Pray, L.C., 1972. Allochthonous carbonate debris flows at Devonian bank ("reef") margins, Alberta, Canada. Bulletin of Canadian Petroleum Geology, v. 20, p. 439-497.
Well documented example of huge debris flows.

Crowell, J.C., 1957. Origin of pebbly mudstones. Geological Society of America, Bulletin, v. 68, p. 993-1009.
The title says it all. For the Pigeon Point examples, see also Howell and Joyce (1981).

Davies, I.C. and Walker, R.G., 1974. Transport and deposition of resedimented conglomerates: the Cap Enragé Formation, Cambro-Ordovocian, Gaspe, Québec. Journal of Sedimentary Petrology, v. 44, p. 1200-1216.
Establishes conglomerate fabric types and uses the results to document paleoflow directions.

Gregory, M.R., 1969. Sedimentary features and penecontemporaneous slumping in the Waitemata Group, Whangaparaoa Peninsula, north Auckland, New Zealand. New Zealand Journal of Geology and Geophysics, v. 12, p. 248-282.
Contains excellent illustrations of some of the largest sedimentary slumps ever described.

Hein, F.J., 1982. Depositional mechanisms of deep sea coarse clastic sediments, Cap Enragé Formation, Québec. Canadian Journal of Earth Sciences, v. 19, p. 267-287.
Describes internal structures and structure sequences for massive and pebbly sandstones.

Hein, F.J., and Walker R.G., 1982. The Cambro-Ordovician Cap Enragé Formation, Québec, Canada: conglomeratic deposits of a braided submarine channel with terraces. Sedimentology, v. 29, p. 309-329.
Conglomerate facies sequences, both lateral and vertical, establish the nature of this deep water braided channel.

Helwig, J., 1970. Slump folds and early structures, northeastern Newfoundland, Appalachians. Journal of Geology, v. 78, p. 172-187.

Hendry, H.E., 1978. Cap des Rosiers Formation at Grosses Roches, Québec – deposits of the mid-fan region on an Ordovician submarine fan. Canadian Journal of Earth Sciences, v. 15, p. 1472-1488
Conglomerate-to-sandstone fining-upward sequences interpreted as backfilling a channel mouth in the mid-fan region.

Heritier, F.E., Lossel, P., and Wathne, E., 1979. Frigg Field – large submarine-fan trap in lower Eocene rocks of North Sea. American Association of Petroleum Geologists, Bulletin, v. 63, p. 1999-2020.
Subsurface data seems to indicate a fan made up of channel levee complexes without prominent smooth depositonal lobes. The authors supply little of their own fan interpretation, however. Reprinted in Tillman and Ali, 1982.

Howell, D.G., and Joyce, J.M., 1981. Field guide to the Upper Cretatceous Pigeon Point Formation. In Frizzell, V., ed., Upper Cretaceous and Paleocene turbidites, central California Coast. Los Angeles, Pacific Section, Society of Economic Paleontologists and Mineralogists, p. 61-70
Describes the classic section where Crowell (1957) first studied and illustrated pebbly mudstones.

Hsu, K.J., Kelts, K., and Valentine, J.W., 1980. Resedimented facies in Ventura Basin, California, and model of longitudinal transport of turbidity currents. American Association of Petroleum Geologists, Bulletin, v. 64, p. 1034-1051.

Johnson, B.A., and Walker, R.G., 1979. Paleocurrents and depositional environments of deep water conglomerates in the Cambro-Orodovician Cap Enragé Formation, Québec Appalachians. Canadian Journal of Earth Sciences, v. 16, p. 1375-1387.
Establishes facies relationships among different types of conglomerate, and suggests initial channel model – see Hein and Walker, 1982.

Link, M.H., Squires, R.L., and Colburn, I.P., eds., 1981. Simi Hills Cretaceous turbidites, southern California. Los Angeles, Pacific Section, Society of Economic Paleontologists and Mineralogists, Field Trip Guide Book, 134 p.
Extremely useful guide book to a superbly exposed and very interesting group of turbidites, and massive and pebbly sandstones.

Link, M.H., and Nilsen, T.H., 1980. The Rocks Sandstone, an Eocene sand-rich deep-sea fan deposit, northern Santa Lucia Range, California. Journal of Sedimentary Petrology, v. 50, p. 583-601.
Sand-rich (channellized) fan based on abundant thinning- and fining-upward sequences.

Link, M.H., and Welton, J.E., 1982. Sedimentology and reservoir potential of Matilija Sandstone: an Eocene sand-rich deep-sea fan and shallow marine complex, southern California. American Association of Petroleum Geologists, Bulletin, v. 66, p. 1514-1534.
Well-documented example of a very sandy fan. Slope facies between fan and shallow marine parts of the section are very enigmatic.

Martin, B.D., 1963. Rosedale Channel – evidence for late Miocene submarine erosion in Great Valley of California. American Association of Petroleum Geologists, Bulletin, v. 47, p. 441-456.
Subsurface example of a partly sand-filled canyon. Reprinted in Tillman and Ali (1982).

Nilsen, T.H., and Abbott, P.L., 1981. Paleogeography and sedimentology of Upper Cretaceous turbidites, San Diego, California. American Association of Petroleum Geologists, Bulletin, v. 65, p. 1256-1284.
Well described and abundantly illustrated forearc basin fan deposits.

Piper, D.J.W., Normark, W.R., and Ingle, J.R., Jr., 1976. The Rio Dell Formation: a Plio-Pleistocene basin slope deposit in northern California. Sedimentology, v. 23, p. 309-328.
Describes slope deposits, with sketches (but no photos) of slumps.

Srivastava, P., Stearn, C.W., and Mountjoy, E.W., 1972. A Devonian megabreccia at the margin of the Ancient Wall carbonate complex, Alberta. Bulletin of Canadian

188

Petroleum Geology, v. 20, p. 412-438.
Good descriptions of debris flow/rockfall?
megabreccias.

Stevens, R.K., 1970. Cambro-Orodovician
flysch sedimentation and tectonics in west
Newfoundland and their possible bearing
on a Proto-Atlantic ocean. *In* Lajoie, J., ed.,
Flysh sedimentology in North America.
Geological Association of Canada, Special
Paper 7, p. 165-177.
Some sedimentological description, but
the thrust of the paper is concerned with
allochthonous flysch complexes.

Sullwold, H.H., 1960. Tarzana Fan, deep
submarine fan of late Miocene age, Los
Angeles County, California. American
Association of Petroleum Geologists, Bulletin, v. 44, p. 433-457.
I believe this is the first interpretation of a
turbidite sequence in terms of submarine
fans. It is based on a radial spread of flow
directions which, if traced upslope, converge at the suggested foot of a canyon.
See next paper.

Walker, R.G., 1966. Shale Grit and Grindslow
Shales: transition from turbidite to shallow
water sediments in the Upper Carboniferous of northern England. Journal of Sedimentary Petrology, v. 36, p. 90-114.
A submarine fan interpretation based on
variability of flow directions, facies relationships and, particularly, the abundance
of channels. Interpretive block diagram
redrawn in Walker (1978).

Walker R.G., 1975a. Generalized facies models for resedimented conglomerates of
turbidite association. Geological Society of
America, Bulletin, v. 86, p. 737-748.
Four "Bouma-like" models are established,
with comments on transport mechanisms
and proximal-distal implications.

Walker, R.G., 1975b. Upper Cretaceous
resedimented conglomerates at Wheeler
Gorge, California: description and field
guide. Journal of Sedimentary Petrology,
v. 45, p. 105-112.
Establishes three major thinning-upward
sequences. This study is put in context by
Walker (in press).

Walker, R.G., 1977. Deposition of upper
Mesozoic resedimented conglomerates
and associated turbidites in south western
Oregon. Geological Society of America,
Bulletin, v. 88, p. 273-285.
Establishes a series of thinning-upward
sequences, and proposes a mechanism for
channel blocking leading to channel fill.

Walker, R.G., 1979. Stop 1. L'Islet Wharf: an
early Cambrian submarine channel com-
plex. *In* Middleton, G.V., *et al.*, eds.,
Cambro-Ordovician submarine channels
and fans, L'Islet to Sainte-Anne-des-
Monts, Québec. Geological Association of
Canada, Guidebook to Field Trip A-6
(Québec, 1979), p. 4-7.
Preliminary interpretation of a superbly
exposed deep submarine fan channel.

Walker, R.G., in press. Mudstones and thin
bedded turbidites associated with the
Upper Cretaceous Wheeler Gorge conglomerates, California: a possible channel-
levee complex. Journal of Sedimentary
Petrology.
Interprets mudstones below conglomerates as basin plain, and mudstones with
turbidites above the conglomerates as
levee.

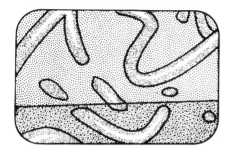

Trace Fossil Facies Models

ROBERT W. FREY
Department of Geology
University of Georgia
Athens, Georgia, U.S.A. 30602

S. GEORGE PEMBERTON
Alberta Geological Survey
4445 Calgary Trail South
Edmonton, Alberta T6H 5R7

INTRODUCTION

Trace fossils are both sedimentological and paleontological entities. They therefore represent a unique blending of potential environmental indicators in the stratigraphic record. Like physical sedimentary structures, trace fossils reflect many of the effects of prevalent environmental parameters, and to an appreciably greater extent than body fossils, trace fossils are a record of the behavior of active, in-situ organisms. The behavioral record of benthic organisms, as dictated or modified by environmental constraints, is thus the mainstay of ichnology.

Biogenic structures appear in many guises (Fig. 1), but here we are concerned mainly with tracks, trails, burrows, and borings. Our ultimate objective is to portray the facies implications of these various structures. But first we must impart something of their behavioral or ethological significance.

ETHOLOGICAL CLASSIFICATION

The single most important ingredient of ichnology is the functional interpretation of individual traces. Numerous categories of behavior are discernible among ancient and recent benthic animals (Frey, 1973). The more important of these categories are depicted in Figure 2. Additional examples are illustrated subsequently (see also Schäfer, 1972; Häntzschel, 1975).

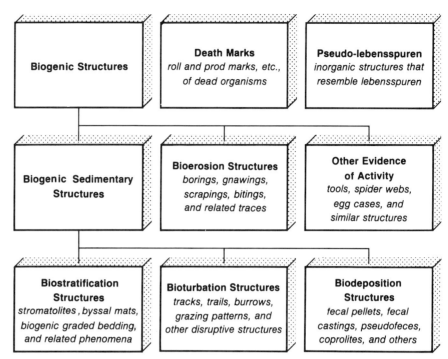

Figure 1
Major relationships among biogenic structures. (Modified from Frey, 1971, 1973).

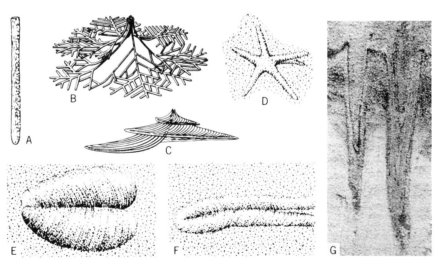

Figure 2
Major categories of benthic behavior represented by trace fossils. Numerous additional categories, such as brooding structures and swimming traces, may be discerned locally. A) Dwelling structure Skolithos. B) Feeding structure Chondrites. C) Grazing trace Zoophycos. D) Resting trace Asteriacites. E) Resting trace Rusophycus. F) Crawling trace Cruziana. G) Escape structures such as those made by anemones. (Adapted from Frey and Seilacher, 1980).

Fundamental behavioral, or ethological, patterns are genetically controlled. Deposit feeders are preadapted to quiet-water environments where deposited foodstuffs are most abundant, for example, and do not fare well in turbulent-water settings. The opposite is true of suspension feeders. Our ability to discern burrows of deposit or suspension feeders in the rock record therefore enhances our environmental interpretations considerably (Fürsich, 1975).

On a smaller, local scale, however, even a singular, preadapted mode of behavior may be modified by specific environmental conditions or fluctuations. In the knobby walled structure *Ophiomorpha,* for instance, vertical components of the burrow system tend to predominate in higher energy settings whereas horizontal components tend to predominate in lower energy settings (Frey *et al.,* 1978). Modal differences in the size of various trace fossils may have similar local environmental significance (Marintsch and Finks, 1982).

We also must recognize that the same basic function may be performed in different ways by different organisms, and that correspondingly different records are left in the sediment. For example, the burrows of some deposit feeders consist of branched feeding probes (Fig. 3) whereas the burrows of other deposit feeders may consist of unbranched, meniscate structures (Fig. 4).

Ethological interpretations of trace fossils thus proceed on two scales. One is the most basic behavioral implication of the trace (Table 1), regardless of its exact mode of fabrication (Figs. 2 to 4). The other is the finite, local variation inherent in many occurrences (e.g., Marintsch and Finks, 1982). In the following discussion we are concerned mainly with the first, most basic implication or behavioral program. These fundamental categories ultimately are most important in broad facies settings. Local variations are important in delineating more specific facies or subfacies characteristics, as explained subsequently.

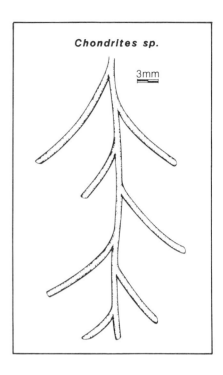

Chondrites sp.

3mm

Figure 3
Branched burrow system representing repetitive feeding probes. (Adapted from Howard and Frey, 1984).

Table 1
Ethological classification of invertebrate trace fossils. (Adapted from Frey and Seilacher, 1980).

Definition	Characteristic Morphology	Examples
Resting Traces *(Cubichnia)* Shallow depressions made by animals that temporarily settle onto, or dig into, the substrate surface. Emphasis is upon brief reclusion.	Trough-like relief, recording to some extent the later-oventral morphology of the animal; structures are isolated, ideally, but may intergrade with crawling traces or escape structures.	*Asteriacites* *Pelecypodichnus* *Rusophycus*
Crawling Traces *(Repichnia)* Trackways and epistratal or intrastratal trails made by organisms traveling from one place to another. Emphasis is upon locomotion. Secondary activities may be involved.	Linear or sinuous overall structures, some branched; footprints or continuous grooves, commonly annulated; complete form may be preserved, or may appear as cleavage reliefs.	*Aulichnites* *Cruziana* *Diplichnites* *Scolicia*
Grazing Traces *(Pascichnia)* Grooves, patterned pits, and furrows, many of them discontinuous, made by mobile deposit feeders or algal grazers at or under the substrate surface. Emphasis is upon feeding behavior analogous to 'strip mining'.	Unbranched, non-overlapping, curved to tightly coiled patterns or delicately constructed spreiten dominate; patterns generally reflect maximum utilization of food resources; complete form may be preserved.	*Helminthoida* *Nereites* *Phycosiphon* *Zoophycos*
Feeding Structures *(Fodinichnia)* More or less temporary burrows constructed by deposit feeders; the structures also may provide shelter for the organisms. Emphasis is upon feeding behavior analogous to 'underground mining'.	Single, branched or unbranched, cylindrical to sinuous shafts or U-shaped burrows, or complex, parallel to concentric burrow repetitions (spreiten structures); walls not commonly lined, unless by mucus. Oriented at various angles with respect to bedding; complete form may be preserved.	*Chondrites* *Gyrophyllites* *Phycodes* *Rosselia*
Dwelling Structures *(Domichnia)* Burrows, borings, or dwelling tubes providing more or less permanent domiciles, mostly for hemisessile suspension feeders or, in some cases, carnivores. Emphasis is upon habitation. Secondary activities may be discernible.	Simple, bifurcated, or U-shaped structures perpendicular or inclined at various angles to bedding, or branched burrow or boring systems having vertical and horizontal components; burrow walls typically lined. Complete form may be preserved.	*Diplocraterion* *Ophiomorpha* *Skolithos* *Trypanites*
Escape Structures *(Fugichnia)* Lebensspuren of various kinds modified or made anew by animals in direct response to substrate degradation or aggradation. Emphasis is upon readjustment, or equilibrium between relative substrate position and the configuration of contained traces. Intergradational with other behavioral categories.	Vertically repetitive resting traces; biogenic laminae either in echelon or as nested funnels or chevrons; U-in-U spreiten burrows; and other structures reflecting displacement of animals upward or downward with respect to the original substrate surface. Complete form may be preserved, especially in aggraded substrates.	*Nested funnels* *U-in-U spreiten* *Down-warped laminae*

Resting Traces

These biogenic structures are formed primarily by mobile epibenthic or endobenthic organisms, although nektobenthic animals may be involved. Most resting traces are made by animals trying to avoid detection by intruders, concealing themselves from their prey, or undergoing a period of inactivity. The trace may record various secondary movements, or may intergrade with crawling traces (Figs. 2E and 2F). In many cases the ventral morphology of the tracemaker is recorded in considerable detail (Fig. 2D). With rapid substrate aggradation, the trace may be repeated vertically; such traces are transitional with escape structures (Table 1).

Crawling Traces

Such traces, made both upon and within the substrate, are a direct record of locomotion. Travel by the animals may involve flight from intruders, forays in search of food, actual food gathering, or such miscellaneous activities as migration or rutting. Many subsurface crawling traces follow interfaces between sedimentary layers; on the outcrop, these might be difficult to distinguish from surficial crawling traces. The traces range in fabrication from simple or ornamented, continuous grooves and ridges (Fig. 2F) to trackways consisting of individual podial imprints. In general, both crawling and resting traces are better preserved as sole casts on the overlying bed than as surficial features on the host bed.

Grazing Traces

Grazing behavior, although exhibited by both epibenthic and endobenthic organisms, tends to be most advantageous in exploiting surficial or relatively shallow subsurface sediments. The organisms are deposit feeders. Most grazing traces are compact, more or less planar structures, and they record efficient utilization of feeding space (Fig. 2C). Typical patterns include coiled or looped meanders, finely dichotomous branches, and closely repetitive or radial traces. Most individual feeding probes avoid contact with previously made probes, the older ones already having been mined and depleted of nutrients. In addition to sedimentary grazing traces, algal grazers such as chitons and limpets rasp hard surfaces along rocky coasts, leaving telltale scrapings or sculptings as records of their activity.

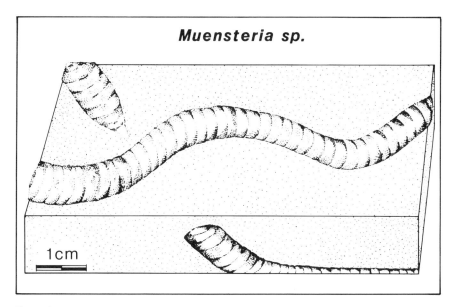

Figure 4
Unlined, essentially cylindrical meniscate burrows representing locomotion and sediment manipulation during deposit-feeding activities. The trace is classified as a feeding structure because locomotion per se was subordinate to feeding activities. (Adapted from Howard and Frey, 1984).

Feeding Structures

Unlike the "strip mining" plan of most grazing traces, feeding structures typically represent extensive subsurface foragings by deposit-feeding organisms. Elaborate, three-dimensional patterns often result (Fig. 2B). Most are produced by endobenthic animals, although a few epibenthos may feed inside the sediment by means of an extensible proboscis or equivalent organ. Endobenthos both feed and dwell within the excavation, yet feeding activities are the main *raison d'être*. Nevertheless, certain types of feeding probes are later converted to permanent domiciles (Frey and Seilacher, 1980, Fig. 3). Some deposit feeders simultaneously pass fine sediment through their gut and coarser sediment around their body, producing meniscate backfills (Fig. 4); other fills may be structureless (Fig. 3).

Dwelling Structures

More or less permanent domiciles are made mainly by endobenthic suspension feeders and certain predators and scavengers. Dwelling structures may approach the size of the tracemaker – a virtual external mold, as with most pholad borers – or they may consist of tubes, simple shafts (Fig. 2A), or an integrated system of shafts and tunnels. Because of their relative permanence, burrow walls ordinarily are reinforced by coats of mucus, agglutinated sediment (including muddy pellets daubed into the walls) or organic tubes of varied composition, all constituting distinctive burrow linings. These wall characteristics help distinguish dwelling structures from feeding structures. Most such domiciles are passively filled with sediment after the demise of the animal.

Escape Structures

Such traces ordinarily are made by organisms that dwell at specific depths within the substrate; they therefore must attempt to maintain constant spatial relationships with respect to the substrate surface, despite episodic intervals of deposition or erosion. Among vertical burrows, a common record of upward migration is nested, funnel-like laminae (Fig. 2G). Numerous additional examples of upward or downward migrations were cited by Howard (1975, Fig. 8.5). Many escape structures thus are precise indicators of substrate aggradation or degradation. However, escape structures such as those shown in Figure 2G must not be confused with certain physical collapse features (Frey *et al.*, 1978, Figs. 7E and 9), which may be equally common locally. Because escape structures represent modifications of preexisting traces, they are not given formal ichnogenus and ichnospecies names.

192

ENVIRONMENTAL GRADIENTS

Environmental zonations are omnipresent in nature, and they strongly influence the disposition of chemical, physical, and biological features. Thus, although local environmental parameters mostly govern individual depositional sites, these parameters tend to change progressively with distance along the regional environmental gradient. Such trends are commonly reflected in the rock record as lithofacies and biofacies successions.

The same is true of behavioral patterns among benthic organisms. Local conditions determine which adaptations (Table 1) are most advantageous at a particular site, and environmental gradients determine their regional distribution (Seilacher, 1958, Fig. 1). These

trends are expressed in the rock record as ichnofacies successions. Numerous modern-day examples occur in the transition from shoreline to deep-sea sites (Fig. 5). Coastal embayments, deltas, back-barrier environments, and the terrestrial realm exhibit comparably extensive zonations and facies successions.

RECURRING ICHNOFACIES

Because of environmental constraints or selectivity, particular assemblages of traces tend to occur at specific depositional sites (Fig. 5). Furthermore, these characteristic assemblages tend to recur, both geographically and temporally, wherever the requisite sets of parameters or environmental sites are repeated. Under equivalent climatic,

hydrographic, and sedimentologic regimes, for example, shoreface lithofacies and ichnofacies everywhere exhibit a certain sameness, whether modern or ancient.

For these reasons, the most prevalent, broadly repetitive ichnofacies have been given formal names (Fig. 5, Table 2) based upon representative ichnogenera. For instance, the *Skolithos* ichnofacies is characterized by a predominance of vertical dwelling structures, of which the namesake (Fig. 2A) is highly exemplary.

This principle is analogous to the concept of recurrent communities among organisms (Walker and Laporte, 1970). Unlike most recurrent assemblages of body fossils, however, trace fossils ordinarily are not subject to dis-

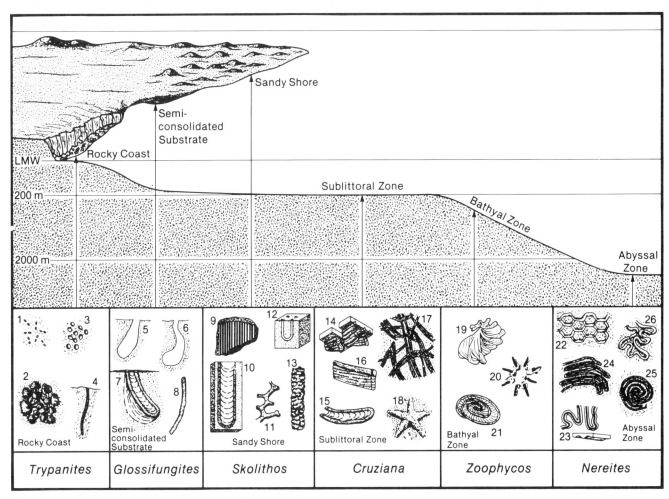

Figure 5

Recurring marine ichnofacies set in a representative, but not exclusive, suite of environmental gradients. Local physical, chemical, and biological factors ultimately determine which traces occur at which sites. Typical trace fossils include: 1) Caulostrepsis; 2) Entobia; 3) echinoid borings, unnamed; 4)

Trypanites; 5,6) Gastrochaenolites or related ichnogenera; 7) Diplocraterion; 8) Psilonichnus; 9) Skolithos; 10) Diplocraterion; 11) Thalassinoides; 12) Arenicolites; 13) Ophiomorpha; 14) Phycodes; 15) Rhizocorallium; 16) Teichichnus; 17) Crossopodia; 18) Asteriacites; 19) Zoophycos; 20) Lorenzinia; 21) Zoophycos; 22) Paleodictyon; 23) Taph-

rhelminthopsis; 24) Helminthoida; 25) Spirorhaphe; 26) Cosmorhaphe. (Modified from Crimes, 1975; Frey and Seilacher, 1980.) Bathymetric terms are those reiterated by Ager (1963), mainly from the Treatise on Marine Ecology and Paleoecology. Not to scale.

Table 2
Recurring trace fossil associations and their general environmental significance. (Adapted from Seilacher, 1967; Frey and Seilacher, 1980; Frey et al., 1984; Pemberton and Frey, 1984b.)

Typical Benthic Environment*	Characteristic Trace Fossils
Scoyenia ichnofacies (preliminary definition): Moist to wet, pliable, argillaceous to sandy sediments at low-energy sites; either very shallowly submersed lacustrine or fluviatile deposits periodically becoming emergent, or waterside subaerial deposts periodically becoming submergent; intermediate between aquatic and nonaquatic terrestrial environments.	Small horizontal, lined, back-filled feeding burrows; curved to tortuous, unlined feeding burrows; sinuous crawling traces; vertical, cylindrical to irregular shafts; tracks and trails. Invertebrates mostly deposit feeders or predators; vertebrates are grovelers, predators, or herbivores. Invertebrate diversity very low, yet some traces may be abundant. Vertebrate tracks may be diverse and abundant around water bodies.
Trypanites ichnofacies (hard substrates):** Consolidated marine littoral and sublittoral omission surfaces (rocky coasts, beachrock, hardgrounds, reefs) or organic substrates (beds of shell, bone). Bioerosion is as important as, and indeed accelerates, physical erosion of the substrate. Intergradational with the *Glossifungites* ichnofacies; somewhat intergradational with the *Teredolites* ichnofacies.***	Cylindrical to vase-, tear-, or U-shaped to irregular domiciles of endoliths, oriented normal to substrate surfaces, or shallow anastomosing systems of borings (sponges, bryozoans); excavated mainly by suspension feeders or 'passive' carnivores. Raspings and gnawings of algal grazers, etc. (chitons, limpets, echinoids). Diversity generally low, although borings or scrapings of given kinds may be abundant.
Glossifungites ichnofacies (firm substrates): Firm but unlithified marine littoral and sublittoral omission surfaces, especially semiconsolidated carbonate firmgrounds, or stable, coherent, partially dewatered muddy substrates either in protected, moderate-energy settings or in areas of somewhat higher energy where clastic, semiconsolidated substrates offer resistance to erosion. Final sedimentary record typically consists of a mixture of relict and palimpsest features.	Vertical cylindrical, U-, or tear-shaped borings or boring-like structures, or sparsely to densely ramified dwelling burrows; protrusive spreiten in some, developed mostly through growth of animals. Fan-shaped *Rhizocorallium* and *Diplocraterion*. Many intertidal species (e.g., crabs) leave the burrows to feed; others are mainly suspension feeders. Diversity typically low, but given kinds of structures may be abundant.
Skolithos ichnofacies (shifting substrates): Lower littoral to infralittoral, moderate to relatively high-energy conditions; slightly muddy to clean, well-sorted, shifting sediments; subject to abrupt erosion or deposition. (Higher energy increases physical reworking and obliterates biogenic sedimentary structures, leaving a preserved record of physical stratification.)	Vertical, cylindrical or U-shaped dwelling burrows; protrusive and retrusive spreiten in some, developed mainly in response to substrate aggradation or degradation (escape or equilibrium structures); forms of *Ophiomorpha* consisting predominantly of vertical or steeply inclined shafts. Animals chiefly suspension feeders. Diversity is low, yet given kinds of burrows may be abundant.
Cruziana ichnofacies: Infralittoral to shallow circalittoral substrates; below daily wave base but not storm wave base, to somewhat quieter offshore-type conditions; moderate to relatively low energy; well-sorted silts and sands, to interbedded muddy and clean sands, moderately to intensely bioturbated; negligible to appreciable, although not necessarily rapid, sedimentation. A very common type of depositional environment, including estuaries, bays, lagoons, and tidal flats, as well as continental shelves or epeiric slopes.	Abundant crawling traces, both epi- and intrastratal; inclined U-shaped burrows having mostly protrusive spreiten (feeding swaths; soft-sediment *Rhizocorallium);* forms of *Orphiomorpha* and *Thalassinoides* consisting of irregularly inclined to horizontal components; scattered vertical cylindrical burrows. Animals include mobile carnivores and both suspension and deposit feeders. Diversity and abundance generally high.
Zoophycos ichnofacies: Circalittoral to bathyal, quiet-water conditions; nearly thixotropic muds or muddy sands rich in organic matter but somewhat deficient in oxygen, below storm wave base to fairly deep water, in areas free of turbidity flows or significant bottom currents. Watery surficial sediments are difficult to exploit by epibenthos, resulting in both low diversity and abundance and poor preservation of epistratal traces. Where relict or palimpsest substrates are present, especially if swept by shelf-edge or deeper water contour currents, this ichnofacies may be omitted in the transition from infralittoral to abyssal environments.	Relatively simple to moderately complex, efficiently executed grazing traces and shallow feeding structures; spreiten typically planar to gently inclined, distributed in delicate sheets, ribbons, or spirals ('flattened' forms of *Zoophycos* or, in pelitic sediments *Phycosiphon*). Animals virtually all deposit feeders. Low diversity; given structures may be abundant.
Nereites ichnofacies: Bathyal to abyssal, mostly quiet but oxygenated waters, in places interrupted by down-canyon bottom currents or turbidity currents (flysch deposits); or highly stable, very slowly accreting substrates. In flysch or flysch-like deposits, pelagic muds typically are bounded above and below by turbidites. In more distal regions, the record is mainly one of continuous deposition and bioturbation. (The stable deep-sea floor is not universally bioturbated, however, at least not equally intensively at every site.)	Complex grazing traces and patterned feeding-dwelling structures, reflecting highly organized, efficient behavior; spreiten structures typically nearly planar, although *Zoophycos* forms are spiraled, multilobed, or otherwise very complex. Numerous crawling-grazing traces and sinuous fecal castings *(Neonereites, Helminthoida, Cosmorhaphe),* mostly intrastratal. Animals chiefly deposit feeders or 'scavengers', although many may have 'farmed' microbe cultures within their more or less permanent, open domiciles *(Paleodictyon).* Diversity and abundance significant in flysch deposits, less so in more distal regions.

*Marine bathymetric zones are those reiterated by Ager (1963, Fig. 2.3).
**The ichnogenus *Trypanites* is presently undergoing extensive taxonomic reevaluation.
***The *Teredolites* ichnofacies has been proposed for woodground borings (Bromley *et al.*, 1984).

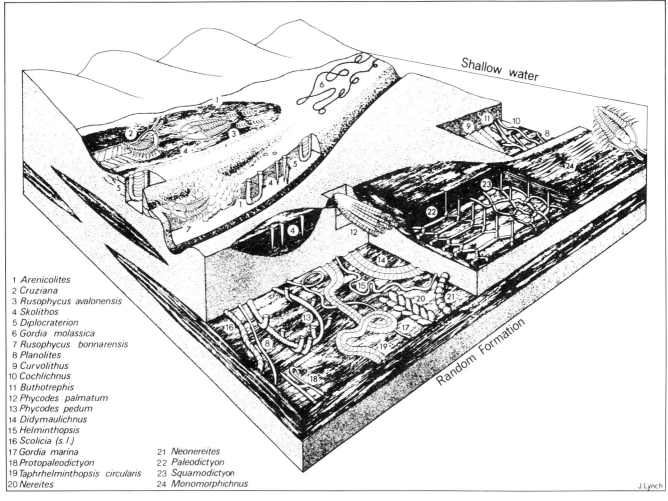

1 Arenicolites
2 Cruziana
3 Rusophycus avalonensis
4 Skolithos
5 Diplocraterion
6 Gordia molassica
7 Rusophycus bonnarensis
8 Planolites
9 Curvolithus
10 Cochlichnus
11 Buthotrephis
12 Phycodes palmatum
13 Phycodes pedum
14 Didymaulichnus
15 Helminthopsis
16 Scolicia (s. l.)
17 Gordia marina
18 Protopaleodictyon
19 Taphrhelminthopsis circularis
20 Nereites
21 Neonereites
22 Paleodictyon
23 Squamodictyon
24 Monomorphichnus

J.Lynch

Figure 6

Trace fossil associations in the Lower Cam-brian of Newfoundland. Nearshore traces (1-7) constitute a mixed Skolithos-Cruziana

ichnofacies. Certain offshore traces (e.g., 22-23) typically indicate deep-sea deposition in post-Cambrian sediments. The overall

assemblage demonstrates substantial di-versity among earliest Paleozoic trace-makers. (Courtesy of T.P. Crimes).

placement, mixing and sorting, or stra-tigraphic leakage. Hence, like physical sedimentary structures, they are more representative of original environmental conditions. In addition, these basic behavioral traits (Table 1) were estab-lished in the late Proterozoic to early Phanerozoic, and have changed rela-tively little to the present day (Frey and Seilacher, 1980; Miller and Byers, 1984). Recurrent ichnofacies therefore have essentially equivalent environmental significance through enormous spans of geologic time.

On a smaller, more specific scale, of course, certain behavioral, temporal, and environmental differences are indeed discernible among otherwise equivalent ichnofacies. Most such dif-ferences fall within two general catego-ries: 1) evolution and extinction of dis-

crete, invidual behavioral patterns, and 2) adaptive radiation of behavioral traits, or their extension into previously unexploited environmental zones.

The first category is exemplified by *Ophiomorpha* and *Cruziana,* among others. *Ophiomorpha* first appeared in the Permian, hence its vertical shafts (Fig. 5.13) are not a component of ear-lier *Skolithos* ichnofacies. Similarly, marine forms of *Cruziana* (Fig. 2F) dis-appeared at the end of the Permian and are not components of later *Cruziana* ichnofacies. Nevertheless, the presence or absence of particular ichnogenera, and the specialized behavioral adapta-tions they represent, in no way alters the basic concept of the respective ichnofa-cies (Table 2). Emphasis is placed upon the definitive character of the entire assemblage of trace fossils, not its indi-

vidual components. In other words, the *Skolithos* ichnofacies is characterized everywhere by vertical dwelling struc-tures whether or not *Ophiomorpha,* or even *Skolithos,* is among them.

The second category, above, is exemplified by progressive colonization of the deep-sea floor by formerly shallow-water lineages of tracemakers. Truly deep-water traces are compara-tively rare in lowest Paleozoic rocks (Frey and Seilacher, 1980; Pickerill, 1980); indeed, some forms now consid-ered to be entirely representative of the deep sea, such as *Paleodictyon* and *Squamodictyon* (Fig. 6), are known from shallow-water Cambrian deposits (Crimes and Anderson, in press). Another adaptive radiation into the deep sea occurred during the Cretaceous, mainly involving opportunistic tracemakers capable of colonizing turbidites (Frey and Seilacher, 1980). Except for the dearth of deep-sea traces during the earliest Paleozoic, these distributions, like *Ophiomorpha* and *Cruziana,* do not detract from the fundamental ichnofacies concepts (Table 2).

Individual recurring ichnofacies therefore should be viewed as archetypical models. While particular components or styles of fabrication may vary, the archetypes everywhere remain recognizable and have the same basic functional and environmental significance.

This principle is especially important in local facies analyses, considering that: 1) most environmental gradients include various heterogeneities or anomalies, which interrupt otherwise smooth transitions, and 2) even in equivalent zones, exact sets of tracemakers and environmental parameters are not apt to recur with perfect fidelity through space and time. Without the archetypes for a framework, these local variants might be difficult to place in proper environmental perspective. Equally important, precisely because environmental transitions are involved (Fig. 5), even the archetypes tend to be intergradational along zonal boundaries.

A final source of potential variation among functionally equivalent ichnofacies is the local inception of strong biological controls, such as competition or predation among the organisms themselves (Kitchell and Clark, 1979; Miller and Johnson, 1981). However, such variations are difficult to evaluate in most instances.

BATHYMETRIC IMPLICATIONS
Because of gradients such as those depicted in Figure 5, certain ichnofacies (e.g., *Skolithos* through *Nereites*) tend to have marine bathymetric significance (Seilacher, 1967). Nevertheless, water depth and distance from shore *per se* are not actual environmental parameters and have little direct influence on local conditions. For instance, the aftermath of storms may permit the incursion of opportunistic, higher energy, *Skolithos*-type tracemakers into a zone otherwise characterized by lower energy, *Cruziana*-type tracemakers (Pemberton and Frey, 1984a); *in-loco* fluctuations of energy levels in such cases seem to exert the major control.

Bathymetric interpretations therefore cannot be made independently of associated physical and biological evidence. When placed in the full context of the sedimentary framework, however, this relative scale of bathymetry has proven useful in numerous applications (Frey and Seilacher, 1980).

ICHNOFACIES MODELS
Of the seven recurrent ichnofacies presently recognized (Table 2), only one is nonmarine. However, this disparity mainly reflects relative proportions of research on marine and nonmarine environments; nonmarine ichnofacies ultimately may prove to be as varied as marine ichnofacies (Frey *et al.*, 1984). The six marine ichnofacies represent adaptations of tracemakers to characteristic changes in substrate consistency, energy levels, depositional processes, food supplies, and related parameters. Each ichnofacies is evaluated in greater detail, below.

These concepts have evolved through many years of ichnologic research. Their origins stem mainly from trace fossil distributions observed in European flysch-molasse sequences (Seilacher, 1958, 1963; Seilacher and Meischner, 1964). The archetypes may be considered as facies models (*sensu* Walker, "General Introduction" to this volume) because each serves as: 1) a norm for comparative purposes, 2) a framework for future observations, 3) a predictor in new situations, and 4) a basis for the interpretation of ancient environments (Frey and Seilacher, 1980).

The main conceptual difference between ichnofacies models and other models presented herein is that the former primarily involve ichnologic links to characteristic sets of environmental parameters. In this sense, ichnofacies models are more abstract than, say, a lithofacies model for a delta. The *Skolithos* ichnofacies, for example, might be equally indicative of conditions along beaches, spits, estuarine point bars, certain delta topsets, or even deep-sea sand fans. Yet, from the organisms' viewpoint, these environments are more or less equivalent: moderately high energy, shifting particulate substrates, suspended food supply, and so on. In short, ichnofacies models should be used in conjunction with, not in lieu of, the various lithofacies models. Conversely, lithofacies models are made

more powerful when ichnologic distributions are incorporated.

Scoyenia Ichnofacies
The original ichnofacies concept stipulated trace fossil associations in continental red beds and similar deposits (Seilacher, 1967). Subsequently, through indiscriminate usage, the concept gradually degenerated to a pigeonhole for nonmarine assemblages in general. As stressed above, part of the problem stems from insufficient ichnological research among diverse nonmarine settings. Furthermore, "red beds" are more enigmatic than originally suspected, which undermines the presumed amenity between these deposits and *Scoyenia*-type tracemakers. Both the ichnofacies and its environmental implication therefore remain somewhat poorly known (Seilacher, 1978).

Yet, a recent analysis of this problem (Frey *et al.*, 1984, Table 1), proffers hope for substantial refinement of the *Scoyenia* ichnofacies concept. Well-documented occurrences of *Scoyenia gracilis, Ancorichnus coronus*, and their ecologic equivalents, ranging in age from Permian to Holocene, suggest a common environmental denominator, namely, the shore zone of ephemeral lakes and sluggish streams. More specifically, respective interpretations indicate that the tracemakers exploited moist to wet sites such as 1) low-lying subaerial deposits subject to inundation by flooding waters and 2) shallowly submersed substrates subject to periodic subaerial exposure. Associated physical sedimentary structures include such features as desiccation cracks, planar and ripple laminae, tool marks, bars in braided channels, and fills of small floodplain channels.

Because of the potential distinctiveness of this association, and as a further test of the model, Frey *et al.* (1984) suggested that all future designations of the *Scoyenia* ichnofacies be restricted to assemblages in which *S. gracilis* and (or) *Ancorichnus coronus* (or their ethologic equivalents) predominate. Associated physical features should be evaluated equally rigorously.

As tentatively redefined, the potential ichnofacies thus consists of relatively small invertebrate traces of low diversity (Fig. 7), made primarily by arthropods. The association consists mainly of

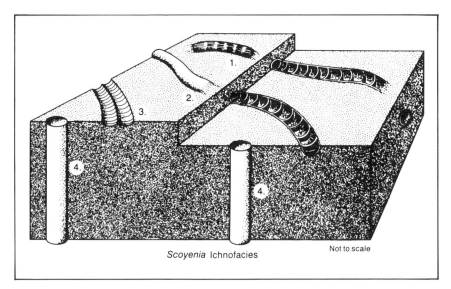

Figure 7
Trace fossil association tentatively considered to be indicative of the Scoyenia ichnofacies sensu stricto. 1) Scoyenia; 2) Ancor- *ichnus; 3) Cruziana, including the "Isopodichnus" of various authors; 4) Skolithos.*

lined, meniscate feeding structures and secondarily of crawling traces and vertical dwelling structures. By analogy with other, modern settings, several additional invertebrate traces might occur locally (Ratcliffe and Fagerstrom, 1980), possibly in juxtaposition with various vertebrate traces. Vertebrate tracks obviously are to be expected around watering holes, and may be diverse and abundant there.

Assuming that the redefined *Scoyenia* ichnofacies proves to be as distinctive as the marine archetypes, the next question concerns its longevity. It could not have become established prior to early-Paleozoic colonization of landscapes by animals (Miller, 1984), yet no *a priori* reason otherwise precludes its inception prior to the Permian. This aspect of the ichnofacies also warrants further study.

Finally, prospects for the recognition of additional nonmarine ichnofacies remain encouraging. In the Triassic of Greenland, for example, four locally recurring, mutually exclusive associations are discernible (Bromley and Asgaard, 1979): the *Arenicolites* and *Fuersichnus* ichnofacies, representing deep lacustrine beds; the *Scoyenia* ichnofacies, representing shallow lacustrine beds; and the *Rusophycus* ichnofacies, representing desiccated fluviatile sediments.

Trypanites Ichnofacies
Substrates most prevalently associated with the *Trypanites* ichnofacies include rocky coasts (Fig. 5), beachrock, reefs, hardgrounds, and other types of discontinuity or unconformity surfaces. Reefs, beachrock, and hardgrounds generally consist of calcium carbonate; yet the others may consist of virtually any lithology, including certain igneous and metamorphic rocks (Bromley, 1970; Warme, 1975; Warme and McHuron, 1978). Diversity of traces is greatest in sedimentary rocks or reefs, of course. On a smaller, subfacies scale, borings also may be common in certain intraformational conglomerates or clast beds and "hiatus concretions", as well as in substrates of bone, shell, or wood (Bromley et al., 1984). The relative hardness of these substances varies considerably, as do the individual adaptations of tracemakers. Although shell and rock borers have existed since the Early Cambrian (Kobluk et al., 1978), post-Paleozoic borings are much more abundant and diverse than Paleozoic ones (Warme and McHuron, 1978).

Because of substrate diversity, and the varied physical and geochemical mechanisms required for their exploitation by organisms, several different trace associations are discernible. The primary common denominator, however, is bioerosion (Fig. 1). Therefore,

the tracemakers not only are ecologic and biologic entities but also function as geologic agents.

For example, many reef developments generally proceed in the periodic repetition of five basic steps (Schroeder and Zankl, 1974): framework growth, encrustation, sedimentation, cementation, and boring. Once a hard substrate is established, these steps may occur penecontemporaneously or in no preferred order. But, in general, fine to coarse sediments and clasts excavated by borers enter the local sediment budget, become cemented, and thereby provide additional foundations for framework growth and encrustation, reef enlargement, and in turn, increased exploitation by boring organisms (Warme, 1977). The process is then repeated.

Somewhat analogous developmental steps may be involved in the geologic history of rocky coasts (Radwański, 1970), unconformities (Pemberton et al., 1980), hardgrounds (Perkins, 1971; Kennedy, 1975), and other kinds of discontinuity or omission surfaces (Bromley, 1975). Many occurrences consist of pre-omission, omission, and post-omission associations of traces, depending upon local depositional and cementational sequences. The pre-omission suite, ordinarily a relict association, may consist of: 1) the *Skolithos* or *Cruziana* ichnofacies – if made originally in an unconsolidated substrate, 2) the *Glossifungites* ichnofacies – if made in early diagenetic, semiconsolidated sediment, or 3) an earlier *Trypanites* ichnofacies – if made in a consolidated substrate. Omission and post-omission suites also may exhibit variations in development. These various relict, palimpsest, and contemporary components are generally detectable by means of cross-cutting relationships. Bioerosion structures characterize *Trypanites* associations *sensu stricto*, however, and many original substrates, such as barren sandstones or crystalline rocks, contain only a *Trypanites* suite.

Most traces in the association (Fig. 8) are dwelling structures excavated by suspension feeders or passive (sessile) carnivores; collectively, these comprise substantial taxonomic and morphologic diversity (Warme, 1975; Warme and McHuron, 1978). Additional ethologic categories (Table 1) are represented locally. Grazing traces (Frey and Seilacher, 1980, Fig. 12A) are made by limpets and chitons as they rasp algae off rock surfaces, and by parrot fish and echinoids as they feed on polyps and other organisms. In a sense, feeding structures are excavated by certain bacteria and fungi while consuming organic residues within skeletal carbonates (Golubic *et al.,* 1975).

Finally, as indicated above, the *Trypanites* and *Glossifungites* ichnofacies tend to be somewhat intergradational. Bioerosion structures generally are much more diverse in the former, however, and burrows are excluded. The *Glossifungites* association typically consists of a mixture of burrows and borings or boring-like structures, and most of the borings are attributable to bivalves. Fortunately, morphological variations among domiciles of pholad bivalves tend to correlate with substrate consistency (Röder, 1977), whether firm substrates of the *Glossifungites* ichnofacies or hard substrates of the *Trypanites* ichnofacies. In addition, borings of the *Trypanites* type penetrate clasts and shells within the substrate as readily as the lithified matrix (Bromley, 1975, Figs. 18.6 and 18.16B); in all other ichnofacies, skeletal parts and rock clasts are skirted by deep excavations.

Glossifungites Ichnofacies
The *Glossifungites* ichnofacies represents firm but unlithified substrates (Table 2), whether stable, cohesive deposits in somewhat protected, moderately low-energy settings, or omission surfaces in settings of higher energy, where semiconsolidated substrates offer resistence to erosion by waves or currents. Such deposits typically consist of dewatered chunky muds (Pemberton and Frey, 1984b) or incompletely cemented carbonates (Bromley, 1975).

Dewatering of noncarbonate muds and consequent firm-substrate burrowing occur most commonly during subaerial exposure, hence these substrates and the ichnofacies tend to develop intertidally or supratidally. Dewatering also may occur with deep burial of sediments, but those deposits are unavailable to tracemakers unless later exhumed by erosion. This exhumation generally occurs in shallow water or intertidal settings because of higher energy there; in the latter case, desiccation enhances the dewatering process. For example, beaches on the Georgia

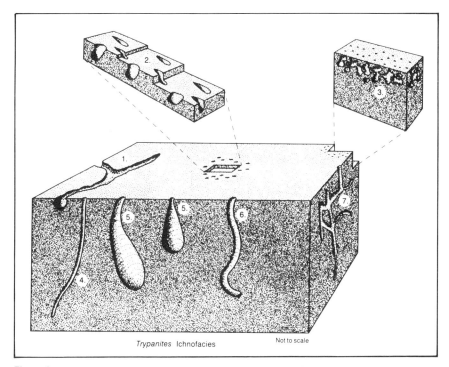

Figure 8
Trace fossil association characteristic of the Trypanites ichnofacies. 1) echinoid grooves, *unnamed; 2) Rogerella; 3) Entobia; 4) Trypanites; 5) Gastrochaenolites; 6) Trypanites; 7) polychaete boring, unnamed.*

coast are presently retreating as sea level rises, and in many places, coastal erosion exposes old salt marsh muds formerly buried beneath beach sands (Frey and Basan, 1981; Pemberton and Frey, 1984b). Comparable substrates occur along the southern part of the North Sea (Schäfer, 1972), where extensive peat deposits are exposed.

Desiccation may produce mud cracks, synersis structures, or large-scale blocky jointing, and these may influence the distribution and configuration of burrows (Schroder, 1982). Conversely, the distribution and configuration of burrows may influence the pattern of desiccation cracking (Pemberton and Frey, 1984b). With the possible exception of shale-like fissility accompanying compaction, few other kinds of physical sedimentary structures are formed in these deposits. In contrast, semiconsolidated carbonates (Bromley, 1975) may occur subtidally and therefore are free of desiccation *per se.*

Whatever their precise origin and individual sedimentary characteristics, firm substrates collectively are much less common than those of other coastal and epeiric settings. The *Glossifungites* ichnofacies therefore tends to

have limited areal extent relative to most other ichnofacies. At present, the association is best known in Mesozoic and Cenozoic deposits. However, firm-substrate excavations surely must extend as far backward in antiquity as hard-substrate excavations of the *Trypanites* association; additional reconnaissance is needed.

As an intermediary between unconsolidated deposits of the *Skolithos* or *Cruziana* ichnofacies and consolidated ones of the *Trypanites* ichnofacies, these semiconsolidated deposits are exploited by an ethologic mixture of tracemakers; most are burrowers, yet others closely simulate borers. Although the distinction between bioturbation and bioerosion ordinarily is quite clear (Fig. 1), here our perception of the difference may be mostly semantic. Substrate hardnesses and endobenthic animal adaptations encompass a broad, gradational spectrum (Bromley, 1975, p. 418; Warme and McHuron, 1978, p. 118-120). Nevertheless, certain organisms, such as the modern bivalve *Petricola pholadiformis,* are almost exclusively adapted to semiconsolidated deposits (Schäfer, 1972) and are profuse in present occurrences of the ichnofacies (Frey and Basan, 1981).

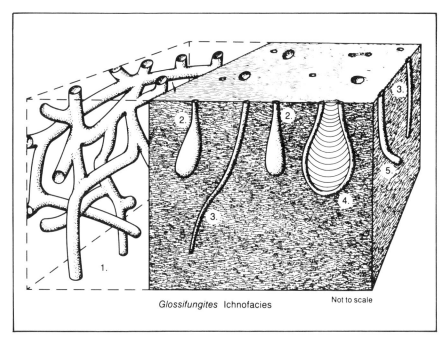

Figure 9
Trace fossil association characteristic of the Glossifungites ichnofacies. 1) Thalassinoides or Spongeliomorpha; 2) Gastrochaenolites or related ichnogenera; 3) Skolithos- or Trypanites-like structures; 4) Diplocraterion or Rhizocorallium; 5) Psilonichnus. (The nomenclature for hardground versus firm-ground ichnogenera presently remains in a state of flux.)

One criterion for the difference between burrowing and boring behavior is whether the excavator cuts through, rather than removing or avoiding, individual sediment grains. But such distinction is difficult in clays or micrites, unless shells or rock clasts are present. Whatever the criteria, certain traces virtually identical with unequivocal borings in hard substrates of the *Trypanites* ichnofacies are common among *Glossifungites* associations. Unlike *Trypanites* associations, however, *Glossifungites* associations consist of a mixture of burrows and borings, and the borings are attributable mainly to bivalves.

Animals exploiting these deposits typically construct permanent, vertical or steeply inclined domiciles (Fig. 9). Sediment cohesiveness generally negates the need for reinforced burrow linings; the walls are sharply defined, and may be sculpted. Substrate firmness also precludes most intrastratal deposit feeding. The tracemakers therefore are predominantly suspension feeders. Among U-shaped burrows, protrusive spreiten develop mainly through growth of the animal and its increased depth of burrowing; the base of the "U" tends to be broader than the top (Seilacher, 1967). Ramified burrow

systems also may be present; most are occupied by communal suspension feeders, although some are inhabited by carnivores or surficial deposit feeders that leave the burrows to forage (Pemberton and Frey, 1984b).

None of the traces indicated in Figure 9 is uniquely restricted to the *Glossifungites* ichnofacies, and individual occurrences may exhibit lesser or greater diversity. But the overall association is everywhere dominated by such combinations of firm-substrate traces, whether modern (Frey and Basan, 1981; Pemberton and Frey, 1984b), or ancient (Fürsich *et al.*, 1981; Schroder, 1982). Like the *Skolithos* ichnofacies, it also may appear in certain deep-water settings (Hayward, 1976). Substrate conditions and requisite endobenthic behavior thus are the main criteria distinguishing this association from the *Trypanites* ichnofacies.

Like the *Trypanites* ichnofacies (especially hardgrounds), most *Glossifungites*-type substrates are palimpsest, i.e., altered by contemporary physical and biogenic processes, and may retain relict features indicative of former conditions. For example, soft original muds might exhibit a *Cruziana* ichnofacies prior to the semiconsolidation of

sediments. This relict association of soft-sediment traces and physical sedimentary structures would then be overprinted by a second association, consisting of firm-sediment traces.

Skolithos Ichnofacies
The *Skolithos* ichnofacies (Table 2) is indicative of relatively high levels of wave or current energy, and typically develops in clean, well-sorted, loose or shifting particulate substrates. Abrupt changes in rates of deposition, erosion, and physical reworking of sediments are frequent. Such conditions commonly occur on the foreshore and shoreface of beaches, bars, and spits; associated stratification features usually consist of fine, parallel to subparallel, gently seaward dipping laminae to large- and small-scale trough cross-beds, including ripple laminae. Physical sedimentary structures ordinarily predominate over biogenic ones (Howard, 1975), because of intense physical reworking of sediments, although some sandstones are literally riddled with vertical shafts.

As dictated by fundamental interrelationships among water agitation, sediment transport, and animal distribution (Purdy, 1964), most tracemakers found here are suspension feeders. Substrates serve mainly as an anchoring medium. The organisms typically construct deeply penetrating, more or less permanent domiciles (Fig. 10). Because of shifting sediments, the dwellings tend to have thick, reinforced wall linings, which may consist of thick layers of mucus, agglutinated sand, or chitinous materials. Most solitary burrows are vertical; burrow systems (Fig. 10.1) consist predominantly of vertical components.

Depth of burrowing in the intertidal zone is controlled in part by tidal range and height of the low-tide water table. During low tide, moist sediments at depth help buffer the organisms against desiccation and salinity or temperature shock, and also help provide respiratory water (Frey, 1971). In both intertidal and high-energy subtidal settings, deep burrowing is one means of escaping the instability of the ever-shifting substrate surface. In compensation, the apertural region of the burrows may be less rigidly constructed than the lower part (Fig. 10.1).

Not all of the traces indicated in Figure 10 need be present in any given occurrence of the ichnofacies, but the recurrent association of traces is dominated by such vertically oriented dwelling structures (e.g., Hallam and Swett, 1966). Because of frequent substrate scour, numerous burrows may be truncated along erosional planes. With renewed deposition, others may grade into escape structures or equivalent manifestations of dynamic equilibrium, such as readjustments in the apertural necks of *Ophiomorpha nodosa* (Frey *et al.,* 1978, Figs. 7 and 8C). Episodic erosion and deposition may result in alternately protrusive and retrusive spreiten structures (Fig. 10.2).

In addition to beaches or beach-like settings, the ichnofacies may occur in higher energy parts of such features as tidal flats, tidal deltas, and estuarine point bars (Frey and Howard, 1980). There, dominant physical sedimentary structures include small-scale ripple laminae on tidal flats and large-scale, tabular or trough crossbeds on tidal deltas or point bars. Mud content and bioturbation of sediments is somewhat greater on high-energy parts of tidal flats than among beach-like facies or the high-energy side of point bars and tidal deltas. With slightly diminished energy, flaser, wavy, and lenticular bedding may appear. Such muds commonly originate as granular fecal pellet layers rather than flocules of clay; fecal pellets move in the traction load, somewhat like sand grains (Frey and Howard, 1980).

Rapid progradation along avalanche faces of bars and similar features excludes most tracemakers, although these deposits tend to be colonized immediately upon inception of more stable conditions (see "Shelf and Shallow Marine Sands", this volume, Fig. 32, Class III). Bioturbation therefore is not strictly coeval with the deposit, and burrows penetrate all pre-existing cross-stratification features.

The *Skolithos* ichnofacies ordinarily grades landward into supratidal or terrestrial zones and seaward into the *Cruziana* ichnofacies (Fig. 5, Table 2). The landward boundary tends to be more abrupt than the latter. Where substrates are suitable, the *Skolithos* ichnofacies may adjoin or intertongue laterally with the *Glossifungites* or *Trypanites* ichnofacies (Radwanski, 1970; Pemberton and Frey, 1984B). With reduced energy, it also may grade into intertidal or shal-

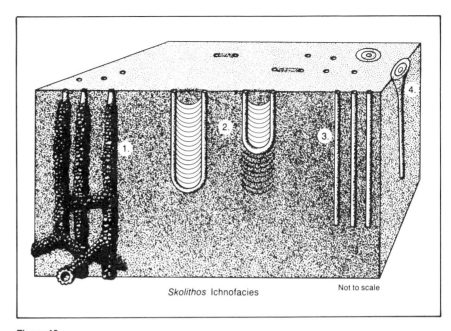

Figure 10
Trace fossil association characteristic of the Skolithos ichnofacies. 1) Ophiomorpha; 2) Diplocraterion, different forms of which may indicate substrate degradation (left) or aggradation (right); 3) Skolithos; 4) Monocraterion.

low subtidal extensions of the *Cruziana* ichnofacies (Radwanski *et al.,* 1975); ecotonal or mixed *Skolithos-Cruziana* associations are common in both recent (Howard and Frey, 1975) and ancient settings (Fig. 6).

Finally, the *Skolithos* ichnofacies may appear in slightly to substantially deeper water deposits wherever energy levels, food supplies, and hydrographic and substrate characteristics are suitable (Crimes, 1977). Potential examples include submarine canyons, deep-sea fans, and bathyal slopes swept by strong contour currents. Therefore, as emphasized previously, paleobathymetric interpretations cannot be based solely on checklists of trace fossil names; evaluation of associated physical sedimentary structures, stratigraphic position, and other evidence is essential, even in normal beach-to-offshore sequences (Howard and Frey, 1984).

Cruziana Ichnofacies
The *Cruziana* ichnofacies is most characteristic of subtidal, poorly sorted, unconsolidated substrates. Conditions typically range from moderate energy levels in shallow waters, below fair-weather wave base but above storm wave base, to low energy levels in deeper, quieter waters. Sediment textures and bedding styles exhibit con-

siderable diversity, including thinly bedded, well-sorted silts and sands, discrete mud and shell layers, interbedded muddy and clean silts and sands, and extremely poorly sorted beds derived from any of the above through intense bioturbation. Physical sedimentary structures, where not modified or destroyed by bioturbation, include parallel, subparallel, or ripple-laminated sand, or trough-crossbedded, megarippled sand. Such substrates and depositional conditions are extremely common in both recent and ancient settings, and include estuaries, bays, and lagoons as well as open continental shelves (Fig. 5) or epeiric seas. Estuarine sediments are apt to include various combinations of wavy, lenticular, and flaser bedding.

With reduced but not negligible energy levels, food supplies consist of both suspended and deposited components (Purdy, 1964); either fraction may predominate locally, or the two may be intermixed. Characteristic organisms therefore include both suspension and deposit feeders, as well as mobile carnivores and scavengers. Because of lowered energy and less abrupt shifts in temperature and salinity levels, burrows tend to be constructed horizontally rather than vertically, although scattered vertical or steeply inclined burrows occur (Fig. 11). Profusions of bur-

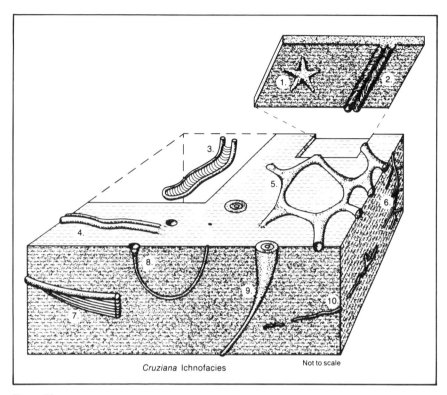

Cruziana Ichnofacies

Not to scale

Figure 11
Diverse trace fossil association characteristic of the Cruziana ichnofacies. 1) Asteriacites; 2) Cruziana; 3) Rhizocorallium; 4)
Aulichnites; 5) Thalassinoides; 6) Chondrites; 7) Teichichnus; 8) Arenicolites; 9) Rosselia; 10) Planolites.

rows may be present at stable, low-energy sites (see Fig. 14). Trails of epibenthic and endobenthic foragers also may be common and reflect the abundance, diversity, and accessibility of food. Indeed, crawling and resting traces predominate in many Paleozoic sandstones, and are sufficiently distinctive that they have biostratigraphic importance (Crimes, 1975).

Pronounced sediment reworking by abundant foragers and burrowers commonly imparts an obscure bioturbate texture to the substrate. In places, this disruption is more typical than are distinctive, identifiable traces (Howard, 1975, Fig. 8.2). Also, thinly interbedded sands, silts, and clays may be converted to thoroughly mixed, poorly sorted, homogeneous sediments.

In shallow waters, periodic scour by storm waves and renewed deposition following their cessation may incorporate storm layers within a sequence of otherwise low-energy deposits (Howard and Frey, 1984; Pemberton and Frey, 1984a). Development of hummocky cross-stratification may involve the introduction of new sediment as well as

the reworking of previously deposited sediment. Any of these conditions may yield burrow truncations and escape structures. Increased energy and allied parameters thus represent a temporary excursion of *Skolithos*-type conditions into a *Cruziana*-type setting. However, this overall bedding style differs from that of the main *Skolithos* ichnofacies, in which stratification features, substrate scour, burrow truncations, and escape structures are contained entirely within sequences of high-energy deposits. Furthermore, the storm layers eventually are overprinted with *Cruziana*-type traces.

Diversity of traces within the ichnofacies may be appreciable (Fürsich, 1974; Pemberton and Frey, 1984a) and populations may exhibit environmental zonations along depositional dip (Farrow, 1966; Howard and Frey, 1984). In certain low-energy, back-barrier or deltaic settings, the *Skolithos* ichnofacies is omitted and the *Cruziana* ichnofacies extends into the intertidal zone.

In low-energy intertidal settings, diagnostic traces may remain essentially like those in subtidal environ-

ments. Major exceptions include the possible appearance of strictly intertidal tracemakers or the exclusion of specific subtidal tracemakers by intolerance for subaerial exposure, lowered salinities, fluctuating temperatures, or reducing conditions in stagnant mud (Purdy, 1964). Sediment textures and physical sedimentary structures may differ markedly, however. Muds tend to be more abundant here than in higher energy intertidal settings, although muddy to nearly pure sands or silts may be present locally. Substrates tend to be totally bioturbated, to the virtual exclusion of primary physical sedimentary structures. With an abundance of potentially cohesive mud, this variant of the *Cruziana* ichnofacies might intergrade locally with the *Glossifungites* ichnofacies.

Zoophycos Ichnofacies
Of all recurrent marine ichnofacies, this assemblage (Table 2) is most debated and least understood. The ichnogenus *Zoophycos* (Fig. 2C) has an extremely broad paleobathymetric range, hence its designation as namebearer for a supposedly depth-related ichnofacies has long been controversial. As stressed previously, however, the most fundamental considerations rest not with water depth *per se* but rather with: 1) the collective interactions of specific, local environmental and biological factors, and 2) the character of the overall association of traces. From these viewpoints, many occurrences of the *Zoophycos* ichnofacies clearly have environmental significance, albeit somewhat varied. The major question remaining is whether these occurrences constitute a single archetypical model, or should be subdivided further.

In popular bathymetric schemes, the *Zoophycos* ichnofacies typically is portrayed as an intermediary between the *Cruziana* and *Nereites* ichnofacies, at a position corresponding more or less to the continental slope (Fig. 5). More specifically, the original designation placed it in flysch-molasse areas below wave base and free of turbidites, within a broad depositional gradient (Seilacher, 1963, 1964). Such areas, ideally being free of contour and turbidity currents, are characterized by extremely low energy. Ichnofaunas dominated by *Zoophycos* are indeed well known from such settings (Chamberlain and Clark, 1973).

As re-evaluated recently (Seilacher, 1978; Frey and Seilacher, 1980), one of the major environmental controls represented by the ichnofacies is lowered oxygen levels associated with organics in quiet-water settings (cf. Rhoads and Morse, 1970). To the extent that these conditions actually obtain on shelf-edge gradients, the popularized bathymetric placement of the ichnofacies (Fig. 5) is suitable. However, such reducing conditions, replete with a dominance of *Zoophycos,* are perhaps even better known in shallower water, epeiric deposits (Marintsch and Finks, 1982).

Considering the above characteristics of the ichnofacies, together with the widespread distribution of individual specimens of *Zoophycos* in both shallow- and deep-water deposits (Osgood and Szmuc, 1972; Ekdale, 1978), we speculate that the *Zoophycos* animal simply was broadly adapted in most ecologic respects. It tolerated not only a considerable range of water depths but also numerous substrate types, variable food resources, and different energy and oxygen levels. Its traces therefore appear in the *Cruziana* through *Nereites* ichnofacies (Frey, 1970; Crimes, 1973; Miller and Johnson, 1981; Crimes *et al.,* 1981). Indeed, in final analysis, its tolerance may be its most distinguishing environmental characteristic. The animal was able to compete successfully with diverse trace-makers under *Cruziana-* and *Nereites-* type conditions, but few other animals were able to compete with it under the restricted conditions outlined above. In some circumstances the *Spirophyton* animal may have been more opportunistic (Miller and Johnson, 1981) but was not nearly so cosmopolitan.

Because of its singular prominence in many restricted settings, the association seems to warrant its own ichnofacies designation. Conversely, the less restrictive the environment at a given site, the less distinctive the ichnofacies as a separate entity. In numerous places the ichnofacies is hardly discernible in the broad transition from the *Skolithos* or *Cruziana* to the *Nereites* ichnofacies, especially on unstable ancient slopes originally subject to turbidity flows or swept by shelf-edge or contour currents.

In its most restricted occurrences, only a few traces (Fig. 12), locally including facies-crossing forms such as

Chondrites, are apt to appear with *Zoophycos* in the main ichnofacies (cf. Chamberlain, 1971; Seilacher, 1978, Fig. 6). In less restricted occurrences, numerous other, generally deeper water traces have been reported (Crimes *et al.,* 1981), some of them in association with proximal turbidites. Under certain conditions, *Phycosiphon* may replace *Zoophycos* as the dominant component of the ichnofacies (Table 2).

Shallow-water occurrences of the ichnofacies *per se* (Osgood and Szmuc, 1972; Seilacher, 1978, Fig. 10) generally represent restricted circulation in near-shore or epeiric environments, or silled basins, rather than open, shelf-edge settings. In the Carboniferous of the east-central United States, the ichnofacies is commonly manifested by shallow, sheet-like traces concentrated in those parts of sandstones or siltstones nearest interfaces with interbedded grey to black shales (Osgood and Szmuc, 1972, Text-fig. 1). In some instances, the only other faunal element is the brachiopod *Lingula.*

Nevertheless, some ichnofaunas dominated by *Zoophycos* do not obviously represent environmental stress, thus the entire ichnofacies concept requires fuller discussion. First, the ichnogenus is extremely broad and poorly known taxonomically (Häntzschel, 1975), and the exact behavioral or functional equivalence of this multiplicity of burrow forms has not altogether been demonstrated. Recent work suggests, for example, that somewhat U-shaped spreiten nets may be related to oxygen deficiencies whereas J-shaped

nets may indicate a respiratory connection with oxygenated bottom waters (Wetzel and Werner, 1981).

Furthermore, although clear exceptions are known, some evidence indicates that Paleozoic forms of *Zoophycos* tend to be most abundant not only in shallow-water deposits but also at relatively shallow depths within the substrate, whereas post-Paleozoic forms tend to be most abundant in deeper water deposits and at greater substrate depths (Miller, 1978; Ekdale, 1978; Wetzel and Werner, 1981). In partial explanation of these trends, admittedly oversimplified, we suggest the following.

1) Relatively deep, epeiric sea slopes or narrow intracontinental trenches of the geologic past were, in places, less well circulated and oxygenated than are modern, unrestricted continental slopes, hence present-day analogs for the ancient shelf-edge ichnofacies (Fig. 5) are rare.

2) The more ancient occurrences of the ichnofacies characterized not only these anoxic, epeiric or intra-continental slopes, but also shallower restricted basins in which low oxygen levels were imparted partly by bottom water and partly by reduced interstitial organics, but then . . .

3) Mesozoic extensions of sublittoral and shallow bathyal tracemakers into the deep sea (Seilacher, 1977) included the *Zoophycos* animal; already tolerant of anoxia, it best competed with contemporary tracemakers there by burrowing

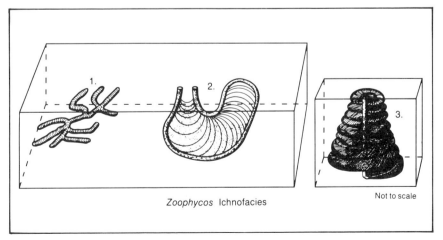

Zoophycos Ichnofacies

Not to scale

Figure 12
Restricted trace fossil association characteristic of the Zoophycos ichnofacies. The ichnogenus Chondrites also may be present. 1) Phycosiphon; 2) Zoophycos; 3) Spirophyton.

more deeply into the substrate, where reduced sediments were prevalent.

An adaptation toward deep burrowing in post-Paleozoic anoxic substrates is strongly suggested by the abundant occurrence of deep *Zoophycos* in various oozes and micrites, including somewhat shallower water chalks. In some of these ichnofacies, however, *Chondrites* (Fig. 3) is even more prevalent (Bromley and Eckdale, 1984) and its architect burrowed to comparable depths.

Deep burrowing also may reflect a preference for firmer sediments at depth, away from the soft or slurry substrate surface. Cohesive sediments are certainly indicated by the fine details of preservation exhibited by numerous specimens of *Zoophycos*. In many local settings, cross-cutting relationships among burrows further indicate that *Zoophycos* was emplaced rather late in the sequence, after some dewatering of sediments. Upper parts of the structure may not routinely be preserved because of a thixotropic boundary layer and intense shallow bioturbation (Berger *et al.*, 1979), yet total absence of the trace is more nearly indicative of original animal absence than of simple nonpreservation of *Zoophycos* in watery muds (cf. Seilacher, 1978).

Explaining the predominance of *Zoophycos* in certain seemingly unstressed, shallower water ichnofaunas of the Paleozoic is more difficult. Many such ichnofaunas are accompanied by diverse body fossils. We simply hypothesize that these environments may have been deceptively less optimal for endobenthos than for epibenthos, hence the relative success of the *Zoophycos* animal. The actual relationship of course warrants further study.

Whatever the major environmental implications of the *Zoophycos* ichnofacies and its variants, the final word is not yet in. The most important factors in the distribution of the animal, in addition to its own opportunism, evidently include water depth, depth of burrowing, sediment cohesiveness, and interstitial or bottom-water oxygen levels. Stressed quiet-water environments, particularly those exhibiting anoxia, seem to be the primary common denominator, even though the animal itself was cosmopolitan. As with the *Scoyenia* ichnofacies, however, this archetype requires further

testing.

Nereites Ichnofacies

In most respects, bathymetric implications of the *Nereites* ichnofacies (Fig. 5) are less equivocal than those of any other recurrent ichnofacies. Although numerous trace fossils otherwise typical of shallow-water deposits occasionally range into deep-sea deposits (Kern and Warme, 1974; Crimes, 1977), the reverse is not ordinarily true. Except for its early-Paleozoic shallow-water occurrences (Fig. 6), the meshwork burrow system *Paleodictyon,* generally considered an index to the deepest, most distal marine environments, is virtually unknown outside the *Nereites* ichnofacies.

This ichnofacies concept, like that of the *Skolithos, Cruziana,* and *Zoophycos* ichnofacies, stemmed from observations on European molasse-flysch sequences (Seilacher, 1958, 1962, 1963). In addition to water depth, turbidite deposition strongly influenced original environmental interpretations of the *Nereites* association. Typical occurrence of the ichnofacies in ancient turbidite sequences has been documented by numerous subsequent studies (e.g., Chamberlain, 1971; Crimes, 1973; Pickerill, 1980). However, depth- and energy-related variables seem to be more important than turbidite deposition *per se* (Crimes *et al.*, 1981). For example, the trace assemblage persists today (Ekdale, 1980) on distant abyssal plains essentially beyond reach of turbidity currents but is absent among well-developed, shallow-water turbidite sequences.

Nevertheless, most *Nereites* associations studied to date occur in turbidites (see "Turbidites and Associated Coarse Clastic Deposits", this volume), probably because the stratigraphic record of deep-water deposits examined in this context mainly represent subsiding basins or subduction zones rather than the broad abyssal plain. Associated sediments thus may consist of virtually any lithology, except that the ratio of turbidite sand to hemipelagic or pelagic mud tends to diminish toward distal extremities of the deposit, and carbonates become increasingly scarce as the calcite compensation depth is approached. Bouma sequences or modified sequences are common locally, and physical

sedimentary structures may include flute, groove, bounce, and load casts, as well as prod marks, flame structures, and linguoid and other ripples. Exceptions to all these generalities are of course known (Crimes *et al.*, 1981).

Animals exploiting lower bathyal to abyssal environments have two major concerns: 1) scarcity of food, relative to more abundant supplies in shallower settings, and 2) periodic disruption by strong down-canyon bottom currents or actual turbidity currents. In response to the last factor, and over long spans of geologic time, the overall community ultimately developed two component parts: pre-turbidite and post-turbidite associations, as documented by their respective traces (Seilacher, 1962; Kern, 1980). The pre-turbidite resident association is characteristic of quiet, normal conditions and is dominant wherever the substrate is free of the influence of turbidity currents. It tends to be overwhelmed or eliminated by severe erosion or turbulence, however, and is replaced by the post-turbidite association after cessation of the turbidity current. As conditions then revert to a normal, low-energy setting, the pre-turbidite association gradually re-establishes itself.

Pre-turbidite animals thus comprise a stable, persistent community well adapted to quiet conditions, derived mainly from original early-Paleozoic colonizers of the deep-sea floor. In contrast, post-turbidite animals represent a more opportunistic, less stable community better adapted to turbidite colonization, derived mainly from subsequent evolutionary immigrants from shallower waters (Seilacher, 1977; Frey and Seilacher, 1980).

From a conceptual viewpoint, considering the ecologic distinctiveness of these two communities, the present *Nereites* assemblage might be separated into two recurrent ichnofacies. The situation is somewhat analogous to *in-loco* alternations of the *Skolithos* and *Cruziana* ichnofacies in shallow offshore sediments punctuated by storm deposition (Pemberton and Frey, 1984a). Here, however, we simply retain the general *Nereites* designation.

A third trace fossil record exists locally but remains poorly documented: syndepositional turbidite escape structures (Seilacher, 1962). As stressed previously, most pre-turbidite tracemakers

203

are overwhelmed during turbidity perturbations; but occasionally a few are able to escape upward through thin layers of episodic sediment, where they are joined by the post-turbidite tracemakers.

Feeding methods employed by these various organisms are generally designed for maximum efficiency, not only with respect to resource utilization, or thorough coverage of space during deposit-feeding activity, but possibly also in response to competition or other biologic pressures (Kitchell and Clark, 1979). Systematic grazing traces and shallow feeding structures predominate. Most are tightly meandrous or spiraled, although some resemble meshworks (Fig. 13.5). The latter, called graphoglyptids, represent open burrows possibly designed to capture microbenthos. Some seem to have been further designed for passive ventilation by gentle background currents, and thus may be indicators of normal, pre-turbidite current directions (Crimes and Crossley, 1980).

In addition to pre- and post-turbidite associations, numerous turbidites display ichnologic gradients along depositional dips (Crimes, 1973; Crimes et al., 1981). Where strong bottom currents issue from submarine canyons or course along fan channels, components of the Skolithos ichnofacies may be present. Otherwise, promixal parts of turbidites may be characterized by rosetted or radiating traces (Fig. 13.3) and gently meandering forms of Scolicia. Medial parts may be indicated by spiraled or tightly meandering traces (Figs. 13.1, 13.6, and 13.7). Distal parts are typified by patterned networks (Figs. 13.2, 13.4, and 13.5) although other traces are generally present. Zoophycos is common locally in various settings, but it tends to be multilobed and in places is more complex than in the Zoophycos ichnofacies.

Finally, the Nereites ichnofacies is recognized via sedimentary coring in ancient, unconsolidated, well-bedded fine sediments, including distal turbidites and pelagic rhythmites, of the present ocean basins. However, the association per se, if present, tends not to be preserved on great expanses of the abyssal plain, where sedimentation and bioturbation are more or less constant rather than episodic (Berger et al., 1979).

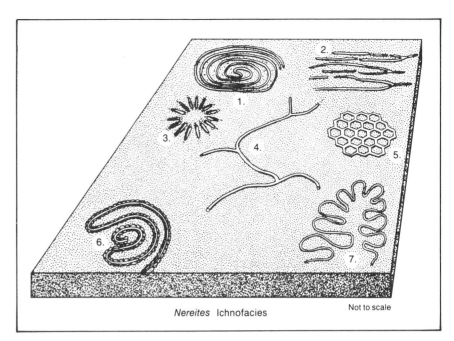

Figure 13
Trace fossil association characteristic of the Nereites ichnofacies. 1) Spirorhaphe; 2) Urohelminthoida; 3) Lorenzinia; 4) Megagrapton; 5) Paleodictyon; 6) Nereites; 7) Cosmorhaphe.

EVALUATION OF THE MODELS

These archetypical models, particularly the marine ones, have proven to be valuable indicators of general environmental conditions. For instance, except for a capping layer of planar bedforms, climbing ripples, or antidunes, primary physical sedimentary structures of fluvial point bars may be strikingly like those of estuarine point bars. However, biogenic sedimentary structures are very different in the two settings.

Perhaps the most misunderstood aspect of these recurrent ichnofacies is their use in paleobathymetry. Although some workers have been too complacent in this aspect of environmental reconstruction (see Byers, 1982), various ichnologists have long and persistently emphasized that local sets of environmental factors are most important in controlling the distribution of tracemakers, whether or not these parameters occur at specific water depths. For instance, many of the estuarine point bars mentioned above exhibit a high-energy, channelward side typified by a Skolithos association and a low-energy, bankward side typified by a Cruziana association (Frey and Howard, 1980). The respective associations occur in close proximity, at the same stratigraphic or bathymetric datum.

On the other hand, many kinds of environmental parameters do tend to change progressively with water depth and distance from shore, and these gradients affect corresponding changes in the distribution of physical and biogenic sedimentary structures. To that extent, trace fossil associations are indeed useful in paleobathymetry.

Equally important is the long temporal duration of most kinds of trace fossils. These basic benthic behavioral patterns are more nearly like stable ecologic niches than individualistic records of particular animal species (Frey and Seilacher, 1980, p. 202-203). As long as the functional niche remains advantageous under given environmental conditions, many different animal species, over long intervals of geologic time, may be expected to exploit it; their preserved traces are strikingly similar and have equivalent significance. Hence, although we conveniently speak of the "Skolithos animal" as the architect for a particular kind of dwelling structure, numerous different animal species actually were involved. The longevity of recurrent ichnofacies thereby exceeds the longevity of recurrent biofacies by a considerable margin, and are correspondingly more useful as archetypical models for environmental

Figure 14
Bioturbate textures, Demopolis Chalk (Upper Cretaceous), Alabama. Outcrop view (A) reveals abundant late-formed, whitish burrows amid a vague background of dense burrow mottles. Identifiable burrows include

Thalassinoides (large), Teichichnus (transverse section through spreite), and Chondrites (small). Coin = 1.9 cm. Fresh subsurface core from approximately equivalent stratigraphic level (B) reveals a more con-

spicuous, thoroughly reconstituted biogenic fabric comprising several generations of burrows. Chondrites (small, white) represents the last burrowing episode. Bar = 1 cm. (Adapted from Frey and Bromley, 1984).

interpretation.

Finally, the models should not be divorced from associated patterns of bioturbation. Numerous local ichnofacies, particularly those representing low-energy conditions and slow rates of deposition, are set in a complex biogenic fabric (Fig. 14). Several generations of burrows may be discernible via their cross-cutting relationships, showing that the same volume of sediment passed repeatedly through various styles of reworking. In environmental reconstruction, such ichnologic fabrics may be equally as important as the individual, named trace fossils (Pemberton and Frey, 1984a; Howard and Frey, 1984).

PERSPECTIVE

The archetypes thus help set the stage for basic environmental discrimination. This first interpretative step is somewhat analogous to deciding between, say, a delta or a fluviatile lithofacies model for a given deposit. Then, just as deltas exhibit considerable diversity of form and subfacies, requiring further evaluation, the ichnologic reconstruction must turn to smaller scaled, more detailed aspects of local ichnofacies for the final analysis (Bromley and Asgaard, 1979; Marintsch and Finks, 1982).

ACKNOWLEDGEMENTS

For their valuable reviews of various parts of the preliminary typescript, we thank R.G. Bromley, T.P. Crimes, H.A. Curran, A.A. Ekdale, and M.F. Miller. Figure 6 was provided by T.P. Crimes; most other ink illustrations were drawn by the staff of the Alberta Geological Survey, as adapted by us from numerous sources.

REFERENCES

PRINCIPLES AND CONCEPTS

Bromley, R.G., 1970. Borings as trace fossils and *Entobia cretacea* Portlock, as an example. *In* Crimes, T.P., and Harper, J.C., eds., Trace fossils. Geological Journal, Special Issue 3, p. 49-90.
One of the first and best general reviews of modern and ancient borings from an ichnological viewpoint.

Frey, R.W., 1971. Ichnology – the study of fossil and recent lebensspuren. *In* Perkins, B.F., ed., A field guide to selected localities in Pennsylvanian, Permian, Cretaceous, and Tertiary rocks of Texas and related papers. Louisiana State University, Miscellaneous Publication 71-1, p. 91-125.
Comprehensive introduction to ichnology, outlining the significance of trace fossils in sedimentology, stratigraphy, paleontology, and paleoecology.

Frey, R.W., 1973. Concepts in the study of biogenic sedimentary structures. Journal of Sedimentary Petrology, v. 43, p. 6-19.
Extensive review of the disciplinary framework of ichnology, including definition of major concepts.

Frey, R.W., ed., 1975. The study of trace fossils. New York, Springer-Verlag, 562 p.
Most comprehensive reference on ichnology presently available. Contains 23 summary chapters treating most aspects of the subject. Chapters cited in this paper include:
Bromley, R.G., Trace fossils at omission surfaces, p. 399-428.
Crimes, T.P., The stratigraphical significance of trace fossils, p. 109-130.
Golubic, S., Perkins, R.D., and Lukas, K.J., Boring microorganisms and microborings in carbonate substrates, p. 229-259.
Howard, J.D., The sedimentological significance of trace fossils, p. 131-146.
Kennedy, W.J., Trace fossils in carbonate rocks, p. 377-398.
Warme, J.E., Borings as trace fossils and the processes of marine bioerosion, p. 181-227.

Frey, R.W., and Seilacher, A., 1980. Uniformity in marine invertebrate ichnology. Lethaia, v. 13, p. 183-207.
Comprehensive evaluation of the uniformitarian approach in ichnology, emphasizing the interaction of benthic behavioral patterns and prevailing environmental conditions.

Fürsich, F.T., 1975. Trace fossils as environmental indicators in the Corallian of England and Normandy. Lethaia, v. 8, p. 151-172.
Major case study of interrelationships between trace fossils and environmental factors, especially hydrology.

Häntzschel, W., 1975. Trace fossils and problematica. In Teichert, C.,ed., Treatise on invertebrate paleontology, Part W, Miscellanea, Supplement 1. Lawrence, University of Kansas Press and Geological Society of America, 269 p.
Best available reference for identification of individual trace fossil genera. Includes copious illustrations and extensive bibliography.

Schäfer, W., 1972. Ecology and palaeoecology of marine environments. Oliver and Boyd, Edinburgh, and University of Chicago Press, 568 p.
An indispensable book on the ethology of modern marine organisms; has important ramifications for the interpretation of trace fossils. Summarizes much early work on the North Sea by researchers at the Senckenberg Institute.

Seilacher, A., 1964. Biogenic sedimentary structures. In Imbrie, J., and Newell, N., eds., Approaches to Paleoecology. New York, John Wiley, p. 296-316.
One of the first review papers in English outlining the paleoecological significance of trace fossils. Probable stimulus for much modern trace fossil work in North America.

Seilacher, A., 1967. Bathymetry of trace fossils. Marine Geology, v. 5, p. 413-428.
Landmark paper outlining basic concepts of the ichnofacies model. The paper has drawn criticism for its extreme emphasis on bathymetry; yet the reader must bear in mind that it appeared in a topical volume devoted entirely to bathymetry.

Seilacher, A., 1978. Use of trace fossil assemblages for recognizing depositional environments. In Basan, P.B., ed., Trace fossil concepts. Society of Economic Paleontologists and Mineralogists, Short Course 5, p. 185-201.
Latest summary by the person most responsible for the ichnofacies concept.

THE SCOYENIA ICHNOFACIES

Bromley, R., and Asgaard, U., 1979. Triassic freshwater ichnocoenoses from Carlsberg Fjord, East Greenland. Palaeogeography, Palaeoclimatology, Palaeoecology, v. 28, p. 39-80.
Excellent account of diverse nonmarine ichnofossil suites. Provides a framework for continued refinement of the Scoyenia ichnofacies concept.

Frey, R.W., Pemberton, S.G., and Fagerstrom, J.A., 1984. Morphological, ethological, and environmental significance of the ichnogenera Scoyenia and Ancorichnus. Journal of Paleontology, v. 58, p. 511-528.
A review of the Scoyenia and related ichnofacies, most of which remain undefined and unnamed. Emphasis upon problems and principles involved.

Ratcliffe, B.C., and Fagerstrom, J.A., 1980. Invertebrate lebensspuren of Holocene floodplains: their morphology, origin and paleoecological significance. Journal of Paleontology, v. 54, p. 614-630.
Documents the potential variety of invertebrate burrows in Holocene floodplain deposits. Superb illustrations of insect lebensspuren.

THE TRYPANITES ICHNOFACIES

Pemberton, S.G., Kobluk, D.R., Yeo, R.K., and Risk, M.J., 1980. The boring Trypanites at the Silurian-Devonian disconformity in southern Ontario. Journal of Paleontology, v. 54, p. 1258-1266.
Detailed study of borings at a major disconformity. The surface is interpreted as a paleokarst, subsequently transgressed.

Perkins, B.F., 1971. Traces of rock-boring organisms in the Comanche Cretaceous of Texas. In Perkins, B.F., ed., A field guide to selected localities in Pennsylvanian, Permian, Cretaceous, and Tertiary Rocks of Texas and related papers. Louisiana State University, Miscellaneous Publication 71-1, p. 137-148.
Excellent account of the use of diverse borings in identifying hardgrounds; presents helpful criteria for differentiating borings from burrows.

Radwanski, A., 1970. Dependence of rock-borers and burrowers on the environmental conditions within the Tortonian littoral zone of southern Poland. In Crimes, T.P., and Harper, J.C., eds., Trace fossils. Geological Journal, Special Issue 3, p. 371-390.
A detailed account of trace fossils at the shallow-water margins of the Central Polish Uplands. The well-represented Trypanites ichnofacies is interpreted as a rocky coast assemblage; adjacent burrows mostly constitute the Skolithos ichnofacies.

THE GLOSSIFUNGITES ICHNOFACIES

Frey, R.W., and Basan, P.B., 1981. Taphonomy of relict Holocene salt marsh deposits, Cabretta Island, Georgia. Senckenbergiana Maritima, v. 13, p. 111-155.
Documents the occurrence and characteristics of modern firmground traces in old tidal creek and salt marsh muds formerly buried beneath modern beach-dune sands.

Fürsich, F.T., Kennedy, W.J., and Palmer, T.J., 1981. Trace fossils at a regional discontinuity surface: the Austin/Taylor (Upper Cretaceous) contact in central Texas. Journal of Paleontology, v. 55, p. 537-551.
A well-documented ancient softground-firmground-omission sequence. The firmground trace fossil assemblage is a good example of the Glossifungites ichnofacies.

Hayward, B.W., 1976. Lower Miocene bathyal and submarine canyon ichnocoenoses from Northland, New Zealand. Lethaia, v. 9, p. 149-162.
Describes firmground ichnofossils that represent a deep-water occurrence of the Glossifungites ichnofacies.

Pemberton, S.G., and Frey, R.W., 1984b. The Glossifungites ichnofacies: modern examples from the Georgia coast. In Curran, H.A., ed., Biogenic structures: their use in interpreting depositional environments. Society of Economic Paleontologists and Mineralogists, Special Publication, in press.
A summary of the Glossifungites ichnofacies concept, including accounts of biogenic structures found in exhumed relict muds on barrier island beaches and along back-barrier tidal streams.

THE SKOLITHOS ICHNOFACIES

Crimes, T.P., 1977. Trace fossils of an Eocene deep-sea sand fan, northern Spain. In Crimes, T.P., and Harper, J.C., eds., Trace fossils 2. Geological Journal, Special Issue 9, p. 71-90.
A major ichnological study of a deep-sea fan. The higher energy, proximal fan contains traces normally associated with shallow-water deposits, a virtual Skolithos ichnofacies. Remaining traces represent the resident Nereites ichnofacies.

Frey, R.W., Howard, J.D., and Pryor, W.A., 1978. Ophiomorpha: its morphologic, taxonomic, and environmental significance. Palaeogeography, Palaeoclimatology, Palaeoecology, v. 23, p. 199-229.
Variations in the morphology and abundance of Ophiomorpha have important environmental ramifications, and help distinguish the Skolithos and Cruziana ichnofacies.

Hallam, A., and Swett, K., 1966. Trace fossils from the Lower Cambrian Pipe Rock of the north-west Highlands. Scottish Journal of Geology, v. 2, p. 101-106.
A classic description of trace fossils from the "pipe rock", which constitutes one of the best examples of the Skolithos ichnofacies.

206

THE CRUZIANA ICHNOFACIES

Farrow, G.E., 1966. Bathymetric zonation of Jurassic trace fossils from the coast of Yorkshire, England. Palaeogeography, Palaeoclimatology, Palaeoecology, v. 2, p. 103-151.
Describes variations in trace fossils along depositional dip, emphasizing the effects of bathymetry and energy levels. Most traces are referable to the *Cruziana* ichnofacies.

Frey, R.W., 1970. Trace fossils of Fort Hays Limestone Member of Niobrara Chalk (Upper Cretaceous), west-central Kansas. University of Kansas Paleontological Contributions, Article 53, p. 1-41.
An example of the *Cruziana* ichnofacies in offshore, quiet-water chalk deposits.

Howard, J.D., and Frey, R.W., 1984. Characteristic trace fossils in nearshore to offshore sequences, Upper Cretaceous of east-central Utah. Canadian Journal of Earth Sciences, v. 21, p. 200-219.
A nearshore *Skolithos* ichnofacies of restricted diversity grades into an offshore *Cruziana* ichnofacies of increased diversity. Storm deposits and patterns of bioturbation also are important.

Pemberton, S.G. and Frey, R.W., 1984a. Ichnology of storm-influenced shallow marine sequence: Cardium Formation (Upper Cretaceous) at Seebe, Alberta. *In* Stott, D.F., ed., The Mesozoic of Middle North America. Canadian Society of Petroleum Geologists, Memoir 9, in press.
Interpretation of ichnofossils associated with quiet-water and storm-influenced deposits, representing the *Cruziana* and *Skolithos* ichnofacies, respectively. Ichnofossils in hummocky cross-stratified sands are thought to represent the activities of opportunistic organisms.

THE ZOOPHYCOS ICHNOFACIES

Chamberlain, C.K., and Clark, D.L., 1973. Trace fossils and conodonts as evidence for deep-water deposits in the Oquirrh Basin of central Utah. Journal of Paleontology, v. 47, p. 663-682.
Study of late Paleozoic sandstones and carbonates containing trace fossil successions characteristic of the *Cruziana*, *Zoophycos*, and *Nereites* ichnofacies.

Marintsch, E.J., and Finks, R.M., 1982. Lower Devonian ichnofacies at Highland Mills, New York and their gradual replacement across environmental gradients. Journal of Paleontology, v. 56, p. 1050-1078.
Excellent account both of restricted, shallow-water occurrences of the *Zoophycos* ichnofacies and of local ichnofacies changes along perceptive gradients.

Miller, M.F., and Johnson, K.G., 1981. *Spirophyton* in alluvial-tidal facies of the Catskill deltaic complex: possible biological control of ichnofossil distribution. Journal of Paleontology, v. 55, p. 1016-1027.
Stresses the possible importance of biological parameters, particularly competition and predation, in explaining the occurrence of *Spirophyton* in shallow-water deposits; *Zoophycos* occurs in some, but not all, beds bearing *Spirophyton*.

Osgood, R.G., Jr., and Szmuc, E.J., 1972. The trace fossil *Zoophycos* as an indicator of water depth. Bulletins of American Paleontology, v. 62, p. 1-22.
Documents an occurrence of the *Zoophycos* ichnofacies in shallow-water deposits of Mississippian age. Reiterates that trace fossil distributions are ultimately linked to prevailing environmental parameters rather than water depth *per se*.

THE NEREITES ICHNOFACIES

Crimes, T.P., 1973. From limestones to distal turbidites: a facies and trace fossil analysis in the Zumaya flysch (Paleocene-Eocene), north Spain. Sedimentology, v. 20, p. 105-131.
Describes trace fossils associated with a typical turbidite sequence, and illustrates the basic ichnological differences between proximal and distal deposits.

Crimes, T.P., Goldring, R., Homewood, P., van Stuijvenberg, J., and Winkler, W., 1981. Trace fossil assemblages of deep-sea fan deposits, Gurnigel and Schlieren flysch (Cretaceous-Eocene, Switzerland). Eclogae Geologicae Helvetiae, v. 74, p. 953-995.
Summary of factors governing the distribution of deep-sea fan ichnofossils, most of which are referable to the *Nereites* ichnofacies. In places, substrate characteristics play a minor role.

Kern, J.P., 1980. Origin of trace fossils in Polish Carpathian flysch. Lethaia, v. 13, p. 347-362.
Outlines criteria useful in distinguishing between pre-depositional and post-depositional traces in turbidite successions.

Pickerill, R.K., 1980. Phanerozoic flysch trace fossil diversity – observations based on an Ordovician flysch ichnofauna from the Aroostook-Matapedia Carbonate Belt of northern New Brunswick. Canadian Journal of Earth Sciences, v. 17, p. 1259-1270.
An account of flysch trace fossils representing a significant radiation of deep-sea behavioral diversity.

Seilacher, A., 1962. Paleontological studies on turbidite sedimentation and erosion. Journal of Geology, v. 70, p. 227-234.
Landmark paper establishing the pre- and post-depositional origin of trace fossils in sediments deposited by turbidity currents.

OTHER REFERENCES CITED IN TEXT

Ager, D.V., 1963. Principles of paleoecology. New York, McGraw-Hill, 371 p.

Berger, W.H., Ekdale, A.A., and Bryant, P.P., 1979. Selective preservation of burrows in deep-sea carbonates. Marine Geology, v. 32, p. 205-230.

Bromley, R.G., and Ekdale, A.A., 1984. *Chondrites:* a trace fossil indicator of anoxia in sediments. Science, v. 224, p. 872-874.

Bromley, R.G., Pemberton, S.G., and Rahmani, R.A., 1984. A Cretaceous woodground: the *Teredolites* ichnofacies. Journal of Paleontology, v. 58, p. 488-498.

Byers, C.W., 1982. Geological significance of marine biogenic sedimentary structures. *In* McCall, P.L., and Tevesz, M.J.S., eds., Animal-sediment relations. New York, Plenum Press, p. 221-256.

Chamberlain, C.K., 1971. Bathymetry and paleoecology of Ouachita geosyncline of southeastern Oklahoma as determined from trace fossils. American Association of Petroleum Geologists, Bulletin, v. 55, p. 34-50.

Crimes, T.P., and Crossley, J.D., 1980. Inter-turbidite bottom current orientation from trace fossils with an example from the Silurian flysch of Wales. Journal of Sedimentary Petrology, v. 50, p. 821-830.

Crimes, T.P., and Anderson, M.M., in press. Trace fossils from Late Precambrian-Early Cambrian strata of S.E. Newfoundland (Canada): temporal and environmental implications. Journal of Paleontology.

Ekdale, A.A., 1978. Trace fossils in Leg 42A cores. *In* Hsü, K.J., *et al.*, eds., Initial Reports of the Deep Sea Drilling Project, v. 42, p. 821-827.

Ekdale, A.A., 1980. Graphoglyptid burrows in modern deep-sea sediment. Science, v. 207, p. 304-306.

Frey, R.W., and Bromley, R.G., 1984. Ichnology of Selma Group chalks (Upper Cretaceous), western Alabama. I. Stratigraphy and biogenic sedimentary structures. Canadian Journal of Earth Sciences, in press.

Frey, R.W., and Howard, J.D., 1980. Physical and biogenic processes in Georgia estuaries. II. Intertidal facies. *In* McCann, S.B., ed., Sedimentary processes and animal-sediment relationships in tidal environments. Geological Association of Canada, Short Course 1, p. 183-220.

Fürsich, F.T., 1974. Corallian (Upper Jurassic) trace fossils from England and Normandy. Stuttgarter Beiträge zur Naturkunde, Serie B, No. 13, p. 1-52.

Howard, J.D., and Frey, R.W., 1975. Estuaries of the Georgia coast, U.S.A.: sedimentology and biology. II. Regional animal-sediment characteristics of Georgia estuaries. Senckenbergiana Maritima, v. 7, p. 33-103.

Kern, J.P., and Warme, J.E., 1974. Trace fossils and bathymetry of the Upper Cretaceous Point Loma Formation, San Diego, California. Geological Society of America, Bulletin, v. 85, p. 893-900.

Kitchell, J.A., and Clark, D.L., 1979. A multivariate approach to biofacies analysis of deep-sea traces from the central Arctic. Journal of Paleontology, v. 53, p. 1045-1067.

Kobluk, D.R., James, N.P., and Pemberton, S.G., 1978. Initial diversification of macroboring ichnofossils and exploitation of the macroboring niche in the lower Paleozoic. Paleobiology, v. 4, p. 163-170.

Miller, M.F., 1978. Ethology and ecology of some Devonian shallow water *Zoophycos* and possible implications for trace fossil evolution. Geological Society of America, Abstracts with Programs, v. 10, p. 457.

Miller, M.F., 1984. Distribution of biogenic structures in Paleozoic nonmarine and marine-margin sequences: an actualistic model. Journal of Paleontology, v. 58, p. 550-570.

Miller, M.F., and Byers, C.W., 1984. Abundant and diverse early Paleozoic infauna indicated by the stratigraphic record. Geology, v. 12, p. 40-43.

Purdy, E.G., 1964. Sediments as substrates. *In* Imbrie, J., and Newell, N., eds., Approaches to paleoecology. New York, John Wiley, p. 238-271.

Radwański, A., Friis, H., and Larsen, G., 1975. The Miocene Hagenir-Birup sequence at Lillebaelt (Denmark): its biogenic structures and depositional environment. Geological Society of Denmark, Bulletin, v. 24, p. 229-260.

Rhoads, D.C., and Morse, J., 1970. Evolutionary and ecologic significance of oxygen deficient marine basins. Lethaia, v. 4, p. 413-428.

Röder, H., 1977. Zur Beziehung zwischen Konstruktion und Substrat bei mechanisch bohrenden Bohrmuscheln (Pholadidae, Teredinidae). Senckenbergiana Maritima, v. 9, p. 105-213.

Schroder, C.H., 1982. Trace fossils of the Oconee Group and basal Barnwell Group of east-central Georgia. Georgia Geological Survey, Bulletin 88, 125 p.

Schroeder, J.H., and Zankl, H., 1974. Dynamic reef formation: a sedimentological concept based on studies of recent Bermuda and Bahama reefs. Proceedings of the 2nd International Coral Reef Symposium, Brisbane, Australia, v. 2, p. 413-428.

Seilacher, A., 1958, Zur ökologischen Charakteristik von Flysch und Molasse. Eclogae Geologicae Helvetiae, v. 51, p. 1062-1078.

Seilacher, A., 1963. Kaledonischer Unterbau der Irakiden. Neues Jahrbuch für Geologie und Paläontologie, Monatshefte, 1963, p. 527-542.

Seilacher, A., 1977. Evolution of trace fossil communities. *In* Hallam, A., ed., Patterns of evolution. Amsterdam, Elsevier, p. 359-376.

Seilacher, A., and Meischner, D., 1964, Fazies-Analyse im Paläozoikum des Oslo-Gebietes. Geologischen Rundschau, v. 54, p. 596-619.

Walker, K.R., and Laporte, L.F., 1970. Congruent fossil communities from Ordovician and Devonian carbonates of New York. Journal of Paleontology, v. 44, p. 928-944.

Warme, J.E., 1977. Carbonate borers – their role in reef ecology and preservation. *In* Frost, S.H., Weiss, M.P., and Saunders, J.B., eds., Reefs and related carbonates – ecology and sedimentology. American Association of Petroleum Geologists, Studies in Geology No. 4, p. 261-279.

Warme, J.E., and McHuron, E.J., 1978. Marine borers: trace fossils and geological significance. *In* Basan, P.B., ed., Trace fossil concepts. Society of Economic Paleontologists and Mineralogists, Short Course 5, p. 77-131.

Wetzel, A., and Werner, F., 1981. Morphology and ecological significance of *Zoophycos* in deep-sea sediments off NW Africa. Palaeogeography, Palaeoclimatology, Palaeoecology, v. 32, p. 185-212.

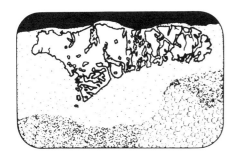

Introduction to Carbonate Facies Models

NOEL P. JAMES
Department of Earth Sciences
Memorial University of Newfoundland
St. John's, Newfoundland A1B 3X5

INTRODUCTION

This paper is a general introduction to facies models in carbonate sedimentary rocks. Here I would like to set the stage for these papers by outlining the inherent differences between siliciclastic and carbonate deposits (Table 1) and discussing some of the attributes of carbonate sediments which are important to the formulation of facies models (Table 2).

CARBONATE SEDIMENTS ARE BORN, NOT MADE

This deceptively simple phrase encapsulates the main theme of the differences between the two sediment types. Siliciclastic sediments made primarily by the disintegration of parent rock are transported to the environment of deposition, and once there, the patterns of texture and fabric are impressed upon the sediment by the hydraulic regimen. The signature of siliciclastic facies is thus in sedimentary structures and grain size variations. Carbonate sediments, on the other hand, are born in or close to the environment of deposition. Thus, in addition to the purely physical sedi-

Table 1
Differences between siliciclastic and carbonate sediments.

Carbonate Sediments	Siliciclastic Sediments
The majority of sediments occur in shallow, tropical environments	Climate is no constraint, sediments occur worldwide and at all depths
The majority of sediments are marine	Sediments are both terrestrial and marine
The grain size of sediments generally reflects the size of organism skeletons and calcified hard parts	The grain size of sediments reflects the hydraulic energy in the environment
The presence of lime mud often indicates the prolific growth of organisms whose calcified portions are mud size crystallites	The presence of mud indicates settling out from suspension
Shallow water lime sand bodies result primarily from localized physicochemical or biological fixation of carbonate	Shallow water sand bodies result from the interaction of currents and waves
Localized buildups of sediments without accompanying change in hydraulic regimen alter the character of surrounding sedimentary environments	Changes in the sedimentary environments are generally brought about by widespread changes in the hydraulic regimen
Sediments are commonly cemented on the sea floor	Sediments remain unconsolidated in the environment of deposition and on the sea floor
Periodic exposure of sediments during deposition results in intensive diagenesis, especially cementation and recrystallization	Periodic exposure of sediments during deposition leaves deposits relatively unaffected
The signature of different sedimentary facies is obliterated during low grade metamorphism	The signature of sedimentary facies survives low-grade metamorphism

Table 2
The sedimentary aspect of modern carbonate producing and binding organisms and their counterparts in the fossil record.

Modern Organisms	Ancient Counterpart	Sedimentary Aspect
Corals	Archaeocyathans, Corals, Stromatoporoids, Bryozoans, Rudistid bivalves, Hydrozoans.	The large components often remain in place, forming reefs and mounds.
Bivalves	Bivalves, Brachiopods, Cephalopods, Trilobites and other arthropods.	Remain whole or break apart into several pieces to form sand and gravel-size particles.
Gastropods, Benthic Foraminifers	Gastropods, Tintinids, Tentaculitids, Salterellids, Benthic Foraminifers, Brachiopods.	Whole skeletons that form sand and gravel-size particles.
Planktonic forminifers	Planktonic foraminifers, Coccoliths (post-Jurassic).	Medium sand-size and smaller particles.
Encrusting foraminifers and coralline algae	Coralline algae, Phylloid algae, Renalcids, Encrusting Foraminifers.	Encrust on or inside hard substrates, build up thick deposits or fall off upon death to form lime sand particles.
Codiacean algae-*Penicillus*	Codiacean algae-*Penicillus*-like forms.	Spontaneously disintegrate upon death to form lime mud.
Blue-green algae (Cyanobacteria)	Blue-green algae (especially in Pre-Ordovician).	Trap and bind fine-grained sediments to form mats and stromatolites.

mentary parameters used in the analysis of non-carbonate sediments, the composition of the sedimentary particles themselves is equally important in characterizing the depositional environment. The particles may either be precipitated out of seawater (e.g., ooids) or formed by organisms (e.g., corals and clams).

VARIATIONS OF CARBONATE PRODUCING ORGANISMS WITH TIME

To interpret ancient sedimentary sequences and construct facies models we rely heavily upon observations in modern environments of deposition. This approach works and is seen to work because the basic composition of most sedimentary particles has remained the same through time; a quartz sand grain or an ooid is generally the same in the Pleistocene, Permian or Precambrian. Because organisms have changed with time it is difficult, at first glance to compare modern and specific ancient carbonate facies.

The approximate diversity, abundance, and relative importance of the principal groups of calcareous marine organisms as sediment producers through the Phanerozoic are outlined in Figure 1. It appears from this diagram that there has been a gradual shift in major players through time. In spite of the variations shown in Figure 1, I think that carbonate secreting organisms in the rock record, when viewed as sediment producers, do have living equivalents in modern oceans, although they may not even be in the same phyla. This is because, despite the numerous groups of organisms with hard parts, there are only two ways in which these hard parts are arranged: 1) as whole, rigid skeletons (foraminifers, snails, corals), and 2) as numerous individual segments held together in life by soft organic matter (trilobites, clams, fish). Table 2 lists the more important carbonate producing and binding organisms their sedimentary aspect and their fossil equivalents.

ZONES OF CARBONATE ACCUMULATION

Because the precipitation of carbonate is easiest in warm, shallow seawater, most carbonate sedimentation takes place on continental shelves or banks in the tropics. Although most sedi-

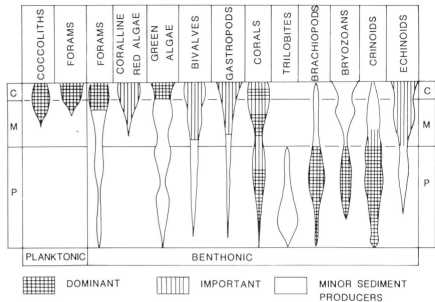

Figure 1
The approximate diversity, abundance and relative importance of various calcareous marine organisms as sediment producers (modified from Wilkinson, 1979). P = Paleozoic; M = Mesozoic; C = Cenozoic

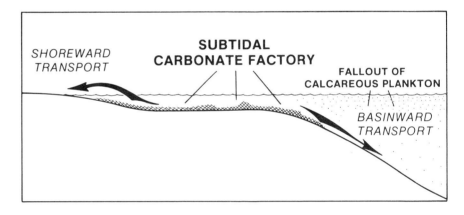

Figure 2
A sketch illustrating the main zones of carbonate accumulation, with most of the carbonate in water less than 30 metres deep.

ments produced in this 'carbonate factory' remain in the source area, some are transported basinward (Fig. 2). Thus, there are three different zones of accumulation: 1) the subtidal, open shelf and shelf margin, characterized by in-place accumulations of lime sands, lime muds and reefs; 2) the shoreline, where sediments are transported from the open shelf onto beaches and tidal flats; and 3) the slope and basin, where shelf-edge sediments are transported seaward, often by mass movements, and redeposited at depth. In the basins, especially in post-Jurassic time, the fallout of calcareous zooplankton and phytoplankton has

also contributed significantly to carbonate sediments.

The characteristics of many carbonate depositional environments have been summarized and profusely illustrated in colour by different authors in the American Assoication of Petroleum Geologists Memoir 33 (Scholle *et al.*, 1983). The reader who wishes a detailed account of different carbonate sedimentary facies through time is referred to outstanding documentation by Wilson (1975).

As each of the three zones of accumulation have distinctive sedimentary environments and produce differing sedimentary facies, they will form a framework for the subsequent articles on carbonate facies models. The shoreline and slope-to-basin facies models are most like siliclastic facies models because sediments are transported from one area and deposited in another. At the other end of the spectrum reefs and reef-like deposits are the most unlike siliclastic facies as they are predominantly accumulations of biologically produced in-place carbonate.

REFERENCES

The reference list on this topic is relatively short because recently several excellent texts on carbonate sediments and facies have appeared. From these the reader can gain access easily to most of the pertinent literature on any specific aspect.

Bathurst, R.G.C., 1975. Carbonate sediments and their diagenesis. Developments in sedimentology No. 12. New York, Elsevier, 658 p.
This book is the most complete reference on the topic of carbonate deposition and diagenesis. Chapters 1 and 2 detail the petrography and occurrence of modern and ancient carbonate particles. Chapters 3 and 4 summarize several different and well-studied environments of carbonate deposition. The book does not cover ancient sedimentary rock sequences.

Flugel, E., 1982. Microfacies analysis of limestones. New York, Springer-Verlag, 633 p.
A thorough and well-illustrated documentation of microscopic aspects of carbonate rocks cast in terms of facies. An excellent reference work to compliment this series of articles.

Folk, R.L., and Robles, R., 1964. Carbonate sands of Isla Perez: Alacran Reef, Yucatan. Journal of Geology, v. 72, p. 255-292.
A classic study illustrating how two different skeletal organisms, corals and the codiacean alga *Halimeda,* break down under different conditions into specific grain sizes.

Ginsburg, R.N., and James, N.P., 1974. Holocene carbonate sediments of continental shelves. *In* Burke, C.A., and Drake, C.L., eds., The geology of continental margins. New York, Springer-Verlag, p. 137-157. A short article summarizing the sedimentology of eight different well-studied areas of carbonate sedimentation in the modern ocean.

Ginsburg, R.N., Lloyd, R.M., Stockman, K.W., and McCallum, J.S., 1963. Shallow water carbonate sediments. *In* Hill, M.N., ed., The sea, Vol. 3, p. 554-578.
The article illustrates how the architecture of modern marine carbonate skeletons governs the grain-size of the resultant sediments.

Ham, W.E., ed., 1962. Classification of carbonate rocks, a symposium. American Association of Petroleum Geologists, Memoir 1, 279 p.
This symposium contains several papers, notably those by W.E. Ham and L.C. Pray, M.W. Leighton and C. Pendexter, R.L. Folk, R.J. Dunham, which by attempting to classify sedimentary carbonates outline succinctly the important factors governing carbonate sedimentation.

Horowitz, A.S., and Potter, P.E., 1971. Introductory petrography of fossils. New York, Springer-Verlag, 302 p.
Chapter 2 is a concise introduction to carbonate sedimentology and the remainder of the book is devoted to the recognition of various skeletal particles in thin section.

Miliman, J.D., 1974. Marine carbonates. New York, Springer-Verlag, 375 p.
This book is devoted wholly to modern carbonate sediments. The first half of the book is an exhaustive documentation of different carbonate particles; the second half is a discussion of modern environments of carbonate deposition – this book is most useful for the specialist.

Scholle, P.A., Bebout, D.G., and Moore, C.H., 1983. Carbonate depositional environments. American Association of Petroleum Geologists, Memoir 33, 708 p.
A superb coverage of all carbonate depositional environments, both modern and ancient, outlined in 12 sections with all illustrations in colour – the best overall coverage of this topic to be found anywhere.

Wilkinson, B.H., 1979. Biomineralization, paleoceanography and the evolution of calcareous marine organisms. Geology, v. 7, p. 524-528.
A short and useful article summarizing amongst other things the relative importance of various skeletal invertebrates as sediment producers through the Phanerozoic.

Wilson, J.L., 1975. Carbonate facies in geologic history. New York, Springer-Verlag, 471 p.
Chapters 1, 2, and 12 of this book are an excellent summary of the principles and stratigraphic aspects of carbonate sedimentation. The bulk of the text is a detailed review of carbonate sedimentary facies at different times in geologic history. This is the best single source book for ancient carbonates.

Wray, J.L., 1977. Calcareous algae. New York, Elsevier, 185 p.
The best single source for information or the sedimentology of various calcareous algae through geologic history.

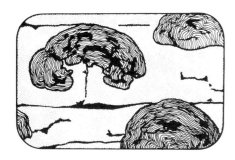

Shallowing-Upward Sequences in Carbonates

NOEL P. JAMES
Department of Earth Sciences
Memorial University of Newfoundland
St. John's, Newfoundland A1B 3X5

INTRODUCTION
Perhaps the most commonly encountered carbonates are laterally persistant, evenly bedded limestones and dolomites of apparent shallow water origin, as demonstrated by abundant fossil mud cracks and stromatolites. These deposits, which are usually found on the continents and in relatively undeformed portions of mountain belts, are not only important sources of paleontological and sedimentological information, but are also common host rocks for hydrocarbons and metallic ores (particularly lead and zinc). As such, it is critical that we be able to determine, as precisely as possible, the environment in which each of the interbedded sediments was deposited.

A quantum jump in our understanding of these deposits occured when modern carbonate tidal flats were examined in detail, notably by Robert Ginsburg and his colleagues in Florida and the Bahamas about 25 years ago. It was quickly realized that there was a host of sedimentary structures and textures on these flats that would allow a much more precise definition of environments of deposition than was possible before: these findings were quickly applied to fossil sequences (Fischer, 1964; Laporte, 1967; Aitken, 1966; Roehl, 1967). This application in turn generated two different lines of investigation: 1) description of other areas of modern tidal flat deposition, in particular the southern shore of the Persian Gulf where evaporites are common, and Shark Bay, Western Australia, where a great variety of modern stromatolites are forming; and 2) documentation of different styles of tidal flat deposits in the geologic record.

THE MODEL
Carbonate sediments characteristically accumulate at rates much greater than the rate of subsidence of the shelf or platform upon which they are deposited (Schlager, 1981). This is because carbonate sediments are produced mainly in the environment of deposition – especially in shallow water where conditions for the biological and physico-chemical fixation of carbonate are optimum. As a result, carbonate accumulations repeatedly build up to sea level and above, resulting in a characteristic sequence of deposits in which each unit is deposited in progressively shallower water. This *shallowing-upward sequence* commonly is repeated many times in a succession of shallow water deposits (Fig. 1).

Readers will recognize that such a shallowing upward sequence also may be termed a 'regressive sequence'. This term has led to much confusion in the past, because it has been used to describe deposits associated with a high rate of sediment production and accumulation under relatively static sea level – sea bottom conditions. I have, therefore, abandoned the term 'regressive' altogether in favor of a rock-descriptive term, albeit interpretive; the *shallowing-upward sequence.*

1) The Model as a Norm. The ideal carbonate shallowing-upward sequence comprises four units illustrated in Figure 2. The basal unit, which is generally thin, records the initial transgression over pre-existing deposits and so is commonly a high energy deposit. The bulk of the sequence, which may be of diverse lithologies, consists of normal marine carbonate, as discussed below. The upper part of the sequence consists of two units: the intertidal unit within the normal range of tides; the other a supratidal unit deposited in the area covered only by abnormal, windblown or storm tides. Each of these units exhibits the characteristic criteria of subaerial exposure.

Figure 1
Bedded carbonates ranging in age from Middle to Late Cambrian near Fortress Lake, B.C. Arrows mark the top of large-scale shallowing-upward sequences (L - Lyell Fm., S - Sullivan Fm., W - Waterfowl Fm., A - Arc-tomys Fm., E - Eldon and Pica Fms.). Striping of the Waterfowl Fm. is caused by repetitive smaller scale shallowing-upward sequences between subtidal-intertidal limestones (dark) and supratidal dolomites (light). Photo courtesy J.D. Aitken.

214

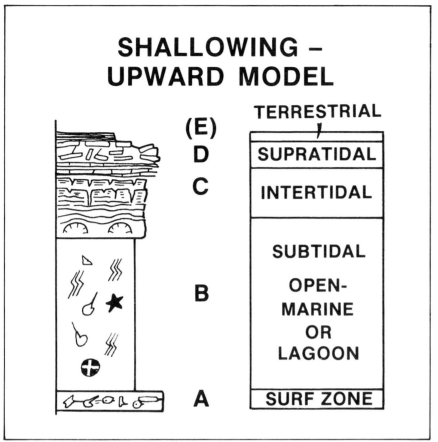

SHALLOWING – UPWARD MODEL

Figure 2

Five divisions of the shallowing-upward model for carbonates: A) lithoclast rich lime conglomerate or sand. B) fossiliferous limestone. C) stromatolitic, mud-cracked crypt-algal limestone or dolomite. D) well lami- *nated dolomite or limestone, flat-pebble breccia. E) shale or calcrete, bracketed to emphasize that the unit is often missing - see text. Symbols used throughout are from Ginsburg (1975).*

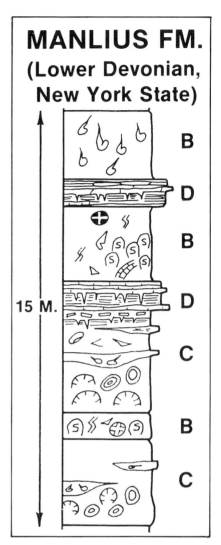

MANLIUS FM.
(Lower Devonian, New York State)

15 M.

Figure 3

Actual sequence of several shallowing-upward sequences from the Manlius Fm., New York State (From Laporte, 1975).

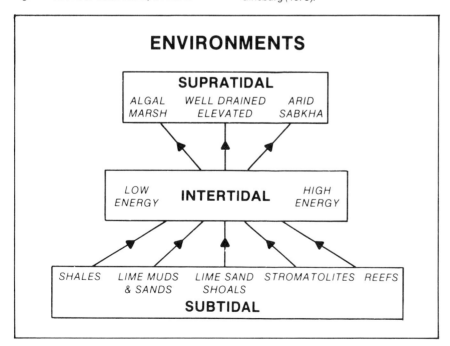

ENVIRONMENTS

Figure 4

A flow diagram indicating the various poss- *ible environmental transitions present in a carbonate shallowing-upward sequence.*

2) *The Model as a Predictor.* The thread that binds all such sequences together is the presence of the distinctive inter-tidal unit, which, once recognized, allows one to interpret the surrounding lithologies in some kind of logical sequence (Fig. 3), and thus predict what lithologies should occur in the rest of the succession under investigation.

First-order variation on the basic model revolves around the two main types of intertidal environment: 1) quiet, low-energy situations, commonly referred to as tidal flats, and 2) agitated, high-energy situations, or quite simply, beaches. Second-order variation involves the kind of subtidal units below and supratidal units above: the subtidal reflects the type of marine environment adjacent to the tidal flat and supratidal reflects the adjacent terrestrial environment, in particular the climate (Fig. 4).

For purposes of discussion I will begin with those sequences that contain low-energy intertidal units (tidal-flats) because they exhibit the greatest variety of distinctive features and consequently are well documented, both in modern and ancient settings. To place the observed features in context we should first examine modern carbonate tidal flats.

SEQUENCES WITH A LOW-ENERGY INTERTIDAL UNIT

Modern Tidal Flats

The main elements of a modern carbonate tidal flat system as exemplified by the narrow shelf and embayments of Shark Bay, Western Australia, the southern coast of the Persian Gulf, and wide platform of the Bahama Banks are shown in Figure 5. The sedimentary features of these tidal flats are beautifully illustrated by Shinn (1983). A characteristic of most modern examples is that they occur in protected locations: protected that is from the open ocean waves and swells, yet still affected by tides and severe storms. This unique setting is commonly afforded by the presence of a semi-protective barrier composed of lime sand shoals, locally associated with reefs and/or islands. The barrier commonly is dissected by tidal channels through which flow high velocity tidal currents. A shallow muddy lagoon lies in the lee of this barrier. The lagoon may be enormous as in the case of the Bahamas, relatively narrow and elongate as in the Persian Gulf, or very small as in the pocket embayments of Shark Bay. In such an arrangement, tidal flats are present as: 1) small flats atop and on the lee side of the emergent sand shoals of the barrier, and 2) large flats along the shoreline of the shallow lagoon (Fig. 5). Thus tidal flats occur in association with two separate carbonate accumulations, high energy sand bodies and low energy lime muds. A third type, which is less common in modern situations, is the association with reefs, especially the interior of large reef complexes.

Intertidal Environments. The intertidal zone, especially along rocky coasts and beaches is commonly a gradual transi-

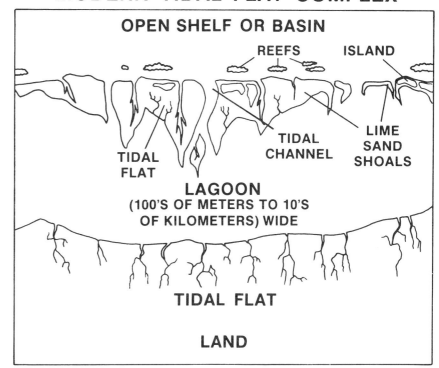

MODERN TIDAL FLAT COMPLEX

Figure 5
Plan view of the geometry of a modern tidal flat complex. Note that tidal flats can be present both adjacent to the land or in the lee of lime sand shoals.

tion from sea to land without much noticeable variation. On wide, gradually sloping tidal flats this zone can be the familiar gradual transition or a complex area of many subenvironments. At one end of the spectrum the flats have few, very shallow, short tidal creeks (Fig. 6). At the other end of the spectrum the flats are dissected by many tidal creeks flanked by levees. Slight depressions between the creeks are occupied by tidal ponds (which fill and partially empty during each rise and fall of the tide) and the whole complex is fronted by small beach ridges or erosional steps (Fig. 6). Perhaps in this case it would be better to refer to the whole zone as the "pond and creek belt" because some of the areas are dry most of the time (levees and beaches) whereas others are continuously submerged (ponds and creeks). These complications have led some workers (e.g., Ginsburg and Hardie, 1975) to despair of conventional terms and instead to relate different zones to the per cent of time that they are exposed rather than to their position.

On some tidal flats where there are many tidal creeks and noticeable relief between levee and tidal pond (about 1 m), as in the Bahamas, the true intertidal zone which lies between the levee and pond may comprise only 60 to 70% of the intertidal environment. In other areas such as the Persian Gulf, where there are fewer creeks and less relief, almost the whole flat is truly intertidal. The most important point to grasp is that numerous environments may exist in very close proximity not only perpendicular to the shoreline but parallel to it as well, so that in the geologic record rapid, local lithological variations are to be expected, both vertically and laterally, rather than a smooth succession of progressively shallower environments.

The tidal flat wedge is built up of fine grained sediments brought onto the flats from the adjacent offshore marine zone by storms rather than by daily tides. Large storms such as hurricanes which flood the flat with sheets of water, white with suspended sediment, are particularly effective. Shinn *et al.* (1969) have suggested that the tidal flat is a river delta turned wrong-side out, with the sea as the "river" supplying sedi-

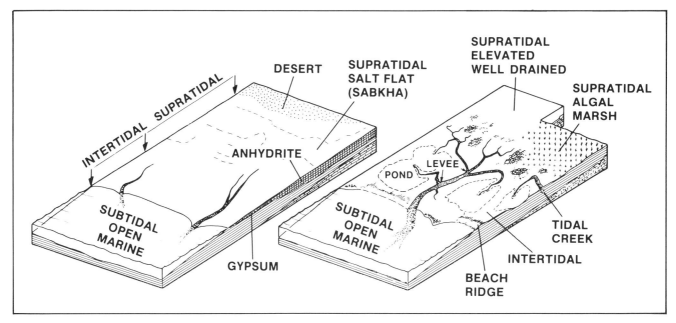

Figure 6

Block diagrams showing the major morphological elements of a tidal flat; left – a hypersaline tidal flat with few channels and bordering a very arid desert (similar to the modern Persian Gulf), right – a normal marine tidal flat with many channels and ponds and bordering an elevated well-drained area of low swamp algal marsh in a humid climate (similar to the modern Bahamas).

ment to the channeled flats as the "delta".

Sediments of the intertidal zone are characterized by three distinctive features, not found elsewhere: 1) algal mats, 2) irregular to even laminations (cryptalgal laminites), with fenestral porosity, and 3) desiccation features.

The algal mats are gelatinous to leathery sheets of blue-green algae which grow on top of the sediment surface. They are widely regarded as the signature of intertidal deposits. These mats are constructed solely or primarily by blue-green algae, which although photo-synthetic like other algal and higher plants, are prokaryotic and have much stronger affinities with bacteria than other eukaryotic forms. They are more correctly called cyanobacteria. It is probably more correct to refer to these mats as cyanobacterial mats or microbial mats (Bauld, 1981) but since the term algal mats is so entrenched in the literature I shall, for the time being, continue to use it in this paper. The mats may occur throughout the intertidal zone but their precise distribution is controlled by climate and the presence or absence of other organisms. The upper limit is controlled by climate; in arid areas they cannot grow above the high intertidal into the supratidal zone, whereas in areas of high rainfall

where the supratidal zone is moist or flooded for days at a time, mats are prolific. The lower limit is more variable and controlled by several factors. Garrett (1970) indicates that the main culprits are gastropods that eat algae. In areas of normal salinity, mats are prevented from developing below the middle intertidal zone because they are browsed by gastropods; in areas of hypersalinity (deadly for gastropods) mats grow down into the subtidal zone. In addition, algal mats will colonize only a temporarily or permanently stable bottom, and will not grow on shifting sand. Pratt (1982) points out that stromatolites are more common in post-Lower Ordovician rocks than generally realized, and that grazing by gastropods may be overemphasized as a limiting factor in their distribution. Rather it may be that substrate competition from various metazoans, together with increased rates of sedimentation during the Phanerozoic are more important controls.

Although the algal mats may themselves vanish with time, evidence of their presence during deposition remains because of the peculiar pores that they help to create, generally referred to as 'laminoid fenestrae'. These are irregular, elongate to mostly sub-horizontal sheet-like cavities (lofer-

ites or birds-eyes of some workers) with no obvious support and much larger than can be explained by grain packing. They are simply due to the fact that the mats are covered with sediment. The mats eventually rot away during burial, leaving voids as well as holes due to entrapped gas and mat shrinkage. Caution should be used when interpreting these structures, however, as similar features can be produced by submarine cementation of pellets, ooids and aggregate grains (Shinn, 1983).

Other sediments recording the presence of blue-green algal mats are the finely laminated carbonates (Fig. 7) ranging from stratiform and lightly crenulated to the familiar arched domes of stromatolites. These have been called cryptalgal (hidden, algal) laminations by Aitken (1967) in reference to the fact that the influence of algae in the rock-forming process is more commonly inferred than observed.

Lower Intertidal Zone. Much of the subtidal character remains evident in sediments from this part of the environment, and the deposits are commonly well burrowed and bioturbated. In hypersaline areas, however, the surface of the sediment is veneered with a thick algal mat, frequently broken into desiccation polygons. Beneath the mat, grains are

Figure 7
Cryptalgal laminites that have been mud-cracked. The intertidal unit of a shallowing-upward sequence in the Petit Jardin Fm. *(Upper Cambrian) on the south shore of the Port-au-Port Peninsula, Nfld. (Photo courtesy R. Levesque).*

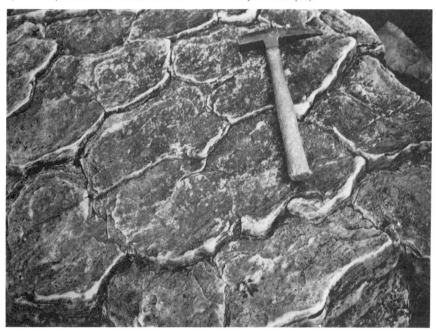

Figure 8
A bedding plane of mud-cracked polygons with the edges of each polygon curled up, probably because the algal mats in the *polygons shrivelled upon exposure and drying out. Near the top of a shallowing-upward sequence in the East Arm Fm., (Upper Cambrian), Bonne Bay, Nfld.*

exchange and which may accumulate as bars of skeletal lime sand. As the channels migrate these skeletal sands commonly form a basal lag deposit.

Middle and Upper Intertidal Zone. Sediments here are commonly light-grey to light-brown (oxidizing conditions), have good fenestral porosity (the variable growth of algal mats), are graded (episodic storm deposition) and are broken into desiccation polygons (prolonged exposure). There is generally good growth of algal mats throughout, and in the lower parts thick leathery mats are separated into desiccation polygons a few centimetres to a metre in diameter with cracks filled by lime mud in the lower parts (Fig. 8). In the central parts, thinner leathery mats have surfaces that are puffed up into blisters and convoluted into crenulated forms. In the upper parts, shriveled, crinkled and split mats are found. Bedding generally is irregular, especially in the upper zones, with mats alternating with graded storm layers.

In some settings, sediment in the upper intertidal zone dries out to form chips of lime mud while in others the sediment below the mats is lithified to a depth of as much as 10 cm.

Although sediments commonly are laminated throughout the intertidal environment, they are also riddled with small-scale tubules produced by insects and worms, and with larger tubes produced by crabs and other crustaceans.

Sediments also may be penetrated by the prolific shallow roots systems of salt tolerant plants.

Supratidal Environment. In all situations (including channel levees) this area is characterized by long periods of exposure. This is reflected by the lithification of storm deposited sediments in the form of surface crusts several centimetres thick, and which in turn are fractured into irregular polygons. These polygons may be pushed up by the force of crystallization (or by plant roots) to form 'teepees', or dislodged completely to form pavements of flat-pebble breccia. Clasts are commonly cemented on modern tidal flats by cryptocrystalline aragonite or calcite, and characteristically contain considerable (25 to 50%) fine crystalline dolomite.

blackened due to reducing conditions and altered by boring algae to peloids of lime mud.

Tidal ponds and the creeks that drain them on hypersaline tidal flats support the most prolific growth of algal mats anywhere on the flat. The algal mat flourishes in water depths greater than those in the immediate offshore area because of relatively elevated salinities in the ponds. On tidal flats where the salinity is closer to normal, marine tidal ponds are populated by a restricted but prolific fauna of foraminifers and gastropods and the gastropods prevent the growth of algal mats. Similarly, if tidal creeks are common in such areas, the channels are devoid of mats but do contain concentrations of the pond fauna that are washed out during total

LOW ENERGY INTERTIDAL -1

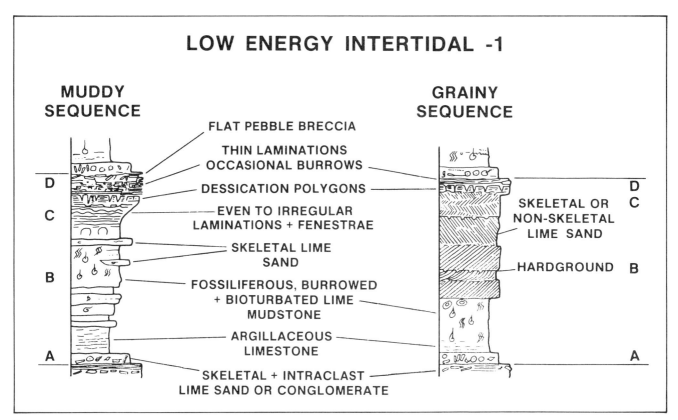

MUDDY SEQUENCE

GRAINY SEQUENCE

FLAT PEBBLE BRECCIA

THIN LAMINATIONS
OCCASIONAL BURROWS

DESSICATION POLYGONS

EVEN TO IRREGULAR
LAMINATIONS + FENESTRAE

SKELETAL LIME
SAND

FOSSILIFEROUS, BURROWED
+ BIOTURBATED LIME
MUDSTONE

ARGILLACEOUS
LIMESTONE

SKELETAL + INTRACLAST
LIME SAND OR CONGLOMERATE

SKELETAL OR
NON-SKELETAL
LIME SAND

HARDGROUND

Figure 9
Two hypothetical sequences with a low energy tidal flat unit developed on a low energy subtidal unit (left) and a high energy lime sand unit (right).

If the creek levees in the intertidal zone have built up above normal high tide level, they consist of hard, finely to very finely laminated sediment, extremely regular and composed of alternating layers of sediment and thin algal mats with excellent fenestral porosity.

The landward parts of the supratidal zone may grade into various terrestrial environments, the end members of which are: 1) areas of elevated, pre-existing bedrock and no sedimentation in which the surface of the rock is characterized by intensive subaerial diagenesis, and the development of caliche (calcrete crusts): 2) areas of contemporaneous sedimentation which grade between: a) low-lying environments in regions of high rainfall occupied by algal marshes, b) low-lying environments in arid, desert regions, characterized by evaporite formation, and c) well-drained zones, often slightly elevated and with little deposition.

Algal marshes, flooded by fresh water during the rainy season, are an ideal environment for the growth of algal mats and these mats are periodically buried by layers of sediment swept in during particularly intense storms. The preserved record is therefore one of thick algal mats alternating with storm layers. With progressive aridity the supratidal zone dries out. If the chlorinity of the groundwaters remains constantly above 39°/oo cementation, particularly by aragonite, is common. Cementation is most common if there is minor but consistent input of fresh water from inland to dilute the hypersaline groundwaters somewhat. If the chlorinity of the groundwaters remains constantly about 65°/oo then authigenic evaporites precipitate within the sediment below ground level. In this setting (called a supratidal sabkha, or salt flat in the Middle East; see "Continental and Supratidal (Sabkha) Evaporites", this volume) dolomitizaiton is also common in the subsurface, saline brine pools occur at the surface, and terrigenous wind-blown sand is common in the sediment.

In relatively well-drained zones the supratidal environment is a deflation surface occasionally cut by the upper reaches of tidal creeks, sometimes damp from rising capillary waters and covered by a thin film of algal mat.

Scoured and rippled sediment is common and clasts are sometimes encrusted with algae to form oncolites.

COMMON SEQUENCES WITH A LOW—ENERGY INTERTIDAL UNIT

Muddy and Grainy Sequences. These sequences developed either by progradation of the wide continental tidal flat or by shoaling the lime sand bodies that formed the barrier offshore (Fig. 9). The climate in the region of deposition was generally too wet or the ground-water table too low or diluted by fresh water to permit precipitation of evaporites.

The muddy sequences, those in which skeletal lime muds or muddy lime sands are the main subtidal unit, are well developed today in well-drained areas of Shark Bay where salinities are too high to permit development of a normal marine fauna as well as browsing of the algal mats by gastropods. Muddy sequences are also well developed in the tidal creek and pond belt of the Bahamas. These sequences are generally regarded as the 'classic' tidal flat sequences. The basal unit, if present, records the initial incursion of the sea onto land and as such is commonly coarse-grained, composed of clasts: all diagnostic of surf-zone deposition. The

Figure 10
Shallowing-upward sequences comprising lower intertidal-subtidal limestones (L) overlain by supratidal dolomites (D – Cryptalgal
laminites, sandy in part) in the Lyell Fm. at Takakkaw Falls, Yoho National Park, B.C. (Photo courtesy J.D. Aitken).

Figure 11
Numerous shallowing-upward sequences comprising thick subtidal oolite lime sands
and thin intertidal-supratidal cryptalgal laminites with fenestrate porosity: Petite Jardin Fm., Port-au-Port Peninsula, Nfld.

sequence (much like that a river), with a basal skeletal lime sand.

Where fenestrae are present they show a zonation: horizontal to laminated in the lower intertidal environments (smooth mat), irregular and, in some cases, vertical in the middle and upper intertidal environments (pustular, shriveled and crinkled mats).

Desiccation polygons are most common near the top, apparently coincident with cementation. The supratidal zone is characterized by very evenly laminated deposits or flat pebble breccias.

Readers interested in the finer details of such sequences are referred to studies by Laporte (1967) and Fischer (1964), the latter outlining and documenting a similar facies sequence but in reverse order, forming a deepening-upward sequence.

A common early Paleozoic subtidal lithology in these sequences is alternating thin-bedded limestone and shale, forming ribbon to parted limestones. Sepkowski (1981) notes that flat-pebble conglomerates are conspicuous in these Cambrian and Ordovician sequences and suggests that they may be formed by early seafloor lithification of true carbonate followed by erosion and redeposition as storm deposits. Thus the presence of flat-pebble conglomerates alone need not indicate tidal flat deposition. Expansion of infauna in middle Ordovician time led to greater burrowing in the subtidal zone and so reduced the opportunity for early lithification in younger sediments. Shoaling sequences also may be present off-shore from the low-energy tidal flat, on the lime-sand shoals. Here low energy tidal flats developed in the lee of the leading edge of the shoal once beach ridges were developed or currents had swept sand together to form islands. This will be reflected in the sequence as a sudden change from obvious high energy deposition to low energy intertidal deposition. The subtidal unit is generally well-sorted, oolitic, pelletoidal or skeletal lime sand (pelmatozoans are particularly common in the Paleozoic), with a few containing oncolites. Bedding is characteristically planar, with herringbone cross-laminations, large at the base and becoming smaller upwards, and individual bedding planes commonly covered with small-scale ripples. Early

subtidal unit is characteristically a bioturbated lime wackestone to packstone with a normal and diverse marine fauna, commonly containing stromatolites in deposits older than middle Paleozoic. In Precambrian and lower Paleozoic deposits the characteristic tidal flat features such as desiccation polygons, well-laminated sediments and fenestrae will occur at the base of the intertidal zones (Figs. 10 and 11). In deposits younger than middle Paleozoic, the prolific

browsing and burrowing activity in the lower intertidal zone (unless the water mass was hypersaline) has homogenized the sediment, so that the signature of intertidal deposition is recorded only within the mid and upper intertidal sediments.

If the tidal flat was extensively channeled, the migration of channels back and forth may also have destroyed some of the subtidal character, forming instead a partial fining-upward

220

cementation is characteristic, and so deposits contain many intraclasts of cemented lime sand, and bored surfaces. Once the shoals, or parts of the shoals are inactive they may be burrowed and much of the original cross-bedding may be destroyed.

The intertidal to supratidal units are similar to those described above but are generally relatively thin. If the shoal is exposed for a long time caliche and soil profiles commonly develop, reflected by brown irregular laminations, breccias, and thin shale zones.

An excellent description of muddy and grainy sequences can be found in Demicco and Mitchell (1982).

Stromatolite and Reef Sequences. One common variation on the model is the development of shoaling-upward sequences in association with abundant stromatolites in the lower Paleozoic/- Precambrian and with reefs in the Phanerozoic in general.

In Shark Bay, Western Australia, where all environments are hypersaline and so stromatolites abound, the interrelationship between stromatolite morphology and environment has only recently been documented (Hoffman, 1976). In the intertidal zone columnar to club-shaped forms up to one metre high

are found rimming headlands. In relatively high energy, exposed environments the relief of the columns is proportional to the intensity of wave action. The columnar forms grade laterally away from the headlands to the lower energy bights, where the stromatolites are more prolate and elongate oriented normal to the shoreline. In tidal pools digitate columnar structures abound.

These growth forms are the result of active sediment movement; algal mats only grow on stablized substrate, thus columns are nucleated upon pieces of rock, or cemented sediment; growth is localized there and does not occur on the surrounding shifting sands. Early lithification of the numerous superimposed layers of mat and sediment turns the structure into resistant limestone. Moving sand continuously scours the bases of the stromatolites. The mounds or pillars are largest in subtidal or lower intertidal environments and decrease in synoptic relief upwards, finally merging with stratiform mats in upper intertidal zones, above the zone of active sediment movement.

The resulting model sequence, summarized in Figure 12, is integrated from the Shark Bay example and the summary sequence of 200 or more shoaling sequences present in the Rocknest

Formation of middle Precambrian age near Great Slave Lake (Hoffman, 1976). In the intertidal zone deposits reflect higher energy than normal, indicating a more exposed shoreline. These sediments underlie and surround the domal (Fig. 13) to columnar stromatolites, which in turn grade up into more stratiform stromatolites, and finally into very evenly bedded structures. The supratidal unit of this sequence will be characterized by both desiccation polygons and flat-pebble breccias as well as occurrences of delicate branching stromatolites (Fig. 14), formed in supratidal ponds. Care should be taken in delineating this sequence because stromatolites that are similar to those in the intertidal zone also occur in the subtidal (Playford and Cockbain, 1976).

Shallowing-upward sequences are also common as the last stage of sedimentation in large bioherms, as numerous successions within the large back-reef or lagoonal areas of reef complexes, and as 'caps' on widespread biostromes. In this type of sequence the shoaling upward is first reflected in the subtidal unit itself, generally as a transition from large massive hemispherical colonial metazoans of the reef facies, to the more delicate, stick-like forms that are common in the shallow protected

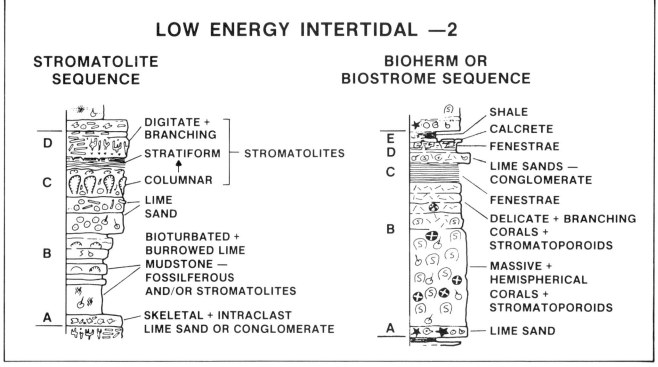

Figure 12
Two hypothetical sequences with a low energy intertidal unit developed in conjunction with stromatolites (left) and on top of a skeletal metazoan bioherm or biostrome (right).

Figure 13
A columnar to club-shaped stromatolite of *Late Cambrian age from the Petite Jardin Formation, Western Newfoundland.*

Figure 14
Digitate stromatolites from a shallowing- *upward sequence of Late Cambrian age Western Newfoundland.*

locations. These stick-like skeletons may be swept together on beaches at the edge of the tidal flat. As a result, the intertidal unit commonly contains a conglomerate within it, or at the base. The upper part of the sequence is otherwise similar to the others described. For a more detailed description of "reefy" sequences see studies by Havard and Oldershaw (1976), Read (1973), and Wong and Oldershaw (1980).

Carbonate-Evaporite Sequences (also see Kendall's paper in this volume). The other major variation on the model proposed at the beginning of this article is at the opposite end of the environmental spectrum, in the supratidal zone, in this case emergent in a very arid environment and flushed by hypersaline groundwaters. The hypersalinity of the groundwaters and attendant high evaporation results in the formation of authigenetic evaporites. This in turn raises the Mg^{++}/Ca^{++} ratio of the groundwaters and induces dolomitization of the sediment. The processes occur within the sediment, above the water table in the intertidal zone, and both above as well as below the water table in the supratidal zone. If the water compositions are barely within the field of gypsum precipitation, and there are fluctuations due to brackish flow of groundwater from the mainland, evaporites will occur in the form of isolated masses or crystals in the upper part of the sequence. If the groundwater compositions are continously well within the field of gypsum precipitation, growth of evaporite minerals takes place: 1) as a mush of gypsum crystals in the intertidal zone or as layers of anhydrite nodules, 2) as complex masses with a characteristic chickenwire texture, and 3) as layers contorted into enterolithic (intestine-like) shapes (Fig. 15). The important point, which is often ignored, is the growth of the evaporites within the sediment, as a diagenetic overprint on depositional facies of various environments. As evaporite growth is porphyroblastic, the host sediment commonly is displaced to intercrystalline areas and earlier fabrics are destroyed. Accompanying dolomitization is commonly intense with sediments of the intertidal and much of the subtidal zones affected.

Evaporites, however, are very soluble when exposed to percolating meteoric waters of low salinity and have a tendency to vanish from the record. Dissolution of the evaporites affects the sequences in several ways, but the most important is the formation of collapse breccias (Fig. 16). This collapse occurs when the evaporites dissolve leaving no support for the overlying sediments which subside into the void created by evaporite removal. Thus the top of the sequence is a breccia of marine limestone from the overlying sequence with a mixture of terrigenous sand, if a terri--genous facies capped the original sequence (Fig. 15). Isolated anhydrite crystals in lower parts of the sequence may be leached out, forming vugs which may be subsequently filled with quartz or chalcedony (usually length-slow). The dolomite, at least in the

222

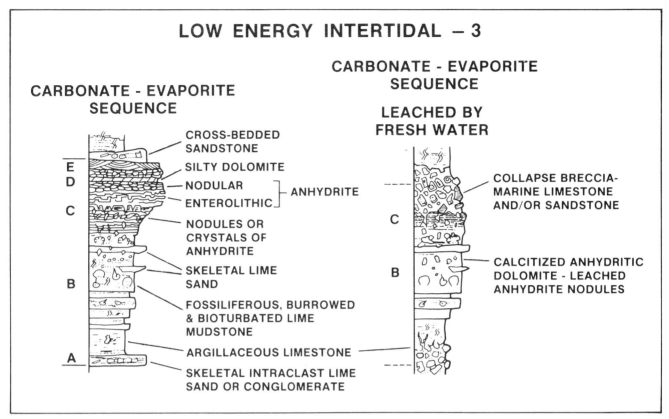

LOW ENERGY INTERTIDAL – 3

CARBONATE - EVAPORITE SEQUENCE

E
D — CROSS-BEDDED SANDSTONE
— SILTY DOLOMITE
— NODULAR ⎤
C — ENTEROLITHIC ⎦ ANHYDRITE
— NODULES OR CRYSTALS OF ANHYDRITE
— SKELETAL LIME SAND
B — FOSSILIFEROUS, BURROWED & BIOTURBATED LIME MUDSTONE
— ARGILLACEOUS LIMESTONE
A — SKELETAL INTRACLAST LIME SAND OR CONGLOMERATE

CARBONATE - EVAPORITE SEQUENCE
LEACHED BY FRESH WATER

C — COLLAPSE BRECCIA-MARINE LIMESTONE AND/OR SANDSTONE
B — CALCITIZED ANHYDRITIC DOLOMITE - LEACHED ANHYDRITE NODULES

Figure 15
Two hypothetical sequences with a low-energy intertidal unit and a supratidal unit developed under arid conditions; on the right the evaporties have been dissolved by percolating fresh waters.

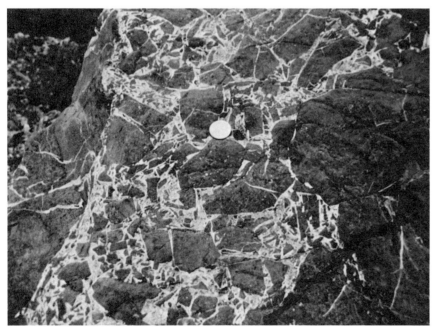

Figure 16
A collapse breccia of subtidal lime mudstone clasts in white calcite: caused by the solution of anhydrite at the top of a shallowing-upward sequence in the Shunda Fm. (Mississippian) at Cadomin, Alberta (Photo courtesy R.W. Macqueen).

upper part, is commoly altered to calcite, in the reverse of the dolomitization process (so-called "dedolomitization").

SEQUENCES WITH A HIGH ENERGY INTERTIDAL UNIT
In contrast to the low-energy intertidal (the tidal flat) the higher energy beach zone is not commonly recognized in the rock record. This may be partly because it resembles many subtidal grainstone deposits and hence is not obviously distinctive. Also, it is relatively narrow compared to the tidal flat, and has a lower preservation potential. Finally, the beach deposits lack the distinctive sedimentary features of the tidal flat. These very reasons illustrate the value of the concept of a shoaling-upward sequence as a guide. Once the potential for such a sequence is recognized in the geologic record, then one can concentrate on the search for subtle features that characterize beach deposition, which otherwise might go unnoticed.

Modern Carbonate Beaches
The sedimentology of carbonate beaches is nicely illustrated by Inden and Moore (1983). The beach is characterized by two zones: 1) the lower foreshore, usually below the zone of wave swash, and 2) the upper foreshore,

the zone of wave swash. Sediments of the lower foreshore are coarse grained, poorly sorted, have a matrix of lime mud (if it is available), and are characterized by small and large-scale festoon cross-bedding, oriented parallel to the shore-line and generally attributed to long-shore drift. The upper foreshore comprises thick-bedded, internally lam-inated, very well-sorted lime sands and gravels in planar cross-bedded accre-tionary beds that dip gently seaward (generally less than 15°). Sediments in the upper foreshore zone may have many open-space structures, the equi-valent of the fenestrae of muddy inter-tidal sediment called keystone vugs (Dunham, 1969) or microcaverns (Purser, 1972). These are due to gas escape, and in the geological record are partly to completely filled with cement.

As on the tidal flat, periodic exposure of beach deposits leads to cementation and partial subaerial diagenesis. The textures thus created are difficult to rec-ognize in the field but are important keys to recognizing the beach environ-ment. The two most important of these diagenetic phenomena are beachrock and calcrete.

Shallowing-Upward Sequence With a High-Energy Intertidal Unit
The lower two units of this type of sequence are similar to those described in the preceding sections on sequences with low-energy intertidal units (Fig. 17). In this sequence, however, characteris-tic subtidal carbonates grade upward into coarse-grained lime sands with all the characteristics of the lower and upper foreshore described above (Fig. 9). The supratidal unit may be present in the form of a thin shale (soil), but more commonly the supratidal environment is represented not by a deposit but by intensive diagenesis of the upper unit (cementation, dissolution, calcrete for-mation and microkarst). This is in many ways similar to the diagenetic overprint of other facies by supratidal evaporite formation.

Beachrock is composed of seaward-dipping beds of lime sand and gravel that are generally cross-laminated and occur in the lower intertidal to middle intertidal environment. It is formed by the precipitation of carbonate cement out of seawater or mixed seawater and rainwater. The beds of limestone may be up to one metre thick, are commonly jointed at right angles to the beach, and

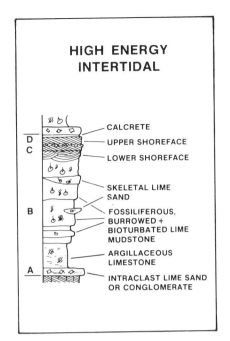

Figure 17
A hypothetical sequence with a high-energy intertidal unit: a beach, developed, in this case adjacent to a low energy subtidal environment.

are encrusted and/or bored by numer-ous intertidal organisms. Lithification disappears seaward and rarely extends higher than the intertidal zone. The partly cemented beds may be broken up and redeposited as conglomerates, made up of cemented sand clasts. In the upper parts of the intertidal zone cementation takes place in intergranular voids partly filled with air: the cements, as a result, are often stalactitic (more extensively developed on the under-sides of grains).

If exposed for long periods of time and if located in an environment where there is at least periodic rainfall, the lime sands will begin to undergo subaerial diagenesis (see Bathurst, 1975, for an extended discussion of subaerial dia-genesis). In addition the upper metre or so of such subaerially exposed deposits develop calcrete or caliche horizons which have many features that closely resemble those produced by laminar to laterally-linked stromatolites and onco-lites. These features are discussed in detail by James (1972) and Read (1976).

The supratidal unit in these sequen-ces may be any of the ones described above, although calcrete (caliche) is very common. Beaches may act as small barriers protecting supratidal ponds and flats so that the cap in such

sequences will be thin beds of lime mud (often dolomitized) with all of the assoc-iated supratidal features. One variation not found elsewhere occurs where the high energy surf zone of the overlying sequence erodes the top of the sequence down to the cemented por-tions, resulting in truncation layers or hardgrounds that separate sequences.

CYCLICITY
The shallowing-upward facies model is demonstrably one of the most useful concepts a sedimentologist can have when working with platform carbo-nates. In the rock record these sequen-ces occur on two scales; *small-scale,* or those less than a metre to a few 10s of metres in thickness at most, and *large-scale* or those many tens to hundreds of metres in thickness, and often likened to the Grand Cycles of Aitken (1967). In spite of the model's obvious utility, the precise mechanisms by which numer-ous sequences are generated remains obscure. Since the first edition of this paper (James, 1979) attention has shifted from the details of the model itself to the possible mechanisms of this accretion.

On the surface the explanation seems simple enough. Because the rate of car-bonate deposition exceeds the rate of platform subsidence or sea level rise, sediments will rapidly accrete to sea level. This is fine for a single shallowing-upward sequence, but how are repeated sequences formed and how do they exist over vast carbonate platforms?

Small-Scale Sequences
Current thinking on how repeated small-scale sequences are formed is succinctly summarized by Wilkinson (1982), who points out that there are currently two end-member models, both of which generate virtually identi-cal sequences (Fig. 18).

The *eustatic model* is one in which the rate of carbonate sedimentation is constant but the rate of subsidence or the absolute position of sea level are not constant and change in a non-uniform or periodic fashion. During periods of stability or slowly rising sea level (Figs. 18 and 2) the whole sequence pro-grades out across the shelf yielding a typical shallowing-upward or regressive sequence. This pattern is interrupted by a sudden and rapid sea level rise, flood-ing the platform (Fig. 18-3) and resulting in a short period of arrested- or

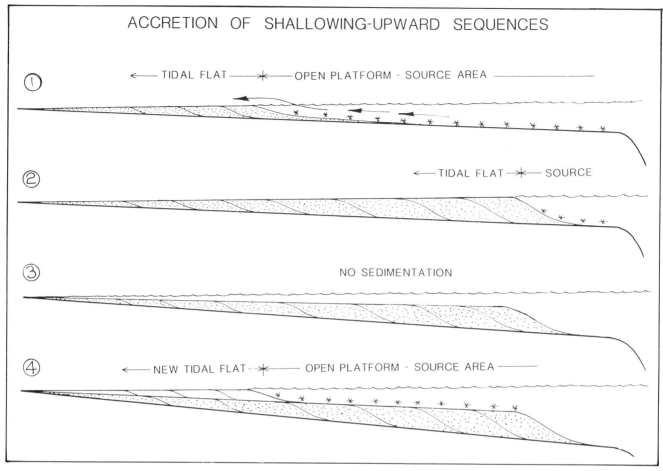

Figure 18
A sketch illustrating how two shallowing- *upward sequences can be produced by progradation of a tidal flat wedge. These* *general conditions apply in the case of both eustatic and autocyclic models.*

non-deposition. Sea level remains relatively stationary in this new position for a time (Fig. 18-4) and progradation begins again with a new shallowing-upward sequence forming over the old one. One variant of this model, calling for sudden platform-wide shifts in sea level has been formalized as "Punctuated Aggradational Cycles" by Anderson and Goodwin (1980).

While this model may be attractive as an explanation for large-scale shallowing-upward sequences it is less compelling for small-scale cycles, because each cycle must record either a sudden eustatic change in sea level or a tectonic event. If it is the cause of small-scale cycles then the problem becomes one of small-scale cyclicity on a global scale (Schwarzacher and Fischer, 1982) which is beyond the scope of this paper.

In the alternative *autocyclic model* the control is intrinsic and lies in the rate of carbonate sedimentation as controlled by source area (Fig. 18). The

model was first proposed by Ginsburg (1971) and has been used for many years as a model in field seminars at the University of Miami. Similar schemes have subsequently been suggested by Matti and McKee (1976), Mossop (1979) and Wilkinson (1982).

As in the eustatic model, sedimentation is envisaged as taking place on a gently inclined shelf under conditions of a gradually subsiding shelf or slowly rising sea level or some combination of both (Fig. 18-1). The source area of the sediments for the prograding wedge is the large subtidal area (Fig. 18-2), which is gradually reduced in size with seaward progradation. Eventually the situation is reached in which the source area is too small or too deep to provide sediments for the prograding wedge (Fig. 18-3), and so sedimentation stops. Relative sea level will continue to rise, however, and soon (Fig. 18-4) the whole platform will once again be subtidal and deep enough for

sediment production and the cycle will begin again.

The second and related problem concerns precisely how tidal flats prograded over the vast areas of epeiric or epicontinental seas. The stratigraphic record illustrates that two situations are common. In one, individual component lithologies of remarkably uniform thickness occur over wide geographical areas. For these sequences Ginsburg (1982) has proposed either continuously prograding tidal-flat wedges which would create time transgressive units and leave large areas exposed to prolonged meteoric diagenesis, or repeated deposition of thin areally-extensive single-event units by wind-driven "tides".

In other examples individual lithologies cannot be correlated between adjacent wells only kilometres apart (e.g., Wong and Oldershaw, 1980) or transitions from supratidal to intertidal to subtidal facies can be walked out in a

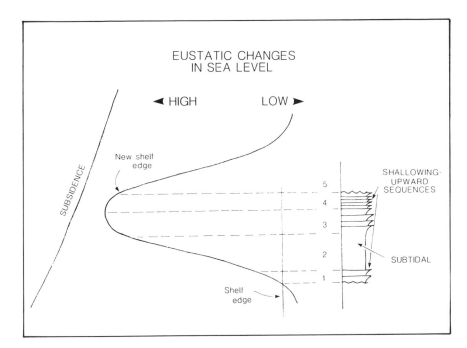

EUSTATIC CHANGES IN SEA LEVEL

◄ HIGH   LOW ►

Figure 19
A diagram illustrating how a large-scale shallowing-upward sequence is produced   *under conditions of slow platform subsidence and a uniform rise and fall in eustatic sea level.*

single bed over distances of only a few kilometres (e.g., Pratt and James, in press). The most appealing explanations for these carbonates is deposition on a platform dotted by a mosaic of exposed banks or islands separated by subtidal areas, with the whole complex shifting both laterally and vertically in response to hydrodynamic conditions through time.

This "island" model has an additional attraction in that a complex facies mosaic of numerous shallowing-upward sequences can be formed everywhere on a subsiding shelf at the same time, and is thus equally applicable to sequences formed under conditions of relatively uniform sea level or under conditions of sporadically changing sea level.

Large-Scale Sequences
These larger-scale packages, the upper parts of which are characterized by many small-scale sequences, are more complex, often involving an interplay of eustatic sea-level fluctuaitons, tectonics and platform geometry (see Aitken, 1978).

An example of how one such large-scale sequence might be developed is outlined in Figure 19. In this case, I have used the concepts formulated by the Exxon Seismic Stratigraphy Group (Vail

pers. commun., 1984). Here subsidence is viewed as constant, with the rise and fall of sea level more or less symmetrical.

(1) As sea level begins to rise slowly over the shelf edge the platform is flooded. During this initial stage carbonate accretion can outpace relative sea level rise and shallowing-upward sequences develop.

(2) During the prolonged period of relatively rapid sea level rise platform subsidence is ongoing and the tendency is to maintain deep water over the shelf. Depending on the rates of each, either subtidal conditions may develop, or if both are slow a few thick shallowing-upward sequences may form.

(3) The rate of sea level rise slows, and shallowing-upward sequences develop easily.

(4) Sea level falls slowly, but subsidence is also continuing, so the net effect is a still stand or close to it. Numerous, thin, shallowing-upward sequences develop with long periods of subaerial diagenesis between.

(5) Sea level begins to fall rapidly, outpacing subsidence and quickly dropping below the shelf edge, which is now higher because of the intervening carbonate accretion; the whole platform is exposed.

The result of this sequence of events is a large-scale shallowing-upward sequence, possibly with a few cycles at the base but mainly a lower half of subtidal sediments and an upper half of numerous shallowing-upward sequences. Obviously this is one sequence formed in response to a given set of variables but other sequences can be easily generated using similar principles. What is important is that a large-scale asymmetrical cycle can be produced by a uniform rise and fall of sea level.

SUMMARY
In the past there has been a natural tendency to use obvious sedimentary structures (e.g., mud cracks, stromatolites) to infer that parts of a carbonate sedimentary sequence had been periodically exposed. Individual structures, however, often have counterparts in other sedimentary environments (e.g., syneresis cracks, subtidal stromatolites) resulting, in many cases, in questionable paleoenvironmental interpretations. With all the data now available on carbonate strandline deposition we can frequently use what have become natural associations of sedimentary features in a vertical succession and define, with precision, specific strandline facies and their interrelationships.

While this is true for low-energy shoreline sequences, it is much less so for high-energy shoreline sequences. To bring all aspects of this type of facies model to comparable levels of understanding much more data is needed on exposed or high-energy intertidal environments, not from the modern, but from the rock record. In addition, the time is ripe to test whether or not the diagenetic features which result from periodic subaerial exposure (cementation, microkarst, calcrete) can be commonly recognized in ancient sequences.

In conclusion, the shallowing-upward sequence is one of the commonest, and with the wealth of sedimentary features, one of the easiest models to apply to the carbonate facies spectrum. As a *norm* this model is constructed from a synthesis of over 40 well-documented fossil examples, but our understanding of the meaning of most diagositc sedimentary features comes from half a dozen modern settings. Carbonate platform deposition, being what it is, a rapidly accreting system, once a shallowing-upward sequence has been recognized, one can *predict* that other similar sequences will be present vertically. If the sequences recur in an orderly fashion (are cyclic) then similar packages should be present laterally as well. Alternatively, if parts of the model are stacked in a less regular fashion, reflecting deposition as a complex of islands and banks on an open shelf, then specific laterally equivalent facies are less predictable. Recognition of the style of the model, which is in turn dependent upon the overall climatic (humid versus arid) and oceanographic (normal versus hypersaline) conditions, then allows the model to be both a *basis for physical and chemical interpretation* as well as a *guide* to the interpretation of other shallow water carbonates of the platform succession.

ACKNOWLEDGEMENTS

Various editions and parts of this manuscript have kindly been read by Roger Macqueen, Bob Stevens, David Kobluk, Brian Pratt, Bob Ginsburg, and Rick Sarg, and I thank them for their help.

REFERENCES

BASIC REFERENCES ON SHALLOWING-UPWARD CARBONATE SEQUENCES

Demicco, R.V., and Mitchell, R.W., 1982. Facies of the Great American Bank in the Central Appalachians. *In* Lyttle, P.T., ed., Central Appalachian Geology, NE-SE GSA'82 Field Trip Guidebook. American Geological Institute, p. 171-266.
An example of comparative sedimentology between Cambrian (Conococheague Limestone) – Ordovician (St. Paul Group) and modern tidal flat sequences with excellent photographs.

Fischer, A.G., 1964. The Lofer cyclothems of the Alpine Triassic. *In* Merriam, D.F., ed., Symposium on cyclic sedimentation. State Geological Survey of Kansas, Bulletin 169, v. 1, p. 107-149.
A regressive sequence of shallow water carbonates, superbly documented and illustrated.

Ginsburg, R.N., ed., 1975. Tidal deposits. New York, Springer-Verlag, 428 p.
The best all around, up-to-date reference on siliciclastic and carbonate tidal deposits.

Hoffman, P., 1973. Recent and ancient algal stromatolites: seventy years of pedagogic cross-pollination. *In* Ginsburg, R.N., ed., Evolving concepts in sedimentology. Bal-timore, MD., Johns Hopkins Press, p. 178-191.
A very readable essay on the evolution of our understanding of stromatolites and related sediments.

Irwin, M.L., 1965. General theory of epeiric clear water sedimentation. American Association of Petroleum Geologists, Bulletin, v. 49, p. 445-459.
The first integrated synthesis of shallow water carbonate sequences and their meaning.

Laporte, L., 1967. Carbonate deposition near mean sea-level and resultant facies mosaic: Manlius Formation (Lower Devonian) of New York State. American Association of Petroleum Geologists, Bulletin, v. 51, p. 73-101.
An extremely clear, well-written analysis of a shallowing-upward sequence.

Lucia, F.J., 1972. Recognition of evaporite-carbonate shoreline sedimentation. *In* Rigby, K.J., and Hamblin, K., eds., Recognition of ancient sedimentary environments. Society of Economic Paleontologists and Mineralogists, Special Publication 16, p. 160-192.
A well-written summary with many examples.

Merriam, D.F., ed., 1964. Symposium on cyclic sedimentation. State Geological Survey Kansas, Bulletin, 2 vols., 636 p.
40 papers, many of which are still basic references on cyclic sedimentary sequences.

Shaw, A.B., 1965. Time in stratigraphy. New York, McGraw-Hill, p. 1-71.
A pedantic, but thought-provoking analysis of epeiric sea carbonate sedimentation.

MODERN CARBONATE TIDAL FLATS

Bathurst, R.G.C., 1975. Carbonate sediments and their diagenesis: Developments in Sedimentology No. 12, New York, Elsevier, p. 178-209, p. 517-543.

Garrett, P., 1970. Phanerozoic stromatolites: non-competitive ecological restriction by grazing and burrowing animals. Science, v. 169, p. 171-173

Hardie, L.A., ed., 1977. Sedimentation on the modern carbonate tidal flats of Northwest Andros Island, Bahamas. Baltimore, MD., The Johns Hopkins Press, 202 p.

Hoffman, P., 1976. Stomatolite morphogenesis in Shark Bay, Western Australia. *In* Walter, M.R., ed., Stomatolites. New York, Elsevier, p. 261-273.

Kinsman, D.J.J., 1966. Gypsum and anhydrite of Recent Age, Trucial Coast, Persian Gulf. Second Symposium on Salt. Northern Ohio Geological Society, Cleveland, p. 1302-1326.

Logan, B.W., Davies, G.F., Read, J.F., and Cebulski, D., 1970. Carbonate sedimentation and environments, Shark Bay, Western Australia. American Association of Petroleum Geologists, Memoir 13, 223 p.

Logan, B.W., *et al.*, 1974. Evolution and diagenesis of Quaternary carbonate sequences, Shark Bay, Western Australia. American Association of Petroleum Geologists, Memoir 22, 358 p.

Kendall, C. St. G.C. and Skipwith, P.A. d'E., 1968. Recent algal mats of a Persian Gulf lagoon. Journal of Sedimentary Petrology, v. 38, p. 1040-1058.

Kendall, C. St. G.C. and Skipwith, P.A. d'E., 1969. Holocene shallow-water carbonate and evaporite sediments of Khor al Bazam, Abu Dhabi, Southwest Persian Gulf. American Association of Petroleum Geologists, Bulletin, v. 53, p. 841-869.

Purser, B.H., ed., 1973. The Persian Gulf. New York, Springer-Verlag, 471 p.

Shinn, E.A., 1983a. Tidal flat. *In* Scholle, P.A., Bebout, D.G., and Moore, C.H. eds., Carbonate depositional environments. American Association of Petroleum Geologists, Memoir 33, p. 171-211.

Shinn, E.A., Lloyd, R.M., and Ginsburg, R.N., 1969. Anatomy of a modern carbonate tidal flat, Andros Island, Bahamas. Journal of Sedimentary Petrology, v. 39, p. 1201-1228.

MODERN CARBONATE SAND BODIES

Ball, M.M., 1967. Carbonate sand bodies of Florida and the Bahamas. Journal of Sedimentary Petrology, v. 37, p. 556-591.

Hine, A.C., 1977. Lilly Bank, Bahamas: history of an active oolitic sand shoal. Journal of Sedimentary Petrology, v. 47, p. 1554-1583.

Halley, R.B., Harris, P.M., and Hine, A.C., 1983. Bank margin. *In* Scholle, P.A., Bebout, D.G., and Hine, A.C., eds., Carbonate depositional environments. American Association of Petroleum Geologists, Memoir No. 33, p. 463-507.

Imbrie, J. and Buchanan, H., 1965. Sedimentary structures in modern carbonate sands of the Bahamas. *In* Middleton, G.V., ed., Primary sedimentary structures and their hydrodynamic interpretation. Society of Economic Paleontologists and Mineralogists, Special Publication 12, p. 149-173.

LOW-ENERGY INTERTIDAL

The papers listed below are studies in which sequences or partial sequences have been well documented. I have omitted papers that simply mention that the rocks are deposited in very shallow environments.

1) Predominantly Muddy or Shaley Sequences

Aitken, J.D., 1966 Middle Cambrian to Middle Ordovician cyclic sedimentation, southern Rocky Mountains of Alberta. Bulletin of Canadian Petroleum Geology, v. 14, p. 405-411.

Aitken, J.D., 1978. Revised models for depositional grand cycles, Cambrian of the southern Rocky Mountains, Canada. Bulletin of Canadian Petroluem Geology, v. 26, p. 515-542.

Assereto, R. and Kendall, C.G. St. C., 1971. Megapolygons in Ladinian limestones of Triassic of Southern Alps: evidence of deformation by penecontemporaneous desiccation and cementation. Journal of Sedimentary Petrology, v. 43, 715-723.

Kahle, C.F. and Floyd, J.C., 1971. Stratigraphic and environmental significance of sedimentary structures in Cayugan (Silurian) tidal flat carbonates, Northwestern Ohio. Geological Society of American, Bulletin, v. 82, p. 2071-2098.

Macqueen, R.W. and Bamber, E.W., 1968. Stratigraphy and facies relationships of the Upper Mississippian Mount Head Formation, Rocky Mountains and Foothills, Southwestern Alberta. Bulletin of Canadian Petroleum Geology, v. 16, p. 225-287.

Mukherji, K.K., 1969. Supratidal carbonate rocks in the Black River (Middle Ordovician) Group of Southwestern Ontario, Canada. Journal of Sedimentary Petrology, v. 39, p. 1530-1545.

Reinhardt, J., and Hardie, L.A., 1976. Selected examples of carbonate sedimentation, Lower Paleozoic of Maryland. Baltimore, Maryland Geological Survey, Guidebook No. 5, 53 p.

Roehl, P.O., 1967. Stony Mountain (Ordovician) and Interlake (Silurian), facies analogs of recent low-energy marine and subaerial carbonates, Bahamas. American Association of Petroleum Geologists, Bulletin, v. 51, p. 1979-2032.

Trettin, H.P., 1975. Investigations of Lower Paleozoic geology, Foxe Basin, Northeastern Melville Peninsula, and parts of northeastern and Central Baffin Island. Geological Survey of Canada, Bulletin 251, 177 p.

Walker, K.R., 1972. Community ecology of the Middle Ordovician Black River Group of New York State. Geological Society of America, Bulletin, v. 83, p. 2499-2524.

2) Grainy Sequences

Lohmann, K.C., 1976. Lower Dresbachian (Upper Cambrian) platform to deep-shelf transition in Eastern Nevada and Western Utah: an evaluation through lithologic cycle correlation. In Robison, R.A., and Rowell, A.J., eds., Paleontology and depositional environments: Cambrian of Western North America. Geological Studies, Brigham Young University, v. 23, p. 111-122.

Smith, D.L., 1972. Stratigraphy and Carbonate petrology of the Mississippian Lodgepole Formation in Central Montana. Summarized in J.L. Wilson, 1975, Carbonate facies in geologic history. New York, Springer-Verlag, p. 283-285.

3) Reef or Stromatolite-rich Sequences

Donaldson, J.A., 1966. Marion Lake map area, Quebec-Newfoundland. Geological Survey of Canada, Memoir 338, 85 p.

Havard, C. and Oldershaw, A., 1976. Early diagenesis in back-reef sedimentary cycles, Snipe Lake reef complex, Alberta. Bulletin of Canadian Petroleum Geology, v. 24, p. 27-70.

Hoffman, P., 1976. Environmental diversity of middle Precambrian stromatolites. In Walter, M.R., ed., Stromatolites. New York, Elsevier, p. 599-613.

Mountjoy, E.W., 1975. Intertidal and supratidal deposits within isolated Upper Devonian buildups, Alberta. In Ginsburg, R.N., ed., Tidal deposits. New York, Springer-Verlag, p. 387-397.

Read, J.F., 1973. Carbonate cycles, Pillara Formation (Devonian), Canning Basin, Western Australia. Bulletin of Canadian Petroleum Geology, v. 21, p. 38-51.

Wong, P.K. and Oldershaw, A.E., 1980. Causes of cyclicity in reef interior sediments, Kabob Reef, Alberta. Bulletin of Canadian Petroleum Geology, v. 28, p. 411-425.

4) Carbonate-Evaporite Sequences

Fuller, J.G.C.M., and Porter, J.W., 1969. Evaporite formations with petroleum reservoirs in Devonian and Mississippian of Alberta, Saskatchewan and North Dakota. American Association of Petroleum Geologists, Bulletin, v. 53, p. 909-927.

Meissner, F.F., 1972. Cyclic sedimentation in Middle Permian strata of the Permian Basin, West Texas and New Mexico. In Elam, J.C., and Chuber, S., eds., Cyclic sedimentation in the Permian Basin, Second Edition. West Texas Geological Society, p. 203-232.

Schenk, P.E., 1969. Carbonate-sulfate-redbed facies and cyclic sedimentation of the Windsorian Stage (Middle Carboniferous), Maritime Provinces. Canadian Journal of Earth Sciences, v. 6, p. 1037-1066.

Shearman, D.J., and Fuller, J.G., 1969. Anhydrite diagenesis, calcitization, and organic laminites, Winnipegosis Formation, Middle Devonian, Saskatchewan. Bulletin of Canadian Petroleum Geology, v. 17, p. 496-525.
For an alternate interpretation see Wardlaw, N.C., and Reinson, G.E., 1971, American Association of Petroleum Geologists, Bulletin, v. 55, p. 1759-1787.

Wilson, J.L., 1967. Carbonate-evaporite cycles in lower Duperow Formation of Williston Basin. Bulletin of Canadian Petroleum Geology, v. 15, p. 230-312.

Wood, G.V., and Wolfe, M.J., 1969. Sabkha cycles in the Arab-Darb Formation of the Trucial Coast of Arabia. Sedimentology, v. 12, p. 165-191.

HIGH-ENERGY INTERTIDAL

There appear to be few well described beach sequences in carbonate successions.

Inden, R.F., 1974. Lithofacies and depositional model for a Trinity Cretaceous sequence. In Perkins, B.F., ed., Geoscience and man, Vol. VIII. Aspects of Trinity Geology. Baton Rouge, LA., Louisiana State University, p. 37-53.

Inden, R.F. and Moore, C.H., 1983. Beach. In Scholle, P.A., Bebout, D.G., and Moore, C.H., eds., Carbonate depositional environments. American Association of Petroleum Geologists, Memoir No. 33, p. 211-267.

Purser, B.H., 1972. Subdivision et interpretation des sequences carbonates. Mémoir Bureau Recherach Géologie et Mineralogie, v. 77, p. 679-698.

CYCLICITY

Anderson, E.J. and Goodwin, P.W., 1980. Application of the PAC hypothesis to limestones of the Helderberg Group. Society of Economic Paleontologists and Mineralogists, Guidebook, Eastern Section, 31 p.

Ginsburg, R.N., 1971. Landward movement of carbonate mud: new model for regressive cycles in carbonates (Abstract). American Association of Petroleum Geologists, Bulletin, v. 55, p. 340.

Ginsburg, R.N., 1982. Actualistic depositional models for the Great American Bank (Cambro-Ordovician). International Association of Sedimentologists, 11th International Congress on Sedimentology, Hamilton, Canada, Abstracts, p. 114.

Matti, J.C. and McKee, E.D., 1976. Stable eustacy, regional subsidence and a carbonate factory: self-generating model for onlap-offlap cycles in shallow water carbonate sequences (Abstract). Geological Society of America, Abstracts with Programs, v. 8, p. 1000-1001.

Mossop, G.D., 1979. The evaporites of the Ordovician Baumann Fiord Formation, Ellesmere Island, Arctic Canada. Geological Survey of Canada, Bulletin 298, 52 p.

Pratt, B.R. and James, N.P., in press. The St. George Group (Lower Ordovician) of Western Newfoundland: tidal flat island model for carbonate sediments in shallow epeiric seas. American Association of Petroleum Geologists, Bulletin.

Schwarzacher, W., and Fischer, A.G., 1982. Limestone-shale bedding and perturbations of the earth's orbit. In Einsele, G., and Seilacher, A., eds., Cyclic and event stratification. New York, Springer-Verlag, p. 72-96.

Wilkinson, B.R., 1982. Cyclic cratonic carbonates and phanerozoic calcite seas. Journal of Geological Education, v. 30, p. 189-203.

OTHER REFERENCES CITED IN TEXT

Aitken, J.D., 1967. Classification and environmental significance of cryptalgal limestones and dolomites with illustrations from the Cambrian and Ordovician of southwestern Alberta. Journal of Sedimentary Petrology, v. 37, p. 1163-1178.

Bauld, J., 1981. Geobiological role of cyanobacterial mats in sedimentary environments: production and preservation of organic matter. Bureau of Mineral Resources, Journal of Australian Geology and Geophysics, v. 6, p. 307-317.

Dunham, R.J., 1969. Early vadose silt in Townsend mound (reef), New Mexico. In Friedman, G.M., ed., Depositional environments in carbonate rocks: a symposium. Society of Economic Paleotologists and Mineralogists Special Publication 14, p. 139-181.

Ginsburg, R.N. and Hardie, L.A., 1975. Tidal and storm deposits, northwest Andros Island, Bahamas. In Ginsburg, R.N., ed., Tidal deposits. New York, Springer-Verlag, p. 201-208.

James, N.P., 1972. Holocene and Pleistocene calcareous crust (caliche) profiles; criteria for subaerial exposure. Journal of Sedimentary Petrology, v. 42, p. 817-836.

James, N.P., 1979. Facies models 10. Shallowing-upwards sequences in carbonates. In Walker, R.G. ed., Facies models. Geological Association of Canada, Geoscience Canada Reprint Series 1, p. 109-119.

Playford, P.E. and Cockbain, A.E., 1976. Modern algal stomatolites at Hamelin Pool, a hypersaline barred basin in Shark Bay, Western Australia. In Walter, M.R., ed., Stromatolites, developments in sedimentology. New York, Elsevier, p. 389-413.

Pratt, B.R., 1982. Stromatolite decline – a reconsideration. Geology, v. 10, p. 512-516.

Schlager, W., 1981. The paradox of drowned reefs and carbonate platforms. Geological Society of America, Bulletin, v. 92, p. 197-211.

Sepkowski, J.J., 1981. Flat-pebble conglomerates, storm deposits and the Cambrian bottom fauna. In Einsele, G., and Seilacher, A., eds., Cyclic and event stratification. New York, Springer-Verlag, p. 371-385. 371-385.

Shinn, E.A., 1983b. Birdseyes, fenestrae, shrinkage pores and loferites: a reevaluation. Journal of Sedimentary Petrology, v. 53, p. 619-628.

Read, J.F., 1976. Calcretes and their distinction from stromatolites. In Walter, M.R. ed., Stromatolites, developments in sedimentology. New York, Elsevier, p. 55-71.

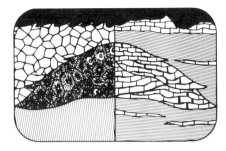

Reefs

NOEL P. JAMES
Department of Earth Sciences
Memorial University of Newfoundland
St. John's, Newfoundland A1B 3X5

INTRODUCTION

A reef, rising above the sea floor, is an entity of its own making – a sedimentary system within itself. The numerous, large calcium carbonate secreting organisms stand upon the remains of their ancestors and are surrounded and often buried by the skeletal remains of the many small organisms that once lived on, beneath, and between them.

Because they are built by organisms, fossil reefs (Fig. 1) are storehouses of paleontological information and modern reefs are natural laboratories for the study of benthic marine ecology. Also, fossil reefs buried in the subsurface contain a disproportionately large amount of our oil and gas reserves compared to other types of sedimentary deposits. For these reasons, reefs have been studied in detail by paleontologists and sedimentologists, perhaps more intensely than any other single sedimentary deposit, yet from two very different viewpoints. This paper is an integration of these two viewpoints. I shall concentrate less on the familiar trinity of back-reef, reef, and fore-reef, but more on the complex facies of the reef proper.

Since the first edition of Facies Models, there has been much new information on both the sedimentology and paleontology of reefs. The model itself has been presented elsewhere (James, 1983) and amplified using numerous examples from the modern and fossil record. In this present version the model remains unchanged but many of the underlying concepts and implications that flow from it have been revised and/or enlarged.

Figure 1
A patch reef of Lower Cambrian age exposed in sea cliffs along the northern shore of the Strait of Belle Isle, Southern Labrador.

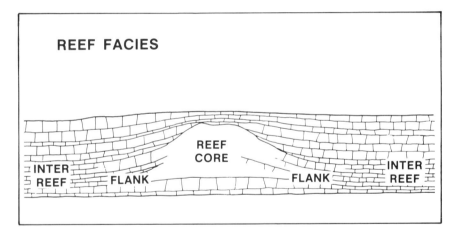

Figure 2
A sketch illustrating the three major reef facies in cross-section.

THE ORGANISM-SEDIMENT MOSAIC

Reefs can generally be subdivided into three facies (Fig. 2).
1) *Reef-core facies* - massive, unbedded, frequently nodular and lenticular carbonate comprising skeletons of reef-building organisms and a matrix of lime mud.
2) *Reef-flank facies* - bedded lime conglomerates and lime sands of reef-derived material, dipping and thinning away from the core.
3) *Inter-reef facies* - normal shallow-water, subtidal limestone, unrelated to reef formation, or fine-grained siliciclastic sediments.

A useful, non-generic term for such a structure is "bioherm" – for discussion of this and other reef terminology the interested reader is referred to papers by Dunham (1970), Heckel (1974), Longman (1981), and James (1983).

Reef facies are best differentiated on the basis of several independent criteria including: 1) the relationship between, and relative abundance of large skeletons and sediments, i.e., the type of reef limestone, 2) the diversity of reef-building species, and 3) the growth form of the reef builders.

Types of Reef Limestone
The present state of any thriving reef is a delicate balance between the upward

230

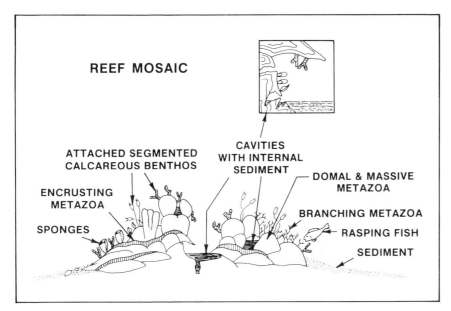

Figure 3
A sketch illustrating the different aspects of   *the organism/sediment mosaic that comprises a reef.*

growth of large skeletal metazoans, the continuing destruction of these same organisms by a host of rasping, boring, and grazing organisms, and the prolific sediment production by rapidly growing, shortlived, attached calcareous benthos (Fig. 3).

The large skeletal metazoans (e.g., corals) generally remain in place after

death, except when they are so weakened by bio-eroders that they are toppled by storms. The irregular shape and growth habit of these reef-builders result in the formation of roofed-over cavities inside the reef that may be inhabited by smaller, attached calcareous benthos. These cavities may also be partly or completely filled with fine-

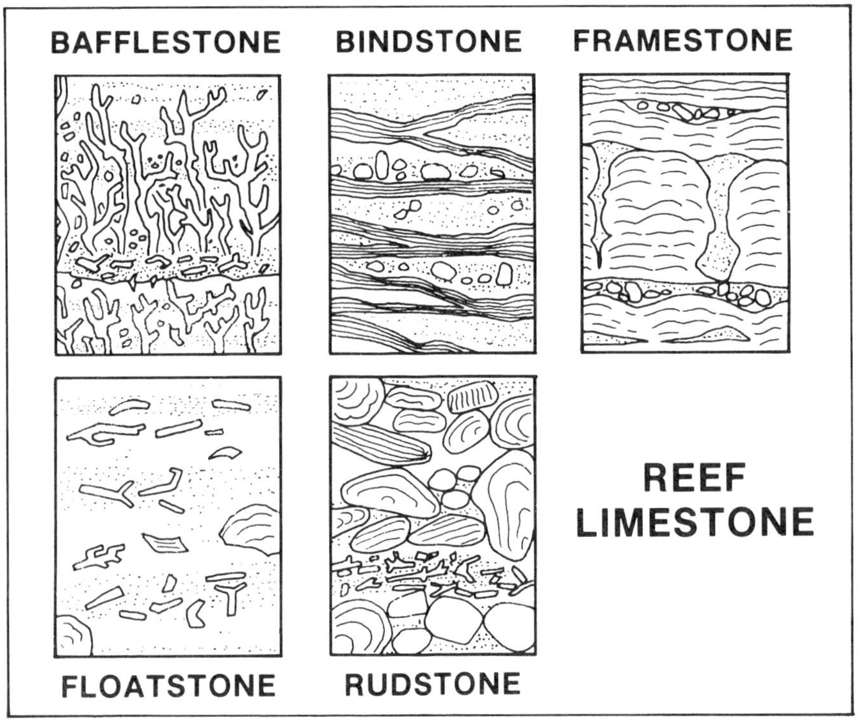

grained "internal" sediment. Encrusting organisms grow over dead surfaces and aid in stabilizing the structure. Branching reef-builders frequently remain in place, but just as commonly are fragmented into sticks and rods by storms to form skeletal conglomerates around the reef.

Most reef sediment is produced by the post-mortem disintegration of organisms that are segmented (crinoids, calcareous green algae) or non-segmented (bivalves, brachiopods, foraminifers). These organisms grow in the many nooks and crannies between larger skeletal metazoa. The remainder of the sediment is produced by various taxa that erode the reef: boring organisms (worms, sponges, bivalves) produce lime mud and rasping organisms that graze the surface of the reef (echinoids, fish) produce copious quantities of carbonate sand, and silt. This material is deposited around the reefs as an apron of sediment, and it also filters into the growth cavities to form internal sediment, which is characteristically geopetal.

Many different classifications have been proposed for the resulting reef carbonates, but the most descriptive and widely accepted is a modification of Dunham's (1970) classification of lime sand mud-rocks proposed by Embry and Klovan (1971) (Fig. 4). They recognize two kinds of reef limestone, allochthonous and autochthonous. The allochthonous limestones are the same as the finer grained sediments, but with two categories added to encompass large particles. If more than 10% of the particles in the rock are larger than 2 mm and they are matrix supported it is a *Floatstone*; if the rock is clast supported it is a *Rudstone.* The autochthonous limestones are more interpretative; *Framestones* contain in-place, massive fossils that formed the supporting framework; *Bindstones* contain in-place, tabular, or lamellar fossils that encrusted or bound the sediment together during deposition; *Bafflestones* contain in-place, stalked fossils that trapped sediment by baffling.

Many reefs also appear to be preferential sites for precipitation of synsedimentary cement (James and Choquette, 1983), and are hard limestone just below the growing surface. The abundance of early cement in many fossil reefs has led some workers to

BAFFLESTONE **BINDSTONE** **FRAMESTONE**

FLOATSTONE **RUDSTONE** **REEF LIMESTONE**

Figure 4
An interpretative sketch of the different types of reef limestone recognized by Embry and   *Klovan (1971). Autochthonous reef limestones are in the upper row, while allochthonous reef sediments are in the lower row. .*

view these buildups as "cementation reefs" rather than biological – sedimentological structures.

Diversity Amongst Reef-Building Metazoans

Relative abundance of different organisms is one of the easiest observations that can be made on a fossil reef, and so potentially one of the most useful. Although intuitively there should be a simple relationship between diversity and environment, recent thinking suggests that this relationship is complex and not straightforward. It seems that diverse faunas (Fig. 5) probably develop when conditions for growth are optimum, i.e., nutrients are in adequate supply and daily chemical and physical stresses are low, *but* when the community is not able to reach competitive equilibrium because of frequent population reduction. If not disturbed, a community will reach competitive equilibrium where a few species dominate, i.e., low diversity. The relative diversity in such settings is probably a complex interplay between frequency of disturbance, population growth rate and nutrient supply. Many of the above concepts have been derived from the study of coral reefs (Connell, 1978) where high diversity is the result of growth in an environment which is relatively nutrient-poor and subject to periodic catastrophic disturbance by tropical storms. (Woodley *et al.*, 1982). An implication of this concept is that we should expect patchiness and evidence of extensive fragmentation and debris formation in the most diverse of fossil reef communities.

Low diversity reef communities are of at least 3 types: 1) those at competitive equilibrium; 2) new communities (those that have moved into a new environment; and 3) those communities subject to severe and continuing chemical and physical stress. Among the factors most likely to stress modern and fossil reef-building communities are: 1) temperature and salinity fluctuations – most modern and likely most ancient reef-builders grow or grew best in tropical sea water of normal salinity; 2) intense waves and swell – the skeletons of most reef-builders will be broken or toppled by strong wave surge: 3) low light penetration – in modern reef-building organisms rapid calcification takes place because light dependent symbionts

Figure 5
A shallow-water (1 m deep) living reef, composed of branching (left), foliose (centre) and hemispherical (centre) corals, off Gouldin Cay, Bahamas.

take over some of the bodily functions of the host; and 4) heavy sedimentation - all reef-builders are sedentary filter-feeders or micro-predators and water filled with fine-grained sediments would clog the feeding apparatus.

The Growth Form of Reef-Building Metazoans

The relationship between organism shape and environment is one of the oldest and most controversial topics in biology and paleobiology. In terms of reef-building metazoans, observations from the rock record (Figs. 6 and 7) of the interrelationship between organisms and surrounding sediments, combined with studies of modern coral distribution on tropical reefs, allow us to make some generalizations about form and environment that are useful in reef facies analysis (Fig. 8).

The limitations of applying these concepts directly to fossil reefs has recently been emphasized by Stearn (1982), who pointed out that no general patterns are applicable to all reefs, and that variations in shape are the result of the interaction between environmental factors with the genetically dicatated growth pattern of the organism. Observations on growth form must be used in conjunction with other parameters, and

are most useful in providing additional information when dealing with low diversity communities.

THE SPECTRUM OF REEF TYPES

Reefs can develop just about anywhere in the carbonate facies spectrum. As isolated structures they are dispersed across shallow carbonate platforms but they also grow, outpacing subsidence, in slope and basinal settings. As more contiguous elements they commonly form long, sinuous barriers along the margins of the same platforms, close to land along the edge of narrow shelves or as halos around positive structural elements.

Modern reefs are best developed and most successful on the windward sides of shelves, islands, platforms and atolls where wind and swell are consistent and onshore. The asymmetry of many ancient reefs and distribution of sediment facies suggests that this was so in the past as well. The reason for the preferential development of reefs on the windward side is by no means established but sedimentation is likely the most important. Shallow water reef-building species characteristically produce abundant fine sediment, yet the major reef-builders, because they are filter feeders and micropredators, are

Figure 6
*An accumulation of branching corals (Por-
ites porites) and bivalves in a late Pleistocene
reef, Barbados, W.I.*

Figure 7
*A small patch of domal shaped corals (Diplo-
ria sp. in cross-section on a cliff exposure of
Late Pleistocene reef limestone, Barbados,
W.I.*

GROWTH FORM AND ENVIRONMENT OF REEF BUILDING SKELETAL METAZOA			
GROWTH FORM		**ENVIRONMENT**	
		Wave Energy	Sedimentation
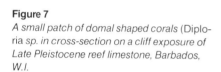	Delicate, branching	low	high
	Thin, delicate, plate-like	low	low
	Globular, bulbous, columnar	moderate	high
	Robust, dendroid, branching	mod-high	moderate
	Hemispherical, domal irregular, massive	mod-high	low
	Encrusting	intense	low
	Tabular	moderate	low

Figure 8
*The growth form of reef-building metazoans
and the types of environments in which they
most commonly occur. From James (1983).*

intolerant of fine sediment. The open ocean and windward locations are the only places in which fine sediment is continuously swept away.

Reefs form a natural breakwater when they grow into the zone of onshore waves and swells and create a relatively quiet environment in the lee of the reef crest. Commonly, this restriction significantly changes water circulation on the shelf, platform, or lagoon behind the reef. In such a marginal location, the symmetrical reef facies model comprising a reef-core facies surrounded on all sides by reef-flank facies is no longer discernable. Instead facies are more asymmetrically distributed with the reef-core facies flanked on the windward side by the fore-reef facies and on the leeward side by the platform facies (often called the back-reef facies).

High-Energy Reefs
In these high energy settings the reef is distinctly zoned (Fig. 9)

Reef Crest Zone. This is the highest part of the reef at any stage in its growth, and if in shallow water, it is that part of the reef top that receives most of the wind and wave energy. Composition of the reef crest depends upon the degree of wind strength and swell. In areas where wind and swell are intense, only those organisms that can encrust, generally in sheet-like forms, are able to survive. When wave and swell intensity are only moderate to strong, encrusting forms still dominate but are commonly also bladed or possess short, stubby branches. In localities where wave energy is moderate, hemispherical to massive forms occur, with scattered clumps of branching reef-builders. The community is still of low diversity. The lithologies formed in these three cases would range from bindstones to framestones.

Reef Front Zone. This zone extends from the surf zone to an indeterminate depth, commonly less than 100 metres, where the zone of abundant skeletal growth grades into sediments of the fore-reef zone. Direct analogy between modern reefs, especially Caribbean reefs, and ancient reefs is difficult because today the sea floor from the surf zone to a depth of about 12 metres is commonly dominated by the robust

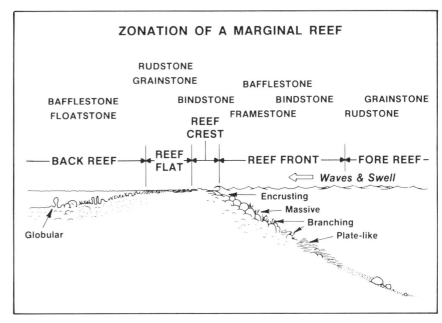

Figure 9
Cross-section through a hypothetical, zoned, marginal reef illustrating the different reef zones, spectrum of different limestones produced in each zone, and environment of different reef-building forms.

branching form *Acropora palmata*, a species which developed only recently in the late Cenozoic. Such branching forms are rarely found in ancient reefs. Instead, the most abundant forms are massive, laminar to hemispherical skeletons, forming framestones and sometimes bindstones.

The main part of this zone supports a diverse fauna with reef-builders ranging in shape from hemispherical to branching to columnar to dendroid to sheet-like. Accessory organisms and various niche dwellers such as brachiopods, bivalves, coralline algae, crinoids, and green segmented calcareous algae (Halimeda), are common. On modern reefs where the reef-builders are corals, this zone commonly extends to a depth of 30 metres or so. The most common rock type formed in this zone would still be framestone, but the variety of growth forms also leads to the formation of many bindstones and bafflestones.

Below about 30 metres wave intensity is almost non-existent and light is attenuated. The response of many reef-building metazoans is to increase their surface area, by having only a small basal attachment and a large but delicate plate-like shape. Rock types from this zone look like bindstones, but binding plays no role in the formation of these rocks and perhaps another term is needed.

The deepest zone of growth of coral and green calcareous algae on modern coral reefs is about 70 metres. The lower limit may depend upon many factors, perhaps one of the most important being sedimentation, especially in shale basins which border many reefs. This lower limit should therefore be used with caution in the interpretation of fossil reefs.

Sediments on the reef front are of two types: 1) internal sediments within the reef structure, generally lime mud giving the rocks a lime mudstone to wackestone matrix, and 2) coarse sands and gravels in channels running seaward between the reefs. These latter deposits have rarely been recognized in ancient reefs.

As a result of numerous observations on modern reefs it appears that most of the sediment generated on the upper part of the reef front and on the reef crest is transported episodically by storms up and over the top and accumulates in the lee of the reef crest. Sediments on the intermediate and lower regions of the reef front, however, are transported down to the fore-reef zone only when it is channelled by way of passes through the reef.

Reef Flat Zone. The reef flat varies from a pavement of cemented, large skeletal debris with scattered rubble and coralline algae nodules in areas of intense waves and swell, to shoals of well-washed lime sand in areas of moderate wave energy. Sand shoals may also be present in the lee of the reef pavement. Vagaries of wave refraction may sweep the sands into cays and islands. These obstructions in turn create small protected environments very near the reef crest. Water over this zone is shallow (only a few metres deep at most) and scattered clumps of reef-building metazoans are common. The resulting rock types range from clean skeletal lime grainstones to rudstones.

Back Reef Zone. In the lee of the reef flat, conditions are relatively tranquil and much of the mud formed on the reef front comes out of suspension. This, coupled with the prolific growth of mud and sand-producing bottom fauna such as crinoids, calcareous green algae, brachiopods, and ostracodes, commonly results in mud-rich lithologies. The two most common growth habits of reef-builders in these environments are stubby, dendroid forms, often bushy and knobby, and/or large globular forms that extend above the substrate to withstand both frequent agitation and quiet muddy periods.

The rock types characteristic of this environment are bafflestones or floatstones to occasional framestones with a skeletal wackestone to packstone matrix. In some reefs there are beds of nothing but dis-articulated branches in lime mud (e.g., *Amphipora* limestones of the Upper Devonian), but there is little evidence of much transport.

Fore-Reef Facies
This facies consists of thin to thick and massively bedded skeletal lime grainstones to lime packstones which are composed of whole or fragmented skeletal debris, blocks of reef limestones and skeletons of reef-builders. These grade basinward into shales or lime muds. In contrast to the reef facies, the beds are rarely dolomitized.

It should be remembered that this high-energy zonation, although most commonly observed on platform margin reefs, is also developed in on-platform isolated reefs and in reefs from slope or basinal settings that rise into the zone of breaking waves.

Low Energy Reefs
As wave energy decreases, so the style

of reef growth changes; distinctive zonation becomes less noticeable, shape of the reef building organisms is different and relative diversity decreases. The relationship between wave energy and reef type has been summarized for modern reefs by Geister (1980) and for fossil reefs by Wilson (1975) and is shown in Figure 10. Lower energy situations are also characterized by sluggish water exchange and so these changes may be amplified by variations in water salinity and nutrient content.

As a result most isolated reefs or patch reefs on carbonate platforms are poorly zoned and more like the ideal reef in Figure 1. They are generally circular to elliptical to irregular in plan and may be large enough to enclose a lagoon themslves. Each reef is zoned with respect to depth, similar to the reef front in higher energy reefs.

Finally, in some settings, reefs as described above do not occur. These settings include the very inner parts of shallow platforms, the deeper (many 10s of metres) lagoons, and those platforms or parts of platforms covered by water of elevated or depressed salinity. There are, however, accumulations of carbonate sand and/or mud, built by organisms that are very close to reefs in composition. In modern seas these range from sea-grass banks to skeletal sand shoals, often bound by algae, to broad banks of corals and algae. Although not common today, these

structures are an important part of the fossil carbonate spectrum and must be integrated into the reef model.

Reef Mounds
Many Phanerozoic carbonate sequences contain structures that some workers call reefs, some call mounds, and some call banks. They lack many of the characteristics we ascribe to reefs yet were clearly rich in skeletal organisms and had relief above the sea floor. The origin of these structures, which I have called *reef mounds* (Fig. 11), has probably caused more discussion than any other topic in the literature on reefs (Heckel, 1974).

Reef mounds are, as the name suggests, flat lenses to steep conical piles with slopes of up to 40° consisting of poorly sorted bioclastic lime mud with minor amounts of organic boundstone. With this composition they clearly formed in quiet water environments and from the rock record appear to occur in preferred locations: 1) arranged just downslope on gently-dipping platform margins (Fig. 12); 2) in deep basins; and 3) spread widely in tranquil reef lagoons or wide shelf areas. When viewed in section, reef mounds display a similar facies sequence in each case (Wilson, 1975) (Fig. 11).

Stage 1. Basal bioclastic lime mudstone to wackestone pile - muddy sediment with much bioclastic debris but no baf-

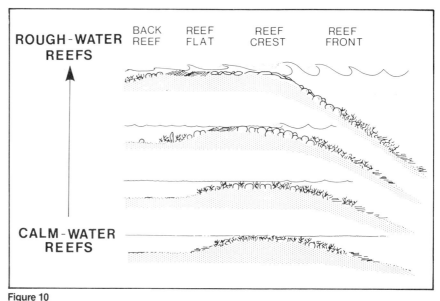

Figure 10
Generalized diagram of the different zonations expected from reefs growing under conditions ranging from calm water to rough water; see Figure 8 for growth forms.

fling or binding organisms.

Stage 2. Lime mudstone or bafflestone core - the thickest part of the mound, consisting of delicate to dendroid forms with upright growth habits in a lime mudstone matrix. The limestone is frequently brecciated, suggesting partial early lithification, dewatering and slumping, and contains stromatactis. Each geologic age has its own special fauna that forms this stage: Lower Cambrian - archaeocyathans; Middle to Lower Ordovician - sponges and algae; Middle Ordovician, Late Ordovician, Silurian, Early Carboniferous (Mississippian) – bryozoans; Late Carboniferous (Pennsylvanian) and Early Permian – platy algae; Late Permian to Middle Triassic – sponges and algae; Late Triassic – large fasciculate dendroid corals; Late Jurassic – lithistid sponges; Cretaceous – rudist bivalves.

Stage 3. Mound cap – a thin layer of encrusting or lamellar forms, occasional domal or hemispherical forms, or winnowed lime sands.

The massive, commonly well-bedded carbonates that flank the reef mounds comprise extensive accumulations of debris and chunks of archaeocyathans, pelmatozoans, fenestrate bryozoans, small rudists, dendroid corals, stromatoporoids, branching red algae or tabular foraminifers along with wholly to partly lithified lime mudstone. Volumetrically these flank beds may be greater than the core itself and almost bury it (Fig. 13).

Carbonate Mud Mounds
One end member of the reef mound category that deserves special attention is a group of structures called either Waulsortian mounds (from the name of a village in Belgium) or more commonly, carbonate mud mounds. These puzzling structures may be just as large and have sides just as steep as reef mounds, but they possess *no* large skeletons. They are made up only of crinoid fragments, sponge spicules or scattered bryozoans that together make up no more than 1/4 of the rock, the rest being lime mud (for a recent review see Pratt, 1982). These mud mounds seem to

Figure 13 ▶
Muleshoe bioherm, a 60 m high reef mound of Late Missippian age exposed along the western escarpment of the Scaremento Mountains, New Mexico.

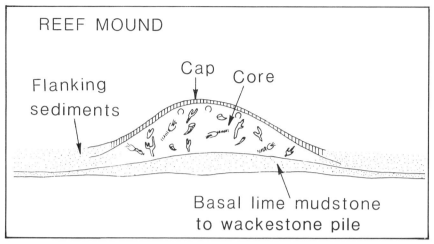

Figure 11
Cross-section through a hypothetical reef *mound illustrating the geometry of the different facies.*

Figure 12
Massive reef limestone (right) of the Nansen Formation (Permo-Pennsylvanian) extending downward and basinward into dark, argillaceous limestones of the Hare Fiord Formation (left). Arrows point out small reef mounds developed on the seaward slopes of the reef front, western side of Blind Fiord, Ellesmere Island, N.W.T.

236

Figure 14
Stromatactis, *sub-horizontal layers of calcite spar illustrating irregular digitate tops and* *smooth bottoms, from Gros Morbe, reef-mound facies, Silurian West Point reef complex, Gaspé, Quebec.*

occur almost exclusively in deep water on carbonate slopes, and are not as common as on-shelf buildups.

Almost all workers have commented on the striking similarity of these structures regardless of their age, which suggests a common origin for all of them. There are, however, no obvious modern analogues. Structures that come closest are seagrass-stabilized, shallow-water mudbanks or deep-water lithoherms, but both also have considerable differences. The localization of the mud is probably some combination of *in situ* production, baffling, and binding by a variety of organisms, among which algae and cyanobacteria are the most important. The seafloor topography is clearly aided by rapid seafloor lithification.

Central to their genesis is the presence of *"Stromatictis"* (Fig. 14) which consists of masses of calcite-filled cavities which have a digitate roof and a flat floor commonly formed by geopetal sediment. This spar occurs in swarms and has a reticulate distribution (see Bathurst, 1982 for an extended discussion). It is clear that cavity development is penecontemporaneous with deposition, but its origin is still a mystery. Current hypotheses include: 1) dewatering,

2) compaction, slumping, and down slope creep of consolidated but unlithified sediment, 3) cementation and/or binding of sediment by algae to form crusts followed by erosion, and 4) decay and collapse of organic tissue (especially sponges) after partial lithification.

A final unsettling fact is that these mud mounds are almost entirely a Paleozoic phenomenon. They range in age from middle Cambrian to late Jurassic but confirmed stromatactis is found only in Paleozoic buildups. There is no clear answer as to why they do not occur in late Mesozoic and Cenozoic carbonates.

Stromatolite Reefs
During the Precambrian and earliest Paleozoic, prior to the appearance of herbivorous metazoans, stromatolites formed impressive build-ups (Fig. 15). These stromatolite complexes clearly had relief above the sea floor and in terms of morphology were surprizingly similar to later skeletal reefs. Mostly developed in shelf margin settings some exhibit excellent lateral zonation (Hoffman, 1974) while others clearly developed in a series of well-defined stages in which stromatolites had different

growth forms (Cecile and Campbell, 1978). Although there has been much study of Precambrian stromatolites, much less attention has been paid to their role in the formation of reefs or reef mounds.

STAGES OF REEF GROWTH
While the composition of the reef core and the different facies can be determined from both modern and ancient examples, information as to the stages of reef growth can only come from the rock record.

It has long been recognized that there is an ecological succession in many Paleozoic reefs (Lowenstam, 1950), i.e., the replacement of one community of reef-building organisms by another as the reef grew. A synthesis by Walker and Alberstadt (1975) of reefs ranging in age from Early Ordocician to Late Cretaceous suggests that a similar community succession is present in reefs throughout the Paleozoic and Mesozoic. Application of this concept to Cenozoic reefs (Frost, 1977), which are dominated by scleractinian corals (the reef-builders in today's oceans), allows us to equate ancient reef community succession with observations on modern reef communities with some measure of confidence.

The reason for this ecologic succession is at present a topic of much debate. Some workers feel that the con-

Figure 15
A large stromatolite mound of Proterozoic age Kuuik Formation, Kilohigok Basin, Northwest Territories. Photograph by M. Cecile.

trol is extrinsic, reflecting a progressive replacement of deep-water communities by shallower water ones as the reef grows to sea level and into more turbulent water; however, there is often abundant evidence that the first two stages are developed in shallow water. Other workers feel that the control is intrinsic, reflecting a natural succession as the organisms gradually alter the substratum and change the energy flow pathways as the community develops; nevertheless, there is abundant evidence of increasing water turbulence as the structure grows.

THE MODEL

The reef model is an integration of information from the modern and the fossil record. The major stumbling block that makes the generation of a model difficult, the ever-changing character of the reef-building fauna and flora through time, is resolvable if the concept of community succession is used as a basis. In the model four separate stages of reef growth are recognized, and these stages, along with the types of limestone, relative diversity of organisms and growth-form of reef-builders in each, are summarized in Figure 16.

1) *Pioneer (Stabilization) Stage.* This first stage is most commonly represented by a series of shoals or other accumulations of skeletal lime sand composed of pelmatozoan or echinoderm debris in the Paleozoic and Mesozoic, and plates of calcareous green algae in the Cenozoic. The surfaces of these sediment piles are colonized by algae (calcareous green), plants (sea grasses) and/or animals (pelmatozoans) that send down roots or holdfasts to bind and stabilize the substrate. Once stabilized, scattered branching algae, bryozoans, corals, soft sponges and other metazoans begin to grow between the stabilizers.

2) *Colonization Stage.* This second stage is relatively thin when compared to the reef structure as a whole, and reflects the initial colonization by reef-building metazoans. The rock is generally characterized by few species, sometimes massive or lamellar forms but more commonly monospecific coppices or clumps of branching forms (Fig. 8). In Cenozoic reefs the one characteristic common to all corals in this stage of reef growth is that they are able to get

STAGES OF REEF GROWTH

STAGE	TYPE OF LIMESTONE	SPECIES DIVERSITY	SHAPE OF REEF BUILDERS
DOMINATION	bindstone to framestone	low to moderate	Laminate encrusting
DIVERSIFICATION	framestone (bindstone) mudstone to wackestone matrix	high	domal massive lamellar branching encrusting
COLONIZATION	bafflestone to floatstone (bindstone) with a mud stone to wackestone matrix	low	branching lamellar encrusting
STABILIZATION	grainstone to rudstone (packstone to wackestone)	low	skeletal debris

Figure 16
A sketch of the four divisions of the reef-core facies with a tabulation of the most common types of limestone, relative species diversity and shape of reef-builders found in each stage.

Figure 17
The diversification stage of an Upper Devonian reef, comprising domal stromatoporoids, and domal to branching tabulate corals, Blue Fiord Formation, south side of Eids Fiord, Ellesmere Island, N.W.T.

rid of sediment and clean their polyps, and so are able to grow in areas of high sedimentation. The branching growth form creates many smaller subenvironments or niches in which numerous other attached and encrusting organisms can live, forming the first stage of the reef ecosystem.

3) *Diversification Stage* This third stage, usually represented by the bulk of the reef mass, is the point at which most pronounced upward-building towards sea level occurs and easily definable,

lateral facies develop. The number of major reef-building taxa is usually more than doubled, and the greatest variety in growth habit is encountered (Fig. 17). With this increase in form and diversity of framework and binding taxa comes increased nestling space, i.e., surfaces, cavities, nooks and crannies, leading to an increase in diversity of debris-producing organisms..

Once a reef reaches the diversification stage, and sometimes even earlier in the colonization stage, the structure is frequently high enough above the sur-

237

Figure 18

A small patch reef built by bryozoans, corals, and stromatoporoids, Long Point Formation *(Middle Ordovician), Port-au-Port Peninsula, Newfoundland.*

Figure 19

Reef and reef-flank deposits (R) ca. 100 m thick (Peechee Formation) of Upper Devo- *nian age in the Flathead Range, southern Rocky Mountains, Alberta. Photograph courtesy B. Pratt.*

rounding sea floor to affect water circulation and thus to alter sedimentation patterns. At this point not only are surrounding sedimentary environments altered but the reef itself develops a zonation, because its margins now reach from shallow to deep water. This zonation is, as outlined in an earlier section, dependent upon wave energy.

4) *Domination (Climax) Stage.* The change to this stage of reef growth is commonly abrupt. The most common lithology is a limestone dominated by only a few taxa with only one growth habit, generally encrusted to laminated. Most reefs show the effects of surf at this stage, in the form of beds of rudstone.

While these four stages are the norm, some reefs only display the upper two or three stages. Careful investigation, however, usually reveals that the reefs began growth on a hardground or lithified substrate.

The Complete Reef Structure

Reefs in the rock record vary widely in size. A complete Ordovician (Fig. 18) or Cretaceous reef, formed by a variety of organisms and displaying several stages of growth, may be only as large as a single coral head in a Devonian, Jurassic, or Pleistocene reef, kilometres long and hundreds of metres thick (Fig. 19).

While some large reefs display all 4 stages of development, most are internally stratified (Fig. 20) to form a series of superimposed or stacked reefs. Individual episodes of reef growth are commonly separated by periods of exposure, reflected in the rock by intensive diagenesis, calcrete horizons, karst, shales (paleosols) or by periods of non-deposition as indicated by hardgrounds, borings, or manganese and phosphate-impregnated bedding planes. When reef growth begins again after a hiatus, because the surfaces are both hard and elevated, it starts at the diversification stage, and so only two stages are present in the next package. Some workers tend to regard these unconformity-bounded layers as the different stages of reef growth which they are not. The different stages of reef growth are found as separate units between these layers.

THE MODEL AS A FRAMEWORK OR GUIDE FOR OBSERVATIONS

Reefs

The reef facies model is predicated on the assumption that a full spectrum of reef-building organisms are present. We see a full spectrum in the tropical oceans today, but this was not the case for much of the Phanerozoic. The critical element that is often missing, and without which the four stages of development in the reef core cannot occur, is the presence of skeletal metazoans that secrete large robust, branching, hemispherical or tabular skeletons. Without them the reef cannot exist in the zone of constant turbulence, usually wave induced, because smaller and more delicate forms would be broken and swept away (unless submarine cementation is very rapid, pervasive, and near-surface). This zone of turbulence is the optimum area for growth and diversity because sediment is constantly removed, water is clear, and nutrients are constantly swept past the sessile organisms. Such large skeletal metazoa were present only at certain times during the Phanerozoic (Fig. 21), and each period has its own specialized group of frame-builders: 1) Middle and Upper Ordovician – bryozoa, stromatoporoids, tabulate corals; 2) Silurian and Devonian – stromatoporoids, atabulate corals; 3) Late Triassic – corals, stromatoporoids; 4) Jurassic – corals, stromatoporoids; 5) Upper Cretaceous – rudist bivalves; and 6) Oligocene, Miocene, Plio-Pleistocene – scleractinian corals. A more detailed review of these reefs during specific periods is given by James (1983).

Although reefs are found in platform margin, on-shelf, and basinal settings during these periods, reef mounds also develop, but only in environments which were inimical to the growth of larger metazoans. At many times during the Phanerozoic, however, the large frame-building metazoans were absent, and during these periods reef mounds were the only buildups in the facies spectrum (Fig. 21).

When viewed against the backdrop of the general reef facies model, I think of reef mounds as half-reefs or incomplete reefs because they represent only stages one, two, and occasionally four of the model. These structures did not develop the other upper stages either

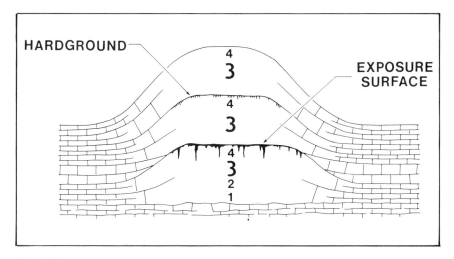

Figure 20

Sketch illustrating a large reef composed of a series of smaller stacked reefs, each with several growth stages (see Fig. 16) and each separated by exposure surfaces or hardgrounds. The size of the numbers represents relative thickness of the stages.

because the environment was not conducive to the growth of large skeletal metazoans or because these larger metazoans simply did not exist at the time when the structure formed.

THE MODEL AS A BASIS FOR INTERPRETATION

The model dictates that reefs, especially large ones, have a series of growth stages. When interpreting an individual structure, which will differ from the model in a variety of ways, special attention must be paid to this internal stratigraphy. If some stages are missing, are thicker or thinner than should be expected, or if the sequence is inverted, then these differences should be a clear signal that extrinsic factors such as sea level fluctuations or changes in subsidence rates occurred during reef growth. In this way the reef is a much more sensitive indicator of such changes than surrounding subtidal facies.

On a larger scale a major question that often arises is whether the reef grew all at once and stood high above contemporaneous basinal strata only to be subsequently buried, or whether it grew in increments, with intervening periods of subaerial exposure and possible continuing off-reef deposition, and so never rose very much above the surrounding sea floor. These two hypotheses not only interpret the reef differently but dictate how surrounding basinal deposition took place and the nature of early diagenesis, and can only

be separated by careful study of reef stratigraphy.

Finally reefs and associated platform facies are commonly important hydrocarbon reservoirs. In exploitation of these resources it is critical to determine whether the reservoir is a more or less uniform structure with good vertical as well as horizontal permeability or whether it is broken into a series of layers with poor vertical connection because of permeability barriers such as hardgrounds or paleosols (shales).

THE MODEL AS A PREDICTOR

If we know the age of a sequence of carbonate rocks and we have some idea of the paleotectonic setting then we can predict, from limited data, the types of reefs we might expect to be present in a shelf or platform setting.

Times When a Complete Spectrum of Reef Builders was Present

The edge of the shelf or platform is occupied by a marginal reef. The reef is well zoned if the front is steep and wave action intense because of the gradation from rough surface waters down the reef front into progressively more tranquil conditions. Zonation is weak, however, if the reef front slopes gradually seaward and the seas are relatively quiet. Patch reefs can occur anywhere on the platform and each is zoned with respect to depth. Reef mounds are found on the linear shallow parts of the shelf in areas of normal salinity but turbid water. Reef mounds also occur at

240

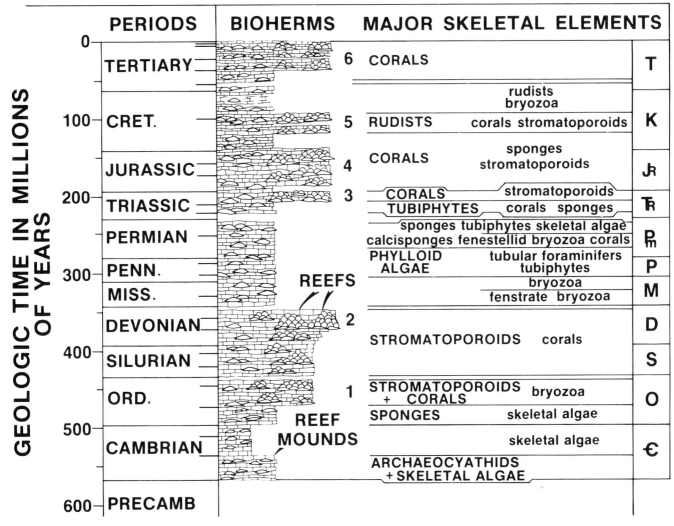

Figure 21

An idealized stratigraphic column representing the Phanerozoic and illustrating times when there appear to be no reefs or bioherms (gaps), times when there were only reef mounds and times when there were both reefs and reef mounds. The numbers indicate different associations of reef-building taxa discussed in the text. (From James, 1983).

depth, in front of the barrier reef down on the reef front or fore-reef.

Patch reefs or reef mounds commonly form a very widespread lithofacies compared to the barrier reef. The stratigraphic thickness of these reefs is dependent upon the rate of subsidence: if subsidence rate is low, reefs are thin; if subsidence rate is high, reefs may be spectacular in their thickness.

Times When Only Delicate, Branching and Encrusting Metazoa Prevail

The margin of the shelf or platform is normally a complex of oolitic or skeletal (generally crinoidal) sand shoals and islands. The only reef structures are reef mounds which occur below the zone of active waves down on the seaward slopes of the shelf or platform and if

conditions are relatively tranquil behind the barrier, on the shelf itself. Mounds may display a zonation, with ocean-facing sides in shallow water armoured with accumulations of fragmented and winnowed skeletal debris.

Not only can we predict adjacent facies with some confidence but given only small outcrops or pieces of core we can, within limits, predict the style of the reef in question. For example, a core composed of lime mudstone to floatstone with scattered bryozoans and stromatactis from a Mississippian sequence, when viewed from the point of view of the model clearly points to a reef mound, which since reefs proper did not form at this time, may be 10's to 100's of metres thick. A similar rock in a Silurian sequence, while predicting a

similar structure if surrounded by slope or inner shelf strata, would in most other cases predict that the sample is from the basal part of a large reef. Alternatively a small Devonian outcrop, composed of a bafflestone of fasciculate stromatoporoids grading up into a framestone of large tabulate corals and many different stromatoporoids would predict that a massive reef should lie above.

The clear limitations of the model are, however, when using small samples. Reefs are generally large and heterogeneous structures so that a drill core for example may pass through areas of sediment between large skeletons, a very likely possibility since 30% to 40% of modern reefs are sediment or pore space, and so give a false picture of the true deposit.

SUMMARY

The purpose of this article has been to marry the sedimentological and paleontological approaches to the study of reefs into a single facies model, useful to both disciplines. This model is an integration of data from two very different sources: from the modern sea floor, predominantly in the horizontal dimension; and from the rock record, predominantly in the vertical dimension as recorded in mountain exposures, quarries and drill core.

To alter and refine this model more information is needed from two areas. We must learn more about the succession of organisms and sediments that underlies the living surface of modern reefs, by drilling into these reefs. We must learn more about reefs from those parts of the stratigraphic record where reefs are known to occur, but have been little studied – the Precambrian, the Lower Paleozoic, and Cenozoic.

The trend in the past has been to compare specific fossil reefs with modern reefs. The comparative approach has just begun on fossil reefs, to compare and contrast the sedimentology and paleoecology of reefs formed by different groups of organisms at different times in geologic history.

ACKNOWLEDGEMENTS

Bob Stevens and David Kobluk kindly read earlier versions of this manuscript and helped clarify many of my ideas. Different parts of the systhesis have grown out of numerous field trips and discussions with Bob Ginsburg and Jim Wilson. By critically editing this version Roger Walker helped greatly in restructuring the basis for the model.

REFERENCES

FOSSIL REEFS – GENERAL

The following references are either syntheses or books with numerous papers on reefs of different ages.

Copper, P., 1974. Structure and development of early Paleozoic reefs. Proceedings of the Second International Coral Reef Symposium, Great Barrier Reef Committee, Brisbane, v. 6, p. 365-386.
An essay on the different types of Paleozoic reefs.

Dunham, R.J., 1970. Stratigraphic reefs versus ecologic reefs. American Association of Petroluem Geologists Bulletin, v. 54, p. 1931-1932.

A thoughtful essay on what is, and is not, a reef – from the point of view of a sedimentologist.,

Harris, P.M., ed., 1983. Carbonate buildups: a core workshop. Society of Economic Paleontologists and Mineralogists, Core Workshop No. 4, 593 p.
Twenty one, short, succinct, well-illustrated papers on reefs of all ages, with emphasis on depositional facies and diagenesis.

Hartman, W.D., Wendt, J.W., and Widenmayer, F., 1980. Living and fossil sponges. University of Miami, Sedimenta VIII, Comparative Sedimentology Laboratory, 274 p.
Notes for a short course with good descriptions of fossil reefs whose major components are sponges.

Heckel, P.H., 1974. Carbonate buildups in the geologic record: a review. In Laporte, L.F., ed., Reefs in time and space. Society of Economic Paleontologists and Mineralogists, Special Publication 18, p. 90-155.
A detailed account of reefs or buildups, their classification, zonation with geologic time and general models for reef formation – more than you ever wanted to know about fossil reefs and an excellent set of references.

Laporte, L.F., ed., 1974. Reefs in time and space. Society of Economic Paleontologists and Mineralogists, Special Publication 18, 256 p.
Seven papers dealing with various aspects of modern and fossil reefs.

Toomey, D.F., ed., 1981. European fossil reef models. Society of Economic Paleontologists and Mineralogists, Special Publication 30, 545 p.
Seventeen papers with emphasis on latest Paleozoic, Mesozoic, and Cenozoic structures; an excellent reference.

Walker, K.R., and Alberstadt, L.P., 1975. Ecological succession as an aspect of structure in fossil communities. Paleobiology, v. 1, p. 238-257.
The first half of this paper outlines succinctly the main theme of ecological succession in fossil reefs.

Wilson, J.L., 1975. Carbonate facies in geologic history. New York, Springer-Verlag, 471 p.
The best overall reference, especially chapters II, IV to VII, XI and XIII.

EXAMPLES OF FOSSIL REEFS

The following papers contain examples of different reef types from the fossil record and/or syntheses of reef types from specific periods; others can also be found in the general references above.

Precambrian

Cecile, M.P., and Campbell, F.H.A., 1978. Regressive stromatolite reefs and asso-

ciated facies, middle Goulburn Group (Lower Proterozoic) in Kilohigok Basin, N.W.T.; an example of environmental control of stromatolite forms. Bulletin of Canadian Petroleum Geology, v. 26, p. 237-267

Hoffman. P., 1974. Shallow and deep-water stromatolites in lower Proterozoic platform-to-basin facies change, Great Slave Lake, Canada. American Association of Petroleum Geologists, Bulletin, v. 58, p. 856-867.

Cambrian

Ahr, W.M., 1971. Paleoenvironment, algal structures and fossil algae in the Upper Cambrian of central Texas. Journal of Sedimentary Petrology, v. 41, p. 205-216.

James, N.P., and Kobluk, D.R., 1978. Lower Cambrian patch reefs and associated sediments, southern Labrador, Canada. Sedimentology, v. 25, p. 1-32.

James, N.P., and Debrenne, F., 1980. Lower Cambrian bioherms; pioneer reefs of the Phanerozoic. Acta Palaeontologica Polonica, v. 25, p. 655-668.

James, N.P., 1981. Megablocks of calcified algae in the Cow Head Breccia, western Newfoundland: vestiges of a lower Paleozoic continental margin. Geological Society of America, Bulletin, v. 92, p. 799-811.

Ordovician

Pitcher, M., 1961. Evolution of Chazyan (Ordovician) reefs of eastern United States and Canada. Bulletin of Canadian Petroluem Geology, v. 12, p. 632-691.

Pratt, B.R. and James, N.P., 1982. Cryptalgal metazoan bioherms of early Ordovician age in the St. George Group, Western Newfoundland. Sedimentology, v. 29, p. 543-569.

Ross, R.J., Jaanuson, V., and Freidman, I., 1975. Lithology and origin of Middle Ordovician calcareous mudmound at Meiklejohn Peak, southern Nevada. United States Geological Survey, Professional Paper 871, 45 p.

Toomey, D.F., and Nitecki, M.H., 1979. Organic buildups in the Lower Ordovician (Canadian) of Texas and Oklahoma. Fieldiana, New Series, v. 2, 181 p.

Webby, B.D., 1984. Ordovician reefs and climate: a review. In Bruton, D.L., ed., Apsects of the Ordovician system. Paleontological Contributions from the University of Oslo, No. 8, p. 87-98.

Silurian

Bourque, P.A. and Gignac, H., 1983. Sponge-constructed stromatactic mud mounds, Silurian of Gaspé Québec. Journal of Sedimentary Petrology, v. 53, p. 521-532.

Fisher, J.H., ed., 1977. Reefs and evaporites – concepts and depositional models. American Association of Petroleum Geologists, Studies in Geology 5, 196 p.

Heckel, P., and O'Brien, D., eds., 1975. Silurian reefs of Great Lakes Region of North America. American Association of Petroleum Geologists, Reprint Series 14, 243 p.

Lowenstam, H.A., 1950. Niagaran reefs in the Great Lakes areas. Journal of Geology, v. 58, p. 430-487.

Narbonne, G.M., and Dixon, O.A., 1984. Upper Silurian lithistid sponge reefs on Somerset Island, Arctic Canada. Sedimentology, v. 31, p. 25-51.

Riding, R., 1981. Composition, structure, and environmental setting of Silurian biohems and biostromes in northern Europe. *In* Toomey, D.F., ed., European fossil reefs models. Society of Economic Paleontologists and Mineralogists, Special Publication 30, p. 41-85.

Scoffin, T.P., 1971. The conditions of growth of the Wenlock reefs of Shropshire, England. Sedimentology, v. 7, p. 173-219.

Shaver, R.H., *et al.,* 1978. The search for a Silurian reef model; Great Lakes Area. Indiana Geology Survey, Special Report No. 15, 36 p.

Devonian

Davies, G.R., ed., 1975. Devonian reef complexes of Canada, I and II. Canadian Society of Petroleum Geologists, Reprint Series 1, 229 p. and 246 p., respectively.

Klovan, J.E., 1974. Development of western Canadian Devonian reefs and comparison with Holocene analogues. American Association of Petroleum Geologists, Bulletin, v. 58, p. 787-799.

Krebs, W., 1971. Devonian reef limestones in the eastern Rhenish Shiefergebirge. *In* Muller, G., and Friedman, G.M., eds., Sedimentology of parts of central Europe. Frankfurt, Kramer, p. 45-81.

Krebs, W., and Mountjoy, E.W., 1972. Comparison of central European and western Canadian Devonian reef complexes. Montreal, Canada, 24th International Geological Congress, Section 6, p. 294-309.

Mountjoy, E.W., 1980. Some questions about the development of upper Devonian carbonate buildups (reefs), western Canada. Bulletin of Canadian Petroluem Geology, v. 28, p. 315-344.

Mountjoy, E.W., and Riding, R., 1981. Foreslope *Renalcis*-stromatoporoid bioherm with evidence of early cementation, Devonian Ancient Wall reef complex. Sedimentology, v. 28, p. 299-321.

Schmidt, V., McDonald, D.A., and McIlreath, I.A., 1980. Growth and diagenesis of Middle Devonian Keg River cementation reefs, Rainbow Field, Alberta. *In* Halley, R.B., and Loucks, R.G., eds. Carbonate reservoir rocks. Society of Economic Paleontologists and Mineralogists, Core Workshop 1, p. 43-64.

Playford, P.E., 1980. Devonian "Great Barrier Reef" of the Canning Basin, Western Australia. American Association of Petroleum Geologists, Bulletin, v. 64, p. 814-840.

Mississippian

Bolton, K., Lane, H.R., and LeMone, D.F., eds., 1982. Symposium on the paleoenvironmental setting and distribution of the Waulsortian facies. El Paso Geological Society and University of Texas at El Paso, 202 p.

Cotter, E., 1965. Waulsortian-type carbonate banks in the Mississippian Lodgepole Formation of central Montana. Journal of Geology, v. 73, p. 881-888

Lees, A., 1964. The structure and origin of the Waulsortian (Lower Carboniferous) "reefs" of west-central Eire. Philosophical Transactions of the Royal Society of London, Series B, No. 740, p. 485-531.

Pennsylvanian

Choquette, P.W., 1983. Platey-algal reef mounds, Parodox Basin. *In* Scholle, P.A., Bebout, D.E., and Moore, C.H., eds., Carbonate depositional environments. American Association of Petroleum Geologists, Memoir 33, p. 454-462.

Heckel, P.H., and Cocke, J.M., 1969. Phylloid algal mound complexes in outcropping Upper Pennsylvanian rocks of midcontinent. American Association of Petroleum Geologists, Bulletin, v. 53, p. 1084-1085.

Pray, L.C., Wilson, J.L., and Toomey, D.F., 1977. Geology of the Sacramento Mountains, Otero County, New Mexico. Midland, Texas, West Texas Geological Society, Guidebook, 216 p.

Toomey, D.F., and Winland, H.D., 1973. Rock and biotic facies associated with a Middle Pennsylvanian (Desmoinesian) algal buildup, Neca Lucia Field, Nolan County, Texas. American Association of Petroleum Geologists, Bulletin, v. 57, p. 1053-1074.

Permian

Davies, G.R., 1970. A Permian hydrozoan mound, Yukon Territory. Canadian Journal of Earth Sciences, v. 8, p. 973-988.

Dunham, R.J., 1972. Guide for study and discussion for individual reinterpretation of the sedimentation and diagenesis of the Permian Capital Geologic Reef and associated rocks, New Mexico and Texas. Midland, Texas, Permian Basin Section, Society of Economic Paleontologists and Mineralogists, Publication 72-14, 235 p.

Hileman, M.E., and Mazzulo, S.J., 1977. Upper Guadalupian Facies, Permian Reef Complex, Guadalupe Mountains, New Mexico and Texas. Midland, Texas, Permian Basin Section. Society of Economic Paleontologists and Mineralogists, Publication 77-16, 508 p.

Mazzullo, S.J., and Cys, J.M., 1979. Marine aragonite sea floor growths and cements in Permian phylloid algae mounds, Sacramento Mountains, New Mexico. Journal of Sedimentary Petrology, v. 49, p. 917-937.

Newell, N.E., *et al.,* 1953. The Permian Reef complex of the Guadalupe Mountains region, Texas and New Mexico. San Francisco, Freeman and Co., 236 p.

Newell, N.E., *et al.,* 1976. Permian Reef Complex, Tunisia. Brigham Young University, Geological Studies, v. 23, p. 75-112.

Triassic

Bosellini, A., and Rossi, D., 1974. Triassic carbonate buildups of the dolomites, northern Italy. *In* Laporte, L.F., ed., Reefs in time and space. Society of Economic Paleontologists and Mineralogists, Special Publication 18, p. 209-233.

Flugel, E., 1981. Paleoecology and facies of Upper Triassic reefs in the northern Calcareous Alps. *In* Toomey, D.F., ed., European fossil reef models. Society of Economic Paleontologists and Mineralogists, Special Publication 30, p. 291-361.

Stanley, G.D., 1979. Paleoecology, structure and distribution of Triassic coral buildups in western North America. University of Kansas Paleontology Contribution, Article 65, 58 p.

Zankl, H., 1971. Upper Triassic carbonate facies in the northern Limestone Alps. *In* Muller, G., and Friedman, G.M., eds., Sedimentology of parts of central Europe. Frankfurt, Kramer. p. 147-185.

Jurassic

Eliuk, L.S., 1979. Abenaki Formation, Nova Scotian Shelf, Canada; a depositional and diagenetic model for Mesozoic carbonate platforms. Bulletin of Canadian Petroluem Geology, v. 24, p. 424-514.

Gwinner, M.P., 1975. Origin of the Jurassic limestones of the Swabian Alb (southwest Germany). Contributions to Sedimentology 5. New York, Elsevier, 75 p.

Palmer, T.J., and Fursich, F.T., 1981. Ecology of sponge reefs from the Upper Bathonian (Middle Jurassic) of Normandy. Palaeontology v. 24, p. 1-25.

Rutten, M.D., 1956. The Jurassic reefs of the Yonne (southeastern Paris Basin). American Journal of Science, v. 254, p. 363-371.

Warme, J.E., Stanley, R.G., and Wilson, J.L., 1975. Middle Jurassic reef tract, central High Atlas, Morocco. Nice, France, International Association of Sedimentologists, Proceedings, Theme VIII, 11p.

Cretaceous

Bebout, D.G., and Loucks, R.G., 1974. Stuart City trend, Lower Cretaceous, south Texas. Bureau of Economic Geology, Report No. 78, 80 p.

Enos, P., 1974. Reefs, platforms, and basins of Middle Cretaceous in northeast Mexico. American Association of Petroleum Geologists, Bulletin, v. 58, p. 800-809.

Kauffman, E.G., and Sohl, N.F., 1974. Structure and evolution of Antillean Cretaceous rudist frameworks. Verhandl. Naturi. Ges. Basel., v. 84, p. 399-467.

Perkins, B.F., 1974. Paleoecology of a rudist reef complex in the Comanche Cretaceous Glen Rose Limestone of central Texas. In Perkins, B.F., ed., Aspects of Trinity Division Geology, Geoscience and Man VIII. Baton Rouge, LA., Louisiana State University, p. 131-173.

Philip, J., 1972. Paleoecologie des formations a rudistes du Cretace Superior-l'example du sud-est de la France. Paleogeography, Paleoclimatology, Paleoecology, v. 12, p. 205-222.

Scott, R.W., 1979. Depsitional model of Early Cretaceous coral-algal-rudist reefs, Arizona. American Association of Petroleum Geologists, Bulletin, v. 63, p. 1108-1128.

Cenozoic

Dabrio, C.J., Esteban, M., and Martin, J.M., 1981. The coral reef model of Nijar, Messinian (Uppermost Miocene) Almeria Province, southwest Spain. Journal of Sedimentary Petrology, v. 51, p. 521-541.

Esteban, M., 1979. Significance of the Upper Miocene coral reefs of the western Mediteranean. Paleogeography, Paleoclimatology, Paleoecology, v. 29, p. 169-189.

Frost, S.H., 1977. Cenozoic reef systems of Caribbean – prospects for paleoecological synthesis. American Association of Petroleum Geologists, Studies in Geology 4, p. 93-110.

Frost, S.H., 1981. Oligocene reef coral biofacies of the Vicentin, northeast Italy. In Toomey, D.F., ed., European fossil reef models. Society of Economic Paleontologists and Mineralogists, Special Publication 30, p. 483-541.

Pedley, H.M., 1979. Miocene bioherms and associated structures in the Upper Coralline Limestone of the Maltese Islands; their lithification and paleoenviroment. Sedimentology, v. 26, p. 577-593.

Pleistocene

Bathurst, R.G.C., 1975. Carbonate sediments and their diagenesis. Amsterdam, Elsevier, 658 p.
Chapters 3 and 4 nicely summarize specific modern reef environments.

Chappell, J., and Polach, H.A., 1976. Holocene sea-level change and coral-reef growth at Huon Peninsula, Papua New Guinea. Geological Society of America, Bulletin, v. 87, p. 235-239.

Crame, J.A., 1980. Succession and diversity in the Pleistocene coral reefs of the Kenya coast. Palaeontology, v. 23, p. 1-37.

Geister, J., 1980. Calm-water reefs and rough water reefs of the Caribbean Pleistocene. Acta Paleontologica Polonica, v. 25, p. 541-556.

James, N.P., Stearn, C.S., and Harrison, R.S., 1977. Field guidebook to modern and Pleistocene reef carbonates, Barbados, West Indies. University of Miami, 3rd International Coral Reef Symposium, Fisher Island, 30 p.

Mesolella, K.J., Sealy, H.A., and Matthews, R.K., 1970. Facies geometries within Pleistocene reefs of Barbados, West Indies. American Association of Petroleum Geologists, Bulletin, v. 54, p. 1899-1917.

Stanley, S.M., 1966. Paleoecology and diagenesis of Key Largo limestone, Florida. American Association of Petroleum Geologists, Bulletin, v. 50, p. 1927-1947.

MODERN REEFS - GENERAL

Darwin, C., 1842. Structure and distribution of coral reefs. Reprinted by University of California Press from 1851 edition, 214 p.
The beginning of modern coral reef research by a young biologist.

Frost, S.H., Wiss, M.P., and Saunders, J.B., 1977. Reefs and related carbonates – ecology and sedimentology. American Association of Petroleum Geologists, Studies in Geology 4, 421 p.
Twenty-eight papers with copious references, mainly on modern reefs.

Ginsburg, R.N., and James, N.P., 1974. Spectrum of Holocene reef-building communities in the western Atlantic. In Ziegler, A.M., et al., eds., Principles of benthic community analysis. University of Miami, Fisher Island Station, Short Course Notes, p. 7.1 - 7.22.
A succinct summary of the major reef types of the Atlantic-Caribbean area.

Hopley, D. 1982. The geomorphology of the Great Barrier Reef. New York, Wiley Interscience, 453 p.
Although concentrating on the Great Barrier Reef this book contains a wealth of information on modern reefs in general.

Stoddart, D.R., 1969. Ecology and morphology of recent coral reefs. Biology Review, v. 44, p. 433-498.
A superb summary of modern coral reefs – an excellent place to start.

Taylor, D.E., ed., 1977. Proceedings of Third International Coral Reef Symposium, Miami Florida 2. Geology: Fisher Island Station, Miami Beach, Florida, 628 p.
Many short papers and guidebooks with up to date research on reefs.

DIFFERENT TYPES OF MODERN REEFS

1) Pacific Atolls
Emery, K.O., Tracey, J.I., and Ladd, H.S., 1954. Geology of Bikini and nearby atolls. United States Geological Survey, Professional Paper 260-A, 265 p.

2) Marginal Reefs
Goreau, T.F., 1959. The ecology of Jamaican coral reefs: I. Species, composition and zonation. Ecology, v. 40, p. 67-90.

Goreau, T.F., and Goreau, N.I., 1973. The ecology of Jamaican coral reefs: II. Geomorphology, zonation and sedimentary phases. Bulletin of Marine Science, v. 23, p. 399-464.

James, N.P., Ginsburg, R.N., Marszalek, D., and Choquette, P.W., 1976. Facies and fabric specificity of early subsea cementation in shallow Belize (British Honduras) reefs. Journal of Sedimentary Petrology, v. 46, p. 523-544.

James, N.P., and Ginsburg, R.N., 1979. The seaward margin of belize barrier and atoll reefs. Blackwells, Oxford, International Association of Sedimentologists, Special Publication 3, 196 p.

Maxwell, W.G.H., 1968. Atlas of the Great Barrier Reef. Amsterdam, Elsevier, 258 p.

3) Pinnacle Reefs
Korniker, L.A., and Boyd, D.W., 1962. Shallow water geology and environment of Aacran reef complex, Campeche Bank, Mexico. American Association of Petroleum Geologists, Bulletin, v. 46, p. 640-673.

Logan, B.W., et al., 1969. Carbonate sediments and reefs, Yucatan shelf, Mexico. American Association of Petroleum Geologists, Memoir 11, p. 1-196

244

4) Patch Reefs

Garrett, P., *et al.,* 1971. Physiography, ecology and sediments of two Bermuda patch reefs. Journal of Geology, v. 79, p. 647-668.

Maiklem, W.R., 1970. The Capricorn Reef complex, Great Barrier Reef, Australia. Journal of Sedimentary Petrology, v. 38, p. 785-798.

5) Reef Mounds

Turmel, R., and Swanson, R., 1976. The development of Rodriquez Bank, a Holocene mudbank in the Florida Reef Tract. Journal of Sedimentary Petrology, v. 46, p. 497-519.

6) Algal Reefs

Adey, W., and Burke, R., 1976. Holocene bioherms (algal ridges and bank-barrier reefs) of the eastern Caribbean. Geological Society of America, Bulletin, v. 87, p 497-519.

Ginsburg, R.N., and Schroeder, J.H., 1973. Growth and submarine fossilization of algal cup reefs, Bermuda. Sedimentology, v. 20, p. 575-614.

7) Stromatolites

Dravis, J.J., 1983. Hardened subtidal stromatolites, Bahamas. Science, v. 219, p. 385-387.

Hoffman, P., 1976. Stromatolite morphogenesis in Shark Bay, Western Australia. *In* Walter, M.R., ed., Stromatolites. Amsterdam, Elsevier, p. 261-273.

Playford, P.E., and Cockbain, A.E., 1976. Modern algal stromatolites at Hamelin Pool, a hypersaline barred basin in Shark Bay, Western Australia. *In* Walter, M.R., ed., Stromatolites. Amsterdam, Elsevier, p. 389-413.

8) Deepwater Mounds

Mullins, H.T., *et al.,* 1981. Modern deep-water coral mounds north of Little Bahama Bank; criteria for recognition of deepwater coral bioherms in the rock record. Journal of Sedimentary Petrology, v. 51, p. 999-1013.

Neumann, A.C., Kofoed, J.W., and Keller, G.H., 1977. Lithoherms in the Straits of Florida. Geology, v. 5, p. 4-11.

9) Linear Mud Banks

Enos, P., and Perkins, R., 1979. Evolution of Florida Bay from island stratigraphy. Geological Society of America, Bulletin, v. 90, p. 59-83.

Pusey, W.C., 1975. Holocene carbonate sedimentation on northern Belize Shelf. *In* Wantland, K.F., and Pusey, W.C., eds., Belize shelf-carbonate sediments, clastic sediments, and ecology. American Association of Petroleum Geologists, Studies in Geology 2, p. 131-234.

OTHER REFERENCES CITED

Bathurst, R.G.C., 1982. Genesis of stromatactis cavities between submarine crusts in Palaeozoic carbonate mud buildups. Journal of the Geological Society of London, v. 139, p. 165-181.

Connell, J.H., 1978. Diversity in tropical rain forests and coral reefs. Science, v. 199, p. 1302-1310.

Embry, A.F. and Klovan, J.E., 1971. A Late Devonian reef tract on northeastern Banks Island, N.W.T. Bulletin of Canadian Petroleum Geology, v. 19, p. 730-781.

Frost, S.H., 1977. Ecologic controls of Caribbean and Mediterranean Oligocene reef coral communities. *In* Taylor, D.L., ed., Miami, Florida, Proceedings of Third International Coral Reef Symposium, p. 367-375.

James, N.P., 1983. Reefs. *In Scholle,* P.A., Bebout, D.G., and Moore, C.H., eds., Carbonate depositional environments. American Association of Petroleum Geologists, Memoir 33, p. 2346-440.

James, N.P., and Choquette, P.W., 1983. Limestone diagenesis: 6 – the sea floor diagenetic environment. Geoscience Canada, v. 10, p. 162-179.

Stearn, C.W., 1982. The shapes of Paleozoic and modern reef-builders: a critical review. Palcobiology, v. 8, p. 228-241.

Pratt, B.R., 1982. Stromatolitic framework of carbonate mud-mounds. Journal of Sedimentary Petrology, v. 52, p. 1203-1227.

Woodley, J.D. *et al.,* 1982. Hurricane Allen's impact on Jamaican coral reefs. Science, v. 214, p. 749-755.

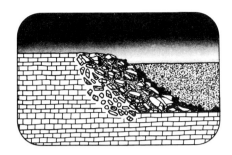

Carbonate Slopes

IAN A. McILREATH
Petro-Canada
P.O. Box 2844
Calgary, Alberta T2P 3E3

NOEL P. JAMES
Department of Earth Sciences
Memorial University of Newfoundland
St. John's, Newfoundland A1B 3X5

INTRODUCTION

To any geologist who has seen them in the field, sediments that comprise the slope facies of carbonate complexes are often the most staggering and long remembered of all. The sheer size of the enormous limestone blocks chaotically intercalated with delicately laminated lime mudstones tests our understanding of sediment genesis and deposition more than for almost any other deposits.

While the sediments themselves are intriguing, they are also useful as the only remaining clues as to the nature and composition of a new dolomitized or tectonically obliterated platform margin. Furthermore, the very presence of huge blocks is an excellent indicator of a nearby carbonate platform or reef complex, and this principle has been successfully used to locate reefs in the subsurface. The lime sands and conglomerates of these deposits, where intercalated with organic-rich basinal sediments, can be reservoirs for oil and natural gas.

We cannot interpret these deposits with the same level of confidence as shallow water carbonate sediments because: 1) modern slope deposits are not easily accessible for field study (the limited use of small research submersibles and seismology is slowly changing this); 2) ancient slope deposits commonly occur in orogenic belts, where facies and tectonic relationships are so complicated that these deposits are often mistaken for tectonic breccias or mélanges; 3) slope sediments in the subsurface generally have not been serious exploration targets as long as adjacent platform margins remained the primary objective; 4) slope sediments are formed in a series of environments that transect major pressure, temperature and oxygen-level boundaries in the ocean and the precise effects of these physiochemical parameters on the sediments are poorly known.

As a result our present facies models are based on the rock record, with some additions from recent sediments. In addition, our understanding of downslope sediment emplacement is based in part upon processes and models determined for siliciclastic deposits (Dott, 1963; Middleton and Hampton, 1973). It has been easy to apply this comparative approach (Cook *et al.*, 1972; Cook and Mullins, 1983) because many similarities do exist, but there are also fundamental differences.

In the paper on "Turbidites and Associated Coarse Clastic Deposits" (this volume), Walker outlined the attributes of a turbidite model and then integrated all associated siliciclastic lithofacies that encompass the slope-to-basin transition into an overall, larger scale, submarine fan model. Similarly our approach in this article will be to outline the major aspects of the slope facies in carbonate sedimentary sequences, first by examining the major sediment types and their modes of emplacement, and second by relating these to general facies models, which are very much dependent upon the nature of the adjacent margin and the depositional setting.

Since the first edition of this summary appeared there has been an increased interest in synthesizing the various aspects of fore-reef and slope carbonates and excellent, well-illustrated summaries have been written by Read (1982), James and Mountjoy (1983), Enos and Moore (1983), and Cook and Mullins (1983).

CARBONATE SLOPE SEDIMENTATION

The slope facies is a transitional one between the rapid and active production of calcium carbonate in shallow water and the slow gentle rain of fine-grained pelagic sediments in the basin. The platform-to-basin transition may in places be abrupt, in the form of a steep cliff, but more commonly is a gently inclined slope decreasing in grade with depth and merging imperceptibly into basinal deposits at some distance, which may be 100s of km from the actual margin. Because the environment as a whole is an incline, short periods of gravity-induced catastrophic sedimentation alternate with long periods of relatively quiet pelagic sedimentation, or to paraphrase Ager (1973, p. 100), "long periods of boredom alternating with short periods of terror".

Pelagic Carbonates

Pelagic carbonates are those sediments deposited in the open sea and derived from the skeletons of planktonic microorganisms which inhabit the overlying water column. Such deposits include ooze and its lithified equivalent, chalk, and consist primarily of the skeletons of various nannofossil groups, especially coccoliths, the tests of planktonic and sometimes benthic foraminifers. Macrofossils such as pteropods, pelecypods, echinoderms and, in older units, ammonites, nautiloids, tentaculitids and styliolinids are present as accessory components. An excellent summary of such deposits can be found in Hsu and Jenkyns (1974), Scholle (1977), and Scholle *et al.* (1983).

True pelagic carbonates are apparently not known from the early Paleozoic and are first recognized from rocks of Upper Silurian age (Tucker, 1974). Planktonic foraminifers and coccoliths appear to have evolved in the Jurassic. During post-Jurassic time pelagic carbonate has increased to the point that in the last 100 Ma it comprises about 67% of worldwide carbonate deposition, and more than 50% of the present sea floor is covered with this type of carbonate sediment (Hay *et al.*, 1976).

Most chalks accumulate a a rate of between one and 30 cm per year. The sedimentary structures and colours depend upon the degree of circulation and oxygenation. Dark colours and preserved laminations reflect stagnation; lighter colours, more burrows and fewer preserved sedimentary structures reflect stronger bottom circulation.

Because of relatively narrow shelves and low sea level stands, Holocene pelagic sediments are restricted largely to deep ocean basins. However, during times of eustatic high stands of sea level, pelagic carbonates can and did accumulate on continental shelves, such as the North American mid-continent seaway in Cretaceous times.

The water depth of Recent pelagic carbonate deposition ranges from less than 100 m to greater than 4500 m. The limiting factors for such accumulations are the relative rates of sedimentation of carbonate versus non-carbonate components, physical erosion by submarine currents and chemical dissolution. Chemical dissolution is particularly important in carbonate slope facies because the environment passes, with depth, through several important increasing pressure and decreasing temperature boundaries (James and Choquette, 1983). Aragonite components, such as pteropods and benthic foraminifers, may be selectively removed by dissolution in water as shallow as 500 m (the aragonite compensation depth) while calcite components are completely dissolved at the carbonate compensation depth, between 4,000 and 5,000 m in today's oceans. Much less is known about the removal or recrystallization of Mg-calcite. This progressive removal by dissolution results in a residual sediment composed largely of siliceous skeletons, red hemipelagic clays and wind-blown silt.

In some ares of the modern ocean the production of siliceous plankton (silicioflagellates, diatoms and radiolaria) exceeds that of calcareous nanno- and microplankton. During thc Paleozoic, when pelagic carbonate was reduced or absent, siliceous sediment was much more widespread in deep-water areas.

Hemipelagic Slope Sediments

Sediments that make up the fine-grained pelagic component of most slope deposits come not only from the water column but from the adjacent platform as well (Wilson, 1969). While the contribution at any one time from the water column is more or less constant, that portion derived from the platform is episodic. Most often storms stir up the wide, shallow, mud-floored areas of the shelf and the milk-white water streams out across the shelf margin to settle in deep water. A less voluminous but more regular transfer process exists at such near-vertical shelf-to-deep-oceanic-basin transitions as St. Croix, Virgin Islands, where warm sediment-rich shelf waters "float" over the cooler

basinal waters by tidal exchange. These fine-grained, shallow-water derived slope sediments have been called "peri-platform ooze" by Schlager and James (1978) because they occur as an apron around the platform and because they are significantly different in their mineralogy and composition from the wholly pelagic sediments of the open sea.

In the Precambrian and Paleozoic most pelagic slope carbonates may well have been almost wholly peri-platform ooze.

The resultant hemipelagic slope deposits are monotonous, uniform dark grey, fine-grained lime mudstones, generally thin-bedded with flat planar contacts and internal micro-laminations (Fig. 1). Mudstone beds are often separated by partings into very thin beds of similar mudstone or beds of shale, forming characteristic "rhythmites" or "ribbon limestones". The original depositional textures and fabrics are often modified by downslope creep leading to sedimentary boudinage, while differential compaction and/or cementation frequently transforms the evenly-bedded sediments into a nodular limestone. The irregular nodules may, in some cases, be so packed together to form a jig-saw puzzle resembling an *in situ* breccia.

From the Mesozoic to Recent, pelagic components become progressively more important. The criteria for distinguishing the relative contribution of

peri-platform vs pelagic ooze is speculative because most fine silt-mud size shallow water indicators are susceptible to early diagenesis (Enos and Moore, 1983),

Peri—Platform Talus

Directly seaward of the shallow water reefs or lime-sand shoals that form a platform margin, there is commonly a debris apron of limestone blocks (Fig. 2), skeletons of reef building metazoa, sediment bounded by submarine cement or encrusting organisms, lime sand and muds. These accumulations are the result of rock-fall and sand-streams from shallow water and, as illustrated in Figure 3, are very common along the seaward margins of modern reef complexes (James and Ginsburg, 1979; Mullins and Neumann, 1979; Schlager and Chermak, 1979; Land and Moore, 1977). The blocks themselves may be multi-generation in composition because the reefs, sand shoals and other deposits at the platform margin are characteristically susceptible to early lithification, either by submarine cementation, or if there are slight fluctuations in sea level, by complex subaerial diagenesis. In addition, parts of the talus wedge are commonly cemented on the sea floor (James and Ginsburg, 1979; Land and Moore, 1977). The lithified portions of these limestones become hard and brittle, and so

Figure 1
Peri-platform ooze; evenly-bedded, grey lime mudstone with thin interbeds of argillaceous lime mudstone, Cooks Brook Formation (Middle Cambrian), Humber Arm, Western Newfoundland.

are particularly susceptible to fracturing and fragmentation.

Large passes through a reef also act as conduits, funnelling back-reef sediments into this zone so that, along strike, areas of chaotic breccia may alternate with fans of lime sand. The later sediment is also commonly cemented, forming numerous hardgrounds.

Examination of sediment dispersal seaward of the platform in areas with low to intermediate slopes (up to 30°) indicates that this talus does not travel any significant distance away from the margin by day-to-day processes.

Carbonate Breccias and Conglomerates

These deposits have been called debris flows (deposits), submarine mass flows, mass breccia flows, breccia and mega-breccia beds, debris sheets, rudite sheets, debris avalanches, or olisto-stromes (in the non-tectonic sense). They are certainly the most impressive parts of the slope sequence. They originate in two very different areas, high up on the slope in shallow water or from lower down the slope profile.

Figure 2
Peri-platform talus; a block of shallow-water reef limestone (approximately 30m high) enclosed in thin-bedded, dark grey, peri-platform lime mudstones. Block occurs approximately 250m down slope from the toe of a near-vertical, 200m high platform margin. Note vertical orientation of bedding within the block, Cathedral Formation (Middle Cambrian), north face Mt. Stephen, British Columbia.

A) Breccias Derived from Shallow Water. These breccias are generally exposed in discontinuous to laterally extensive sheets, channels with lenticular cross sections or irregular masses. They stand out as resistant masses of light-coloured carbonate against a background of dark-coloured, well-bedded limestone and shale (Figs. 4 and 5). They are characterized by blocks of all sizes and shapes, but often equi-dimensional and somewhat rounded. Some of the blocks are so enormous that they have been mistaken for bioherms (see Mountjoy et al., 1972). One exceptional clast in the Cow Head Group (Cambro-Ordovician) at Lower Head, Newfoundland is 0.2 km x 50 m in size, with surrounding blocks often 30 x 15 m in size, (Kindle and Whittington, 1958). The breccias commonly have a matrix of lime mud, lime sand or argillaceous lime mud.

The deposits are bedded, with a planar to undulating basal contact accentuated by differential compaction and a planar to irregular and often hummocky upper contact. The nature of the bedding contacts often cannot be determined accurately because the bedding planes are stylolitic, and so any original bedding-plane features are often destroyed. Bedding thicknesses range up to tens of metres. Davies

(1977) made the interesting observation that the common occurrence of crinoids, bryozoa and ammonites at the upper surface of Permo-Pennsylvanian debris deposits on Ellesmere Island may represent an indigenous fauna inhabiting the "reef-like" upper surface of the deposit.

The polymict nature of the clasts reflects the complexity of the source area, namely the platform margin, which consists of partly lithified reefs and/or limesand shoals, downslope (yet still shallow) reef mounds, or peri-platform talus. Among the talus blocks, expected types include well-sorted and well-bedded lime sands which can be differentially submarine cemented (Fig. 6), individual colonies of reef builders, multigeneration reef rock, limestones with subaerial karst features, tidal flat lithologies, and even cemented talus that has been refractured to give breccia clasts within breccia.

The fabrics of "analagous" coarse siliciclastic deposits have been discussed by Walker (1976). In lime breccias they range from mainly chaotic to imbricated to horizontal to vertical, and rarely include graded or even reverse graded bedding. They range from clast-supported to most commonly matrix-supported with extremely poor sorting. The matrix ranges from shale to argil-

Figure 3
Peri-platform talus; looking across the steeply dipping fore-reef slope at a depth of 130m seaward of the Belize barrier reef complex. The slope is composed of blocks of limestone, plates of coral and lime sand composed of the plates of the green alga Halimeda; the small block at the center (arrow) is about one metre high.

247

Figure 4
Lime breccias; light grey, shallow-water reef-derived limestone breccias occurring in a 'channel' – a (approximately 8m thick); sheets – b (approximately 2m thick); and irregular masses – c (up to 12m thick), all enclosed in thin-bedded, dark grey, peri-platform lime mudstones, Cathedral Formation (Middle Cambrian), southface Mt. Field, British Columbia.

Figure 5
A sequence illustrating two different types of carbonate slope deposits; debris flows with large limestone clasts (right) and thin-bedded, graded calcarenites (the thin, grey limestone beds), interbedded with black fissile shale. This overturned sequence (top at lower left) of Middle Ordovician age occurs at Cape Cormorant, Port-au-Port Peninsula, Western Newfoundland.

laceous lime mud to lime mudstone with occasional lime sand. As Hopkins (1977) points out, however, what is often taken to be lime mud in outcrop turns out to be peloid lime sand in thin section, so that sand-sized matrix may be more common than supposed.

The exact mechanisms by which these sediments are transported are not yet clear. Submarine debris flows (Hampton, 1972) are sediment gravity flows in which granular solids such as boulders, pebbles and sand are more or less "floated" during transport by the yield strength of the matrix which is composed of interstitial fluid and fine sediment. Buoyancy of the fluid matrix also contributes to the support. Because not all such deposits have a clay mineral matrix, the transport mechanism is thought to be a combination of debris flow and grain flow (Middleton and Hampton, 1973). A major problem in this regard is that almost all experimental work to date has been done on clay-water mixtures; none of the experiments has been carried out on sediments with a clay-lime or lime mud matrix.

B) Breccias Derived from the Slope. The evenly-bedded calcilutites or lime muds of the slope facies are often prone to downslope creep. Individual beds can be seen to neck or wedge out, or whole intervals will move downslope within a series of slump folds (Fig. 7). Dislocation and movement of large masses of slope material downslope leads to the formation of breccias or submarine glide masses composed of numerous tabular clasts of slope limestone that have been bent or fractured, that are poorly-sorted and that exhibit random to subparallel orientations, often resembling shallow-water "flat pebble conglomerates" (Fig. 8). Enormous blocks of bedded slope sediments, often internally folded, are caught up in the breccias.

The source of these breccias is thought to be the large "intraformational truncation surfaces" (Fig. 9) or "cut-and-fill structures " (Wilson, 1969) which are sharp concave-up discontinuity surfaces that truncate underlying beds and are overlain by a downslope thickening wedge of sediment with an angular relationship on the truncated beds. In these deposits, reduction of shear stress occurs by displacement of

Figure 6
Thinly-bedded, nodular foreslope sequence comprising cemented nodules in compacted calcarenite (N) and a laterally continuous bed of cemented calcarenite (S). These cal- *carenites form the predominant foreslope facies below the Miette and Ancient Wall buildups (Upper Devonian), Alberta. Photo courtesy of J.C. Hopkins.*

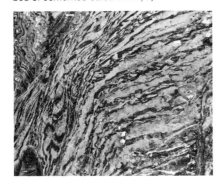

◄ **Figure 7**
Extensive syn-sedimentary distortion of bedding developed by creep in thin to very thin-bedded, upper basinal slope, peri-platform lime mudstones, Eldon Formation (Middle Cambrian), Wapta Mountain, British Columbia.

Figure 8
Slope-derived breccia; clasts of partly lithified peri-platform ooze (see Fig. 1) that have been eroded and transported as a *clast-supported breccia, Cooks Brook Formation (Middle Cambrian), Humber Arm, Western Newfoundland.*

coherent masses along discrete shear planes and not usually by deformation within the mass as occurs in slumps.

The tabular clasts of slope material, although derived by separation along bedding planes, clearly indicate that the slope sediments were partly consolidated very early, probably by submarine cementation. Cementation may have been similar to that in shallow-water with lithified and unlithified layers reflecting times of slow and rapid sedimentation respectively. If cementation and neomorphism took place below the thermocline, dissolution of aragonite and possible precipitation of calcite may have caused the same effect in layers of different original composition (Schlager and James, 1978). Alternatively, if the lime mudstone is interlaminated with shale, cementation of the carbonate may have taken place while the shale remained soft.

Deposits of the two end members, one originating high on the slope and the other down on the lower slope are sometimes found intermixed in extensive breccia masses (Fig. 10). Such deposits are similar to what Schlager and Schlager (1973) term marl-flaser breccia, characterized by a chaotic fabric of plastically deformed, dark grey, argillaceous lime mudstone lithoclasts separating irregular lenses of sub-angular limestone and other lithoclasts, with the deformed marls forming the flaser fabric. There are thought to be shallow-water derived breccia flows that incorporated lime mudstone clasts from the floor of the slope environment as they moved basinward and they may grade downslope into turbidites.

Graded Calcarenites
A large proportion of any slope sequence commonly consists of size-graded beds of clastic textured limestone, mainly of sand size, interpreted to be the carbonate equivalent of silici-clastic turbidites (Fig. 5). They are envisaged to be deposited from turbidity currents that formed by the sudden surge-type release of dense fluid rather than from a steady state flow such as described by Harms (1974). These deposits have also been called allodapic limestones (Meischner, 1964). Such sediments are well-bedded and characteristically have sharp planar bases that can be coplanar with, or locally scour and truncate underlying

Figure 11

A bed of light grey calcarenite composed of a graded lower portion, planar laminated middle unit, and the upper portion having climbing ripples (A,B and C Bouma subdivisions respectively), capping a lime breccia, Sekwi Formation (Lower Cambrian), Cariboo Pass, Mackenzie Mountains. Photo courtesy of F.F. Krause.

Figure 9

Large intraformational truncation surface in agrillaceous and cherty limestones of the Hare Fiord Formation (Permo-Pennsylvanian), north side of Svartfjeld Peninsula, Ellesmere Island. Note smooth, *curved concave-up (listric) geometry of the truncation surface and the lack of macro-scale deformation of beds below or above truncation surface. Shadow at lower left centre is of heliocopter: width of view 150m. Photo courtesy of G.R. Davies.*

Figure 10

A large deformed clast of well-bedded peri-platform ooze that was eroded, transported and redeposited as part of a debris flow, Cow Head Group (Middle Ordovician), Cow Head, Western Newfoundland.

slope beds. Sole marks and load structures are usually absent although in some cases they may be obliterated because of stylolitization and solution along bedding contacts. Calcareous turbidites can exhibit all five of the typical ABCDE division of the Bouma sequence but most commonly it is the A, and sometimes the B and C divisions that characterize the deposits (Fig. 11). The particles in the basal parts of division A are often cobble size and larger and the more common grain types are lithoclasts, skeletal debris and ooids, the petrology of which indicates a shallow water origin in contrast to the surrounding pelagic deposits.

The most obvious sources for these units are the unstable accumulations of lime sand and gravel that build up near the platform margin and are occasionally set into motion. It is also possible that they are the distal parts of carbonate debris flows representing the uppermost more dilute turbulent portions of the debris flow (Krause and Oldershaw, 1979). Davies (1977) has suggested a third origin, that skeletal material produced on the slope particularly by pelmatozoans may be easily remobilized.

Post-Paleozoic graded calcarenites derived from sediments further down the slope profile can be virtually indistinguishable compositionally from pelagic limestone. These calcarenites are generally rich in pelagic components such as coccoliths and foraminifers but may also contain lesser amounts of pteropods, sponge spicules, radiolarians, and coarser-grained skeletal debris (especially pelmatozoans). The sediments are size-sorted and may be mixed with clastic terrigenous or volcaniclastic sediment if they have travelled great distances. Although the sedimentary structures such as horizontal laminations, convolutions, occasional channels, flute and groove casts and trace fossils may be present, the A and B divisions of the Bouma sequence are commonly missing and they generally start with the C or D divisions.

Turbidity currents and debris flows appear to be the dominant transport mechanisms for the downslope movement of coarse detritus in modern carbonate slopes (Cook and Mullins, 1983; Enos and Moore, 1983).

Non-Graded Calcarenites

Massive to cross-bedded and ripple-marked calcarenites are an enigmatic type of deposit found in many slope sequences. These deposits are fine- to coarse-grained wackestones to grainstones with occasional large clasts or fossils. Individual beds have sharp bases and vary in geometry from lenticular to irregular masses. The fabric may be random or grains may be aligned parallel to the paleoslope.

The grains in these deposits are variable, ranging in composition from shallow-water derived particles to pelagic grains.

Non-graded calcarenites occurring below a carbonate margin of considerable slope and having an abundant supply of lime sand may have formed from grain flows or more likely, through a modified grain flow mechanism whereby the addition of lime mud matrix and turbulence may have aided dispersive pressures in supporting the grains during transport (Lowe, 1976). It is unlikely that liquified flow, or fluidized flow contribute significantly to the formation of these particular slope calcarenites. Another viable mechanism is reworking of previously deposited slope sediments by bottom currents. Perhaps the mas-

sive deposits having an apparent lack of sedimentary structures are nothing more than the product of downslope mass movement of well-sorted lime sands produced at a rapid rate near the platform margin such as occurs on modern leeward open margins during large storms (Hine et al., 1981).

Sedimentary structures in the cross-bedded deposits indicate some sort of bottom currents, often running parallel to the slope (contour currents). Well-sorted, rippled ooid lime sands, sometimes with large scale bed forms, occur in the deeper parts of the slopes around the margins of the Tongue of the Ocean, Bahamas, and are also common on the slopes along the western parts of the Bahama Banks (Mullins and Neumann, 1979) where currents flow along and parallel to the slope at speeds of 60 cm/sec and more (although such velocities are high and not characteristic of today's oceans). These currents may rework bank-derived sands (Hine and Neumann, 1977) or rework pre-existing pelagic slope deposits, leaving only the larger foraminifers and pteropods together with lithoclasts of cemented pelagics to form a deep-water grainstone. They may also winnow the upper parts of turbidites, removing the finer layers and leaving a sequence composed only of shallow-water clasts, and divisions A and B of the Bouma sequence, capped by a cross-bedded lime sand.

Such clean, well-sorted sands are commonly sites of submarine cementation and hardground formation. In such areas precipitation of cement may lead to displacive expansion of grain-to-grain distance, resulting in fracturing and the formation of in situ breccias.

THE DEPOSITONAL SETTING

Even though there may be a continuous rain of pelagic sediment on the slope, most slope sediments come from the platform, as re-sedimented gravity flows or peri-platform ooze. Thus, the nature of slope deposition closely reflects events on the platform, or more specifically whether the platform is close to sea level, drowned or exposed (Fig. 12). If the platform surface is close to sea level, then there is a constant source of carbonate sediment being produced and so slope as well as adjacent basin deposits are correspondingly abundant. If sea level drops, the platform is

exposed to meteoric diagenesis and the platform sediments are turned to limestone, thus shutting off the supply of sediment to the slope. Starved deep-water sedimentation can also reflect rapid sea level rise. If carbonate production is outpaced, a tranquil deep-water shelf consisting primarily of muddy, skeletal carbonates can develop.

The style of shelf-slope break in the fossil record also reflects the interaction between rates of carbonate production and relative sea-level movement (James and Mountjoy, 1983; Bossellini, 1984), the latter being due to the combined effect of subsidence (tectonic controls) and sea level fluctuations (Schlager and Ginsburg, 1981). If the rate of carbonate accretion is more or less equal to the rate of relative sea level rise, the shelf break will remain more or less in the same position and ultimately the relative relief will increase between the margin and the basin. When relative sea level rise is less than carbonate accretion, the slope facies prograde out over older slope deposits, and will consist of thick accumulations of many re-sedimented lime sands and conglomerates. Opposite circumstances create onlap margins which can be drowned or will move shelfwards in steps. In this situation, little sediment is transported seaward so slope and basin deposits are thin and mostly carbonate muds. Drowned and emergent margins due to large changes in relative sea level result ultimately in starved basinal sedimentation.

In the drowned situation, the style of carbonate shelf is close to what Ahr (1973) has termed a "carbonate ramp", where the high energy zone is the shoreline and the carbonate facies pass progressively into deeper water lithologies. Ginsburg and James (1974) have called these "open shelves" and good modern examples are present on the Yucatan Shelf, West Florida Shelf and in the Persian Gulf. If the ramp has a marked increase in slope at the seaward edge, slope facies will have abundant slumps, slope breccias and turbidites. This situation is termed by Read (1982) a "distally steepened ramp". The absence of a slope break results in a lack of significant slump and sediment gravity flow deposits in the deeper water facies and the formation of a "homoclinal ramp".

The nature of slope facies is also

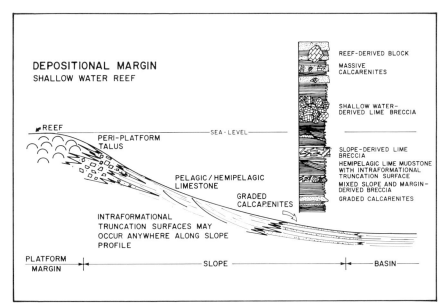

Figure 12
Variations in the style of slope sedimentation as a function of water depth on an adjacent carbonate platform.

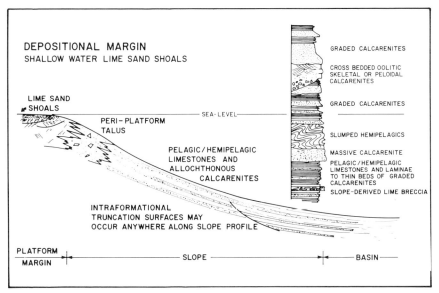

Figure 13
Schematic model for a shallow-water, reef dominated, depositional carbonate margin and illustration of a hypothetical sequence of deposits within the adjacent basin slope.

dependent on the direction and magnitude of off-shelf sediment transport resulting from the net effects of waves, storms and tides. Antecedent topography in the form of islands or subtidal rock ridges create energy barriers which can control the volume of sediment flux on or off the shelf. Oceanic circulation (bottom currents) can modify, through physical transport and erosion, pre-existing slope sediments as well as promote submarine cementation and hardground development on the slopes. For additional details on these parameters and how they affect slope sedimentation along the Northern Bahamas, the reader is referred to Hine *et al.* (1981) and Mullins and Neumann (1979).

In discussing the topic of sea level fluctuation and slope deposition, Schlager and Ginsburg (1981) make the important point that in siliciclastic systems, a lower sea level results in increased erosion and delivery of terrigenous material to the deep; the reverse is true in carbonate systems.

Carbonate slope sedimentation also differs from that adjacent to terrigenous shelves in another important way. Carbonate sand is delivered all along the platform margin. Deep sea fans are absent because no submarine dendritic drainage systems are developed that would funnel sediment into canyons. Instead, the reefs or sand shoals of the platform act as a line source, creating a continuous belt of overlapping turbidites and gravity-flow deposits at the toe-of-slope (Schlager and Chermak, 1979); the resulting deposit is more appropriately termed a debris apron (McIlreath, 1977b; Mullins *et al.*, 1984) which has a geometry that is distinct from a fan.

Carbonate sedimentation providing slope stability results in another distinction from terrigenous shelf-basins. Massive failure of a partly lithified carbonate slope will reduce the possibility of the simple evolution of a single flow (slump → debris flow → turbidity current) as postulated for siliciclastics (Middleton and Hampton, 1973).

FACIES MODELS
Because of the preceding variables we have chosen not to integrate the spectrum of carbonate slope deposits into one model. Instead, we have chosen to model carbonate slope sedimentation adjacent to a platform near sea level. In this situation, the style of slope and basinal sedimentation is dependent upon the relief between platform and basin, and the nature of the shallow portion of the margin. Where the margin itself is a facies transition with a gradual slope profile, then the sequence of slope deposits is very much different from the sequence where the margin is abrupt. We have differentiated between these two types of margins and called them depositional and by-pass margins respectively (Fig. 12 to 16)

The nature of the slope sediments in each case also depends on whether the shallow-water margin is formed: 1) by metazoan, calcareous algal or stromatolitic reefs, and occurs either at the edge or slightly downslope below the zone of the most wave movement, or 2) by skeletal algal or oolitic lime-sand shoals. In the case of reefs, the nature of the reef-building biota changes with the

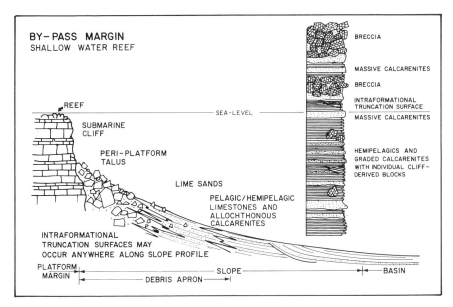

Figure 14
Schematic model for a depositional carbonate margin dominated by shallow-water lime sands and illustration of a hypothetical sequence of adjacent basinal slope deposits.

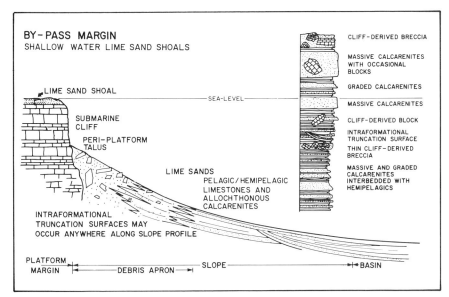

Figure 15
Schematic model for a shallow-water, reef-dominated, by-pass type of carbonate margin in a shallow-basin and illustration of a hypothetical sequence of deposits within the adjacent basin slope. In a deep basin there is an extensive by-pass slope below the peri-platform talus. Debris, including turbidites is funnelled through gullies onto the basin floor.

time and therefore the composition and nature of the resulting debris correspondingly changes.

It should be noted that none of the models is mutually exclusive and within a buildup or platform margin all four (depositional reef, depositional shoal, by-pass reef, by-pass shoal) may be present an any one time. They may be repeated in time and space; in the case of a buildup, it may even be possible to have all four occurring simultaneously in different places along the buildup margin. It is quite common in ancient platforms to progress from a ramp or depositional margin to a by-pass type and even to an erosional margin.

Depositional Margins
The slopes are generally gentle and decrease basinward to merge with the flat basin floor. Because ramps have even lower gradients, slope sediments are normally much finer and consist of pelagic carbonates and shales with minor slumping and slide development.

A) Shallow-Water Reef. The zone of peri-platform talus is relatively narrow but the full spectrum of allochthonous deposits is present downslope (Fig. 12). Because most of the allochthonous material comes from the reef or talus pile many of the allochthonous deposits generated high on the slope are deposited far down on the slope or in the basin. Consequently that zone seaward of the peri-platform talus is often composed of hemipelagic limestones and is often by-passed by the mass movements. This type of depositional slope occurs most frequently around reef complexes and basinward of platform-margin barrier reef systems along paleotopographic highs, structurally positive elements or hingelines in fairly stable cratonic or miogeosynclinal basins. Examples of this style of slope deposit occur in the Upper Devonian and the Cambrian of Western Canada (McIlreath, 1977a) and the Devonian of the Canning Basin, Australia (Conaghan *et al.,* 1976).

B) Shallow-Water Lime Sands. The slope flanking this style of margin is generally a calcarenite wedge of proximal-to-distal turbidite plain (Fig. 13). These slopes probably represent a depositional equilibrium in that sedimentation controls the slope angle and is active all along the profile. Turbidity currents and grain flows are the predominant transport mechanisms, and debris sheets and breccias rare. Some minor debris sheets composed of cemented lime-sand clasts or other slope-derived lithologies may be present. Hardgrounds and incipient brecciation are common.

Examples of this style of slope deposit includes the Pennsylvanian Dimple Limestone, Texas (Thomson and Thomasson, 1969); Silurian of California and Nevada (Ross, 1965); several of the Devonian Fairholme carbonate complexes of Western Canada, and Devonian encrinite banks in Arctic Canada.

By-Pass Margins
In these situations the magin is on top of a cliff or submarine escarpment so

254

that sediments are transported directly from shallow to deep-water. They may bypass much of the slope along a wide front, or be funnelled through channels and canyons to accumulate at the toe-of-slope and adjacent basin. In shallower basins the submarine cliff is the actual by-pass slope, below which accumulates a debris apron of coarse peri-platform talus fining basinwards into peri-platform and pelagic oozes with occasional turbidites. Flows are triggered on the upper slope by over-steepening of peri-platform talus, collapse of the reef wall or by slumping of previously deposited sediments, and are seen to erode gullies on modern slopes (Schlager *et al.,* 1976). The cliffs may result from faulting, large fluctuations in sea-level or just rapid upbuilding of the platform as compared to the basinal deposits. This style of margin is particularly common along block-faulted oceanic margins or at the structural hingeline where a basin is subsiding faster than the adjacent platform.

A) Shallow-Water Reef. Since the reef crowns the escarpment, the most characteristic and spectacular style of accumulation is the wedge of peri-platform talus (Fig. 14). This wedge of material may be enormous, especially if the area is subject to tectonics, with the main transport mechanisms being a combination of rock-fall, sandstreams and gravity-induced downslope mass movement. If the cliff is dissected by channels or canyons, the peri-platform talus may interdigitate along strike with carbonate submarine fans similar to those described for siliciclastic deposits (Evans and Kendall, 1977). Slumps creep and sliding are more active in the deposit than on the adjacent slope due to the variations in lithification. The talus wedge grades downslope into a relatively narrow zone of lime sands and then into pelagic calcilutites to form a debris apron.

This is the style of many modern slope deposits in Belize (Ginsburg and James, 1973), Puerto Rico (Conolly and Ewing, 1967), Jamaica (Goreau and Land, 1974), the Bahamas (Mullins and Newmann, 1979; Schlager and Chermak, 1979), and the Pacific Atolls (Emery *et al.,* 1954). Perhaps the most spectacular fossil example is in the Cretaceous of Mexico (Enos, 1977). Other fossil examples include the Cam-

brian Cathedral Escarpment, Western Canada, and Upper Devonian margins in the Front Ranges of Western Canada.

B) Lime Sand Shoals. If the shallow-water margin facies is lime sand, the peri-platform talus will also consist predominantly of lime sand intercalated with calcilutites (Fig. 15) with fewer limestone blocks than in the previous model (unless there have been substantial movements in sea level exposing the margin to subaerial diagenesis). Away from the escarpment the lime sands grade relatively quickly into slope or basinal pelagic lime muds. There are minor contributions from turbidites.

A fossil example of such a debris apron of calcarenite is the Cambrian Boundary Limestone (McIlreath, 1977b). Modern examples have been found in the northern Bahamian slopes (Mullins and Newmann, 1979).

The Models as a Norm
In these models we have not consciously placed the slope lithologies in any particular sequence because we feel that the sequence on such a broad scale represents more the complex interactions of sea level and tectonics at the shallow rim than any secondary sedimentary process on the slope. As a result unusual features are likely to record not so much the style of sedimentation on the slope, as the style of sedimentation and tectonics at the shallow margin.

The Models as a Framework and Guide for Description
The differences in carbonate deposition through time are, in large part, a function of the appearance and disappearance of different types of carbonate secreting organisms and thus affect the use of these facies models as a guide in two ways: 1) shallow-water benthic organisms build massive reefs, cause relief at the platform margin, and contribute major amounts of sediment to the slope; however, they are present only at specific times in geologic history; 2) the pelagic calcareous zooplankton and phytoplankton are insignificant in the early Paleozoic, minor in the middle and late Paleozoic, and prolific in the Mesozoic and Tertiary.

As a result, the hemipelagic slope deposition is almost entirely peri-platform ooze in the Precambrian and early Paleozoic, and perhaps one-half peri-platform ooze and one-half true pelagic carbonate in the Mesozoic and Tertiary. Interruptions in the fallout of peri-platform ooze in the Paleozoic sometimes resulted in shale interbeds, whereas in the Mesozoic and Tertiary interbeds are thinner but are wholly pelagic carbonate.

The Models as Predictors in New Situations
Based on a few observations, and bearing in mind the age of the deposits as well as their tectonic setting, one can extrapolate and formulate three critical

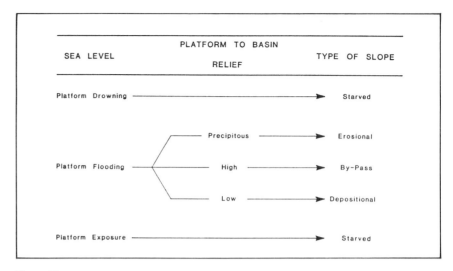

Figure 16
Schematic model for a by-pass type of carbonate margin dominated by shallow- *water lime sands in a shallow-basin, and illustration of a hypothetical sequence of adjacent basinal slope deposits.*

conclusions: 1) examination of the overall sequence indicates the relative position on the slope and possible proximity of the platform; 2) the lithology of the lime-sand beds and relative calcarenite to hemipelagic ratio gives some idea as to the nature of the slope facies; depositional versus by-pass; and 3) the composition of the clasts indicates the nature of the margin, which has often been obliterated or is inaccessible.

The Models as Basis for Interpretation
The interpretation of carbonate sediment gravity flows has, to date, been based primarily on an analogy with siliciclastic deposits which have similar sedimentary characteristics. One of the important differences between carbonate and siliciclastic sediment gravity flows, however, is that a dispersal model for the hypothetical evolution of a single flow of carbonate platform-derived debris into deep water remains speculative. In contrast to the relatively unconsolidated sediments on continental shelves, carbonate sediments in similar environments tend to be stabilized by organisms and/or well-lithified. This results in distinctively different slope deposits being produced by a variety of gravity-driven transport processes rather than different types of deposits evolving from the same flow. Unequivocal examples of an ancient deposit evolving from the same flow are rare. It should be noted, however, that the concept of a singular flow spawning a series of deposits may apply where slide failure occurs in the lower portion of the slope, remobilizing and transporting these mixed deposits even further basinward.

SUMMARY
Carbonate slope sediments have, in the past, often been either ignored or interpreted as tectonic in origin. Their identification as deposits, separate from tectonically formed mélanges has come largely from a detailed analysis of not only the chaotic deposits but the fine-grained interbeds as well. Our understanding is increasing as more deposits are documented and the first timid steps are being taken beyond the reef into deeper water by submersibles. This latter aspect of carbonate sedimentology is still very much in its infancy.

Refinements of the models presented in this paper must come from two directions, experimentation and more observations from modern carbonate slope environments (in addition to those from current studies on Bahamian slopes). The hydrodynamic parameters and processes for gravity-induced mass movements involving only carbonate materials must be carefully documented and contrasted with the results from siliciclastic materials. A combination of detailed observations from submersibles, and high resolution seismic and bottom sampling is needed to make an inventory of the spectrum of sediments and structures that make up carbonate slope environments in the modern ocean.

ACKNOWLEDGEMENTS
Many of the original ideas presented here came about as a result of stimulating discussions with John Harper and Bob Stevens. John Hopkins, Dave Morrow and Federico Krause critically read the first manuscript and Roger Walker the present version. Gary Allwood and Dave Haden drafted the figures and Oralie Shearing typed the current manuscript.

REFERENCES

BASIC REFERENCES ON CARBONATE BASIN SLOPE FACIES
Cook, H.E., and Enos, P., eds., 1977. Deep-water carbonate environments: Society of Economic Paleontologists and Mineralogists, Special Publication 25, 336 p.

Cook, H.E., and Mullin, H.T., 1983. Basin margin environment. In Scholle, P.A., Bebout, D.G., and Moore, C.H., eds., Carbonate depositional environments. American Association of Petroleum Geologists, Memoir 33, p. 540-617.

Enos, P., and Moore, C.H., 1983. Fore-reef slope environment. In Scholle, P.A., Bebout, D.G., and Moore, C.H., eds., Carbonate depositional environments. American Association of Petroleum Geologists, Memoir 33, p. 508-537.

Hsu, K.J., and Jenkyns, H.C., eds., 1974. Pelagic sediments on land and under the sea. International Association of Sedimentologists, Special Publication 1, 448 p.

James, N.P., and Mountjoy, E.W., 1983. Shelf-slope break in fossil carbonate platforms: an overview. In Stanley, D.J., and Moore, G.T., eds., The shelfbreak: critical interface on continental margins. Society of Economic Paleontologists and Mineralogists, Special Publication 33, p. 189-206.

Mountjoy, E.W., Cook, H.E., Pray, L.C., and McDaniel, P.N. 1972. Allochthonous carbonate debris flows – worldwide indicators of reef complexes, banks or shelf margins. Proceedings of 24th International Geological Congress, Section 6, p. 172-189.

Read, J.G., 1982. Carbonate platforms of passive (extensional) continental margins: types, characteristics and evolution. Tectonophysics, v. 81, p. 195-212.

Scholle, P.A., 1977. Deposition, diagenesis and hydrocarbon potential of "deeper-water" limestones. American Association of Petroleum Geologists, Continuing Education Course Notes, Series No. 7, 25 p.

Scholle, P.A., Arthur, M.A., and Ekdale, A.A., 1983. Pelagic environment. In Scholle, P.A., Bebout, D.G., and Moore, C.H., eds., Carbonate depositional environments. American Association of Petroleum Geologists, Memoir 33, p. 620-692.

Wilson, J.L., 1969. Microfacies and sedimentary structures in "deeper-water" lime mudstones. In Friedman, G.M., ed., Depositional environments in carbonate rocks. Society of Economic Paleontologists and Mineralogists, Special Publication 14, p. 4-19.

EXAMPLES OF ANCIENT CARBONATE BASIN SLOPES
The following papers contain examples of ancient carbonate basin slopes, with a bias towards examples in Canada. However as with reefs, the location of the country in temperate to boreal latitudes during much of the Mesozoic and, unfortunately, the Cenozoic results in Canadian examples being mainly Paleozoic in age.

Bosellini, A., 1984. Progradation geometries of carbonate platforms: examples from the Triassic of the Dolomites, northern Italy. Sedimentology, v. 31, p. 1-24

Conaghan, P.J., Mountjoy, E.W., Edgecombe, D.R., Talent, J.A., and Owen, D.E., 1976. Nubrigyn algal reefs (Devonian), eastern Australia: allochthonous blocks and megabreccias. Geological Society of America, Bulletin, v. 87, p. 515-530.

Cook, H.E., McDaniel, P.N., Mountjoy, E.W., and Pray, L.C., 1972. Allochthonous carbonate debris flows at Devonian bank ("reef") margins Alberta, Canada. Bulletin of Canadian Petroleum Geology, v.20, p. 439-497.

Davies, G.R., 1977. Turbidites, debris sheets and truncation structures in upper Paleozoic deep-water carbonates of the Sverdrup Basin, Arctic Archipelago. In Cook, H.E., and Enos, P., eds., Deep-water carbonate environments. Society of Economic Paleontologists and Mineralogists, Special Publication 25, p. 221-249.

Enos, P., 1977. Tamabra limestone of the Poza Rica trend, Cretaceous, Mexico. *In* Examples of ancient carbonate slope-to-basin systems. Cook, H.E., and Enos, P., eds., Deep-water carbonate environments. Society of Economic Paleontologists and Mineralogists, Special Publication 25, p. 273-314.

Hopkins, J.C., 1977. Production of fore-slope breccia by differential submarine cementation and downslope displacement of carbonate sands, Miette and Ancient Wall buildups, Devonian, Canada. *In* Cook, H.E., and Enos, P., eds., Deep-water carbonate environments. Society of Economic Paleontologists and Mineralogists, Special Publication 25, p. 155-170.

Hubert, J.F., Suchecki, R.K., and Callahan, R.K.M., 1977. Cow Head breccia: sedimentology of the Cambro-Ordovician continental margin, Newfoundland. *In* Cook, H.E., and Enos, P., eds., Deep-water carbonate environments. Society of Economic Paleontologists and Mineralogists, Special Publication 25, p. 125-154.

Hurst, J.M., and Surlyk, F., 1983. Depositional environments along a carbonate ramp to slope transition in the Silurian of Washington Land, North Greenland. Canadian Journal of Earth Sciences, v. 20, p. 473-449.

Kindle, C.H., and Whittington, H.B., 1958. Stratigraphy of the Cow Head Region, Western Newfoundland. Geological Society of America, Bulletin, v. 69, p. 315-342.

Krause, F.F., and Oldershaw, A.E., 1979. Submarine carbonate breccia beds – a depositional model for two-layer, sediment gravity flows from the Sekwi Formation (Lower Cambrian), Mackenzie Mountains, Northwest Territories. Canadian Journal of Earth Sciences, v. 16, p. 189-199.

Mackenzie, W.S., 1970. Allochthonous reef-debris limestone turbidites, Powell Creek, Northwest Territories. Bulletin of Canadian Petroleum Geology, v. 18, p. 474-492.

McIlreath, I.A., 1977a. Stratigraphic and sedimentary relationships at the western edge of the Middle Cambrian Carbonate Facies Belt, Field, British Columbia. Ph.D. Thesis, University of Calgary, Calgary, Alberta, 269 p.

McIlreath, I.A., 1977b. Accumulation of a Middle Cambrian, deep-water, basinal limestone adjacent to a vertical, submarine carbonate escarpment, southern Rocky Mountains, Canada. *In* Cook, H.E., and Enos, P., eds., Deep-water carbonate environments. Society of Economic Paleontologists and Mineralogists, Special Publication 25, p. 113-124.

Morrow, D.W., 1978. The Prairie Creek Embayment and associated slope, shelf and basin deposits. Geological Survey of Canada Paper 78-1A, p. 361-370.

Ross, D.C., 1965 Geology of the Independence Quadrangle, Inyo County, California. United States Geological Survey, Bulletin 1181-0, 64 p.

Srivastava, P.C., Stearn, C.W., and Mountjoy, E.W., 1972. A Devonian megabreccia at the margin of the Ancient Wall carbonate complex, Alberta. Bulletin of Canadian Petroleum Geology, v. 20, p. 412-438.

Thomson, A.F., and Thomasson, M.R., 1969. Shallow to deep water facies development in the Dimple Limestone (Lower Pennsylvanian), Marathon Region, Texas. *In* Friedman, G.M., ed., Depositional environments in carbonate rocks. Society of Economic Paleontologists and Mineralogists, Special Publication 14, p. 57-78.

Tyrrell, W.W., Jr., 1969. Criteria useful in interpreting environments of unlike but time-equivalent carbonate units (Tansill-Capitan-Lamar), Capitan Reef Complex, West Texas and New Mexico. *In* Friedman, G.M., ed., Depositional environments in carbonate rocks. Society of Economic Paleontologists and Mineralogists, Special Publication 14, p. 80-97.

Unfortunately a number of excellent papers on Mississippian and Permian basin slope carbonates occurring in New Mexico and Texas exist in difficult-to-obtain guidebooks of local societies. For example, the "Guidebook to the Mississippian Shelf-edge and Basin Facies Carbonates, Sacramento Mountains and Southern New Mexico Region", published by the Dallas Geological Society (1975).

EXAMPLES OF MODERN CARBONATE BASIN SLOPES

Andrews, J.E., 1970. Structure and sedimentary development of the outer channel of the Great Bahama Canyon. Geological Society of America, Bulletin, v. 81, p. 217-226.

Andrews, J.E., Shepard, F.P., and Hurley, R.J., 1970. Great Bahama Canyon. Geological Society of America, Bulletin, v. 81, p. 1061-1078.

Bushby, R.F., 1969. Ocean surveying from manned submersibles. Marine Technological Society Journal, v. 3, p. 11-24.

Conolly, J.R., and Ewing, M., 1967. Sedimentation in the Puerto Rico Trench. Journal of Sedimentary Petrology, v. 37, p. 44-59.

Emery, K.O., Tracey, J.I., Jr., and Ladd, H.S., 1954. Geology of Bikini and nearby atolls. United States Geological Survey Paper 260-A, p. 1-262.

Ginsburg, R.N., and James, N.P., 1973. British Hondoras by submarine. Geotimes, v. 18, p. 23-24.

Goreau, T.F., and Land, L.S., 1974. Fore-reef morphology and depositional processes, North Jamaica. *In* Laporte, L.F., ed., Reefs in time and space. Society of Economic Paleontologists and Mineralogists, Special Publication 18, p. 77-89.

Hine, A.C., Wilber, R.J., and Neumann, A.C., 1981. Carbonate sand bodies along contrasting shallow bank margins facing open seaways; northern Bahamas. American Association of Petroleum Geologists, Bulletin, v. 65, p. 261-290.

James, N.P., and Ginsburg, R.N., 1979. The deep seaward margin of Belize barrier and atoll reefs. International Association of Sedimentologists Sepcial Publication 3, 201 p.

Land, L.S., and Moore, C.H., 1977. Deep fore-reef and upper island slope, North Jamaica. *In* Frost, S.H., Weiss, M.P., and Saunders, J.B., eds., Reefs and related carbonates: ecology and sedimentology. American Association of Petroleum Geologists, Studies in Geology No. 4, p. 53-67.

Moore, C.H., Graham, E.A., and Land, L.S., 1976. Sediment transport and dispersal across the deep fore-reef and island slope (-55m to -305m), Discovery Bay, Jamaica. Journal of Sedimentary Petrology, v. 46, p. 174-187.

Mullins, H.T., and Neumann, A.C., 1979. Deep carbonate bank margin structure and sedimentation in the northern Bahamas. *In* Doyle, L.J., and Pilkey, O.H., eds., Geology of continental slopes. Society of Economic Paleontologists and Mineralogists, Special Publication 27, p. 165-192.

Mullins, H.T., Heath, K.C., VanBuren, H.M., and Newton, C.R., 1984. Anatomy of a modern open-ocean carbonate slope: northern Little Bahama Bank. Sedimentology, v. 31, p. 141-168.

Paulus, F.J., 1972. The geology of site 98 and the Bahama Platform. Initial reports of the deep sea drilling project. National Science Foundation, Washington, D.C., v. 11, p. 877.

Schlager, W., and Chermak, A., 1979. Sediment facies of platform-basin transition, Tongue of the Ocean, Bahamas. *In* Doyle, L.J., and Pilkey, O.H., eds., Geology of continental slopes. Society of Economic Paleontologists and Mineralogists, Special Publication 27, p. 193-208.

ADDITIONAL REFERENCES CITED IN TEXT

Ager, D.V., 1973. The nature of the stratigraphical record. New York, J. Wiley and Sons, Inc., 114 p.

Ahr, W.M., 1973. The carbonate ramp: an alternative to the shelf model. Transactions of the Gulf Coast Association of Geological Sciences , v. 23, p. 221-225.

Dott, R.H., Jr., 1963. Dynamics of subaqueous gravity depositional processes. American Association of Petroleum Geologists, Bulletin, v. 47, p. 104-128.

Evans, I., and Kendal, C.G. St. C., 1977. An interpretation of the depositional setting of some deep-water Jurassic carbonates of the central High Atlas Mountains, Morocco. *In* Cook, H.E., and Enos, P., eds., Deep-water carbonate environments. Society of Economic Paleontologists and Mineralogists, Special Publication 25, p. 249-261.

Ginsburg, R.N., and James, N.P., 1974. Holocene carbonates of continental shelves. *In* Burk, C.A., and Drake, C.L., eds., Geology of continental margins. New York, Springer-Verlag, p. 137-155.

Hampton, M.A., 1972. The role of subaqueous debris flow in generating turbidity currents. Journal of Sedimentary Petrology, v. 42, p. 775-793.

Harms, J.C., 1974. Brushy Canyon Formation, Texas: a deep-water density current deposit. Geological Society of America, Bulletin, v. 85, p. 1763-1784.

Hay, W.W., Southam, J.R., and Noel, M.R., 1976. Carbonate mass balance – cycling and deposition on shelves and in deep sea (Abst.). American Association of Petroleum Geologists, Bulletin, v. 60, p. 678.

Hine, A.C., and Neumann, A.C., 1977. Shallow carbonate-bank-margin growth and structure, Little Bahama Bank, Bahamas. American Association of Petroleum Geologists, Bulletin, v. 61, p. 376-406.

James, N.P., 1978. Facies models 10: reefs. Geoscience Canada, v. 5, p. 16-26.

James, N.P., and Choquette, P.W., 1983. Diagenesis 6, limestones – the sea floor diagenetic environment. Geoscience Canada, v. 10, p. 162-179.

Lowe, D.R., 1976. Grain flow and grain flow deposits. Journal of Sedimentary Petrology, v. 46, p. 188-199.

Meischner, K.D., 1964. Allodapische Kalke, Turbidite in riff-nahen Sedimentations – Becken. *In* Bouma, A.H., and Brouwer, A., eds., Turbidites. Amsterdam, Elsevier, p. 156-191.

Middleton, G.V., and Hampton, M.A., 1973. Sediment gravity flows; mechanics of flow and deposition. *In* Middleton, G.V., and Bouma, A.H., eds., Turbidites and deepwater sedimentation. Society of Economic Paleontologists and Mineralogists, Short Course, p. 1-38.

Schlager, W., and Schlager, M., 1973. Clastic sediments associated with radiolarites (Tauglboden-Schichten, Upper Jurassic, eastern Alps). Sedimentology, v. 20, p. 65-89.

Schlager, W., Hooke, R.L., and James, N.P., 1976. Episodic erosion and deposition in the Tongue of the Ocean, Bahamas. Geological Society of America Bulletin, v. 87, p. 1115-1118.

Schlager, W., and James, N.P., 1978. Low-magnesian calcite limestones forming at the deep-sea floor, Tongue of the Ocean, Bahamas. Sedimentology, v. 25, p. 675-702.

Schlager, W., and Ginsburg, R.N., 1981. Bahama carbonate platforms – the deep and the past. Marine Geology, v. 44, p. 160-181.

Tucker, M.E., 1974. Sedimentology of Palaeozoic pelagic limestones: the Devonian Griotte (Southern France) and Cephalopodenkalk (Germany). *In* Hsu, K.J., and Jenkyns, H.C., eds., Pelagic sediments: on land and under the sea. International Association of Sedimentologists Special Publication 1, p. 71-92.

Walker, R.G., 1976. Facies models 2: Turbidites and associated coarse clastic deposits: Geoscience Canada, v. 3, p. 25-36.

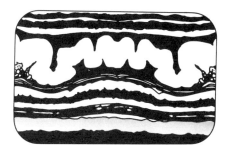

Evaporites

ALAN C. KENDALL
Sohio Petroleum Company
50 Fremont Street
San Francisco, California 94105

Table 1
Major Constituents of Marine Evaporites

Sulphates	
Anhydrite	$CaSO_4$
Gypsum	$CaSO_4 \cdot 2H_2O$
Langbeinite	$K_2Mg_2(SO_4)_3$
Polyhalite	$K_4CaMg(SO_4)_4 \cdot 2H_2O$
Kieserite	$MgSO_4 \cdot H_2O$
Kainite	$KMg(SO_4)Cl \cdot 3H_2O$
Clorides	
Halite	$NaCl$
Sylvite	KCl
Carnallite	$KMgCl_3 \cdot 6H_2O$

A fuller listing of evaporite minerals can be found in Stewart, 1963.

INTRODUCTION

Evaporites are rocks composed of minerals that form by precipitation from concentrated brines (Table 1). Concentration necessary for this precipitation is generally attained by evaporation at the air-water interface but can also be achieved by brine freezing or by subsurface processes such as ion-filtration of residual connate fluids. The usual source for aerially-extensive evaporite deposits is seawater, but saline ground waters are the sources of many smaller evaporite deposits in continental settings. Evaporite minerals may precipitate within a saline water body, at the brine surface, at a sediment-brine interface, or interstitially within the sediment, either beneath a body of brine or subaerially. They may develop anywhere there is a substantial deficit in the water budget due to evaporation. Many evaporites are not strictly primary precipitates, but are diagenetic minerals emplaced within non-evaporite sediments. Still others are diagenetic replacements of true primary precipitates.

Evaporites can be viewed in terms of two classes of models: 1) sedimentary models that relate structures and textures to hydrodynamic and other depositional parameters, and 2) post-depositional models that relate present mineralogical compositions to the physico-chemical environments of diagenetic processes. Because evaporite deposition is controlled mainly by physico-chemical parameters and because many changes occur during early diagenesis (where they are controlled by depositional settings), the dis-

tinction between the two classes is blurred. This paper discusses sedimentary models but will mention diagenetic changes when these are early, or when the origin of the diagenetic change is disputed.

Evaporite Models

Four main factors make evaporites probably the least suitable of sedimentary rocks for facies modelling.

1) Only recently have evaporites been considered as sediments rather than just chemical precipitates. The initial success of the chemical approach caused this to dominate evaporite studies and only recently have sedimentary aspects been stressed. For many evaporite deposits therefore, the basic data upon which facies models are based is lacking. When models have been constructed they all too commonly have been based upon a few occurrences. Thus distillation of essential from local details may be far from complete. The chemical approach has also generated a host of depositional models based upon theoretical concepts of seawater evaporation but which ignore sedimentological evidence. These cannot rightly be considered facies models, yet these aspects cannot be ignored.

2) Observations upon evaporites may be limited. Only rarely are unaltered evaporites exposed in outcrop. Most evaporite studies are confined to subsurface materials – cores or mine openings. Drill cuttings rarely provide enough information. For many poorly sampled evaporite units the

gross three-dimensional characteristics are established but internal details (upon which facies modelling depends) are poorly known.

3) Areas of present day evaporite deposition comparable in size with those of the past are absent. The Holocene transgression has not been conducive to the formation of large-scale evaporitic environments. Ancient evaporite deposits reach stratigraphic thicknesses and aerial extents up to two or three orders of magnitude greater than those forming today. It is uncertain whether or not modern small depositional areas (or even artifical salt-pans) are fully representative. Thus the opportunity to utilize modern sediments to construct facies models is either denied to us or is controversial.

4) Lastly, but most importantly, evaporites are most susceptible to wholesale post-depositional change. The solubility of evaporite minerals, the tendency for metastable hydrates to be precipitated, and the susceptibility of many salts to flowage under burial conditions, are features unique to evaporites and have the common result of obliterating original sedimentary characteristics during diagenesis. The profound effects of these changes mean that some evaporites are better considered metamorphic rocks than sediments. Recognition of primary features and formulation of depositional models for many evaporites may thus be impossible. The situation with respect to many bittern salt deposits is most extreme for

they commonly lack any vestige of original fabrics, structures or mineralogy. They commonly are also the products of diagenetic/metamorphic processes rather than being primary sedimentary accumulates. There is a corresponding dearth of facies models for these deposits.

In the light of these four factors it is hardly surprising that basic disagreements exist about almost all aspects of evaporite genesis. Most significant amongst them are whether basin-central evaporites were deposited in deep or shallow water, and whether many evaporite structures and textures are of primary or post-depositional origin.

There is probably not a single Holocene depositional environment that is strictly analogous to those that generated most ancient evaporite sequences. Although there may be many similarities, there are always one or more aspects (commonly scale) that cannot be fitted into the analog scheme. The technique used to interpret ancient evaporites is to take items of information from several modern settings and relate them to their ancient counterparts.

No single facies model can be applied to so heterogeneous a grouping of rocks as the evaporites. A persistant dogma since the 1960s that evaporites represent deposits of supratidal or sabkha environments became much too one-sided. Yet today we face the danger of the other end of the pendulum, for some supratidal evaporites appear to be interpreted as subaqueous on insufficient grounds.

Given the correct environmental conditions, evaporites can mimic most other sediment types. There are evaporite turbidites and oolites; 'reefs' composed of huge gypsum crystals that formed mounds standing proud of the basin floor, and shallow-water clastic evaporites that resemble in texture and sedimentary structure their clastic or carbonate equivalents. Since evaporites may exhibit detrital as well as crystalline precipitate textures, these sediments constitute one of the most variable of sedimentary rock groups.

Evaporite minerals may form only a minor component of some deposits (isolated gypsum crystals in continental redbeds would be an example) and these are best considered part of other facies models.

At the present day, areas of sufficient evaporation (and negative water balance) to cause evaporite deposits to form are present between 10 and 40° north and south of the Equator (subtropical high-pressure atmospheric circulation zones). These zones have been wider in the past, particularly during periods of low sea level. The presence of evaporitic sodium sulfate deposits in seasonally-frozen lakes in Antartica and Western Canada deomonstrate that negative water balances are not exclusively a condition of low latitudes.

DEPOSITIONAL ENVIRONMENTS OF EVAPORITES
Evaporite sequences have been generated in a variety of geographic settings (Fig. 1): 1) coastal intertidal and supratidal environments (marine sabkhas), 2) lagoons on coasts, 3) large basins, with brine level below sea-level and marine inflow; brine level within the basin may be high (giving deep-water evaporites) or low, and 4) non-marine interior basins. These environments may be present in a wide spectrum of tectonic settings. They occur within 1) continental margins and shelves, 2) interior cratonic basins of varying

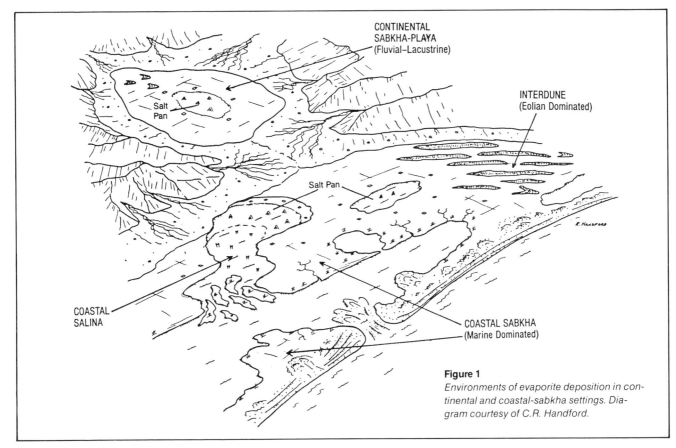

Figure 1
Environments of evaporite deposition in continental and coastal-sabkha settings. Diagram courtesy of C.R. Handford.

depths and 3) rifted continental margins – in which case evaporites may be present in areas that are now oceanic.

Of the many possible environments of evaporite precipitation, five major categories (or regimes) were identified by Schreiber *et al.* (1976) with a further subdivision in each category as to whether the evaporites are calcium sulphates or halides (with or without complex sulphates) (Fig. 2). Regimes grade into each other such that the identification may depend more upon associated facies than upon internal characteristics. Continental sabkha deposits commonly are internally identical with coastal sabkha deposits, differing only by being inserted within continental deposits. Furthermore, the degree of restriction required to generate halite and/or subaqueous sulphate deposits ensures that all these environments have some of the attributes of the continental regime. Distinction between large hypersaline inland lakes and partially desiccated small seas can be a somewhat academic exercise.

Three main environmental groupings are recognized here: continental, coastal sabkha, and subaqueous marine. Many ancient evaporites were deposited subaqueously within enclosed and hypersaline basins. The primary composition, textures and form of these subaqueous deposits are now only partially understood because, in part, so few hypersaline water bodies occur at the present day for study; none of them of large size.

The origins of small, thin evaporite deposits and marginal-marine evaporites composed of numerous superimposed sabkha cycles are readily discernable. In contrast, the formation of vast, thick, basin-central evaporites, some which cover millions of square kilometres and exceed several kilometres in thickness or which may directly overlie oceanic basement, present very different problems.

Some authors suggest that the enormous evaporite deposits form by lateral and vertical accretion within depositional environments similar to those of

the present time (in supratidal flats, lagoons and salinas; Shearman, 1966; Friedman, 1972) whereas others consider that the great difference in scale between recent and ancient deposits requires explanations that are drastic departures from the present day settings of evaporites. They suggest either that precipitation occurred from vast bodies of hypersaline water (Schmalz, 1969; Hite, 1970; Matthews, 1974), or that evaporites were precipitated on the floors of desiccated seas (Hsu *et al.*, 1973).

Theoretical models, which were developed to answer the major compositional problems posed by large evaporite bodies, must be integrated with evidence from rock textures and structures (facies models). Unfortunately this integration is not yet possible because of basic disagreements concerning the depositional paleogeography of evaporites, and because many evaporite rock characteristics still have to be studied in detail or have disputed origins. Many evaporites are not just passive chemical precipitates or displacive growth structures, but are transported and reworked in the same ways as siliciclastic and carbonate deposits. For these sediments, sedimentary structures are a major key to unravelling the facies and will be emphasized here. Internal characteristics of evaporites alone can provide the necessary information about depositional environments. The most pressing environmental concern has been, and still is, the depth of water in which evaporites form.

Schreiber *et al.* (1976) recognize three main environmental settings for subaqueous evaporites. These are identified on the basis of sediment characteristics, believed to reflect the depth at which deposition occurs. Criteria used include: 1) structures indicative of wave and current activity, identifying an intertidal and shallow subtidal environment; 2) algal structures (in the absence of wave and current-induced structures), which are believed to identify a deeper environment but one that still resides with the photic zone; and 3) widespread evenly-laminated sediments (rhythmites) that lack evidence of current and algal activity (perhaps associated with gravity-displaced sediments), and characterize the deep, subphotic environment.

Considerable difficulty exists in using

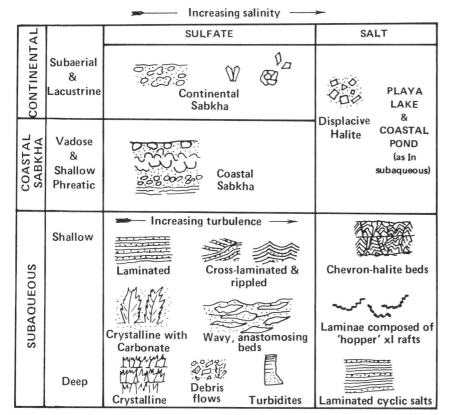

Figure 2

Summary of physical environments of evaporite deposition and the main facies present (modified from Schreiber et al., 1976).

the presence or absence of algal and current structures as relative depth indicators. Because stromatolites commonly grow in protected, quiet-water, shallow environments, the absence of current structures from algal-bearing sediments is no criterion of greater depth. In addition, the photic limit in hypersaline waters probably always occurs at shallow depths, because suspended organic residues (preserved because of the poorly-oxygenated nature of brines), surface nucleated and floating evaporite crystals, and numerous anaerobic bacteria (commonly red in colour) all reduced light penetration – sometimes to depths of only a few decimetres. Such turbid brines also trap radiant heat and may reach temperatures of up to 90° C; another adverse environmental factor that will inhibit or curtail algal growth.

The presence of widely-correlatable laminations is not a definitive feature of deep-water environments because such laminations have also been found in evaporites that were deposited in sub-aerial, but ephemerally flooded, environments.

For these reasons, only two sub-aqueous environments are here distinguished; the deep-water environment characterized by the presence of laminites and gravity-displaced sediments and the shallow-water environment that represents a plethora of subenvironments which, as yet, are poorly characterized.

CONTINENTAL EVAPORITES

Evaporites formed exclusively from continental groundwaters are not commonly recognized in rock record. Many evaporites formed in continental settings were derived partly from marine input, but it is difficult to identify the relative importance of continental and marine influences. Compared with seawater, river waters are generally richer in calcium bicarbonate and calcium sulphate than sodium chloride. Non-marine evaporites thus commonly contain sodium carbonates (such as trona, $Na_2CO_3 \cdot NaHCO_3 \cdot 2H_2O$) or sodium sulphates (such as mirabilite, $Na_2SO_4 \cdot 10H_2O$). The presence of these minerals, which are not precipitated from seawater, is evidence that non-marine waters were important in the evaporite basin. An association of evaporites with alluvial fan and fluvial dep-

osits, aeolian sediments, redbeds and lacustrine carbonates all suggest non-marine origins.

The rarity of continental evaporites (particularly pre-Tertiary) also reflects the ephemeral nature of many evaporite minerals in the depositional environment. Many are recycled or moved upwards at the same rate as sediment accretion and are thus non-accumulative. Their former presence may leave evidence in the form of crystal molds or disrupted lamination.

Continental evaporites occur in saline soils and as sedimentary bodies in central parts of playa (continental sabkha) basins, particularly in association with playa lakes. With the possible exception of gypsum crust (gypcrete) which forms in the same manner as caliche (calcrete) but in more arid areas, the accumulation of pedogenic evaporites is unlikely to be preserved in the rock record. Watson (1979) describes several proposed origins for gypsum crust in areas peripheral to hot deserts.

PLAYA (CONTINENTAL SABKHA) EVAPORITES

These evaporites, whether precipitated from brine lakes or emplaced within desiccated sediments, are usually precipitated in the lowest areas of enclosed area drainage basins – environments that are characterized by almost horizontal and largely vegetation-free surfaces of fine-grained sediments (Figs. 3 and 4). These base-level plains are a distinctive feature of arid regions and are

given many different names (sabkha, sebkha, playa, salina, pan, chott). The name playa is employed here for these features. Playa evaporites are one component of a complex of different subenvironments, of which Hardie et al. (1978) recognize 10: 1) alluvial fan, 2) sandflat, 3) mudflat, 4) ephemeral saline lake, 5) perennial saline lake, 6) dune field, 7) perennial stream floodplain, 8) ephemeral stream floodplain, 9) springs, and 10) shoreline features. Sediments deposited in subenvironments 1, 6, 7, and 8 are covered in other chapters of this book.

Alluvial fans at basin edges trap most coarse detritus so that only the finest material is carried into the basin. Apart from sheetwash flow during storms, water circulation is generally confined to the subsurface although ephemeral or perennial streams may cross the playas.

At the base of the fans occurs a flat sandy apron where the braided channels of the fans lose their identity and sheetflow during flooding-events is the dominant depositional process. Sediments are planar and wavy-laminated sands (Fig. 5a) which may become cemented by carbonate or gypsum if groundwaters are already concentrated.

Some playas have water tables so deep that no groundwater discharge occurs at the surface. These playas possess smooth, hard and dry surfaces and evaporites are commonly lacking. Most evaporites accumulate within playas where groundwater discharge

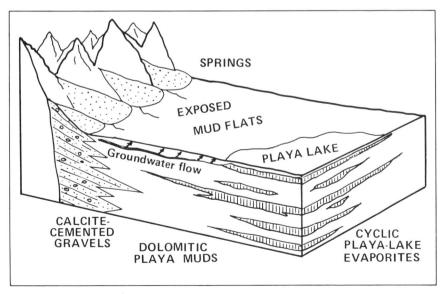

Figure 3
Schematic block-diagram showing depo-   *sitional framework in the Playa Complex model (after Eugster and Hardie, 1975).*

Figure 4
View to the west over Bristol Dry Lake (California) toward alluvial fans. Photograph courtesy of C.R. Handford.

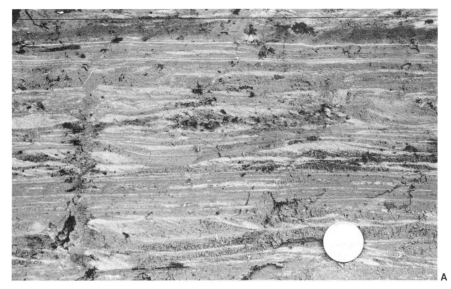

Figure 5
A) Flaser-bedded clastic playa sediments with clay drapes (5 cm coin for scale).

B) Contorted gypsum and red mud (5 cm coin for scale). Both photographs from Bristol Dry Lake and courtesy of C.R. Handford.

occurs and this may be: 1) indirect, caused by capillary rise, evaporative pumping or evapotranspiration by phreatophytes from a shallow water table, or 2) directly from the water table (perennially or seasonally at the playa surface) or from springs. Many playas are equilibrium deflation-sedimentation surfaces with topography controlled by the water table level and its gradients.

The closeness of the water table to the surface allows great evaporative loss and concomitant concentration of pore fluids. Playas are thus sites of brine formation irrespective of the salinities of peripheral groundwaters that feed into them. The brine type and the mineralogy of evaporites that precipitate are, however, dependent upon the chemical composition of the groundwater supply.

Hydrographic lows on the surface may be occupied by perennial or seasonal bodies of shallow water (playa lakes), fed directly by groundwater seepage, by springs or by accumulation of storm waters. Playa lakes exist only at times when water input (precipitation and inflow) is less than the water lost by evaporation. The latter is dependent upon climate, water salinity and the geometry of the water body.

Continuing evaporation and evapotranspiration generate a pronounced groundwater concentration gradient towards the basin centre or along the flow paths taken by the groundwater. Saturation with respect to calcium and magnesium carbonates is reached at an early stage, causing precipitation of calcite cement and caliche layers in alluvial fans, or of soft micron-sized high Mg-calcite and protodolomite in playa fringes, or of travertines and pisolitic caliche when precipitation occurs from surface waters associated with peripheral springs (Fig. 7A). Deposition on playa flats occurs as a mud because sediments here are kept permanently moist by the groundwater discharge (Eugster and Hardie, 1975). The carbonates should be considered evaporites because they form in exactly the same manner as gypsum and more saline minerals further into the basin. Together with any detrital sediments, the carbonate muds are transported toward the basin centre by storm sheet-floods which imparts the laminated or cross-laminated (Fig. 7B) structure. This lamination, however, is also continuously being disrupted and destroyed by

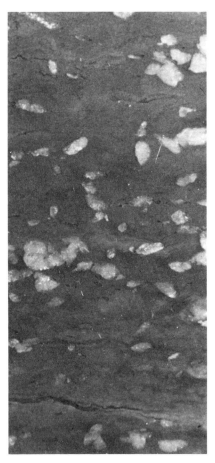

Figure 6
*Red dolomitic mudstones with anhydrite
pseudomorphs after gypsum crystals.
Watrous Formation, Saskatchewan. Probable
playa flat deposit. Slab 9 cm wide.*

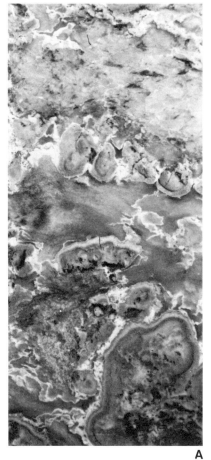

A

Figure 7
*Anydrite (after gypsum crystals) displacing
(and replacing?) pisolitic caliche in (A) and
possible laminated dolomite-calcium sul-*

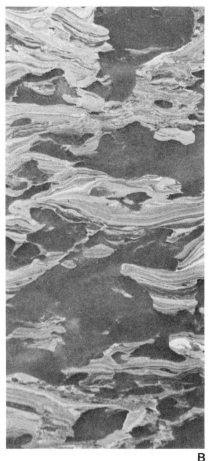

B

*phate playa flat deposits in (B); both from the
Whitkow Anhydrite (Prairie Evaporite Formation; Middle Devonian), Saskatchewan. Slabs
about 9 cm wide.*

further groundwater discharge (creating
porous 'putty-ground' surfaces), by the
growth and dissolution of ephemeral
evaporite crystals and crusts, and by
episodes of surficial drying that cause
extensive and multiple mud-cracking.
Mine tailings on playas have been destroyed by these processes in less than
50 years.

Hardie *et al.* (1978) distinguish
between two types of mudflat. The first,
(the dry mud-flat) lying closer to the
basin edge is characterized by preservation of sedimentary structures (Fig. 5a),
whereas in saline mudflats all structures
are destroyed by growth of evaporite
crystals (Fig. 6). Dry mudflats are commonly covered with thin saline efflorescent crusts and are composed of laminated sediments which may be partially
disrupted by mudcracks, sheetcracks
and saline mineral growth.

Removal of the less soluble mineral

phases (Ca-Mg carbonates and calcium
sulphates) profoundly modifies the
groundwater composition and thus the
sequence and type of saline minerals
that will precipitate in the basin centre.
A mineral zonation is formed with the
most soluble minerals located at the
most distal parts of the groundwater
flow and segregated from the less soluble phases.

Drying of the playa surface may
cause sediment deflation. Gypsum crystals, precipitated displacively in the
uppermost playa sediments, are concentrated as lag deposits and may be
swept together to form gypsum dunes.
Surficial gypsum may also dehydrate to
bassanite or anhydrite and, in some
playas, calcium sulphate is emplaced
directly as nodular anhydrite that is
seemingly identical with that in coastal
sabkha environments (Fig. 5b).

Efflorescent crusts of saline minerals

accumulate on playa surfaces during
groundwater discharge and evaporation, or by the evaporation to dryness of
ponded stormwaters. Because evaporation is rapid and complete, the crusts
include metastable and highly soluble
salts. Rain and storm waters dissolve
the most soluble saline minerals of the
crusts to form concentrated, but chemically 'simple', brines that owe their
highly modified compositions to this
fractional dissolution. Ultimately these
brines, which are dominated by only
one or two major solute species (e.g.,
NaCl, Na_2SO_4 or Na_2CO_3), reach the
basin centre.

Evaporite crusts may reach 30 cm or
more in thickness. Continual growth of
salt crystals causes great volume
increases and formation of salt-thrust
polygons (and other types of patterned
ground) or highly irregular surfaces
with relief perhaps reaching several

TOP

BASE

Figure 8
Cores exhibiting upward passage from displacive halite (haselgeberge)—some crystals with hopper morphology—into bedded halite with thin anhydrite and clay laminae. Sequence marks the change from a saline mud flat to a salt pan deposit. Lotzberg Salt, northern Alberta.

metres.

Even the salts that initially survive dissolution by storm waters and become buried are ephemeal if underlying groundwaters are undersaturated. Upward movement of the less saline water dissolves the salt crust and repricipitates it at the new surface. Towards the basin centre groundwaters become increasingly saline and calcium sulphate and even halite may become stable in the sediment. It is important to note that minerals in surface crusts do not necessarily reflect the character of evaporite minerals that are preserved in underlying sediments. Many fine-grained dolomitic red-bed sequences, such as the Keuper of Europe and the Watrous-Amaranth-Spearfish Formation of the Williston Basin (Fig. 6), probably represent deposits of these evaporitic but essentially non-evaporite-preserving environments. Halite within playa sediments has been described from modern environments by Gornitz and Schreiber (1981) and Handford (1982), but the details of its precipitation are still unclear. Smith (1971) described displacive halite in Permian red mudstones which he interprets as forming in a playa flat. Euhedral to subhedral halite cubes occur in abundant matrix but with increasing halite content the matrix becomes discontinuous, then confined to isolated polyhedral pockets as the halite becomes a near-continuous interlocking mosaic (Fig. 8). In more coherent sediments, however, halite occurs interstitially, as veneers around sand grains or as skeletal 'hopper' crystals (Fig. 9) – the last mentioned sometimes assuming extreme forms.

Playa lakes lie at the termination of groundwater flow paths and also accept concentrated brines formed when overland flows dissolved efflorescent crusts on the playa flats. These ponded brines continue to suffer evaporation and saline minerals are precipitated on the brine surface, at the brine-sediment interface and, perhaps also within the bottom sediments to form bedded crystal-brine accumulates. The characteristics of these accumulates are similar to those of marine-derived subaqueous evaporites.

Shallow playa lakes expand enormously during flooding events so that the saline mudflats, and perhaps parts of the dry mudflats, become inundated. Sediment deposition during such times

is largely the result of "settle-out" after the turbulence of the floodwaters subsides, giving rise to laminae of mud (which may be reworked by waves) that become disrupted by saline crystal growth and mudcracking as the evaporating lake retreats. Bacterial reduction of sulphate to produce H_2S and iron sulphides in the mud layers makes them black and anaerobic. Blue-green algae may bloom in the freshened lakes to form lake-bottom mats. However, these form after sedimentation has occurred. As the lake slowly evaporates and shrinks in size, the ponded brines eventually precipitate halite or trona.

In the saltpan single storm sheets thus result in deposition of a couplet of a thin mud layer (mm-scale, iron-sulphide-rich) overlain by a thicker crystalline salt-layer (upper part of Fig. 8). Repeated storms will superimpose couplets upon each other, although continued growth of salt crystals from groundwater after the lake completely dries up may destroy this bedding.

Evaporation in perennial playa lakes (lasting all year) produces an orderly succession of saline minerals with the more soluble overlying the less soluble. Freshening of lakes after storms or during the 'wet' periods dissolves the uppermost, more soluble minerals if water mixing is complete (as in shallow lakes). In deeper playa lakes the brine may become stratified with less saline water overlying a denser, more saline brine which protects the salt-layer from dissolution.

The crystal accumulates become exposed to the air during 'dry' episodes

Figure 9
Displacive halite hopper crystal in dolomite. Souris River Formation (Upper Devonian), Saskatchewan. Core is 12 cm across.

in many shallow playa lakes. The interlocking salt crystals have high porosities and interstices between crystals are occupied by saturated brine. The salt surface is kept moist by evaporative draw and by precipitation of dew on hydrophilic salt surfaces during cold nights. The evaporation rate falls to values as low as 1/170th of the rate from standing bodies of the same brine, and thus the brine level rarely drops more than a few metres beneath the surface. The crystalline surface is dissected by salt-thrust polygons and much eolian dust is trapped on the rough and damp surface. During 'wet' episodes or seasons, lakes are flooded by storm waters which dissolve surficial salts and introduce clastic material. Since new saline material is introduced during such times, generally less salt is dissolved than was precipitated during preceeding 'dry' seasons. Evaporation during the suceeding 'dry' period creates a new salt layer. Each salt layer is thus largely composed of recycled material. Layers are separated by mud partings composed of detrital material introduced by storm waters and the eolian sediment deposited on the emergent salt surfaces.

The order of salt deposition in ephemeral playa-lake deposits is commonly not that which would be predicted by the theoretical crystallization sequence from the brine. More soluble salts are found beneath less soluble, forming 'inversely stratified' salt deposits. Such sequences form because: 1) the more soluble salts in surface layers are dissolved during lake-flooding episodes, and 2) concentrated, dense brines created by evaporation during the emergent episodes sink through the crystal accumulate and displace the less concentrated brines, which emerge to the surface, there to cause further dissolution of more saline phases. It is from the descending, dense brines that the permanent, more saline salts precipitate. They must be regarded as early diagenetic additions. Density mixing of brines during emergent phases probably also encourages the replacement of metastable by stable minerals and the recrystallization of earlier formed salt; it thus contributes towards the early diagenetic lithification of the salt deposit. These effects are absent or less efficient within deposits formed from permanent brine lakes.

Perennial saline lakes, that persist for tens to thousands of years without drying up, require substantial perennial inflow, usually a large river which keeps the lake supplied with water, solutes and clastic sediment. Solutes may also be supplied by springs, and flashfloods introduce clastic sediments.

Evaporation occurs from the lake surface and creates a concentrated surface brine within which saline minerals nucleate and grow. The concentrated brine and the saline crystals sink toward the lake bottom and less-dense and less-concentrated inflow floats in over the brine, there to suffer evaporation. Unless the entire brine is saturated throughout, however, the crystals will dissolve before reaching the lake bottom. This will increase the brine concentration until, ultimately, the crystals no longer dissolve and begin to accumulate on the lake floor.

The minerals that precipitate from the surface waters depend upon the evaporation/inflow ratio, the chemical composition of the inflow and the stage in history of the lakes. If evaporation only slightly exceeds inflow, only minerals of low solubility (for example, alkaline earth carbonates) will be precipitated; but in order to precipitate a highly soluble mineral (such as halite) not only must the evaporation/inflow ratio be higher, but also the bottom brine must be dense enough to support the concentrated surface brine for a sufficient time to allow it to become supersaturated with respect to the saline material. If the bottom brine is not dense enough, the surface brine will sink before saturation is reached.

A lake that suffers a progressive decrease in its inflow will show a progressive change in chemical sedimentation from low to highly soluble salts. In contrast, a perennial lake that experiences a short-term decrease in inflow may experience no change in precipitation because the change in evaporation/inflow ratio is not matched by a sufficient change in the concentration and density of the lake brine which would allow more soluble precipitates to form in the surface brines.

Perennial saline deposits are laterally continuous, comprising saline mineral layers and clastic (mud) partings. Because evaporation is normally continuous throughout each year, the layering does not represent annual varves.

Instead it appears to result from non-periodic storm-influxes of mud that interrupt, or punctuate, the continuous rain of chemical sediment. Some clastic influxes could be seasonal, but are more likely to be irregularly spaced. Thicknesses of chemical layers are normally fractions of a millimetre for carbonates; several millimetres for gypsum laminae and thin beds of several centimetres for halite.

Where organic matter has accumulated in the bottom sediment, interstitial brines undergo sulphate reduction so that sulphate minerals dissolve. Gypsum precipitated from surface brines of the Dead Sea is absent in the bottom sediments. Sulphate reduction may result in the precipitation of iron sulphides, calcium carbonates or phosphate.

Variations in the Playa Model
Climate, groundwater source and composition, and the size of the playa complex are the main factors that dictate the type and distribution of evaporites within the playa setting.

A) Geologic/Geographic Setting. Three main settings are distinguished by Hardie et al. (1978), each characterized by associations of subenvironments.
1) Rain-shadow tectonic basins, like the block-fault desert basins of the western U.S.A., where there is both arid climate and hydrologic closure. The environment is characterized by huge alluvial fans and salt-encrusted ephemeral saline lakes ringed by narrow dry-mudflats and sandflats. Inflow into the lake is confined to groundwater influx and ephemeral storm runoff.
2) Wide shallow basins, which are dominated by ephemeral stream flood plains and dunes. Large areas become episolically inundated by ponded floodwaters which slowly evaporate, precipitating a saline crust. Complete desiccation gives rise to a salt pan (perhaps only one hundredth the area of the innundated region) fringed by a saline mudflat. The Lake Eyre basin of Southern Australia is a recent example of this association.
3) Perennial lakes, supplied by perennial streams, vary considerably according to the steepness of the basin flanks. Steep-sided basins

with perennial lakes (e.g., Dead Sea) are unlikely to change into ephemeral lakes and accumulate massive evaporite deposits. In contrast, wide basins have shallow perennial lakes (e.g., Lake Chad; Great Salt Lake, Utah) and decreased inflow rates cause significant lake shrinkage, exposing large parts of the lake bottom, or may cause the lake to dry up completely, converting it into an ephemeral lake.

B) Climate. Temperature influences evaporation rate but may also control the type and sequence of salt deposition more directly (Fig. 10). For example, in warm climates brines may precipitate halite before any sodium sulphate is deposited as thenardite (Na_2SO_4). Lakes in colder climates (as in the Prairie Provinces) precipitate mirabilite ($Na_2SO_4 \cdot 1OH_2O$) prior to halite.

Water input into the playa basin determines whether evaporites will precipitate and be preserved or not. They accumulate only at times when the water budget is a negative one. The history of playa lake complexes is one of alternating wet (pluvial) and dry (arid) conditions with corresponding transgressive, freshened, non-evaporite-precipitating lakes and regressive (shrinking) saline lake or dry playa stages. Pluvial phases (Fig. 10) are marked by partial to complete dissolution of earlier formed salts, by deposition of basal transgressive conglomerates and beach deposits over former playa flat deposits, and by deposition of non-saline lacustrine sediments (among which oil-shales may be conspicous). Increasing aridity (Fig 10A) is recorded by shrinkage of the lake area, a decrease in lake depth, and an increase in salinity ultimately leading to bedded evaporite deposition.

Climate changes may also be reflected in non-lacustrine playa sediments. Widespread rhythms of increasing evaporite content in red, dolomitic mudstones and siltstones of the Keuper (Upper Triassic) of Europe can be interpreted as indicating gradual reductions in the water influx to the depositional site and a corresponding increase in the persistence of evaporites in the sediments (Wills, 1970). Similar cyclic-Keuper sediments (alternations of laminated and structureless

268

mudstone/siltstones; dry mudflat-ephemeral halite saline mudflat deposits?) have recently been beautifully documented by Arthurton (1980). Cycles, however, are attributed to eustatic control (with sea-level perhaps controlling groundwater residency and concentration?).

Playas fed by artesian flow or from rivers may possess water tables that are located higher than those of neighbouring areas. Groundwater moves and becomes compositionally modified towards the basin-edge – in directions opposite to that in the ideal model. Mueller (1960) has shown that saline waters from the Andes evaporate on the floor of the central valley. Residual brines containing nitrates and iodates move upslope through the soil of the coastal mountain slopes by capillary migration and eventually evaporate to complete dryness.

C) Groundwater Composition. The mineralogy of salts precipitated in closed basins is controlled by the groundwater composition which, in turn, depends mainly upon the rock types in the source area and their mode of weathering. Commonly the evaporite minerals are similar to those precipitated from oceanic waters (hence the difficulty of distinguishing between them) and there is a predominance of alkaline-earth carbonates and various sulphates. This reflects the dominance of the same ions (Ca, Mg, Na, CO_3, HCO_3, SO_4, Cl), but they may be in different proportions from those in sea water. Such differences are most evident when the more saline salts are precipitated. Commonly calcium, sodium,

and bicarbonate are present in excess, leading to precipitation of salts such as pirssonite ($CaCO_3 \cdot Na_2CO_3 \cdot 2H_2O$), gaylussite ($CaCO_3 \cdot Na_2CO_3 \cdot 5H_2O$), and trona ($Na_2CO_3 \cdot NaHCO_3 \cdot 2H_2O$). When groundwaters are sulphate-rich then (dependent upon the dominant cations) glauberite ($CaSO_4 \cdot Na_2SO_4$), epsomite ($MgSO_4 \cdot 7H_2O$), bloedite ($MgSO_4 \cdot Na_2SO_4 \cdot 4H_2O$), thenardite ($Na_2SO_4$) and mirabilite ($Na_2SO_4 \cdot 10H_2O$) may be precipitated. Variation in playa and playa-lake mineralogy constitutes a vast field of study, one that cannot be discussed here. Reference should be made to Hardie and Eugster (1970) and Eugster and Hardie (1978).

D) Groundwater Source. It has been assumed that groundwaters move radially from the hinterland, converging toward the basin centre, which also marks the hydrographic low point of the basin. Flow is also assumed to be essentially horizontal and shallow subsurface (except during storms). This produces a concentric pattern of increasing groundwater salinity and a 'bulls-eye' pattern of salt deposition (more saline salts in the centre, Fig. 11). When the deepest part of the basin floor is not centrally located, or when groundwater enters the basin from one side, this ideal pattern is disturbed and becomes asymmetric. The compositions of brines in lakes fed by rivers are not modified by the prior precipitation and retention of less saline salts in peripheral playa flats. These brines retain their carbonate and sulphate contents and low-solubility salts may precipitate within the lake. Consequently there is less mineral

segregation in river-fed than in groundwater-fed playa systems.

Chaotic and disturbed sediments with irregularly distributed salt lenses occur beneath playas fed by artesian groundwater. The rise of less saline water dissolves previously deposited evaporites except where they are protected by impermeable clay seals. Removal of deep-lying salts results in localized subsidence, creation of depressions occupied by small playa lakes and pools, and deposition of small, isolated salt deposits.

E) Size of the Playa Complex. Much of the surface water introduced during storms will reach the basin centre in small playa basins. Lakes will thus exhibit many cycles of salt dissolution and precipitation and the efficiency of leaching salts from playa flats will be high. In contrast, storm waters may not reach playa lakes that are surrounded by vast playa flats: the water evaporates before it reaches the basin centre. Even during the 'wet' seasons waters may fail to reach lakes, which then become flooded only during exceptional circumstances. Such 'lakes' spend much of their time with emergent salt surfaces. Salt leaching on adjacent playa flats is inefficient and crystal accumulates will suffer more early-diagenetic changes at depth than those deposited in small playa basins.

SUPRATIDAL (COASTAL SABKHA) EVAPORITES
Coastal sabkha evaporites were briefly described by James (this volume) under the heading of arid-zone variants of

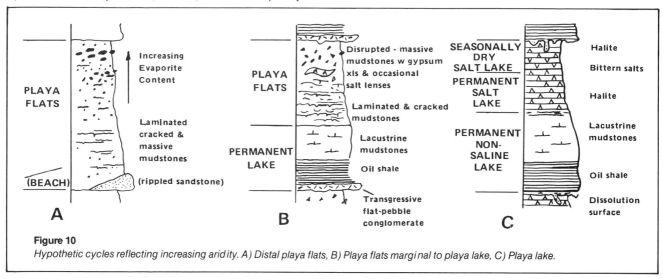

Figure 10
Hypothetic cycles reflecting increasing aridity. A) Distal playa flats, B) Playa flats marginal to playa lake, C) Playa lake.

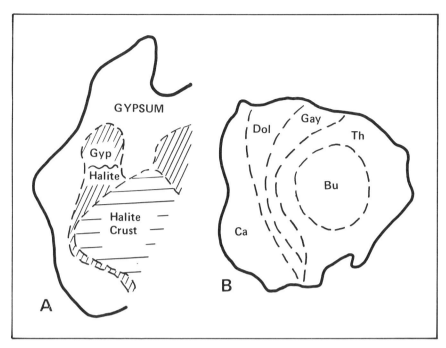

Figure 11
*Saline mineral zonation in playas. A) Yotvata
Sabkha (Israel) after Amiel and Friedman
(1971). B) Deep Spring Lake, California. Ca =
calcite/aragonite. Dol = dolomite. Gay =
gaylussite. Th = thenardite. Bu = burkeite
(after Jones, 1965).*

carbonate shallowing-upwards sequences. This style of shallowing-upward
sequence (Fig. 12) is composed of (in
upwards sequence): (1) carbonates, or
less commonly clastics, (2) similar sediments but with angular anhydrite
nodules, pseudomorphic after gypsum
crystals (Fig. 13), and (3) nodular-
mosaic anhydrite, commonly terminated by a sharp erosive contact (Fig.
14). The evaporites are interpreted as
diagenetic emplacements within supratidal environments because of their
close resemblance to the sequence of
lithologies in the progradational wedge
along the Abu Dhabi coast of the Persian Gulf (Fig. 15) (Shearman, 1966;
Kinsman, 1969; Butler, 1970; Bush,
1973). Our knowledge of these important sedimentary environments is dominated by the results of the numerous
studies of the sabkhas at Abu Dhabi.
This probably gives an unbalanced view
of sabkha systems as a whole.

On shallow stable shelves with arid
climates and low eolian sand influx the
seaward progradation of subtidal and
intertidal facies generates broad coastal
flats (or sabkhas) that lie just above high
tide level and extend between the offshore water body (commonly with coastal lagoons) and regions of arid contin-

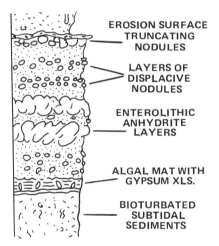

Figure 12
*Characteristic features of coastal sabkha
evaporites (after Shearman, 1966).*

ental sedimentation. This environment
is a product of both depositional and
diagenetic processes, the most important of the latter being the displacive
growth of early diagenetic calcium sulphate (or halite). Modern cratonic areas,
such as the Arabian coasts of the Persian Gulf and the coasts of Australia
and North Africa, provide the most
favorable settings for Recent sabkhas
and are associated with wide offshore

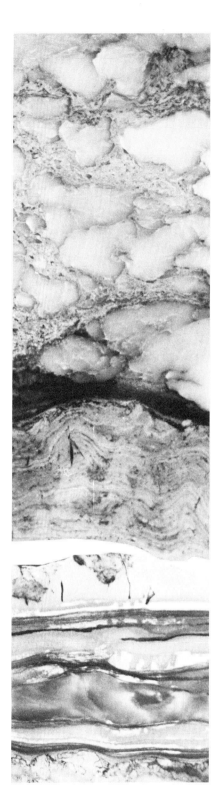

Figure 13
*Laminated microdolomites (probably hyper-
saline lagoonal) overlain by algal mat, with
gypsum pseudomorphed by anhydrite, and
nodular and mosaic coastal sabkha anhydrite. Frobisher Evaporite (Mississippian)
Saskatchewan. Core fits together but was
rotated during slabbing—slab is 10 cm wide.*

270

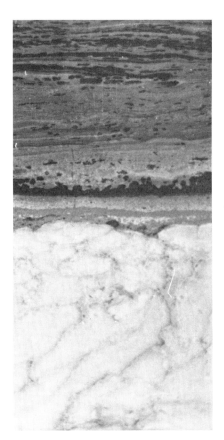

Figure 14
Upper part of sabkha cycle illustrated in Figure 13. Mosaic anhydrite cut across by erosion surface and surmounted by laminated micrites (with late-diagenetic anhydrite) of next lagoonal member. Frobisher Evaporite, Saskatchewan. Slab is 10 cm wide.

Figure 15
Oblique view of NW of Abu Dhabi sabkha environment. Sabkha in foreground; intertidal algal belt is the dark zone (1 to 2 km wide) and seaward is the lagoon, barrier islands and the open Persian Gulf shelf in the far distance. Photograph courtesy R.K. Park.

platforms or shelves. The sabkha is an equilibrium geomorphic surface whose level is dictated by the local level of the groundwater table. Sediment above the capillary fringe dries and is blown away by the wind unless cemented by salt.

Indigenous sediments of the supratidal flats are a reflection of the offshore sediment mosaic but may contain a substantial proportion of detrital sediment from the hinterland. Offshore sediments are washed over the sabkha during storms that periodically inundate seaward parts with marine floodwaters. Depressions (filled and buried tidal channels) act as conduits for flood and seepage waters.

Groundwaters beneath the sabkha are responsible for transporting materials precipitated as solid phases (evaporites, dolomite) and for removing byproducts of diagenetic reactions and non-accumulating ions. These waters become progressively concentrated as

they advance into the interior of the sabkha and all but the very seaward and landward margins may be saturated with respect to halite. Concentration occurs by evaporation from the capillary fringe and by dissolution of earlier-formed evaporites (particularly halides). Groundwaters lost by evaporation are replenished by: 1) downward seepage of storm-driven floodwaters (flood recharge), 2) gradual intrasediment flow, fluxing from the seaward margin, and 3) intrasediment flow, fluxing from a continental groundwater reservoir that affects landward parts of the sabkha (Fig. 16). Renfro (1974) believes that groundwater flow through continental clastics adjacent to coastal sabkhas (flow induced by evaporative pumping from the sabkha surface) is an important feature in the reddening of these sediments.

Our information about the hydrology of sabkhas is based almost entirely upon studies undertaken in Abu Dhabi (Kinsman, 1969; Butler, 1969; McKenzie et al., 1980; Patterson and Kinsman, 1981). After marine flooding, seawater sinks into the sabkha sediment, raising the water table. Capillary evaporation subsequently lowers the water table, increases salinity and promotes upward water movement within the phreatic

zone by evaporative pumping.

The water table inclines seaward (Patterson and Kinsman, 1981) but the seaward migration of interstitial brines is slow and is insufficient to explain the extensive dolomitization that occurs in the sabkha sediments. Salinity also decreases downwards (caused by the effects of surface evaporation and the upward movement of less saline brines induced by evaporative pumping). Such upward movement precludes evaporative reflux of the dense brines.

Interstitial water movement is limited by the impermeable nature of the sediments (commonly carbonate muds in part compacted by displacement growth of evaporites) and impermeable barriers in the form of buried algal mats (Bush, 1973) and cemented layers (McKenzie et al., 1980) act as aquitards and divide the sabhka sedimentary prism into several hydrostatic zones. Upward movement of groundwater between these zones only occurs where these impermeable barriers are broken.

The relative importance of the groundwater sources is dependent upon local geomorphic conditions. Beach ridges seaward of the sabkha prevent inundation by marine floodwaters, whereas lack of hinterland relief will restrict continental groundwater

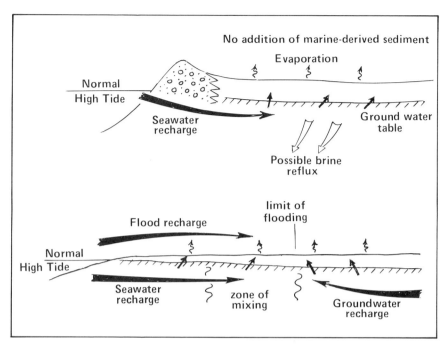

Figure 16
Contrasting water supply in sabkhas. Above sabkha plain bordered by beach ridge. Seawater recharge is entirely intrasediment flow (based upon a Sinai coastal sabkha; Gavish, 1974). Below, sabkha groundwaters are replenished by flood recharge and seepage from seawater and continental reservoir (based upon Abu Dhabi sabkha).

as products of reactions between ground-water brines and earlier-deposited sediments. Gypsum is not precipitated on the exposed sediment surface but grows displacively within algal mat or other upper intertidal sediments (forming cyrstal mushes up to 1 m thick) or grows poikilitically within supratidal sand sediments where it occurs as large, lenticular crystals that include sand grains arranged in herring-bone patterns.

Gypsum precipitation in the intertidal and near-shore supratidal environments causes groundwaters to become depleted in calcium. The increased Mg/Ca ratio of brines induces dolomitization of pre-existing aragonite and the precipitation of magnesite. The dolomite is calcium-rich and poorly ordered. Dolomitization of aragonites releases strontium that is precipitated as celestite. Dolomitization may be favored by the 1) increase in the Mg/Ca ratio of the brine (to about 10), 2) the presence of organic matter within the fine aragonitic muds, or 3) to the removal of sulphate ions – the presence of which inhibits dolomite precipitation.

In the Abu Dhabi sabkha, anhydrite first appears one km inland from the normal high water mark, in the capillary zone. It occurs as discrete nodules and as bands of coalesced nodules, some of which may take the form of ptygmatic (enterolithic) layers. Growth of nodules occurs by host sediment displacement and by replacement of the intervening sediment matrix. Dilution of the host sediment may occur to such an extent that it is relocated to internodule areas and its fabrics are destroyed. In extreme cases host sediments are confined to mere partings between the anhydrite nodules (mosaic anhydrite; Fig. 17). Some nodules are formed by alteration

inflow. Marine waters have greater effects along the seaward edge of sabkhas and along former tidal channels (which are still depressions on the sabkha surface) while inner parts of the sabkha are less prone to marine influence as the sabkha becomes wider as a result of sedimentary accretion. Cemented sediment layers and algal mat sediments beneath the sabkha surface inhibit upward movement of deeper-lying groundwaters, thus increasing the importance of marine flooding.

Concentration of groundwater causes precipitation of diagenetic minerals: some as direct precipitates, others

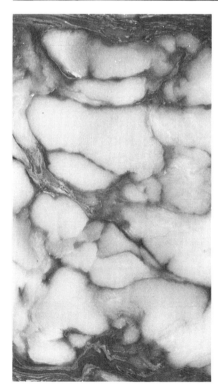

Figure 17
Mosaic anhydrite (displacing subaqeous laminated anhydrite) with individual nodules distorted against each other (a natural consequence of displacive growth). Ordovician Stonewall Evaporite, Saskatchewan. Slab is 8.5 cm wide.

Figure 18
Surface trench about 50 cm deep in Abu Dhabi sabkha with diapiric layers of anhydrite (after gypsum); upper layer truncating anhydrite is a storm washover and aeolian carbonate-clastic unit. Photograph courtesy R.K. Park.

272

of earlier formed gypsum crystals (Butler, 1970). Pseudomorphs lose shape because of flowage (adjustment during compaction) and the continued growth of primary anhydrite laths in and between pseudomorphs. Some doubt concerning this mechanism of anhydrite nodule formation has arisen following the discovery by West *et al.* (1979) of primary gypsum nodules from an Egyptian sabkha. The possibility exists that some of the anhydrite nodules from the sabkhas of Abu Dhabi also possessed a gypsum *nodule* precursor. Composite anhydrite nodules are remnants of gypsum crystal clusters and massive-appearing anhydrite forms from gypsum mush in former upper intertidal sediments. Such soft anhydrite layers become deformed into enterolithic folds and microdiapers (Fig. 18). The displacive growth of anhydrite and gypsum in intertidal and supratidal sediments is believed to raise (jack-up) the sediment surface. If the water table does not rise a corresponding amount, the upper parts of the sediment dry out and blow away. Deflation exposes anhydrite and gypsum at the surface, concentrating nodules and crystal fragments as a regolith, or breaking up nodules into laths that become strewn across the sabkha surface. Isolated anhydrite laminae at the top of some ancient sabkha sequences may have formed by such nodule and crystal destruction.

Halite occurs as salt crusts on the surface, as veneers around grains in the upper part of the capillary zone and as solid cubes in sand sediments. High humidities, particularly at night, contribute to surface water supply (as dew) and result in the diurnal dissolution of surface halite crusts. Within fine grained sediments the displacive halite cubes assume a skeletal hopper form commonly to extreme degrees (Fig. 8). In most described modern sabkhas halite is not an accumulative phase but is blown away or dissolves in floodwaters. Repeated growth and dissolution of halite can so disrupt the host sediment that all its original fabrics are destroyed.

VARIATIONS IN THE COASTAL SABKHA MODEL
Variations in size and setting of sabkhas, the nature of the host sediment, the character of the offshore water body, the type of diastrophic control and the

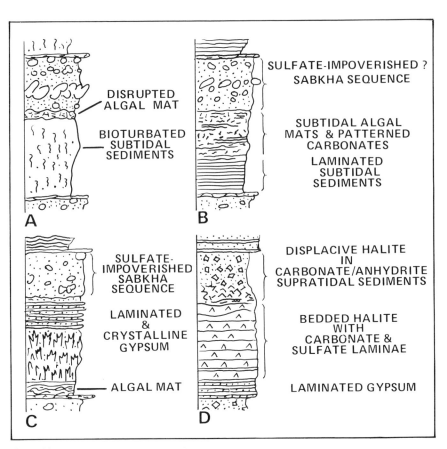

Figure 19
Hypothetical shoaling-upwards cycles: A) marginal to a normal marine to slightly hypersaline water body; B) marginal to a hypersaline water body within which sulphates are bacterially reduced; C) marginal *water body precipitates and preserves gypsum; D) marginal water body is salt-precipitating supratidal sequence largely composed of displacive (and replacive?) halite.*

effects of differing local topography all may cause profound modifications from the 'norm', as represented by the Abu Dhabi sabkha (Fig. 19).

A) Size and Setting of Sabkhas. Since coastal sabkhas form the uppermost parts of accreting sedimentary bodies the development and size of sabkhas is dependent upon the topography off- and on-shore. Only narrow, discontinuous sabkhas are to be expected at locations where the offshore gradient is steep (such as the coasts of the Red Sea or Iran) whereas broad sabkhas can form on low gradient, stable shelves. Patterson and Kinsman (1981), however, sound a word of warning for they maintain that a regional groundwater flow system that causes the water table to rise as the sabkha progrades is necessary for the preservation of broad sabkhas. Without such a groundwater system evaporative losses in the areas beyond the zone of seawater flood-

recharge would lower the water table, resulting in deflation and removal of the sabkha sedimentary sequence. The requirement of a seaward dipping gradient to the sabkha groundwater surface requires the presence of a large landmass with sufficient relief to act as a recharge area for the groundwater system.

Small sabkhas, such as Sabkha Faishakh in Qatar may be more frequently flooded by marine waters and thus generally have lower interstitial-water salinities. This may partly account for why, despite the almost identical climate to that of Abu Dhabi, the sabkha contains only minor traces of anhydrite.

B) Nature of the Host Sediment. This determines the amount of drainage, the subsequent history of sabkha brines and the compactional history of the evaporite deposit. In some cases evaporites may not form in sabkha settings, despite elevated salinities well above gypsum saturation. Amdurer and Land (1982) describe the situation in part of Laguna Madre (Texas) where so much calcium has been removed from the brine by algal precipitation (which subsequently blows away in the wind) that gypsum is unable to precipitate. Doubtless the high resultant sulphate concentrations in the brine prevent dolomitization of any carbonate that does survive. Impermeable sediments inhibit brine reflux and, by curtailing downward seepage of floodwaters, extend the width of the area affected by flood recharge. This surface flooding, however, causes little dilution of existing groundwaters. Finer grained sediments also allow thicker capillary fringes to form. Thicker evaporite sequences should be formed in fine-grained sediments because of this but the control has yet to be demonstrated in ancient examples.

Sabkhas composed of permeable sands may allow brine reflux. DeGroot (1973) identified a downward and seaward increase in salinity of interstitial brines within the Umm Said Sabkha of Qatar. This suggests the presence of a reflux system of brine movement but dolomitization as a result of this still has to be demonstrated.

Carbonates (particularly aragonite) in host sediments are of major importance. Dolomitization of carbonates releases calcium which reacts with sulphate in groundwaters to form more gypsum and anhydrite. This additional sulphate precipitation and dolomitization reduces the sulphate and magnesium content of brines in carbonate sabkha interiors to low levels and causes magnesite (precipitated earlier) to redissolve. In non-carbonate sediments, dolomitization does not occur, the sabkha interior brines retain 60 to 70 per cent of their sulphate, much less gypsum and anhydrite is emplaced, and brines remain magnesium rich so that magnesite remains stable. The sulphate

Figure 20
Alternations between mosaic anhydrite (top and bottom) and microdolomites much disrupted by growth of halite (now pseudomorphed by anhydrite) and gypsum crystals (now anhydrite). Dolomite intervals probably represent former inter- and subtidal sediments partially obliterated by sulphate growth during reflux dolomitization, Frobisher Evaporite (Mississippian), Saskatchewan. Slab is 10.5 cm wide.

and magnesium rich brines formed in non-carbonate sabkha sediments react with earlier-formed gypsum to form polyhalite (Holser, 1966):

$$2CaSO_4 \cdot 2H_2O + 2K + Mg + 2SO_4 = K_2MgCa_2(SO_4)_4 \cdot 2H_2O + 2H_2O$$

gypsum + brine = polyhalite

Reflux of brines capable of dolomitizing deeper-lying carbonates (well beneath the sabkha vadose zone) causes calcium sulphate precipitation (gypsum, perhaps anhydrite) in these deeper-lying sediments. Growth of sulphates in subtidal carbonate intervals between sabkha evaporites by this reflux dolomitiation may obliterate evidence of the cyclic nature of an evaporite deposit and create a single thick, composite unit of nodular anhydrite. Alternations between nodular and mosaic anhydrites and disrupted dolomite intervals full of gypsum pseudomorphs in parts of the Mississippian Frobisher Evaporite in Saskatchewan may represent such partially obliterated cycles (Fig. 20).

Differences in sediment coherency dictate subsequent compactional history. Lithified or coherent sediments preserve gypsum peseudomorphs or the moulds of dissolved halite crystals. Compressible sediments (particularly organic-rich varieties), on the other hand, allow anhydrite nodules to grow, to coalesce and compact perhaps to form vuggy or even laminar anhydrites (Shearman and Fuller, 1969). Mossop (1979) believes laminar anhydrites in the Ordocician Baumman Fiord Formation (Fig. 21) were originally nodular and have been drastically altered by early diagenetic compaction and flowage.

C) Nature of the Offshore Water Body. Most commonly the offshore water body is normal marine to slightly hypersaline (well below gypsum saturation). Here subtidal-intertidal sediments are bioturbated and skeletal rich, and algal-mat sediments (if present) are confined to upper intertidal to low supratidal environments (Fig. 19A) where they may become disrupted by subsequent growth of gypsum (James, 1977).

When sabkhas border hypersaline (gypsum precipitating) water bodies, the sediments beneath sabkha evaporites are laminated (burrowing biota absent) and algal mats extend well into

274

Figure 21
Numerous superimposed sabkha cycles. Baumann Fiord Formation. Ellesmere Island (photo courtesy G. Mossop).

subtidal environments where they may be preserved. When precipitated gypsum persists in the bottom sediment, the overlying sabkha sequence forms the uppermost member of a largely subaqueous evaporite sequence (Fig. 19B). However, the abundance of organic matter and dissolved sulphate in hypersaline waters normally induces reducing conditions within which sulphate-reducing bacteria thrive. Their activites cause reduction of gypsum, the formation of hydrogen sulphide with precipitation of carbonates and pyrite as by-products (Friedman, 1972) and perhaps formation of patterned carbonates (Dixon, 1976; Kendall, 1977; Fig. 19B). Removal of calcium and sulphate from the offshore water body may severely restrict gypsum and anhydrite formation in adjacent sabkha environments (Fig. 19B and C). On the other hand, the shallow subaqueous evaporites may be transported onto the sabkha by storms, there to form clastic beds of gypsum, anhydrite or even halite debris. Such sabkhas could be largely composed of such beds (which would be difficult to distinguish from shallow subaqueous evaporites) or the clastic units could be intercalated with non-storm sabkha sediments.

The atmosphere adjacent to large bodies of normal marine water is too humid for halite to persist in the sub-aerial environment (Kinsman, 1976). If the water body is a concentrated brine, however, its water vapour pressure may be low enough not to increase atmospheric humidity. Halite can thus become an accumulative phase in sabkhas that neighbour hypersaline water bodies (particularly those saturated or near-saturated with respect to halite). Shearman (1966), Friedman (1972) and Smith (1971, 1973) have described halite rocks that appear to have formed by displacing or replacing earlier carbonate-sulphate sabkha sediments. Such sediments form adjacent to halite-precipitating water bodies (Fig. 19D).

D) Diastrophic Control. Shoaling-upwards sequences terminated by coastal sabkha deposits can form as a result of three different events. The most commonly offered interpretation is that each sequence is a separate progradational event. Sabkha plains are generated by sediment accretion with little or no significant sea-level fall. Mossop (1979) and Ginsburg (*in* Bosellini and Hardie, 1973) have independently developed hypotheses which generate successive shoaling-upwards cycles in carbonate-producing areas in a regime of continuous subsidence.

On the other hand, sediment emergence, with formation of supratidal surfaces, can also be achieved by relative falls in sea-level, independently of any sediment up-building. Sea-level changes may be the result of external events (glaciations?) or of restriction of the water body from the world ocean and subsequent removal of water by evaporation (evaporative downdraw). Criteria for distinguishing cycles that form from progradational events from those that reflect episodes of evaporative downdraw are not evident. Taylor (1980) argues that cycles resulting from sealevel falls (or drops in the brine level within isolated evaporating basins) will be stunted. Rates of evaporation would cause rapid regression and basinward migration of the shoreline. Taylor calculated rates of shoreline regression that could have occurred during deposition of the Werraanhydrit (Permian) of the North Sea of 150 m/year – 20 times as fast as the progradation of the Trucial Coast sabkhas. Meagre algal mat development, precipitation of small quantities of calcium sulphate and only

negligible dolomitization would be expected for such single-batch dessication cycles. On the other hand, evaporative downdraw need not be as fast as Taylor suggests. Evaporation may be reduced by high humidities (Kinsman, 1976), or evaporation losses may be more nearly balanced by marine inflow or seepage. In either case, rates of shoreline retreat might be more compatable with those caused by sediment progradation in which case the sabkha sequences may be difficult to distinguish.

When greater subsidence occurs towards the basin centre it is possible to recognize distal from proximal locations (Mossop, 1979). Basinwards the cycles are thicker and are dominated by thick subtidal units. Short-lived or less extensive transgressive events may not reach basin margins so that marginal successions contain fewer and thinner cycles that are dominated by supratidal (sabkha) members. Coalescence of several supratidal units may also generate thick evaporite sequences at marginal locations.

E) Topographic Control. The Abu Dhabi 'norm' is associated with a relatively simple progradational sediment wedge undissected by active channels, maritime lakes or ridges formed by former beach or offshore spit deposits (Fig. 22). This situation reflects the constant conditions (slightly falling sea-level) that have occurred since the sabkha began to form and the protection afforded by an offshore island chain. When protective barriers are absent, or if sediment supply or rates of sea-level change are variable the accumulation of supratidal sabkha sediments are more discontinuous and parts of the intertidal and subtidal environment are isolated by growth of beach bars and spits. Here we have an arid-zone equivalent of the chenier plain – an environment recently described by Picha (1978) from Kuwait but to date one that has not been recognized in the ancient.

Drowned valleys or former tidal channels, isolated by spit development or by the formation of beach barrier ridges, may occur within the sabkha environment. If connection is retained with the sea, flow into the former channels occurs in response to a lowered water level caused by evaporation from the standing body of water. Such

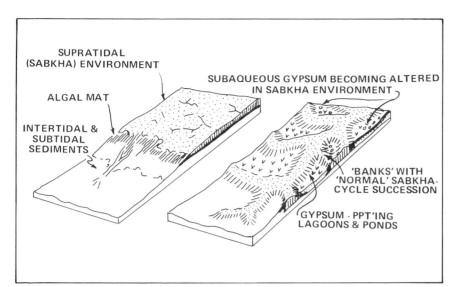

Figure 22
Contrasting patterns of supratidal sedimentation. A) simple sediment wedge. Recent Abu Dhabi sabkha; B) inferred environment for

part of Frobisher Evaporite (Mississippian) in southeastern Saskatchewan—numerous shallow maritime lakes isolated by narrow strips of supratidal sabkha.

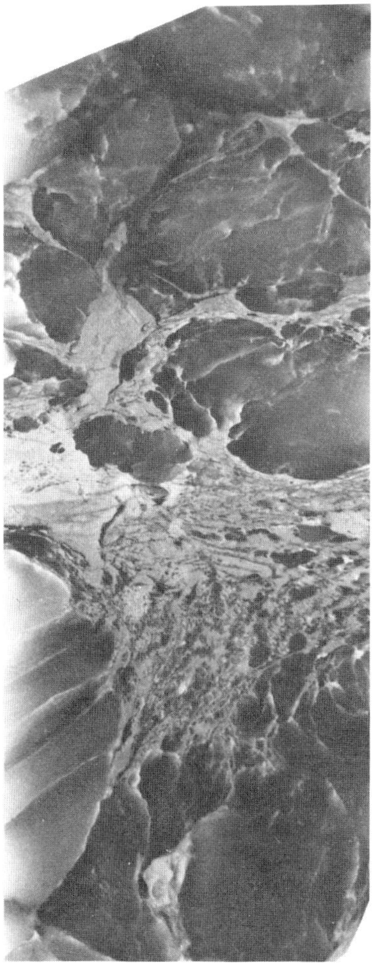

Figure 23
Displacive gypsum crystals (centre) distorted by growth of later but still early-diagenetic anhydrite nodules. Frobisher Evaporite. Saskatchewan. Slab is 10.5 cm wide.

depressions will also attract groundwaters from beneath the surrounding sabkha and disrupt the more normal pattern of groundwater flow. The Sebkha el Melah (Busson and Perthuisot, 1977) was such a depression but has since been filled with evaporites including a halite sequence 30 m thick. Beds of subaqueous gypsum, patterned dolomites (representing bacterially-reduced calcium sulphates) or halite beds within 'normal' sabkha deposits may represent the fills of depressions on the sabkha surface.

The evaporite portion of sabkha cycles in the Mississippian Frobisher Evaporite of Saskatchewan (Figs. 13, 14, 20, and 23) is dominated by large, subaqueously-precipitated gypsum crystals (now pseudomorphed by anhydrite). They pass laterally into more 'normal' sabkha sequences composed of nodular and mosaic anhydrite. The former gypsum crystals are also deformed by anhydrite nodule growth (Fig. 23) indicating they were transformed to anhydrite or bassanite during early diagenesis. Since more than 90 per cent of the sulphate was precipitated subaqueously a provisional environmental reconstruction having resemblance to the humid sub-tropical environment of Florida Bay is suggested. Deposition occurred in hypersaline lagoons separated by narrow barriers upon which 'normal' sabkha sequences were formed. The gypsum crystals were precipitated in the lagoons

but as progradation of the lagoon complex occurred, older lagoons became more distant from the open sea and dried out to become part of the sabkha plain. In this desiccated environment gypsum dehydrated and new anhydrite grew displacively as nodules.

It is probable that most environments which include supratidal sediments have arid-zone equivalents within which evaporites have formed. We have still to look for them in the rock record.

SHALLOW WATER EVAPORITE FACIES
Deposition of shallow-water evaporites occurs in brines that were at or near saturation with respect to gypsum or halite and in environments that may have been subject to strong wave and current action, causing sediment scour, transport and redeposition. Algal activity was significant in more protected (or deeper?) environments and many sediments were subject to periodic drying. Whereas water depths may range from a few centimetres to 20 m or more, most facies probably formed in water less than 5m deep. In fact, many evaporites considered subaqueous may have been deposited on evaporitic flats that only became flooded during storm surges or particularly high tides. Since all depositional events are subaqueous, the interpreted environment is so identified even though the depositional site may have been subaerially exposed for most of the time. Evaporite precipitation may occur at the air-water interface, at the sediment-water interface or beneath the sediment surface and varying amounts of continental and marine-derived sediments may be periodically transported into the evaporitic environment.

Most of our knowledge of shallow water evaporites has come from the interpretation of ancient examples – particularly from the Miocene of the Mediterranean (Schreiber et al., 1973, 1977; Hardie and Eugster, 1971; Vai and Ricci Lucchi, 1977; Garrison et al., 1978). More recently, however, studies of Holocene and Recent salinas (saline lakes adjacent to the ocean in which the salina water level is below that of the ocean and is replenished by seawater seepage; Warren, 1982; Kushnir, 1981 and Arakel, 1980) have provided valuable information confirming the older interpretations of ancient evaporites and suggesting others.

A) Laminated Sulphates. These may be similar in character and origin to deep-water sediments but most apparently consisted of current-deposited micrite and clastic gypsum particles in reverse and normally-graded laminae. Laminae were originally composed of silt and sand-sized gypsum crystals or cleavage fragments which grew: 1) as crusts on the depositional surface and so were easily broken and reworked, or 2) as acicular crystals precipitated at the air-water interface which sank and became reworked on the bottom. Other crystals may have grown displacively within the bottom sediment and then were reworked. All crystals and fragments suffer overgrowth on the bottom and laminae become converted into interlocking gypsum mosaics.

In some sediments the gypsum crystals have suffered little if any transport, and in many the crystals displace or poikilitically enclose algal mat carbonate and organic material. Lamination in these sediments is largely a reflection of algal mat lamination (Fig. 24). Similar algal-laminated gypsum may form by the encrusting of mats, or the mats may act as sediment traps for carbonate or gypsum muds and silts. Conversion of the gypsum to anhydrite during burial will normally obscure the differences between these types of laminite.

Cross-bedding, ripple-drift bedding (Fig. 25), basal scoured surfaces and rip-up breccias testify to environments with periodic high energy events, such as storms. Some small asymmetric ripple-marks with oversteepened sides at the tops of some laminae may represent adhesion ripples and indicate depositon of wind-blown gypsum detritus onto moist surfaces . Shallow-water deposition is also shown by the occurrence of micritic, organic-rich stromatolites between, or within, some laminae; by bird or dinosaur footprints, or by fossil brine shrimp.

Clastic sedimentation is apparently a dominant feature in the shallower, higher-energy environments of inter-tidal or supratidal-lagoonal (marine or salina) settings with layering due to tide- or wind-induced influx of sediment or seawater.

Laminae are interpreted as storm deposits. Each lamina forms during a storm when evaporitic tidal flats are flooded by sediment-charged water. Blue-green algal mats, which cover the

A

Figure 24
A) Anhydrite after displacive gypsum crystals which grew within mud-cracked stromatolitic carbonate. Each gypsum crystal is now represented by a small, angular anhydrite 'nodule'. Souris River Formation (U. Devonian, Saskatchewan), core is 9 cm across. B) Anhydrite after incorporative gypsum crystals which grew within an algal stromatolite, Souris River Formation, Saskachewan. Core is 8 cm wide.

B

flats, collect and bind evaporite sediment and, as the storm subsides, the coarser load is deposited as a traction layer or as a settle-out to produce a normally graded lamina. Algae grow through the new lamina, re-establish themselves on the surface and protect the underlying sediment from erosion. The analogy may be made with the

formation of storm laminae in other tidal-flat sediments.

Reverse-graded laminae are variously interpreted. They may record episodes of brine dilution that induce recrystallization of gypsum in the upper-most parts of laminae, or this feature may be of depositional origin. Upward segregation of coarser particles may have

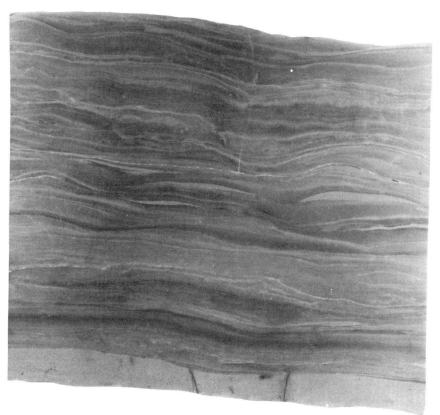

Figure 25

Laminated anhydrite containing minor amounts of disseminated dolomite that define lamination, ripples, minor cross-stratification and scoured surfaces, Poplar Beds (Mississippian). Saskatchewan. Core is 10.5 cm across.

Figure 26

Deformed (slumped?) laminated to thin-bedded anhydrite which can easily be confused with displacive nodular anhydrite. Ordovician (Herald Fm.), Saskatchewan. Core is 10.5 cm across.

occurred within highly concentrated flowing sand sheets in very shallow waters upon tidal flats during storm surges. The reverse grading may then be emphasized by early diagenetic recrystallization and lithification during quiet periods between storms. Inversely graded layers, adhesion ripples, algal mats and early-diagenetic cementation of gypsum are recorded from evaporitic flats of the Laguna Mormona (Baja California; see Horodyski and Vonder Haar, 1975).

Gypsum laminites that have been altered to anhydrite rarely provide sufficient evidence for environmental reconstruction. Some laminites suffer pervasive recrystallization to coarse gypsum mosaics which transect all earlier fabric elements. If replaced by nodular anhydrite such crystals may yield rocks that superficially resemble sabkha anhydrite.

It was originally believed that although shallow-water laminite units could be laterally persistent they typically contained fewer laminae than deeper-water facies and that individual laminae could not be traced for long distances. Now it is known that depositional environments that suffer widespread floods (salinas, some tidal flats) undergo periodic episodes of surface dissolution and reprecipitation as the floodwaters evaporate with the formation of a sedimentary sequence composed of laterally persistant thin beds or laminae – some of which are traceable over the whole environment or over the extent of the flooding.

Shallow-water laminites may also be distinguished by their association with other facies. Possibly the manner in which laminites deform provides evidence for different environments. Evaporitic flat sediments, which become emergent and suffer extensive early-diagenetic cementation, fracture and become incorporated into rip-up breccias. In contrast, some laminites interpreted as subaqueous, have suffered folding, slumping and plastic stretching (Fig. 26) suggesting that they did not become lithified during early diagenesis.

B) Coarsely Crystalline, Selenitic Gyp-

sum. This occurs as single crystals, clusters, crusts and as superimposed beds. This facies is best known from the Miocene of Italy but is also recognized in older sequences, now altered to anhydrite. Similar gypsum has been described from man-made salinas.

Beds of crystalline gypsum are mainly composed of orderly rows of vertically-standing, elongate and commonly swallow-tail twinned crystals that range from a few centimetres to a few metres in height (Figs. 27, 28, and 29). Crystals are commonly euhedral and in aggregate define a vertical pallisade fabric or may be arranged into radiating upwards conical clusters (cavoli). Individual crystals are separated from each other by micritic carbonate, fine-grained gypsum or gypsum sands; or secondary overgrowth produces an interlocking crystal mosaic. Other gypsum crystals exhibit more bizarre growth and twin-

278

Figure 27
*Coarsely crystalline, selenitic gypsum facies.
A) Palisades of gypsum crystals, Miocene of
Sicily. Photo courtesy B.C. Schreiber.
B) Layered anhydrite with pseudomorphs*

*after gypsum crystals, Otto Fiord Fm.
(Pennsylvanian), Ellesmere Island. Photograph courtesy N.C. Wardlaw. Scale divisions in cm.*

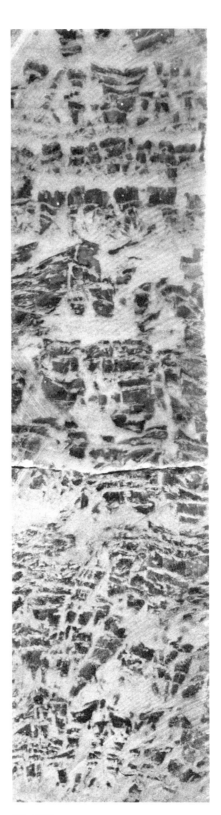

Figure 28
*Swallow-tail twinned gypsum crystal (25 cm
across) with dissolution surface at arrow.
Inset is a cleavage plane surface of the same*

*crystal revealing numerous inclusion-defined
growth layers. Miocene of S.E. Spain. Photograph courtesy B.C. Schreiber.*

Figure 29
*Swallow-tail gypsum crystals pseudo-
morphed by halite and anhydrite. Gypsum is
unstable in contact with halite-saturated
brines and dissolves to create molds that are
subsequently plugged with halite. Clear Fork
Formation (Permian) Texas. Photograph
courtesy C.R. Handford. Core is 8 cm wide.*

ning patterns and suffer crystal splitting to generate palmate to fan-shaped clusters of subparallel crystals (Fig. 30; for details see Schreiber, 1978; Orti-Cabo and Shearman, 1977). Twinning occurs at a variety of angles, probably as a consequence of the inclusion of organic matter along curved crystal faces (the greater the amount of impurity, the more obtuse the twinning angle). Other results of impurity absorbtion are that one twin arm may fail to grow or the crystals split into a wide and bizzare group of growth forms.

The crystals contain faint lamination (Fig. 28), defined by carbonate and anhydrite inclusions, which pass through the crystalline beds, parallel to bedding. Inclusions lie parallel to crystal faces, recording successive positions of the growing crystal, or defining solution surfaces. Many crystals include algal filaments and appear to have invaded algal mats (Fig. 24B).

Most authors now conclude that these gypsum crystals are primary and are mostly of very shallow-water origin. Schreiber (1978) notes that in salinas gypsum growth occurs mainly at depths shallower than five metres. Observations made in solar ponds reveal that the largest gypsum crystals form in environments of constant and active brine flow. The crystals record nucleation and slow incremental growth, presumably in quiet waters. The internal lamination and included algal mats indicate the crystals grew poikilitically, enclosing surficial veneers of sediment. Phases of slight undersaturation create minor dissolution surfaces that truncate the crystals. Renewed precipitation, however, commonly takes place upon

the etched surfaces, burying the surface within the crystal (Fig. 28). More severe interruptions may include: 1) a new phase of nucleation, producing a new bed of crystals, 2) lateral dissolution along crystal sides, perhaps with accumulation of residual impurities in the dissolution cavities, or 3) in extreme cases, crystals become disoriented and form residual gypsum breccias.

Beds originally composed of gypsum crystals may be difficult to identify when converted to anhydrite. Inclusions may define crystal faces within massive or mosaic anhydrite, but if the original crystals possessed numerous inclusions that defined laminae, the replacement can be mistaken for laminar sulphate. Gypsum crystals are most easily identified when the pseudomorphs are set within abundant carbonate matrix (Fig. 31). Much of the polyhalite from the Permian of New Mexico appears to have replaced and pseudomorphed selenitic gypsum (see Schaller and Henderson, 1932, Pls. 29 and 30).

Beds of gypsum crystals can become replaced during burial by mosaic anhydrite (Rouchy, 1976) which can closely resemble, and thus can be confused with, sabkha displacement-nodular anhydrite. Furthermore, if the gypsum-to-anhydrite transformation occurs in a low-permeability hostrock, the expelled water cannot easily escape. The sulphate becomes thixotropic and flows or fractures to nodular-anhydrite replacements of gypsum. I would interpret the peculiar anhydrite–structures in the Ferry Lake Anhydrite, describe by Loucks and Longman (1982), in this manner.

Figure 30
Anhydrite pseudomorphs of extensively twinned and split gypsum crystals within a dolomite matrix. Frobisher Evaporite (Mississippian), Saskatchewan. Cores are 10 cm across.

Figure 31
Parallel laminated, cross-stratified and load-casted gypsum sandstones (gypsarenites).

Miocene of Sicily. Photo courtesy B.C.Schreiber. Penknife gives scale.

280

C) Coarse Clastic Gypsum. Gypsum sands and pebbly sands, composed of worn gypsum cleavage fragments with variable amounts of carbonate and other materials, may be locally abundant but only rarely constitute major rock units. They do indicate, however, that gypsum may be transported and deposited in the same manner and environments as other clastic sediments, so long as the water body is gypsum-saturated. Such sands exhibit structures indicative of current or wave activity or may be penecontemporaneously disturbed and contain load cast or ball-and-pillow structures (Fig 31). Clastic gypsum occurs as shoestring sands or in sand sheets; represents channel, beach, offshore shoal or spit deposits or may occur as intercalations between beds of laminar or selenitic gypsum.

Vai and Ricci Lucchi (1977) have interpreted wavy bedded and laminar gypsum (composed of mm-sized gypsum) with accompanying poorly-sorted, broken gypsum-crystal sands, as fluvial deposits that prograded into a basin. This facies first appears between beds of subaqueous selenite but increases in abundance upwards and includes selenitic nodules interpreted to have been supratidal anhydrite. It grades into a facies of disoriented large gypsum crystals and fragments in a clayey matrix

that represents deposits of subaerial debris-flows. Growth of subaqueous gypsum apparently became more and more interrupted by sheet-floods that carried selenite fragments. Progradation caused development of wide supratidal flats composed of this transported material and in this environment sabkha anhydrite was emplaced.

D) Halite. At least three main facies are present: detrital halite, halite crusts, and halite that grows displacively in pre-exisiting sediments. It is uncertain what controls which particular facies will be developed.

Halite crusts constitute the best understood facies – one for which there are detailed descriptions from the ancient (Wardlaw and Schwerdtner, 1966), from Recent salt pans (Shearman, 1970) and from experimental studies (Arthurton, 1973). Crusts form: 1) by the foundering of, and continued growth upon, rafts of halite crystals which nucleated on the brine surface; 2) by upward and lateral growth of floor-nucleated crystals; and 3) by accumulation of, and overgrowth upon, detrital halite particles. Various halite growth habits are observed but the most common is layered halite, formed by the superposition of crusts (each crust separated by films or thin beds of detri-

tal carbonate, sulphate or terrigenous sediment) and identified as 'chevron halite' (Fig. 32 A-C). Each halite layer is composed, in part, of vertically elongate crystals that contain abundant brine-filled inclusions. The crystal fabric results from an upward competitive crystal growth on the sea or lake floor such that crystals with coigns uppermost are the most favoured. Inclusions are concentrated in layers parallel to cube faces (100), so that in the elongate halite crystals with coigns uppermost, the zoning appears as chevrons with upwardly-directed apices. The upper surfaces of halite layers: 1) may exhibit crystal growth faces (interruption in growth caused by only temporary and slight brine undersaturation), 2) are truncation surfaces associated with cavities in the underlying halite crust (recording more extreme episodes of brine undersaturation and halite dissolution), or 3) are flat truncation surfaces (possible deflation surfaces cut during episodes of emergence). Each halite layer is usually composed of two types of halite; the zoned chevron halite and clear halite which fills former dissolution cavities made in the crust.

Inclusion-rich layers *in zoned halite crystals* form where brines are highly supersaturated and growth is rapid. Reduced brine concentrations (the

Figure 32
Chevron halite. A) Layers of chevron halite interbedded with laminated anhydrite, Souris River Fm. (U. Devonian), Saskatchewan. Core is 10 cm across. B) Thin-section through chevron halite layer containing cloudy inclusion-rich and clear void-filling crystals, the former truncated by an anhydrite lamina. Prairie Evaporite, Saskatche-wan. (Thin section loaned by N.C. Wardlaw). C) Isolated crystals from halite crust on bottomof brine pool in a Saskatchewan potash mine. Largest crystal is 3.5 cm long.

result of halite precipitation) then allow slower and more perfect (inclusion-free) halite layers to be deposited. Zonal laminae are 0.1 to 0.3 mm thick: thicknesses that could be expected to result from precipitation caused by diurnal fluctuations of evaporation rate and/or temperatures. Because brine reconcentration (necessary to cause deposition of succeeding inclusion-rich halite layers) can only occur by evaporation of the brine, the numerous alternations between inclusion-rich and inclusion-poor layers in chevron halite, indicate that rapid changes in brine concentration occured. This can only be achieved in bodies of brine of small volume. The layering in chevron halite is thus indicative of shallow water precipitation and contrasts with the clear halite crystals of deep-water deposits.

Displacive halite has been described previously in connection with playa-flat and sabkha evaporites but may also be of subaqueous origin. It is recorded from the floor of the Dead Sea where it occurs as large (5 to 10 cm) cubes with hopper-like pyramidal hollows on each face (Fig. 33). Zoned inclusions of the enclosing sediment, parallel to all cube faces, indicate the crystal grew displacively within the mud. Sediments containing significant quantities of displacive halite cubes are termed Haselgebirge (see Arthurton, 1973) and rock units composed of displacive halite (with host sediment reduced to mere pockets or thin film between crystals) constitute the upper parts of the Prairie Evaporite and other Devonian halites in Saskatchewan.

Detrital halite is probably more important than published studies would suggest, perhaps because this facies seems particularly susceptible to recrystallization – so that depositional fabrics are lost. Detrital halite is composed of fragmentary surface-grown hopper crystals and small cubes that may represent overgrown hoppers, crystals precipitated during brine-mixing (Raup, 1970) or reworked material from bottom-growing crusts. Detrital halite is commonly ripple-marked and may exhibit cross-bedding and include other detrital material. Crystal growth may continue after deposition, by means of small-scale sediment displacement, and the detrital origin can become obscured.

Weiler et al. (1974) suggest that halite

Figure 33
Displacive halite crystals (with hopper faces) that grew in micritic ooze at southern end of the Dead Sea (Photo courtesy B.C. Schreiber).

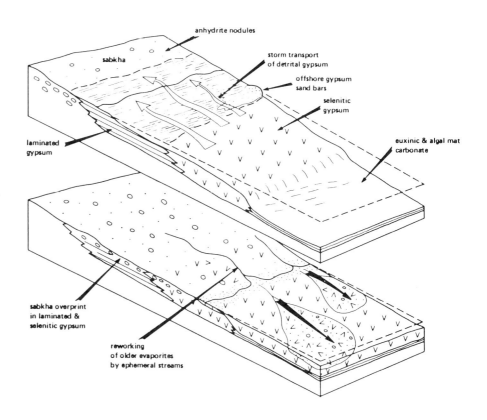

Figure 34
Models for deposition of shallow water sulphate evaporite facies. Above, after Hardie and Eugster (1970); below Vai and Ricci Lucchi (1977).

282

crusts grow preferentially in shallow, quiet-water environments, whereas detrital halite, commonly ripple marked, dominates in higher energy environments because there the sunken surface-grown crystals are subject to bottom movement sufficient to prevent crust development.

Halite deposits may become consolidated early in their history by early diagenetic processes of crystallization and re-crystallization. Garrett (1970) concluded from studies of brine ponds, that in shallow-water deposits, much of the salt deposited in the evening redissolves during the day and subsequently recrystallizes. This tends to consolidate the deposit and with time and burial the porosity decreases progressively and rapidly (40% initially, 20% under 30cm of salt, 5 to 10% under 6 to 12 m of salt and to 0% with deeper burial). Not all salts, however, appear to follow this trend and the Holocene salt of Lake Macleod (Western Australia), up to 12 m thick, has porosities of 25% throughout its thickness and acts as an aquifer (Logan, pers. commun., 1982).

Much less is known about the textures and structures of potash-magnesia salts. Halite-sylvite in the Oligocene of the Rhine Valley exhibits varve-like banding (Baar and Kuhn, 1962). Because sylvite solubility is much more temperature-dependent than that of halite, the sylvite bands are interpreted to represent precipitation during periods of higher (summer) evaporation.

Most potash-magnesia salts, however, appear to be diagenetic replacements of, or additions to, earlier halite or sulphate deposits. All textures and structures may be diagenetic, but less-altered beds may still exhibit surprisingly well-preserved depositional features. Lowenstein (1982) describes primary textures in halite and anhydrite (after gypsum) from the potash ore beds of the Permian Salado Formation of West Texas-New Mexico.

Wardlaw (1972) has described crusts of bottom-grown carnallite (KCl·MgCl$_2$·6H$_2$O) interbedded with layers of detrital and surface-grown (?) halite. The salts are deformed by synsedimentary folds and by the displacive growth of large carnallite crystals within the sediment. Deformation of the sedimentary layering suggests that the salts were never subaerially exposed or lithified and that subaqueous salts remain unlithified and are capable of being deformed by slumping and differential loading. The occurrence to tachyhydrite (CaCl$_2$·2MgCl$_2$·12H$_2$O) in these evaporites, a mineral that cannot survive exposure to the atmosphere, also indicates evaporite deposition was entirely subaqueous.

Shallow Water Evaporite Models
Two models are proposed for shallow-water sulphates; both created for the Messinian evaporites of Italy (Fig. 34). Hardie and Eugster (1971) invoke deposition of coarsely crystalline selenite in the quiet waters of a shallow lagoon or gulf, adjacent to a littoral belt of laminated gypsum. Gypsum in the laminites and in associated gypsum sand bodies (beach or offshore-shoal deposits) was derived from the area of selenite deposition and transported shorewards onto the marginal evaporitic flats during storms.

Vai and Ricci Lucchi (1977), on the other hand, working on a sequence that lacked gypsum laminites, suggest transport of gypsum toward the basin centre. Gypsum was reworked from older, emergent beds of selenitic gypsum by ephemeral slope-controlled agents (torrential streams and debris flows) which built up shallow alluvial cones that enchroached the basin. This cannibalistic model can be integrated with Hardie and Eugster's model: Vai and Ricci Lucchi's interpretation applicable to times of regression, when older evaporites become exposed in marginal areas and subject to reworking, and Hardie and Eugster's interpretation appropriate to times of transgression or when the regression occurs entirely as a consequence of sediment outbuilding (when gradients will be low).

Whereas we possess a reasonable idea about details of the depositional environment of shallow-water halite (since we have a modern-day equivalent; Shearman, 1970), interpretation of the mechanism for depositing the enormous volumes of this material that occur in many evaporite formations remains problematical. As an example, the lower part of the Middle Devonian Prairie Evaporite consists almost entirely of chevron halite with carbonate-anhydrite laminae (Wardlaw and Schwerdtner, 1966) and represents deposition in shallow brine pools and salt flats. This environment apparently stretched across Saskatchewan from Central Alberta and the source of the brine was from the northwest and would have had to have travelled more than 1600 km. It is difficult to imagine how this brine could have travelled across brine pools and salt flats without evaporating away before it had travelled for more than a small part of its journey. Interpretations of other large units of shallow-water halite would appear to be afflicted by the same problem.

DEEP WATER EVAPORITE FACIES
In this environment the brine is at or near saturation with respect to gypsum and/or halite. Crystal growth probably occurs mainly at the air-water interface and crystals settle through the water column as a pelagic rain. Regular interlamination of minerals of different solubilities (calcite and gypsum, with or without halite) reflect variations in brine influx, temperature or evaporation rate. Some calcium sulphate may grow within the upper layers of the bottom sediment and some salt may be precipitated during the mixing of brines in a stratified water body (Raup, 1970). Evaporite turbidites and mass-flow deposits, derived from shallower water carbonate and evaporite accumulations, may also be emplaced within this environment.

The depth of water in which "deep water" evaporites accumulate is difficult to determine. Where turbidites (composed of basin-marginal materials) occur at the basin centre, the centre to basin-margin distance combined with a minimal 1° slope suggests a minimum depth. Such a calculation for the Sicilian Basin during the Messinian (Upper Miocene) suggests depths exceeding 175 m (Schreiber et al., 1976).

A minimum water depth can also be obtained by observing the relation of basinal evaporites to topographic elevations. Laminated evaporites at the base of the Muskeg-Prairie Evaporite Formations (Middle Devonian of the Elk Point Basin described by Wardlaw and Reinson, 1971; Davies and Ludlam, 1973) cover flanks of Winnipegosis – Keg River carbonate buildups to heights of at least 20 m. Persistence of laminae up such slopes and the lack of associated lithologic change suggest deposition occurred from a brine body at least 40 m deep.

Detailed log correlations aross basin

margins can sometimes be used to identify the basin configuration and thus be used to determine the depths at which basin-central evaporites were deposited. Colter and Reed (1980) and Taylor (1980) have attempted this procedure for Zechstein (Permian) evaporites of the North Sea. They trace individual evaporite units from the basin up onto a pre-existing carbonate depositional shelf and this implies basinal evaporites were depostied in up to 200 metres of brine. Evaporite units identified as deepwater by this method include thick anhydrites, halites and halite-polyhalite which implies the presence of a deep basin filled with brine capable of precipitating bittern salts. Such an environment is not even remotely approached in the Recent.

Geochemical evidence can sometimes be employed to calculate water volume and, by implication, water depth. The smaller the volume of brine, the less the evaporative system is buffered and therefore the greater the possibility for larger variations in salinity and trace-element concentration.

Katz et al. (1977) have used the strontium content of aragonite laminae, some interlaminated with gypsum (Begin et al., 1974), from the Pleistocene Lisan Formation of the Dead Sea region to establish a water depth of between 400 and 600 m.

A) Sulphate mm-Laminites (Figs. 35 and 36). Laminar sulphate (originally gypsum), either alone or in couplets or triplets with carbonate and/or organic matter, is probably the commonest deep-water evaporite facies and occurs in the Permian Castile Formation of Texas and New Mexico (Anderson and Kirkland, 1966; Anderson et al., 1972), in the Permian Zechstein group of Germany (Richter-Bernurg, 1957; Anderson and Kirkland, 1966), in the Jurassic Todilto Formation of New Mexico (Anderson and Kirkland, 1966) and in the Middle Devonian Muskeg and Winnipegosis Formations of Western Canada (Davies and Ludlam, 1973; Wardlaw and Reinson, 1971).

Laminae are thin (1 to 10 mm thick) and although they are typically bounded by perfectly smooth, flat surfaces they may be uneven, crenulated or plastically disturbed. Over short sections, laminae are nearly of uniform thickness and individual laminae are

Figure 35
Cycles of varve-like laminated carbonate (light coloured) passing upward (in figure up and to the left) into interlaminated carbonate-anhydrite and into highly disturbed and distorted laminated anhydrite. Each cycle is abruptly overlain by the lower carbonate laminite of the succeeding cycle. Ratner Member (basal Priarie Evaporite), Middle Devonian, central Saskatchewan. Top left is top of core, lower right is bottom of core: core is 8 cm wide.

Figure 36
Lateral correlation of individual carbonate-anhydrite laminae within Ratner Member of *Saskatchewan. Cores are from wells located several kilometres apart: cores about 8 cm wide.*

---

traceable over long distances (Fig. 36), (up to several hundred kilometres). The Castile – Lower Salado laminites are 440 m thick, comprise more than 250,000 anhydrite-carbonate couplets and some laminae have been traced laterally for more than 110 km (Anderson *et al.,* 1972).

Some anhydrite laminae exhibit evidence that they were originally composed of small lenticular gypsum crystals, arranged parallel to bedding (Shearman, 1971) and are similar to those in gypsum laminae from the Lisan Formation. Similar lenticular gypsum crystals precipitate from the water column (?) in shallow solar-salt ponds or grow displacively in algal sediments (Schreiber, 1978). Laminae that lack evidence of lenticular gypsum may have accumulated on the basin floor from a rain of fine gypsum or primary anhydrite needles precipitated at the air-water interface.

Nodular anhydrite intervals occur within the Castile Formation but are the result of a reorganization of pre-existing sulphate laminae, the nodular anhydrite rarely completely losing its laminated appearance. However, some intervals

do approach, in appearance, those formed in supratidal settings. Some authors (notably Friedman, 1972) would use the presence of nodular anhydrite to suggest that the entire Castile succession is shallow water in origin, whereas others (Dean *et al.,* 1975) conclude that this type of nodular anhydrite is not diagnostic of supratidal environments. The occurrence of nodular anhydrite at horizons where anhydrite laminae are thick or immediately beneath halite layers suggests nodule formation was associated with increased salinity.

Laminated sulphates record the precipitation and deposition of sediments in a water body whose bottom was unaffected by wave action and currents. Such stagnant, permanently stratified water bodies need not be particularly deep and carbonate laminae form in comparatively shallow waters of the Dead Sea (Neev and Emery, 1967) as a result of "whitings"at the brine surface. Lenticular and needle gypsum crystals precipitate in shallow brine ponds and also are non-diagnostic of water depth. The interpretation of some laminated sulphate deposits as deep-water thus rests primarily upon: 1) the wide-spread

occurrence of individual laminae, 2) the lack of other facies indicative of shallow water, 3) the size of the evaporite unit, and possibly 4) the presence of gravity-displaced sediments.

Unfortunately the utility of criterion 1 is questionable in that laminae of wide distribution are found in some shallow-water to subaerially exposed environments (see below). It has been held that shallow-water laminites are prone to current and wave reworking. Unfortunately abrupt brine stratification in the brine column can dampen wave motion at shallow depths, leading to a false impression of "depth".

B) Laminated Halite. Deep-water halite is difficult to recognize because many examples have suffered recrystallization, obliterating original characteristics. Even so, deep-water halite is invariably finely laminated and contains anhydrite-carbonate laminae (Jahresringe) similar to those of deep-water laminated sulphates (which commonly underlie or are interbedded with the halite). Lamination within the salt beds bounded by anhydrite-carbonate laminae is common and is defined by variations in inclusion content (liquid inclusions or very fine grained sulphate or pelitic material). Salt layers and laminae have been traced for many kilometres (Schreiber *et al.,* 1976; Richter-Bernburg, 1973; Anderson *et al.,* 1972).

Many halites are thus banded with alternations of clear translucent halite and dark grey to black halite. Dark colours are caused by light dispersion that is caused by anhydrite and/or talc inclusions. In some banded halite the dark layers contain clay or quartz silt and suggest episodes of clastic influx into the basin that alternated with periods of basin-floor halite growth.

The classic description of a sub-aqueous basin-central halite deposit is that of the Salina (Silurian of Michigan Basin) by Dellwig (1955) and Dellwig and Evans (1969). Salina salts exhibit a clear salt- cloudy salt banding (in 2 to 9 cm thick couplets) in addition to dolomite-anhydrite laminae. Banding is absent or only poorly developed in some basin-marginal locations where there is additional evidence for shallow-water conditions. Cloudy layers are inclusion-rich and are described by Dellwig as being composed of numerous pyramidal-shaped hopper crystals that grew on the brine surface. When broken or disturbed, these skeletal crystals were swamped, sank and accumulated on the bottom as a sediment. They subsequently developed syntaxial inclusion-free overgrowths, and assumed cubic habits.

Cloudy and clear salt banding was interpreted by Dellwig (1955) as a product of variations in halite saturation on the basin floor. Sinking hopper crystals caused bottom brines to become saturated with respect to halite. A temperature rise in the bottom brines, however, caused undersaturation and some dissolution of previously accumulated hopper crystals. Subsequent cooling of the brine allowed the brine to become supersaturated and promoted growth of clear, inclusion-free halite as overgrowths of surviving bottom hopper crystals and as a new, clear, halite layer. Supply of new hopper crystals from the brine surface formed a new layer of cloudy halite on top of the clear layer. The early diagenetic origin of clear salt layers and of hopper overgrowths is shown where carbonate-anhydrite laminae drape over overgrowth crystal faces or when similar carbonate-anhydrite laminae overlie flat dissolution surfaces that cut across both hoppers and their overgrowths.

If Dellwig's interpretation of the clear halite is correct, then this may account for the recrystallized appearance of other deep-water halites. It is not known, however, whether a deep body of brine would suffer sufficient variation in bottom temperatures to promote this wholesale solution-reprecipitation.

Many of Dellwig's conclusions have been challenged by Nurmi and Friedman (1977). They identify much of the cloudy salt as having grown on the basin floor as crusts of upwardly-directed crystals and infer a shallow-water origin for it (see section on shallow-water halite). However, Dellwig categorically describes some halite crystals as being downwardly-directed so that both bottom-grown and surface-grown (hopper) halite may be present. Nurmi and Friedman also identify some clear halite crystals, interpreted as recrystalized halite by Dellwig, as primary. Such halite occurs as well-developed cubes and is interbedded with stringers of carbonate and anhydrite which drape over underlying halite crystals (Fig. 37). The clear character of

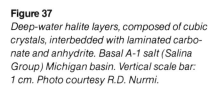

Figure 37
Deep-water halite layers, composed of cubic crystals, interbedded with laminated carbonate and anhydrite. Basal A-1 salt (Salina Group) Michigan basin. Vertical scale bar: 1 cm. Photo courtesy R.D. Nurmi.

Figure 38
Carbonate and anhydrite turbidites from a facies that flanks M. Devonian (Winnipegosis Fm.) carbonate buildups: Saskatchewan. Graded carbonate turbidites at left are inserted within laminated carbonate and anhydrite. At right poorly-graded anhydrite layers occur in association with thinner (autochthonous?) anhydrite laminae. Cores are 8.5 cm across.

these crystals reflects slow precipitation from a brine body that did not suffer rapid compositional changes. This, together with a restriction of this facies to the lower part of the lowest (A-1) Salina salt and to the basin centre, suggests deposition in somewhat deep-water environments. All other salt is reinterpreted to be of shallow-water origin.

C) Gravity-Displaced Evaporites. Clastic evaporite intervals, interbedded with deep-water laminated evaporites or with non-evaporite sediments, are interpreted as slump, mass-flow and turbidity-current deposits. Their presence is possibly the best indication of a large body of brine during deposition.

Gypsum or anhydrite turbidites are seemingly identical with non-evaporite equivalents. Sometimes the entire Bouma sequence is present (Schreiber *et al.,* 1976) but most beds are only composed of graded units or have poorly developed, parallel laminae in uppermost parts (Schlager and Bolz, 1977). Beds may be entirely evaporite in composition or contain carbonate and

other types of clastic material. Gypsum-rich turbidites from the Miocene of the Periadriatic Basin (Parea and Ricci Lucchi, 1972) constitute a thin horizon within a thick siliciclastic flysch sequence, interpreted as a deep-sea fan deposit. Turbidites within some evaporite deposits are entirely carbonate in composition (Davies and Ludlam, 1973) indicating an entirely carbonate upslope source, or that evaporites at such locations contained no coarse-grained material. Centimetre-thick anhydrite beds (Fig. 38), some exhibiting poorly-developed grading, associated with carbonate turbidites in flanking beds around Winnipegosis banks in Saskatchewan, suggest that the deposits of turbidity currents which only carried fine-grained sulphate may be difficult to distinguish from "normal" basinal evaporites that are deposited as a pelagic rain.

Mass-flow deposits are represented by breccias composed of clasts of reworked sulphate, either alone or with carbonate fragments. They occur in well-defined beds; clasts are tightly packed and large fragments (up to a

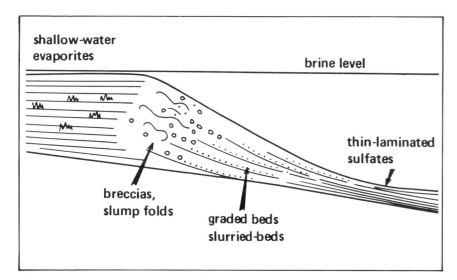

shallow-water evaporites

brine level

breccias, slump folds

graded beds
slurried-beds

thin-laminated sulfates

Figure 39
Schematic diagram of deep water and slope evaporite environments (after Schlager and Bolz, 1977).

metre in size) may be concentrated at the base of beds. They are commonly associated with beds affected by slump-folding. Confinement of deformation to certain horizons and possible truncation of deformed beds beneath undisturbed beds are indications that sediment transport down slope was penecontemporaneous.

Deep Water Evaporite Model
The deep-water evaporite model is only just beginning to be understood and to be recognized in ancient sulphate evaporites. When initial basin slopes are gentle, the basin periphery becomes the depositional site of thick shallow-water evaporites that build upwards and outwards into the basin and construct a ramp or platform (Schlager and Bolz, 1977) (Fig. 39).

In large part, this difference in sedimentation rate between basin centre and flanks is the result of the greater degree of evaporation that can occur in shallower waters. Additionally, deeper waters (below the photic zone) have little or no free oxygen, so that sulphate-reducing bacteria are able to prevent gypsum-precipitation or dissolve that which had been precipitated in shallower oxic waters. Deepwater sulphates must be transported to their final resting site from oxic waters either by settling from surface waters or by lateral displacement. Rate of sulphate supply must also exceed rates of removal by bacterial activities. Because evaporite

deposition at the deep basin centre is slower than upon the platform, steep depositional slopes develop at the platform edge. Upper parts of slopes are sites of slumping and mass flow, whereas lower parts of slopes contain graded beds that were emplaced by turbidity currents. Laminated sulphates (gypsum) are deposited on basin floors and slopes.

Not all deep-water evaporite basins are flanked by sulphate platforms. Basins flanked by lithified carbonate build-ups, for example, possess no source of evaporite detritus and are largely composed of laminites, possibly with minor carbonate turbidites at basin flanks.

Conversely, not all deep-water evaporites need have been emplaced under saturated waters. Some mass-flow deposits described by Parea and Ricci Lucchi (1972) were deposited after evaporites had ceased forming on the platform, and were presumably preserved in the undersaturated waters of their new environment by their fast mode of transport and burial beneath protective non-evaporite sediments.

Deep water halite accumulates in the same general environment as sulphate laminites but the brines became supersaturated with respect to halite. Periodic returns to sulphate precipitation, forming Jahresringe, suggest pulses of seawater entry into the basin – perhaps seasonally. Restriction of clear, cubic halite facies to central parts of the Michigan Basin suggest gradual desiccation of the basin occurred so that deep-water deposition became progressively restricted to the basin centre (Nurmi and Friedman, 1977).

Colter and Reed (1980) have shown that the same pattern of basin filling that occurs when calcium sulphates are deposited may occur during deposition of deeper-water halites and potash salts. Individual units are traceable from basin to depositional shelf and are arranged in a foresetting pattern with units exhibiting a thinning towards both the basin and shelf.

EVAPORITE SEQUENCES
Facies models are developed from the characteristics of individual facies and from the succession and arrangement of these facies. The thickness of many shoaling-upwards subaqueous sedimentary sequences also have commonly been used to estimate a minimum depth of water at the time deposition commenced. It is not possible to use this method for subaqueous-evaporite successions (although it has been attempted) because the upper depositional limit, the brine surface, is rarely static. Cycles in subaqueous evaporites can result as much from brine-level lowering (due to evaporation) as from any sedimentary upbuilding. Thus the "minimum" estimate of brine depth (for lower parts of the cycle) can be very much an underestimate. Conversely, because subaqueous evaporite deposition occurs in locations where the brine surface may be lowered by evaporative downdraw, the thickness of cycles need not even record minimal water depths at the start of deposition. Unlike sea-level, which is commonly a more or less static confining surface for marine sedimentation, the level of a brine surface may rise to offset the effect of sediment upbuilding, so maintaining a similar depth of water. In this way, shallow water evaporites may accumulate for many tens of metres without necessarily passing vertically into shallower facies. Shoaling-upwards cycles reflect a gradual decrease in brine depth but this need not occur at the same rate as sedimentary accretion.

It cannot be expected that brine depth will be stable over any great length of time. The very fact of evaporite precipitation means that the brine volume has been depleted by evaporation. In the absence of significant water input, precipitation of evaporites must be accompanied by dramatic lowering of the brine surface (evaporative downdraw) and even when water input offsets this brine-loss it is most unlikely to balance the evaporation rate exactly and brine-level fluctuations will occur. Downdraw and desiccation may cause shallow-water and supratidal sediments to be located only a short distance above those formed in deep water. Conversely, basin refill and dilution may cause episodes of non-evaporite deep-water sedimentation. Thus deep depositional basins may contain both deep and shallow-water deposits. Application of a single depositional model throughout the history of basin filling is unlikely.

Three types of vertical succession occur within marine evaporite sequences and each corresponds to deposition in a different part of a basin (Fig. 40).

Basin-marginal sequences (which in shallow basins may extend well into the basin) are characterized by sabkha deposits, with evaporites growing *within* the sediments. Calcium sulphate saturation is only achieved in upper intertidal-supratidal environments and shallow water evaporites are either absent or are confined: 1) to existing depressions on the sabkha surface, or 2) to brine-flats that develop if the rate at which the supratidal surface is raised by displacive evaporite growth falls below the rate of subsidence, and the former sabkha surfaces thus becomes flooded with brine. Leeder and Zeidan (1977) interpret laminar sulphates above nodular anhydrite as forming in this last-mentioned situation but, because the brines would have been derived from sabkha groundwaters (therefore calcium and sulphate depleted), salt-pan halite is more likely to be precipitated in such a situation. Halite in the Stettler Formation (Upper Devonian of Alberta; Fuller and Porter, 1969) may have been deposited in such supra-sabkha depressions.

In shallow basin or shelf sequences (which may also be located on the floors of partially desiccated deep basins) gypsum saturation is reached in the shallow subaqueous environment. Vertical variation is caused: 1) by sediment upbuilding, 2) by lowering of brine level by evaporation or drainage (commonly associated with cannibalism of earlier-formed evaporites), or 3) by changes in the rate of brine-recharge that occur as a result of brine-level rise toward the world sea-level, brought about by sediment upbuilding. Decreased recharge will result in desiccation and regressive sequences, whereas increased recharge

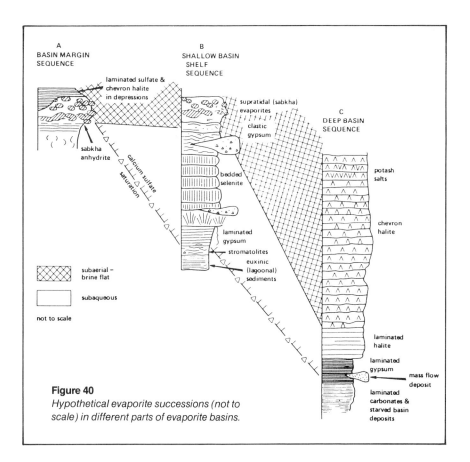

Figure 40
Hypothetical evaporite successions (not to scale) in different parts of evaporite basins.

will produce transgressive sequences. Changes in recharge will also affect the salinity of brines. Salinity increases are recorded by upward transitions from carbonates into sulphates, perhaps via patterned (or pyritic) carbonates that record sulphate precipitation and contemporaneous sulphate-reduction (Fig. 41). By the time halite saturation is reached, the brine-level in the shallow basin or shelf environment has been lowered to such an extent that only shallow subaqueous or brine-pan salt is deposited.

Lowenstein (1982) describes cycles of magnesite, anhydrite and halite (with diagenetic potash mineral overprints) from the Salado Formation of the Delaware Basin. They involve numerous (74 cycles in 160 m of core) passages from shallow lagoonal gypsum-carbonate deposits upwards into shallow lagoon – salt pan mud-free halites and, at the top, dry salt pan, displacive muddy halites. These sequences were compared with those described by Arakel (1980) from Hutt and Leeman Lagoons of Western Australia although the factors that caused these Holocene cycles (progressive restriction of the lagoons by growth of barrier beach and dune com-

plexes) are unlikely to be similar to the Permian examples.

A most valuable Holocene analog for interpreting sequences of shallow-water gypsum has been described by Warren (1982) (Figs. 42 and 43). From a comparison of the inferred hydrologic changes that have occurred in South Australian salinas and the depositional sequences present, Warren has been able to make sense of some of the depositional features. The salinas began as perennial brine lakes up to 10 m. deep. The volume for the brine pond was large and its waters were strongly density-stratified. Sediments were initially precipitated therefore from a stable, gypsum-saturated brine that was unaffected by seasonal input of meteoric waters that affected the shallow water-layers of the salina. This stable setting allowed continuous deposition of gypsum and aragonite in, and on, a surface covered by an algal mat. Gypsum crystals pushed aside the aragonite to form an interlocking mosaic of large gypsum crystals with an intercrystalline matrix.

Later, as the salina began to fill with sediment, the volume and depth of the brine ponds decreased and seasonal freshening of surface waters became

288

A

B

Figure 41

A) Part of Souris River Fm (U. Devonian, Saskatchewan) evaporite cycle. Light coloured laminated carbonates at base pass up into pyritic-stained carbonates (marking episode when brines were gypsum saturated but gypsum failed to accumulate because of bacterial reduction in the sediment) and then into laminated anhydrite (deposited when rate of gypsum precipitation exceeded the rate of its removal). A further salinity increase is revealed by the highly dendritic halite crystals that grew within the laminated carbonates. Core is 8 cm across. B) Evaporite cycle in Ratner Member (M. Devonian, south Saskatchewan) composed of varved

dolomite passing rapidly but gradationally into laminated and varved anhydrite (perhaps representing several cycles like those seen in Fig. 19), abruptly overlain by massive anhydrite (after gypsarenite ?) and chevron, layered halite. Cycle represents a period of increasing salinity and decreasing water depth. It starts with subaqueous (deep ?) calcium carbonate and sulphate and abruptly is overlain by shallow subaqueous to subaerial (salina) subphate and salt-pan halite.

progressively more important in controlling salina sedimentation. This induced a pronounced aragonite-layering within the gypsum crystals and poikilitic enclosure of some of the carbonate matrix. Initially carbonates were deposited upon the upturned crystal faces of the gypsum crystals (outlining them) but eventually the seasonal freshening caused the dissolution of the upper parts of the newly-precipitated gypsum

crystals to form truncation surfaces.

As the sediment surface approached sea-level, the brine-pond became ephemeral with rapid changes in salinity and saturation conditions. This promoted multiple gypsum-crystallite nucleation and gypsum precipitated as an annual crop of sand-sized crystals. Deposition changed from precipitation of large gypsum crystals (typical of more stable conditions) to a laminated

gypsarenite unit. During the transitional period, gypsarenite forms in the shallower margins of the salina and selenitic gypsum in the deeper, more central, parts. Similar sequences of gypsum to those which formed in the South Australian salinas have been described from the Miocene of Italy (Schreiber *et al.*, 1973; Vai and Ricci Lucchi, 1977; Fig. 42–4).

Calcium sulphate saturation is reached in the central deep-water parts of some basins and laminar sulphates overlie starved basin deposits. Some pyritic basal limestones may represent the by-product of subaqueous sulphate reduction (Friedman, 1972) and the change from carbonate to sulphate marks an increase in the rate of sulphate production so that some of the sulphate survives bacterial reduction. Halite saturation may be reached in shallow or deep-water environments but some basins seem to pass directly from deep-water sulphate laminites into brine-pan halite. The absence of deep-water halite from these basins presents a considerable problem. Upward sequences are produced: 1) by brine-level lowerings, caused by net evaporative loss, which causes precipitation of more saline and shallower water evaporites above deeper, less saline deposits; and 2) by flooding events that may cause deeper water, less saline deposits to abruptly overlie shallower, more saline evaporites. Taylor (1980) suggests that cycles in the Werraanhydrit of the North Sea (Fig. 42–5), which are composed of laminar carbonates that overlie laminate anhydrite and nodular anhydrite at the base, formed during conditions of progressively lower supersaturation and during episodes of transgression. To date this is the only transgressive evaporite deposit recognized. Most halite appears to have precipitated upon brine-flats, and thick sequences of chevron halite (the lower part of the Prairie Evaporite for example) must record sediment upbuilding coincident with a similar rise in brine-level on the floor of a fairly deep desiccated basin.

DEPOSITIONAL SETTINGS OF EVAPORITES (DEPOSITIONAL MODELS)

Rather than discuss the classic models that have been applied to subaqueous evaporites (such as the bar model of

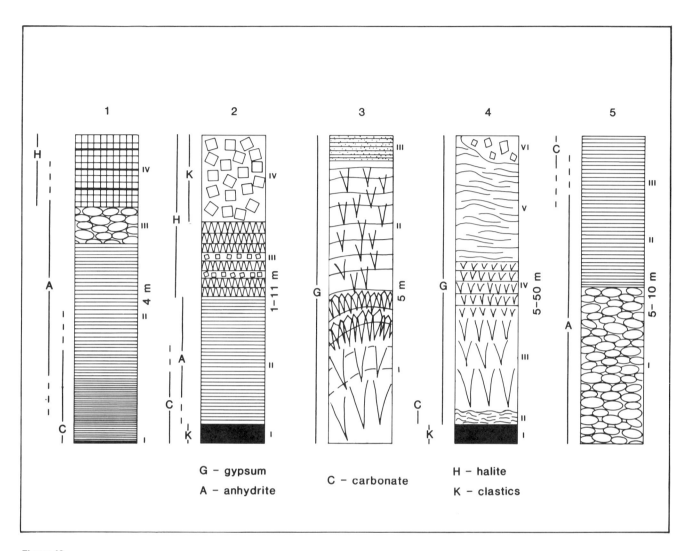

Figure 42

Evaporite cycles

1) Salinity cycle composed completely of deepwater laminites from the Castile Formation (Permian) of west Texas—New Mexico (after Dean, in Handford et al., 1982). Laminites are initially calcitic and very fine (i) but pass up, via calcite-anhydrite couplets into thicker laminites composed of anhydrite (ii) which at their top become nodular (iii). The cycle is terminated by thin-bedded halite containing anhydrite laminae (iv). Below the halite the carbonate-anhydrite laminite sequence closely resembles that seen in the Ratner Member of Saskatchewan (see Fig. 35) but there the deepwater anhydrites pass directly into salt-pan halite (Fig. 41B).

2) Lagoonal to salt-pan cycle from Salado Formation (Permian) of west Texas and New Mexico (after Lowenstein, 1982). (i) Mud containing magnesite is followed by alternations of anhydrite (after gypsum) and magnesite and then by anhydrite laminae after clastic and in-situ gypsum (ii) which represent shallow lagoon or hypersaline lake deposits. Mud-free halite with chevron and hopper structures (iii) were deposited in a perennial lagoon or lake that eventually dried

up, forming a dry salt pan or saline mud-flat within which chaotically-bedded muddy halite was deposited (iv). All parts of the Salado cycle may contain potash minerals that are diagenetic overprints. The cycle records the progressive increase in salinity and the desiccation of a lagoon or lake. It is the reverse of the sequence seen at the base of the Lotzberg Salt of northern Alberta (Fig. 8) which must illustrate the passage of a saline mud-flat into a halite-precipitating saline lake.

3) Salina cycle from New Lake, South Australia (after Warren, 1982). Selenite domes composed of coarsely-crystalline gypsum and with indistinct layering (i) pass transitionally upward into selenite with aragonitic laminae that drape over and define gypsum-crystal terminations. Overlying bedded, vertically-oriented gypsum crystals (ii) contain solutional surfaces overlain by aragonite laminae, all poikilitically enclosed within the gypsum crystals. The uppermost part of the cycle is composed of laminated gypsarenites (iii). The cycle was formed by the progressive filling of a coastal salina, the sediments of which were progressively more affected by

seasonal freshening events.

4) Gypsum cycle from Messinian (Miocene) of Northern Apennines, Italy (after Vai and Ricci Lucchi (1977). (i) Bituminous shale is overlain by carbonate-gypsum algal laminite (ii) and massive selenite that has enclosed algal-mat sediment (iii). Upward the coarsely-crystalline gypsum becomes bedded and more finely-crystalline with the appearance of dissolution surfaces. The upper part of the cycle is composed of lenticular to laminated gypsum (iv) with beds of chaotic selenite (v) interpreted to be cannabilized parts of older gypsum deposits. The sequence of selenite types closely resembles that from South Australian salinas (Warren, 1982).

5) Anhydrite—carbonate cycle from Werrannhydrit (Permian) of North Sea (after Taylor, 1980). Nodular to nodular-mosaic anhydrite (i) passes up into finely laminated anhydrite (ii) and carbonate (iii). This sequence is the reverse of that seen in the Castile Formation or the Ratner Member (Fig. 35) and has been interpreted to result from a progressive decrease in basin-water salinity, perhaps brought about by a slow transgression.

290

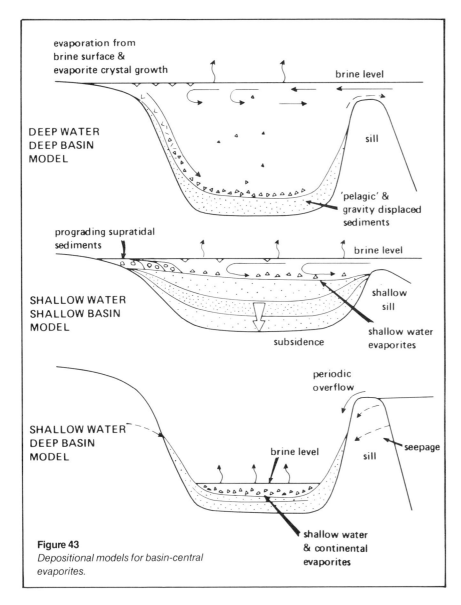

Figure 43
Depositional models for basin-central evaporites.

evaporites in the Muskeg-Prairie Evaporite Formations of the Elk Point Basin (western Canada) were deposited in the time interval corresponding to a fraction of a conodont zone – possibly only 500,000 years. Such rates require that deposition was initiated within a pre-existing deep basin.

Carbonate buildups (reefs or mud-mound complexes) are commonly associated with basin-central evaporites and occur in marginal or basin-central locations. They accumulated either before evaporite deposition was initiated or are (in part) contemporaneous with evaporite deposition. The height of pre-evaporite portions of the buildups can be used to determine depth for the basin and such evidence commonly indicates pre-evaporite basins were at least hundreds of metres deep.

Evaporite deposits also commonly include intercalations of euxinic sediments, such as black shales. These are considered, by some, as evidence for deep-water deposition (Schmalz, 1969).

There is thus considerable evidence for the postulate that many evaporites were deposited on the floors of deep basins. Unfortunately, most of these criteria identify the basin depth but not the depth of water in which the evaporites formed. Many evaporites and genetically related sediments exhibit evidence for shallow-water or subaerial deposition. Nevertheless, there are some evaporite deposits *whose internal characteristics* strongly suggest deep water deposition and, as will be seen, the shallow water, deep basin model must progress through a deep water, deep basin stage in its development.

Shallow Water Shallow Basin Model
The shallow water, shallow basin model accounts for the sedimentologic and geochemical evidence for shallow water and/or subaerial depositional environments for basin-central evaporites; evidence that commonly is overwhelming. The main argument against the applicability of the shallow water, shallow basin model is the structural and stratigraphic evidence that deposition occurred within pre-existing deep topographic depressions – depressions that, from the evidence of the evaporite facies themselves, must have been only partially filled with brine. There are also difficulties in generating thick evaporite

Ochsenius, the surface reflux model of King and the seepage reflux model developed by Adams and Rhodes) – models that are adequately described and discussed by Stewart (1963), Hsu (1972), and Kirkland and Evans (1973) – attention is directed towards three currently accepted and competing depositional models (Fig. 43). Deep- and shallow-water evaporites are also contrasted in Table 2.

Deep Water Deep Basin Model
The deep water, deep basin model is founded upon evidence that giant evaporite basins were deep togographic depressions. Evidence of this comes from: 1) the rate of evaporite deposition compared to possible rates of basin-floor subsidence, and 2) from paleogeographic reconstructions.

The Zechstein (Permian) of Germany locally contains almost 2,000 m of evaporites which accumulated at an average rate, based upon varve measurements (assumed to be annual), of 10 mm/year. Even if the Zechstein basin subsided at rates comparable with those of geosynclines (0.1 mm/year), a postulate for which there is no confirming evidence, the initial depth of the Zechstein basin could not have been less than 1,165 m (Schmalz, 1969). The depositional rate may be disputed because the annual nature of the evaporite varves is uncertain (see Shearman, 1970). Other evidence, however, indicates that evaporite depositonal rates can be very high. More than two km of salt in the Messinian of the Mediterranean accumulated in less than two million years and more than 300 m of

Table 2
Sedimentary Aspects of Deep-Water and Shallow-Water Evaporite Deposits.

Mineralogy	Deep Water	Shallow Water
Sulphate Laminites	thin, traceable over long distances.	thicker than in deep water, individual laminae may be laterally impersistent.
		evidence of deposition by currents: clastic textures, ripple drift and X-bedding, rip-up breccias, reverse and normal grading.
		associated stromatolites, footprints.
	nodular anhydrite developed from laminated sulphates.	nodular anhydrite developed displacively in inter-and supratidal sediments.
Clastic Sulphates	in form of gravity flows, slumps and turbidites.	in form of offshore bar, channel, beach and sand spit deposits and as intercalations between other facies.
Selenitic Gypsum		layers of swallow-tail twinned crystals.
Halite	finely laminated with carbonate-sulphate laminae. Inclusion-defined laminae traceable over long distances.	layers separated by terrigenous or carbonate-sulphate laminae.
		associated with potash salts.
	clear, inclusion-free halite cubes.	inclusion-rich 'chevron' halite with clear cavity-filling halite.
		detrital halite, ripple-marked and cross-bedded.
		emersion surfaces, salt-thrust polygons.

Note that recrystallization and other diagenetic changes commonly destroy the evidence necessary to place evaporites into environmental settings. No single criterion is diagnostic.

deposits by this model because it must be assumed that the basin floor subsides at approximately the same rate as the evaporites were deposited – unlikely in most tectonic environments. Furthermore, it is also necessary to postulate that the barrier zone, which controls ingress of oceanic water (needed to account for the volume of evaporites precipitated) and egress of refluxing brines (required to prevent isochemical successions from being formed), remains at approximately the same altitude. The barrier can neither subside (as does the basin) nor rise. The first would permit entry of fresh sea-water, which would dissolve previously deposited salts, and reflux out of the basin the concentrated brines. The second, uplift

of the barrier, would permit the basin to dry out and no further deposition of marine derived salts would occur. Because the rates of evaporation and corresponding rates of salt deposition are high in arid climates, the rates of basin subsidence would have to be both rapid and constant. Estimated rates of evaporite deposition thus do not support theories of shallow-water deposition with contemporaneous subsidence for the formation of vast bodies of salt. On the other hand, the shallow water, shallow basin model is certainly applicable to evaporite formation in satellite basins and to formation of thin evaporite deposits in basin-central locations. The latter occur at the top of sedimentary cycles which can be numerous and

superimposed such that, in aggregate, the evaporites constitute a major proportion of the sedimentary sequence. Examples of such sequences in the Williston Basin occur within the Ordovician (Kendall, 1976), the Upper Devonian (Wilson, 1967; Dunn, 1975) and the Poplar Beds of the Mississippian, although the subaqueous nature of much of these evaporites has not been previously recognized or is disputed.

Basins bound by active faults are locations where rates of subsidence could be fast enough to keep pace with evaporite deposition. Rates of isostatic readjustment deduced from the Lake Bonneville (Utah) area indicate that such movements can be both rapid and responsive to very small differences in load – in this instance, the weight of water in Pleistocene Lake Bonneville. This leads to an interesting possibility (so far unexplored) that varying climatic conditions control the volume of brine in some basins and the weight of these brines induces isostatic subsidence or uplift with the formation of sedimentary cycles that appear to be of purely tectonic origin. Windsor (Mississippian) evaporites of the Maritimes accumulated in graben (Evans, 1970) and could theoretically, have been deposited in shallow water, shallow basin environments that suffered continuous subsidence.

Shallow Water Deep Basin Model
The shallow water, deep basin model was developed to account for pre-existing deep basins that become filled by evaporites with internal evidence for shallow water and/or subaerial depositional environments.

Calculations made by Lucia (1972) on the degree of basin restriction required to promote gypsum and halite precipitation suggest that the barrier between the open sea and the hypersaline basin must be almost complete. Sea-water-supplying channels into gypsum-precipitating basins can only be of very small dimensions and salt deposition implies complete surface disconnection from the ocean. The source for the halite is from episodic flooding over the barrier. A corollary to Lucia's argument is that when a deep basin undergoes restriction and loses connection with the world ocean (a requirement needed before evaporites can be precipitated) there may be little to prevent desiccation or a pronounced depression of the brine level in the basin well below sea level.

The shallow water deep basin model was developed largely to account for two major evaporite deposits – the Middle Devonian Elk Point evaporites of western Canada (Muskeg and Prairie Evaporite Formations) and the Miocene Messinian evaporites of the Mediterranean. Fuller and Porter (1969) and Shearman and Fuller (1969) identified laminated dolomites and anhydrites at the base of the Prairie Evaporite, located between carbonate buildups, as algal mat and sabkha deposits and so postulated desiccation of the Elk Point Basin. The laminated beds are now interpreted as subaqueous deposits (Wardlaw and Reinson, 1971; Davies and Ludlam, 1973) but immediately overlying halites (described by Wardlaw and Schwerdtner, 1966; re-interpreted by Shearman, 1970) testify to deposition of salt flats and imply basin desiccation. Most support or the shallow-water deep basin model, however, comes from the DSDP program in the Mediterranean (Hsü et al., 1978). During the Late Miocene the Mediterranean basins were covered by deep marine waters when evaporites were not being formed, but the evaporites were deposited in shallow waters, brine-flats or subaerially on the floor of the basins, thousands of metres below sea level.

Evaporation of the entire Mediterranean Sea would yield only enough salts to reach 60 m in thickness locally. Part of the Messinian evaporites may have been derived from the salt content of waters that drained into the desiccated Mediterranean, but Hsü et al. (1973) estimated that at least 11 flooding-desiccation events would have been required to generate the Messinian evaporite sequence. In this calculation no attention was paid to groundwater contribution. Deep basins must intersect the groundwater pattern of neighbouring areas and, if deep enough, would constitute a major sink for groundwater flow. Much shallow water, deep basin evaporite may thus be derived from groundwaters. The low bromine halite of the Lower Elk Point in Alberta may have been entirely derived from such a groundwater source (Holser et al., 1972).

During basin desiccation and after basin isolation from the world ocean the desiccating sea must pass through a deep water, deep basin stage within which deep water sulphates and halite are precipitated. Hsu (1972) calculates that the Mediterranean would have reached saturation with respect to gypsum while still more than a thousand metres deep. Friedman (1972), however, argues that deep water sulphates will not be preserved because organic matter in the brine promotes bacterial reduction of dissolved sulphate or of already precipitated gypsum. This argument assumes that the rate at which sulphate is bacterially reduced will always exceed the rate at which sulphates are precipitated, itself dependent upon the evaporation rate. The assumption is clearly incorrect in locations where subaqueous sulphates are being precipitated today, like the brine ponds described by Schreiber et al. (1977) and Schreiber and Kinsman (1975).

Upon complete desiccation the floors of basins in which major bodies of evaporite formed (such as the Mediterranean and Zechstein basins) must have lain one or more kilometres below sea level. Such large depressions would provide conditions that are unlike any now present on the earth's surface. Air temperatures would be high (perhaps exceeding 60° C), brine temperatures even higher (80° C or more) and humidities would be very low because of the extreme continentality of basin floors and because of reduced vapour pressures, caused by the high temperatures. Such conditions should markedly influence the type of evaporite minerals formed and it is possible that primary subaqueous anhydrite might have been able to form during the extreme desiccation stages of the Mediterranean.

SUMMARY

Ths paper has emphasized interpretations based upon evaporite fabrics and structures but has largely ignored geochemical evidence. Postash and similar evaporites have also been little mentioned because few sedimentologic studies have been attempted for these rocks. In part, this sparsity reflects the major changes imposed by diagenesis causing few dispositional characters to survive. The treatment given to other evaporites has also been subject to considerable personal bias. Interpretation of evaporites is still very much an art and many stratigraphic units have been interpreted in very different ways. Important new interpretations seem to appear each year.

ACKNOWLEDGEMENTS
Noel P. James read an earlier version of this manuscript and suggested many worthwhile changes. The paper was partially written when the author was a member of the Saskatchewan Geological Survey and an employee of Amoco Canada.

BIBLIOGRAPHY
Of the numerous papers dealing with the sedimentology, few deal with facies models or summarize previous work. Many facies were first, or are best, described from Canadian deposits but others have yet to be adequeately described from Canada. Canadian sources are thus not listed separately but are identified by asterisks.

INTRODUCTORY READING
Busson, G., 1974. Sur les evaporites marines: sites actuels on Recents de deposits d'evaporites et leur transposition dans les series du Passe. Revue de Geographie Physique et de Geologie Dynamique (2), v. XVI, p. 189-208.

Dean, W.E., and Schreiber, B.C., eds., 1978. Notes for a short course on marine evaporties. Society of Economic Paleontologists and Mineralogists Short Course No. 4. A comprehensive, but uneven, compilation of work upon evaporites. The paper by Schreiber upon subaqueous sulphates remains essential reading and the section upon halite fabrics by Shearman is clearly written and illustrated. Other papers deal with environments, geochemistry and geophysical-log evaluation of evaporites.

Handford, C.R., Loucks, R.G., and Davies, G.R., eds., 1982. Depositional and diagenetic spectra of evaporites – a core workshop. Society of Economic Paleontologists and Mineralogists Core Workshop No. 3, Calgary, Canada, 395 p. A beautifully illustrated collection of papers concerned with both Recent and ancient evaporites. Provides an interesting contrast to Kirkland and Evans (1973) in that subaqueous evaporites are perhaps over-represented. Includes a useful summary paper by Schreiber, Roth and Helman.

Hosler, W.T., 1976. Mineralogy of evaporites. In Burns, R.G., ed., Mineralogical Society of America Short Course Notes, v. 6 Marine Minerals. Washington, Mineralogical Society of America, p. 211-294.

Kirkland, D.W., and Evans, R., 1973. Marine evaporites: origin, diagenesis and geo-

chemistry. Benchmark Papers in Geology. Stroudsburg, Penn., Dowden, Hutchinson and Ross.
Probably the best starting point, particularly the introductions to the papers written by the editors. A carefully selected collection of papers, but now outdated in that subaqueous evaporites are under-represented. This failing is filled by Dean and Schreiber, eds., 1978.

Perthuisot, J-P., 1980. Sites et processus de la formation d'evaporites dans la nature actuelle. Bulletin Centre Recherche Exploration Production Elf Aquitaine, v. 4 p. 207-233.
Two critical reviews of Recent evaporite environments.

Strakhov, N.M., 1970. Principles of lithogenesis v. 3. New York, Oliver and Boyd, 557 p.
A survey of Soviet ideas on arid-zone sedimentation, concentrating upon evaporites. Particularly good in its use of evidence from Recent salt lakes and ancient deposits.

MODERN CONTINENTAL EVAPORITES

Amiel, A.J., and Friedman, G.M., 1971. Continental sabkha in Arava Valley between Dead Sea and Red Sea: significance for origin of evaporites. American Association of Petroleum Geologists Bulletin, v. 55, p. 581-592.

Cook, R.U., and Warren, A., 1973. Geomorphology in deserts. London, B.T. Batsford Ltd.
Parts 2 upon desert surface conditions, 2 and 3.5 on playa systems provide an excellent geomorphic background to continental evaporites. Also see: Glennie, K.W., 1970. Desert sedimentary environments. Developments in sedimentology 14. Amsterdam, Elsevier, 222 p.

Eugster, H.P., and Hardie, L.A., 1978. Saline lakes. In Lerman, A., ed., Chemistry, geology and physics of lakes. New York, Springer-Verlag, p. 237-293.

Handford, C.R., 1982. Sedimentology and evaporite genesis in a Holocene continental – sabkha playa basin – Bristol Dry Lake, California. Sedimentology, v. 29, p. 239-253.

Hardie, L.A., and Eugster, H.P., 1970. The evolution of closed-basin brines. Mineralogical Society of America, Special Publication 3, p. 273-290.

Hardie, L.A., Smoot, J.P., and Eugster, H.P., 1978. Saline lakes and their deposits: a sedimentological approach. In Matter, A., and Tucker, M.E., eds. Modern and ancient lake sediments. Special Publication 2. International Association of Sedimentologists. Blackwell Scientific Publications, p. 7-41.
Excellent summary papers dealing with

the sedimentology and brine-geochemistry of saline lakes and surrounding environments.

Jones, B.F., 1965. The hydrology and mineralogy of Deep Springs Lake, Inyo Cunty, California. United States Geological Survey, Professional Paper 502-A, 56 p.
Describes concentric zonation of carbonate-sulphate evaporite minerals in a small playa lake.

Kinsman, D.J.J., 1969. Modes of formation, sedimentary associations and diagnostic features of shallow-water and supratidal evaporites. American Association of Petroleum Geologists Bulletin, v. 53, p. 830-840.

Neal, J.T., ed., 1965. Geology, mineralogy and hydrology of U.S. playas. United States Air Force, Cambridge Research Laboratory, Environmental Research Paper 96, 104 p.

Valyashko, M.G., 1972. Playa lakes – a necessary stage in the development of a salt-bearing basin. In Richter-Bernburg, G., ed., Geology of saline deposits. Proceedings of the Hanover Symposium 1968, UNESCO, Paris, p. 41-51.

Watson, A., 1979. Gypsum crusts in deserts. Journal of Arid Environments, v. 2, p. 3-20.

ANCIENT CONTINENTAL EVAPORITES

No detailed studies appear to have been made of possible continental evaporites and associated evaporitic sediments in Canada. They occur in the basal Mississippian of the Maritimes, parts of Arctic Canada and in the Juro-Triassic Watrous-Amaranth Formations of Saskatchewan and Manitoba.

Arthurton, R.S., 1980. Rhythmic sedimentary sequences in the Triassic Keuper Marl (Mercia Mudstone Group) of Cheshire, northwest England. Geological Journal, v. 15, p. 43-58.

Deardorff, D.L., and Mannion, L.E., 1971. Wyoming trona deposits. University of Wyoming Contributions to Geology, v. 10, p. 25-37.

Dyni, J.R., Hite, R.J., and Raup, O.B., 1970. Lacustrine deposits of bromine-bearing halite, Green River Formation, north-western Colorado. In Rau, J.L., and Dellwig, L.F., eds., Third Symposium on Salt. Northern Ohio Geological Society, p. 166-180.

Eugster, H.P., 1980. Lake Magadi, Kenya, and its precursors. In Nissenbaum, A., ed., Hypersaline brines and evaporitic environments. Amsterdam, Elsevier, p. 195-232.

Eugster, H.P., and Hardie, L.A., 1975. Sedimentation in an ancient playa-lake complex. The Wilkins Peak Member of the Green River Formation of Wyoming. Geological Society of America Bulletin, v. 85, p. 319-334.

Although not dealing primarily with evaporites, contains an excellent summary of the playa environment which was used as the basis for the section upon continental evaporites in this paper.

VanHouten, F.B., 1965. Crystal casts in Upper Triassic Lockatong and Brunswick Formations. Sedimentology, v. 4, p. 301-313.

Wills, L.J., 1970. The Triassic succession in the central Midlands in its regional setting. Quarterly Journal of the Geological Society of London, v. 126, p. 225-285.

MODERN COASTAL SABKHAS AND SALT-FLATS

Amdurer, M., and Land, L.S., 1982. Geochemistry, hydrology and mineralogy of the Sand Bulge area, Laguna Madre Flats, south Texas. Journal of Sedimentary Petrology, v. 52, p. 703-716.

Bush, P.R., 1973. Some aspects of the diagenetic history of the sabkha in Abu Dhabi, Persian Gulf. In Purser, B.H., ed., The Persian Gulf. Berlin, Springer-Verlag, p. 395-407.

Butler, G.P., 1970. Holocene gypsum and anhydrite of the Abu Dhabi Sabkha, Trucial Coast: an alternative explanation of origin. In Rau, J.L., and Dellwig, L.F., eds., Third Symposium on Salt. Northern Ohio Geological Society, p. 120-152.

Gavish, E., 1974. Geochemistry and mineralogy of a recent sabkha along the coast of Sinai, Gulf of Suez. Sedimentology, v. 21, p. 397-414.

Holser, W.T., 1966. Diagenetic polyhalite in Recent salt from Baja California. American Mineralogist, v. 51, p. 99-109.

Kinsman, D.J.J., 1966. Gypsum and anhydrite of Recent age. Trucial Coast, Persian Gulf. In Rau, J.L., ed., Second Symposium of Salt. Northern Ohio Geological Society, p. 302-326.

Matthews, R.K., 1974. Dynamic stratigraphy. Englewood Cliffs, N.J., Prentice-Hall, 370 p.

McKenzie, J.A., Hsu, K.J., and Schneider, J.F., 1980. Movement of subsurface waters under the sabkha, Abu Dhabi, UAE, and its relation to evaporative dolomite genesis. Society of Economic Paleontologists and Mineralogists, Special Publication 28, p. 11-30.

Patterson, R.J., and Kinsman, D.J.J., 1976. Marine and continental ground-water sources in a Persian Gulf coastal sabkha. In Frost, S.J., Weiss, M.P., and Saunders, J.B., eds., Reefs and related carbonates – ecology and sedimentology, p. 381-399.

Patterson, R.J., and Kinsman, D.J.J., 1981. Hydrologic framework of 2 sabkhas

294

along the Arabian Gulf. American Association of Petroleum Geologists Bulletin, v. 65, p. 1457-1475.

Phleger, F.B., 1969. A modern evaporite deposit in Mexico. American Association of Petroleum Geologists Bulletin, v. 53, p. 824-829.

Picha, F., 1978. Depositional and diagenetic history of Pleistocene and Holocene oolitic sediments and sabkhas in Kuwait, Persian Gulf. Sedimentology, v. 25, p. 427-449.

Shearman, D.J., 1970. Recent halite rock, Baja California, Mexico. Transactions of the Institute of Mining and Metallurgy, v. 79B, p. 155-162.

West, I.M., Ali, Y.A., and Hilmy, M.E., 1979. Primary gypsum nodules in 2 modern sabkhas on the Mediterranean coast of Egypt. Geology, v. 7, p. 354-358.

ANCIENT COASTAL SABKHAS AND SALT-FLAT DEPOSITS.

Bosellini, A., and Hardie, L.A., 1973. Depositional theme of a marginal marine evaporite. Sedimentology, v. 20, p. 5-27.

Handford, C.R., 1981. Coastal sabkha and salt-pan deposition of the lower Clear Fork Formation (Permian), Texas. Journal of Sedimentary Petrology, v. 51, p. 761-778.

*Jansa, L.F., and Fischbuch, N.R., 1974. Evolution of a Middle and Upper Devonian sequence from a clastic coastal plain – deltaic complex into overlying carbonate reef complexes and banks. Sturgeon – Mitsue area, Alberta. Geological Survey of Canada, Bulletin 234, 105 p.

Kerr, S.D., and Thomson, A., 1963. Origin of nodular and bedded anhydrite in Permian shelf sediments, Texas and New Mexico. American Association of Petroleum Geologists Bulletin, v. 47, p. 1726-1732.

*Mossop, G.D., 1974. The evaporites of the Baumann Fiord Formation, Ellesmere Island, Arctic Canada. Geological Survey of Canada Bulletin 298, 52 p.

Renfro, A.R., 1974. Genesis of evaporite-associated stratiform metalliferous deposits – a sabkha process. Economic Geology, v. 69, p. 33-45.

*Schenk, P.E., 1969. Carbonate-sulphate-redbed facies and cyclic sedimentation of the Windsorian Stage (Middle Carboniferous), Maritime Provinces. Canadian Journal of Earth Sciences, v. 6, p. 1037-1066.

Smith, D.B., 1971. Possible displacive halite in the Permain Upper Evaporite Group of northeast Yorkshire. Sedimentology, v. 17 p. 221-232.

Smith, D.B., 1973. The origin of the Permian middle and upper Potash deposits of Yorkshire: an alternative hypotheses. Proceedings of the Yorkshire Geological Society,

v. 39, p. 327-346.

Wood, G.V., and Wolfe, M.J., 1969. Sabkha cycles in the Arab/Darb Formation off the Trucial Coast of Arabia. Sedimentology, v. 12, p. 165-191.

SUBAQUEOUS EVAPORITES – GENERAL

*Bebout, D.G., and Maiklem, W.R., 1973. Ancient anhydrite facies and environments, Middle Devonian Elk Point Basin, Alberta.Bulletin of Canadian Petroleum Geology, v. 21, p. 287-343.

Schreiber, B.C., Friedman, G.M., Decima, A., and Schrieber, E., 1973. Depositional environments of the Upper Miocene (Messinian) evaporite deposits of the Sicilian Basin. Sedimentology, v. 23, p. 729-760.

Schreiber, B.C., Roth, M.S., and Helman, M.L., 1982. Recognition of primary facies characteristics of evaporites and the differentiation of these forms from diagenetic overprints. Society of Economic Paleontologists and Mineralogists Core Workshop 3, p. 1-32.
Three recent studies that stress the range of subaqueous evaporite environments.

DEEP WATER EVAPORITES

Anderson, R.Y., Dean, W.E., Kirkland, D.W., and Snider, H.I., 1972. Permian Castile varved evaporite sequence. West Texas and New Mexico. Geological Society of America Bulletin, v. 83, p. 59-86.

Anderson, R.Y., and Kirkland, D.W., 1966. Intrabasin varve correlation. Geological Society of America Bulletin, v. 77, p. 241-256.

Begin, Z.B., Ehrlich, A., and Nathan, Y., 1974. Lake Lisan, the Pleistocene precursor of the Dead Sea. Geological Survey of Israel Bulletin, v. 63, 30 p.

Colter, V.S., and Reed, G.E., 1980. Zechstein 2 Forden Evaporites of the Atwick No. 1 borehole, surrounding areas of N.E. England and the adjacent southern North Sea. Contributions to Sedimentology, v. 9, p. 115-129.

*Davies, G.R., and Ludlam, S.D., 1973. Origin of laminated and graded sediments. Middle Devonian of western Canada. Geological Society of America Bulletin, v. 84, p. 3527-3546. For a contrary view see Shearman and Fuller, 1969.

*Dean, W.E., Davies, G.R., and Anderson, R.Y., 1975. Sedimentological significance of nodular and laminated anhydrite. Geology, v. 3, p. 367-372.

Dellwig, L.F., 1955. Origin of the Salina Salt of Michigan. Journal of Sedimentary Petrology, v. 25, p. 83-110.

Nurmi, R.D., and Friedman, G.M., 1977. Sedimentology and depositional environments of basin-center evaporites, Lower

Salina Group (Upper Silurian), Michigan Basin. In Fisher, J.H., ed. Reefs and evaporites – concepts and depositional models. American Association of Petroleum Geologists, Studies in Geology 5, p. 23-52.

Parea, G.C. and Ricci Lucchi, F., 1972. Resedimented evaporites in the Periadriatic Trough. Israel Journal of Earth Science, v. 21, p. 125-141.

Schlager, W., and Bolz, H., 1977. Clastic accumulation of sulphate evaporites in deep-water. Journal of Sedimentary Petrology, v. 47, p. 600-609.

*Shearman, D.J., and Fuller, J.G., 1969. Anhydrite diagenesis, calcitization, and organic laminites, Winnipegosis Formation, Middle Devonian, Saskatchewan. Bulletin of Canadian Petroleum Geology, v. 17, p. 496-525.
Presents contrary view to that of Davies and Ludlam, 1973.

Taylor, J.C.M., 1980. Origin of the Werraanhydrit in the U.K. southern North Sea – a reappraisal. Contributions to Sedientology, v. 9.

*Wardlaw, N.C. and Reinson, G.E., 1971. Carbonate and evaporite deposition and diagenesis, Middle Devonian Winnipegosis and Prairie Evaporite Formations of Saskatchewan. American Association of Petroleum Geologists Bulletin, v. 55, p. 1759-1786.

RECENT SHALLOW WATER EVAPORITES

Arakel, A.V., 1980. Genesis and diagenesis of Holocene evaporitic sediments in Hutt and Leeman lagoons, Western Australia. Journal of Sedimentary Petrology, v. 50, p. 1305-1326.

Horodyski, R.J., and VonderHaar, S.P., 1975. Recent calcareous stromatolites from Laguna Mormona (Baja California) Mexico. Journal of Sedimentary Petrology, v. 45, p. 894-906.

Kushnir, J., 1981. Formation and early diagenesis of varved evaporitic sediments in a coastal hypersaline pool. Journal of Sedimentary Petrology, v. 51, p. 1193-1203.

Neev, D., and Emery, K.O., 1967. The Dead Sea – depositional processes and environment of evaporites. Geological Survey of Israel, Bulletin 41, 147 p.

Schreiber, B.C., Catalano, R., and Schreiber, E., 1977. An evaporitic lithofacies continuum: the latest Miocene (Messinian) deposits of the Salemi Basin (Sicily) and a modern analog. In Fisher, J.H., ed. Reefs and evaporites –concepts and depositional models. American Association of Petroleum Geologists, Studies in Geology 5 p. 196-180.

Schreiber, B.C., and Kinsman, D.J.J., 1975
New observations on the Pleistocene evaporites of Montallegro, Sicily and modern
analog. Journal of Sedimentary Petrology,
v. 45, p. 469-479.

Shearman, D.J., 1970. Recent halite rock.
Baja California, Mexico. Institute of Mining
and Metallurgy Transaction, v. 79B,
p. 155-162.

Warren, J.K., 1982. The hydrological setting,
occurrence and significance of gypsum in
late Quaternary salt lakes in South Australia. Sedimentology, v. 29, p. 609-637.

Weiler, Y., Sass, E., and Zak, I., 1974. Halite
oolites and ripples in the Dead Sea, Israel.
Sedimentology, v. 21, p. 623-632.

ANCIENT SHALLOW WATER EVAPORITES
Arthurton, R.S., 1971. The Permian evaporites of the Langwathy Borehole, Cumber-
land. Report of the Institute of Geological
Sciences U.K. 71-17, 18 p.

Arthurton, R.S., 1973. Experimentally produced halite compared with Triassic
layered halite-rock from Cheshire, England. Sedimentology, v. 20, p. 145-160.
Possibly the best illustrated paper written
upon evaporites and one that reveals the
potential of detailed fabric and experimental studies for environmental
interpretation.

Dellwig, L.F., 1968. Significant features of
deposition in the Hutchinson Salt, Kansas
and their interpretation. In Mattox, R.B.,
ed., Saline deposits. Geological Society of
America Special Paper 88, p. 421-426.

Dellwig, L.F. and Evans, R., 1969. Depositional processes in Salina Salt of Michigan,
Ohio and New York. American Association
of Petroleum Geologists Bulletin, v. 53,
p. 949-956.
See also Dellwig, 1955.

Garrison, R., Schreiber, B.C., Bernoulli, D.,
Fabricius, F.H., Kidd, R.B., and Melieres, F.,
1978. Sedimentary petrology and structures of Messinian evaporitic sediments in
the Mediterranean Sea. Leg 42A. Deep Sea
Drilling Project. In Hsu, K.J., and
Montaderi, L., et al., Initial Reports of the
Deep Sea Drilling Project v. 42,
p. 571-611. Washington, D.C., United
States Government Printing Office. See
also Schreiber et al., 1976; and Schreiber et
al., 1977.

Hardie, L.A., and Eugster, H.P., 1971. The
depositional environment of marine evaporites: a case for shallow, clastic accumulation. Sedimentology, v. 16, p. 187-220.

*Kendall, A.C., 1976. The Ordovician
carbonate succession (Bighorn Group) of
southeastern Saskatchewan. Saskatchewan Department of Mineral Resources
Report 180, 185 p.

Lowenstein, T., 1982. Primary features in a
potash evaporite deposit, the Permian
Salado Formation of West Texas and New
Mexico. Society of Economic Paleontologists and Mineralogists, Core Workshop 3,
p. 276-304.

*Nassichuk, W.W., and Davies, G.R., 1980.
Stratigraphy and sedimentation of the Otto
Fiord Formation – a major Mississippian –
Pennsylvanian evaporite of subaqueous
origin in the Canadian Arctic Archipelago.
Geological Survey of Canada Bulletin 286,
87 p.

Orti-Cabo, F., and Shearman, D.J., 1977.
Estructuras y fabricas deposicionales en
las evaporitas del Mioceno superior (Mes-
siniense) de San Miguel de Salinas (Ali-
cante, Espana). Inst. Investigaciones Geo-
logicas Diputacion Provincial Universidad
de Barcelone, v. 32, p. 5-54.

Richter-Berburg, G., 1973. Facies and paleogeography of Messinian evaporites in Sicily. In Drooger, C.W., ed., Messinian events
in the Mediterranean. Amsterdam, North
Holland, p. 124-141.

Vai, G.B., and Ricci Lucchi, F., 1977. Algal
crests, autochthonous and clastic gypsum
in a cannibalistic evaporite basin: a case
history from the Messinian of Northern
Appenines. Sedimentology, v. 24,
p. 211-244.

Wardlaw, N.C., and Schwerdtner, W.M., 1966.
Halite-anhydrite seasonal layers in Middle
Devonian Prairie Evaporite Formation.
Saskatchewan, Canada. Geological
Society of America Bulletin, v. 77,
p. 331-342.

DEPOSITIONAL MODELS
Hite, R.J., 1970. Shelf carbonate sedimentation controlled by salinity in the Paradox
Basin, southeast Utah. 4th symposium on
salt. Northern Ohio Geological Society,
p. 48-66.

Hsü, K.J., 1972. Origin of saline giants: a critical review after the discovery of the Mediterranean evaporite. Earth Science
Reviews, v. 8, p. 371-396.

Hsü, K.J., Cita, M.B., and Ryan, W.B.F., 1973.
The origin of the Mediterranean evaporites. In Ryan, W.B.F., Hsü, K.J., et al., Initial
Reports of the Dead Sea Drilling Project. v.
13. Washington, United States Government Printing Office, p. 1203-1231.
The deep basin, shallow-water model applied to Miocene evaporites from the Mediterranean. Hsü's paper contains a useful
review of other depositional models.

Kinsman, D.J.J., 1976. Evaporites: relative
humidity control of primary mineral facies.
Journal of Sedimentary Petrology, v. 46,
p. 273-279.

Lucia, F.J., 1972. Recognition of evaporite-
carbonate shoreline sedimentation. In
Rigby, J.K. and Hamblin, W.K., eds.,
Recognition of ancient sedimentary
environments. Society of Economic
Paleontologists and Mineralogists, Special
Publication 16, p. 160-191.
Includes calculation of the degree of
restriction required for subaqueous eva-
porite deposition.

Matthews, R.D., and Egleson, G.C., 1974.
Origin and implications of a mid-basin
potash facies in the Saline Salt of Michigan. 4th symposium on salt. Northern
Ohio Geological Society, p. 15-34.
Discusses aspects of the deep-basin deep-
water model.

Schmalz, R.F., 1969. Deep-water evaporite
deposition: a genetic model. American
Association of Petroleum Geologists Bulletin, v. 53, p. 798-823.
Discusses aspects of the deep-basin,
deep-water model.

Shaw, A.B., 1977. A review of some aspects
of evaporite deposition. Mountain Geologist, v. 14, p. 1-16.
A thought-provoking analysis of deep-
water evaporite models which should
command more attention than it has.

REFERENCES CITED IN TEXT
Baar, A., and Kühn, R., 1962. Der Werdegang
der Kalisalz-lagerstätten am Oberrhein.
Neues Jahrbuch fuer Mineralogie,
Abhandluhgen, v. 97, p. 289-336.

Busson, G., and Pethuisot, J.P., 1977. Interêt
de la Sebkha el Nelah (sud-tunisien) pour
l'interpretation de series evaporitiques
anciennes. Sedimentary Geology, v. 19,
p. 139-164.

de Groot, K., 1973. Geochemistry of tidal-flat
brines at Umm Said, S.W. Qatar, Persian
Gulf. In Purser, B.J., ed., The Persian Gulf.
Berlin, Springer-Verlag, p. 377-394.

Dixon, J., 1976. Patterned carbonate – a
diagenetic feature. Bulletin of Canadian
Petroleum Geology, v. 24, p. 450-456.

*Dunn, C.E., 1975. The Upper Devonian
Duperow Formation in southeastern
Saskatchewan. Saskatchewan Department
of Mineral Resources, Report 197, 151 p.

*Evans, R., 1970. Sedimentation of the Mis-
sissippian evaporites of the Maritimes: an
alternative model. Canadian Journal of
Earth Sciences, v. 7, p. 1349-1351.

Friedman, G.M., 1972. Significance of Red
Sea in problem of evaporites and basinal
limestones. American Association of Petroleum Geologists Bulletin, v. 56,
p. 1072-1086.

*Fuller, J.G.C.M., and Porter, J.W., 1969.
Evaporite formations with petroleum

296

reservoirs in Devonian and Mississippian of Alberta, Saskatchewan, and North Dakota. American Association of Petroleum Geologists Bulletin, v. 53, p. 909-926.

Garrett, D.E., 1970. The chemistry and origin of potash salts. *In* Rau, J.L., and Dellwig, L.F., eds., 3rd symposium on salt. Northern Ohio Geological Society, v. 1, p. 211-222.

*Holser, W.T., Wardlaw, N.C., and Watson, D.W., 1972. Bromide in salt rocks: extraordinarily low content in the Lower Elk Point salt, Canada. *In* Richter-Bernburg, G., ed., Geology of saline deposits. Paris, UNESCO, p. 69-75.

Katz, A., Kolodny, Y., and Nissenbaum, A., 1977. The geochemical evolution of the Pleistocene Lake Lisan-Dead Sea system. Geochimica et Cosmochimica Acta, v. 41, p. 1609-1626.

Kendall, A.C., 1977. Patterned carbonate – a diagenetic feature (by James Dixon): Discussion. Bulletin of Canadian Petroleum Geology, v. 25, p. 695-697.

Leeder, M.R., and Zeidan, R., 1977. Giant late Jurassic sabkhas of Arabian Tethys. Nature, v. 268, p. 42-44.

Loucks, R.G., and Longman, M.W., 1982. Lower Cretaceous Ferry Lake Anhydrite, Fariway Field, East Texas: product of shallow-subtidal deposition. Society of Economic Paleontologists and Mineralogists, Core Workshop 3, p. 130-173.

Mueller, G., 1960. The theory of formation of north Chilean nitrate deposits through capillary concentration. Report of the 19th International Geological Congress, Norden 1960. Part 1, p. 76-86.

Raup, O.B., 1970. Brine mixing: an additional mechanism for formation of basin evaporites. American Association of Petroleum Geologists Bulletin, v. 54, p. 2246-2259.

Richter-Berburg, G., 1957. Isochrone Warven in Anhydrite des Zechstein. Geol. Jahrb., v. 74, p. 601-610.

Rouchy, J.M., 1976. Sur la genèse de deux principaux types de gypse (finement lité et en chevrons) du Miocène terminal de Sicile et d'Espagne méridionale. Revue de Géographie Physique et de Géologie Dynamique (2), v. 18, p. 347-364.

Schaller, W.T. and Henderson, E.P., 1932. Mineralogy of drill cores from the potash field of New Mexico and Texas. United States Geological Survey Bulletin 833, 124 p.

Schreiber, B.C., Friedman, G.M., Decima, A., and Schreiber, E., 1976. Depositional environments of Upper Miocene (Messinian) evaporite deposits of the Sicilian basin. Sedimentology, v. 23, p. 729-760.

Shearman, D.J., 1971. Marine evaporites: the calcium sulphate facies. American Association of Petroleum Geologists, Seminar, University of Calgary, 65 p.

*Shearman, D.J., and Fuller, J.G., 1969. Anhydrite diagenesis, calcitization and organic laminites, Winnipegosis Formation Middle Devonian, Saskatchewan. Bulletin of Canadian Petroleum Geology v. 17, p. 496-525.

Stewart, F.J., 1963. Data of Geochemistry, 6th Edition, Chapter Y. United States Geological Survey Professional Paper 440-Y, 52 p.

von der Borch, C.C., 1977. Stratigraphy and formation of Holocene dolomitic carbonate deposits of the Coorong area, South Australia. Journal of Sedimentary Petrology, v. 46, p. 952-966.

Wardlaw, N.C., 1972. Syn-sedimentary folds and associated structures in Cretaceous salt deposits of Sergipe, Brazil. Journal of Sedimentary Petrology, v. 42, p. 572-577.

*Wilson, J.L., 1967. Carbonate-evaporite cycles in Lower Duperow Formation of Williston Basin. Bulletin of Canadian Petroleum Geology, v. 15, p. 230-312.

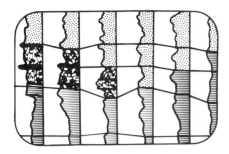

Subsurface Facies Analysis

DOUGLAS J. CANT
Alberta Geological Survey
Alberta Research Council
4445 Calgary Trail South
Edmonton, Alberta T6H 5R7

INTRODUCTION
This article will attempt to bridge the gap between "academic" sedimentology based largely on outcrop and modern sediment studies and the techniques of resource geologists who investigate sedimentary rocks in the subsurface. It is written for an audience which is unfamiliar with subsurface techniques, and is intended to be an introduction to subsurface data and procedures, particularly 1) geophysical logs, 2) cores and cuttings, 3) correlation, 4) facies analysis. Seismic methods are reviewed elsewhere in this volume;

readers interested in these methods are also referred to the American Association of Petroleum Geologists Memoir 26 (Payton, 1977), a collection of papers which summarizes a great deal of information about seismic stratigraphic analysis.

Subsurface studies will probably become more important in academic facies modelling in the future. Many details of individual facies have been worked out, but we know relatively little about stacking of individual facies, or the migration of facies through time. One specific example of this is the very small number of studies documenting how fluvial point bar sequences (see "Sandy Fluvial Systems", this volume) are stacked together into meander belt sands, and how meander belt sands relate to one another. This kind of study is impossible to carry out in most outcrop areas, but a subsurface study in an appropriate unit may succeed.

DIFFERENCES FROM SURFACE WORK
In many ways, subsurface data differs from the kinds of data collected from outcrops and modern sediments. Most fundamentally, subsurface data provides a differently-biased sample of the characteristics of a rock unit than does outcrop data. Drill holes and cores are concentrated in localities and zones of economic interest while outcrops preferentially expose harder, more resistent

rocks occurring near the margin of a basin. Drill holes "sample" a complete section while outcrops rarely do. Some common sedimentological techniques such as paleocurrent analysis are much less applicable in the subsurface because of difficulties in obtaining data. No matter how closely spaced wells may be, data from 3 to 20 cm diameter holes cannot provide as much local information as an outcrop. However, because outcrops are in most cases two-dimensional and restricted in size, subsurface data from an extensively drilled unit may be superior for larger scale or regional studies. For example, the sizes and shapes of offshore bars are known entirely from subsurface studies (see "Shelf and Shallow Marine Sands", this volume). The variation in the most appropriate scale of investigation may be the most important difference between the two situations.

GEOLOGICAL USES OF WELL LOGS
Well logs are extensively used in the petroleum industry for the evaluation of fluids in rocks, but this aspect will not be covered here. The interested reader is referred to the numerous logging company manuals or other manuals such as Merkel (1979) or Asquith (1982). In most subsurface studies, geophysical logs are the fundamental source of data because virtually every oil and gas well is logged from near the top to the bottom. Coal and mineral exploration drill

Table 1
Log types, properties measured, and geologic uses

Log	Property Measured	Units	Geologic Uses
Spontaneous potential	Natural electric potential (compared to drilling mud)	Millivolts	Lithology (in some cases), correlation, curve shape analysis, identification of porous zones
Resistivity	Resistance to electric current flow	Ohm-metres	Identification of coals, bentonites, fluid evaluation
Gamma-ray	Natural radioactivity - related to K, Th, U	API units	Lithology (shaliness), correlation, curve shape analysis
Sonic	Velocity of compressional sound wave	Microseconds/metre	Identification of porous zones, coal, tightly cemented zones
Caliper	Size of hole	Centimetres	Evaluate hole conditions and reliability of other logs
Neutron	Concentrations of hydrogen (water and hydrocarbons) in pores	Per cent porosity	Identification of porous zones, crossplots with sonic, density logs for empirical separation of lithologies
Density	Bulk density (electron density) includes pore fluid in measurement	Kilograms per cubic metre (gm/cm³)	Identification of some lithologies such as anhydrite, halite, non-porous carbonates
Dipmeter	Orientation of dipping surfaces by resistivity changes	Degrees (and direction)	Structural analysis, stratigraphic analysis

Table 2

Lithology as determined by well logs

Lithology	Primary Log(s) Used	Important Property	Notes
Limestone	Gamma-ray	Low radioactive K-content	Porous limestone best distinguished from sandstone in cores or cuttings
Dolomite	Gamma-ray Density	Low radioactivity Density of 2.87	Best distinguished from limestone in cores or cuttings
Sandstone	Gamma-ray (SP)	Low radioactive K-content	Arkosic sandstone may not be identified
Shale	Gamma-ray	High radioactivity	
Conglomerate	Gamma-ray	Low radioactivity	Best distinguished from sandstone in cores or cuttings
Anhydrite	Density	Density of 2.96	
Halite	Density	Density of 2.03	
Sylvite (and other K-bearing evaporites)	Gamma-ray	Very high radioactivity	
Coal	Gamma-ray and sonic or density	Low radioactivity, long sonic travel time, low density	Argillaceous material in coal may raise radioactivity
Bentonite	Resistivity	Low resistivity	Impure ones may have high radioactivity

holes may provide well log data on shallow rock units. Other relevant information about subsurface methods and procedures can be found in Rees (1972), Allen (1975), Jageler and Matuszak (1972) and Krumbein and Sloss (1963).

Types of Logs

Different types of logs, with the properties they measure and their geological uses are shown in Table 1 and discussed below.

1) Spontaneous Potential (SP) Log. This log measures the electric potential between an electrode pulled up the hole in contact with the rocks and a reference (zero) electrode on the surface. The log is measured in millivolts on a relative scale only (Fig. 1) because the absolute value of the potential depends not only

Figure 1 ▶

Example of SP and resistivity logs. A shale line, or line of zero deflection is shown on the SP log – any deviation from this reflects porous rock. Two resistivity curves are shown, one of medium depth, and one which reads deep into the formation beyond the influence of fluids from the drilling mud. The deep induction tool reads lower resistivity in porous zones, probably indicating salt water saturation. The coarsening-upward (C-U) sandstones and shales are Cretaceous Mannville Group rocks, lying unconformably on Devonian Winterburn dolomite (from core).

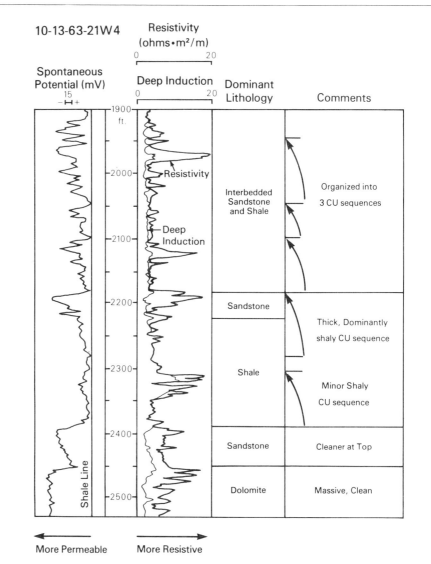

on the properties of the rock and interstitial fluid, but also on the properties of the drilling mud. In shaly sections, the SP response is relatively constant, and it can be used to define a "shale line" (Fig. 1). Zones of permeable rock containing interstitial fluid with a salinity contrast to the drilling mud are indicated by deflections from this line.

The SP log is run in most wells, and while it is not a good lithologic indicator in many areas, in others it provides the only available data which can be used. In areas of low-permeability rock such as the Deep Basin of Alberta, or the bitumen-saturated Athabasca Oil Sand it is useless for lithologic interpretation. In freshwater-bearing units such as many Upper Cretaceous formations in Alberta, SP deflection is suppressed where low salinity drilling mud is used. However, in other areas such as the Ventura basin in California, the sandstones are all permeable and saturated with salt water (or hydrocarbons), with the result that the SP log delineates them very well (Hsu, 1977). Experience in an area, and calibration against cores and cuttings are the best criteria for the reliability of the SP log as a lithologic indicator. In Figure 1, the coarsening-upward sequences are shown by progressively increasing deflection from the shale line of the SP curve, indicating more porosity/permeability upward.

2) Resistivity Logs. These logs measure resistance of the interstitial fluid to flow of electric current. The current flow is created either directly by electrode contact, or indirectly by passing alternating currents through transmitting coils, thus inducing a magnetic field and secondary currents in the rock (induction log). By varying the length of the tool and focussing the current, resistivities can be measured at different distances from the hole. Several resistivity measurements are commonly shown on the same track (Fig. 1) with the scale in ohm-metres, increasing to the right. Resistivity logs are used mainly for evaluation of the fluid content of the rocks, but are also useful for identifying coals (high resistivity), thin limestones in shaly sequences (high resistivity), and bentonites (low resistivity) (Table 2). In areas where only SP and resistivity logs are available, resistivity logs are used for "picking" or identifying formations and correlation. Freshwater-saturated por-

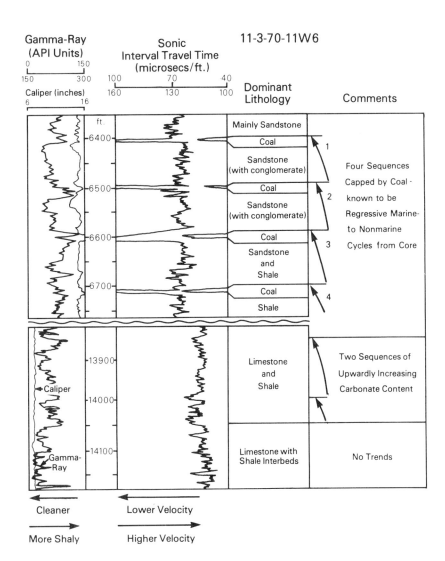

Figure 2

Example of gamma-ray and sonic logs. Siliciclastic (Lower Cretaceous Spirit River Formation) and carbonate-dominated (Devonian Ireton and Leduc Formations) sections are shown. Because of space limitations in the diagram, coaly shales (with higher gamma-ray readings) are also labelled as coals. In these carbonaceous rocks, the *sonic log has gone off-scale to the left and re-appeared on the right. The arrows at the bottom of the logs show the directions of variation of the important rock properties. Sequences 1 and 2 coarsen upward while sequence 3 shows no real pattern because the well is very close to the limit of this trangression.*

ous rocks (usually very shallow) have high resistivities. Resistivity logs are therefore useful in near-surface units for separating shales from porous sandstones or carbonates.

3) Gamma-Ray Log. This is probably the single most useful log for geological purposes (Fig. 2). It measures the natural gamma emissions of the rock, a property which is closely related to the content of potassium, thorium, and uranium. Because these elements (particularly potassium) are most common in clay minerals, the log reflects the

"cleanness" or conversely the "shaliness" of the rock. This property is very useful because gamma-ray patterns in many cases mimic vertical grain-size trends of sedimentary sequences. This will be discussed in more detail later in the paper. Gamma-ray logs are calibrated in API units, with radioactivity increasing to the right (Fig. 2). It should be emphasized, however, that a gamma-ray reading is *not* a function of grain size; that is, a clean, well sorted, fine sandstone composed of quartz grains will give a similar gamma-ray reading to a coarse sandstone of the

300

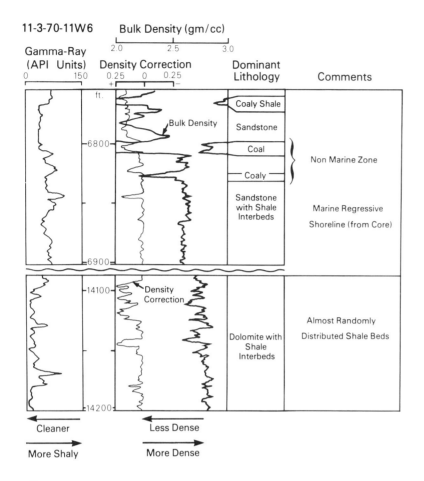

11-3-70-11W6

Gamma-Ray
(API Units)
0   150

Bulk Density (gm/cc)
2.0   2.5   3.0

Density Correction
0.25   0   0.25
+   -

ft.

Bulk Density

-6800-

-6900-

-14100-

Density
Correction

-14200-

Dominant
Lithology

Coaly Shale

Sandstone

Coal

Coaly

Sandstone
with Shale
Interbeds

Dolomite with
Shale
Interbeds

Comments

Non Marine Zone

Marine Regressive

Shoreline (from Core)

Almost Randomly
Distributed Shale Beds

Cleaner
More Shaly

Less Dense
More Dense

Figure 3
Example of density (along with gamma-ray) log from the Spirit River and Leduc Formations. The bulk density and density correction curves are shown. The density correction is calculated from the caliper log and is designed to compensate for mud cake build-up on the side of the hole. It has already been applied to the density value, and gives an indication of its reliability. Where density corrections are greater than .1gm/cm³, the density values are suspect. Because of the very low density of coaly material, the density log has gone off-scale to the left and reappeared on the right. Direction of rock property changes are shown at the bottom of the log.

same mineralogy. Clean lime mudstone also gives the same low gamma-ray response as a much coarser grained limestone.

The log can be affected by diagenetic clay minerals precipitated in the pores of rocks. Different clay types affect the log by different amounts because of their composition. Shales rich in illite (higher K) are more radioactive, on average, than those rich in montmorillonite or chlorite (low K).

4) Sonic Log. This is run with the gamma-ray log and measures the travel time of compressional sound waves through the formation (Fig. 2). The velocity of the sound depends on: 1) the lithology of the rock, 2) the amount of interconnected pore space, and 3) the type of fluid in the pores. This log is useful for delineating beds of low-velocity material such as coal or very porous rock, or high velocity material such as tightly cemented carbonate or sandstone, or igneous basement. The interval travel time is measured in time per unit length (microsecond/m) with longer travel times to the left (Fig. 2).

5) Density Log. This log is again run with a gamma-ray log (Fig. 3). The density tool emits gamma radiation which is scattered back to a detector in amounts proportional to the electron density of the formation. Electron density is directly related to density of the rock (except in evaporites) and the amount and density of pore-filling fluids. The log is plotted in gm/cm³ or kg/m³ with higher densities to the right (Fig. 3). Because the major classes of sedimentary rocks have somewhat different densities, this log is useful where porosities are known for lithologic identification.

6) Neutron Log. This log is used primarily to estimate porosities (Fig. 4) because it measures the concentration of hydrogen (in water or hydrocarbons) in the rock. The tool emits neutrons of a known energy level which collide with atomic nuclei in the formation, and the detector measures the energies of returning neutrons. Because energy is transferred most readily to particles of similar mass, energy loss is a function of hydrogen ion concentration. The log is useful in many cases in conjunction with other logs for empirical calibration of rock type against log response. Neutron porosity is commonly shown in the same track as a porosity calculated from the density log by assuming a density of the rock material (2650 kg/m³ for sandstone, 2710 kg/m³ for limestone) and fluid (1000 kg/m³ for water) (Fig. 4). Higher porosities are on the left.

7) Caliper Log. This log records the diameter of the well bore measured with a caliper device. It gives an indication of the conditions of the borehole. A very large hole indicates that a great deal of caving or falling in of the rock has occured. While most logging tools are designed to compensate for the size of the hole, anomalous or unreliable readings can occur where a very much enlarged hole has developed. A hole size smaller than the drill bit results because the fluid fraction of the drilling mud invades very permeable zones leaving the solid fraction (mud or filter cake) plastered to the inside of the well bore. The caliper log is usually plotted on the same track as the gamma-ray log (Fig. 2), with hole size increasing from left to right.

8) Dipmeter Log. This log is made by a resistivity tool with 3 or 4 electrodes, each capable of detecting changes in lithology, mounted on separate arms with a common centre point (Fig. 5). The orientation of the tool in the hole is also continuously recorded. Where a dipping bed is encountered, the response to the lithologic change occurs at slightly different elevations for each electrode. Because the orientations of the electrodes are known, correlation of the resistivity records yields the magnitude and direction of dip.

The tool can measure structural dip or fractures in the rock, but can also detect various types of sedimentary dips such as compaction drape over a reef, a mud drape on a point bar surface, and even some cross-stratification. In many cases it is difficult to determine the nature of a dipping surface unless a core has been taken of the interval. Dipmeter results are shown in "tadpole plots" which indicate the magnitude (0 to 90 degrees) laterally, and the direction of dip by the small tail (Fig. 5).

INTERPRETATION OF LITHOLOGY FROM LOGS

Interpretation of lithologies in the subsurface from logs, without any other data, is very difficult. In sections where lithologies are known in general, lithologic interpretation can be made with much more confidence, based on the properties measured by each log. It should be emphasized however, that the interpretation procedure is somewhat subjective because of 1) unusual minerals in the rock, 2) anomalously high or low porosity, 3) thinly interbedded lithologies, 4) poor hole condition, and 5) poor log quality. A few specific problems will be discussed.

1) Sandstone vs. Carbonate. Many sedimentary units contain either one or the other, so discrimination is not a problem in thsese cases. However, where they are mixed, distinguishing them solely on the basis of logs can be difficult. Because carbonates have higher densities, the density log can be successful; however, it should be noted that this log records bulk density so it will read values less than pure carbonate where porosity is present. The density log should be checked against other data.

2) Sandstone vs. Shale. The gamma-ray discriminates clearly in most cases. The log can be calibrated by establishing minimum and maximum readings corresponding to sandstone and shale end members (Fig. 6), and scaled between. Where a thick section is being considered, several estimates of the position of the maximum "shale" end member should be obtained over the entire depth range under study. As

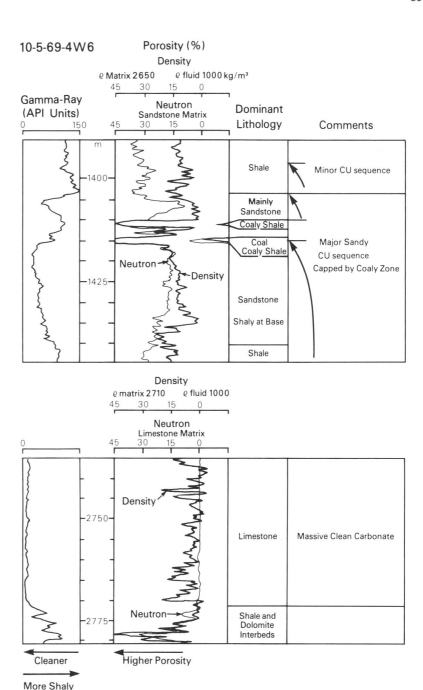

Figure 4
Example of neutron-porosity and density-porosity logs. In shales, the neutron-porosity log reads anomalously high because of water bound into the clay minerals. In the limestone (Mississippian Pekisko Formation), the density log records higher porosity because of light natural gas in the pores, and the neu-tron log records low porosity because of low concentrations of hydrogen in the gas (compared to water or oil). Porosities in coals (Spirit River Formation) are anomalously high because of its low density compared to the reference matrix material. Readings in the coaly material go off-scale to the left and reappear on the right.

shales compact, the amount of radioactive material per unit volume increases, so the shale line will drift to the right on the gamma-ray log with increasing depth. The tool response is non-linear (Fig. 7). A cutoff can be established by drawing a line at some appropriate value (Fig. 6). This calibration works well for thick beds, but log response in thin beds (less than 2 m) is affected by surrounding lithologies and registers an intermediate value. It is extremely difficult to distinguish thinly interbedded sandstone and shale from shaly sand-

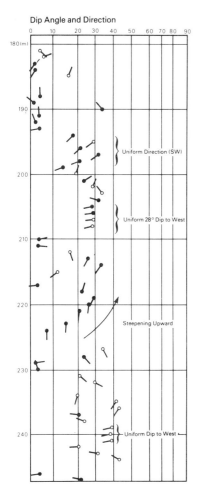

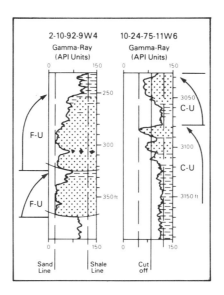

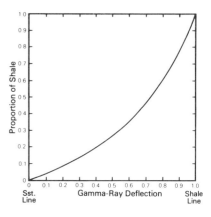

Figure 7
The relationship between gamma-ray reading and the proportion of shale. A reading half-way between maximum and minimum log values corresponds to about 28 per cent shale. Modified from Schlumberger basic manual.

Figure 5
Example of a dipmeter log from the Paleocene Paskapoo Formation of Alberta indicating direction and magnitude of dip. Vertical tails mean northward dip. Zones with clear dip patterns are indicated. On some dipmeter logs, regional dip can be identified by (a) a consistent minimum dip, (b) a consistently recurring dip separated by zones with other dips.

Figure 6
Examples of fining-upward (F-U) and coarsening-upward (C-U) sequences (actually upwardly increasing shaliness and upwardly decreasing shaliness). A clean sand line and shale line is drawn on each. Note the difference in spacing of these on the two logs. On the 10-24 log, a cutoff halfway between the sand and shale lines is drawn. The 2-10 well shows meandering stream sand bodies (with intraclast zone) of the Lower Cretaceous Athabasca Oil Sands. The 10-24 well shows shallow marine sequences from the Spirit River Formation of Alberta.

stone or siltstone. The gamma-ray log run with the density log may provide slightly better resolution of thin beds because it is run at a slower logging speed. Another problem is that the gamma-ray log does not satisfactorily separate sandstone and shale where the sandstone contains much K-bearing feldspar or granite fragments. If this is known from cores or cuttings, the SP log can be used in some cases to discriminate between sandstone and shale. This has proved successful in evaluating lithologies in the so-called "Granite Wash", a wedge of porous Devonian arkoses and conglomerates shed from the Peace River Arch in northwestern

Alberta. In this case, checking against cores showed that SP logs are more reliable for lithologic interpretation than gamma-ray logs.

3) Sandstone vs. Conglomerate. No general method is available to discriminate between these two rock types, especially for conglomerates with a sandy matrix. In local areas, by calibration from cores or cuttings, some differences in log response can be found. For example, in some cases conglomerates show a "cleaner" gamma-ray log signature. An empirical solution can be applied to the same unit in the local area where it was developed.

4) Dolomite vs. Limestone. The greater density of dolomite (2.85 vs. 2.71) in some cases allows a distinction to be made by the density log. However, porous dolomites have a lower bulk density than the rock material itself, making distinction difficult. The best solution is calibration of logs against cores and cuttings.

One general problem of interpretation of lithologies occurs where two or more rock types are interbedded on a small scale. Where the beds are less than about 2 m in thickness, log measurements are influenced by each of the rock types, and an intermediate response results. In this case, logs cannot be used effectively, and cores are necessary to identify lithology.

In many cases, empirical calibration of logs against cores or cuttings depends not on any intrinsic property of the rock, but on the observation that in some areas each rock type present has a range of porosity and permeability values which do not overlap with others. This causes different responses on logs which then can be interpreted by means of the empirical calibration. This approach is commonly very effective, but constant re-calibration should be done to check the results.

Recently, the concept of electrofacies has been introduced. An electrofacies is defined as the set of log responses which characterizes a sediment and permits it to be distinguished from others (Serra and Abbott, 1982). Sets of log responses can be separated into discrete classes by n-dimensional cluster analysis (n depends on the number of logs used). Each class is termed an electrofacies. Where facies defined by direct examination have lithologic differences (i.e., shaly facies vs. carbonate facies) electrofacies may correlate well with observed facies assuming observed facies do not vary in porosity, mineralogy, or fluids. Facies can also be defined on criteria which do not reflect changes in mineralogy, porosity, or fluid content (i.e., trough crossbedded sandstone vs. planar crossbedded sandstone). In this case, log responses for the two facies may be identical, and electrofacies cannot be correlated directly to observed facies. The concept of electrofacies, therefore, is not directly analogous to the concept of facies. However, this kind of quantitative approach to subsurface sedimentology will become of great value in the future when it is developed more fully.

In conclusion, it must be emphasized that lithologic interpretation from logs depends on understanding the properties measured by the logs. In some cases, a unique solution cannot be found, and empirical calibration can be used effectively.

CORE DESCRIPTION
In general, core description is much like measuring an outcrop section, and all the usual methods and procedures should be followed. This section will deal with some problems specific to core studies.

The most obvious limitation of cores is their width. Not only are large features such as channels or bioherms undetectable in them, but also much smaller sedimentary structures such as hummocky cross-stratification are difficult to recognize. In some cases, trough and planar crossbeds (Fig. 8) cannot be distinguished, especially in unslabbed core. Another general problem with core is less than perfect recovery. Because of stresses on the rock during drilling and later handling, soft or very brittle lithologies may be poorly represented, or even totally absent from the core. Lines of weakness such as contacts commonly are broken for the same reason. Bedding surfaces are rarely exposed, with the result that sole markings are difficult to detect in core.

To minimize the possibilities of error, before a core is logged, the order of the boxes should be checked. Oil industry cores and boxes are numbered from the top downwards, and notations are usually recorded on the tops of core segments. Cores should be described with the geophysical logs present to check for completeness of core recovery, thicknesses, core-log correlations, and log response.

Figure 8
Two photographs of core segments showing slabbed and unslabbed core. The flat face on the slabbed core makes most observations easier, but the cut may not be in the most advantageous plane. Some unslabbed core (unlike this example) is scratched and shows sedimentary features very poorly. The hole in the side of the unslabbed core was drilled to obtain a sample for porosity and permeability measurements. Both cores are 9 cm in diameter, and are from fluvial deposits of the Spirit River Formation.

Cores are very unevenly distributed. Many rock units without economic interest are essentially uncored. Other units, particularly those forming hydrocarbon reservoirs have many thousand of metres of core distributed over wide areas, allowing for better three-dimensional control than virtually any outcrop. In Canada, Devonian stromatoporoid-dominated reefs, clastic shoreline and clastic shallow marine deposits are particularly well represented in cores.

RELATING CORES AND CUTTINGS TO LOGS
In many cases, recorded core depths do not correspond precisely to depths on the well logs. Where a core-gamma log (made by passing a detector down the core) is available, this can be compared to the gamma-ray log of the well to establish a correlation. When this kind of record cannot be obtained, a sedimentological log of the core relating grain size or "cleanness" of the rock can be used. This can be inspected and compared to patterns in any of the logs, but particularly the gamma-ray log from the well. In many cases, distinctive patterns, commonly fining- or coarsening-upward are present (Fig. 6) which allow the cored interval to be located precisely on the log. Distinctive lithologic units such as coals, bentonites, or any isolated bed different from other lithologies in the core can also provide a good correlation point to the log. When a core analysis (porosity and permeability measurements) is available, it can also be used to check core depths.

After a core-log correlation has been established, lithologic data from the core can be used to check or recalibrate the lithologic interpretations made from the logs. For example, sandstone-shale cutoffs (Fig. 6) can be adjusted to match the core data more closely.

Well cuttings are fragments of rock from 1 to 5 mm diameter ground out by the drill. Two main difficulties are associated with their study: (1) the time lag required for the cuttings to reach the surface, and (2) caving of rock from higher in the hole. The first problem can be overcome by carefully logging the proportions of lithologies present, working down the hole. The first occurrence of a new lithology, or increase in proportion of a lithology can be correlated to the logs. The problem of caving is alleviated because the cavings are larger and more angular in many cases. In some wells a steel liner termed casing is cemented to the wall of the hole when a certain depth is reached. Where casing was set (noted on logs) caving from higher up was prevented. By careful work, cuttings can provide valuable data on lithologies where no cores are present. However, cuttings should be used with caution because of the possibilities of error in the original collection of the sample.

CORRELATION OF LOGS

To conduct regional facies analysis, to map, and make cross-sections, logs must be correlated. Three major methods applicable to well logs will be discussed: correlation by (1) marker beds, (2) sequence analysis, and (3) slice techniques. Biostratigraphic and mineralogic correlation methods will not be discussed.

1) Marker Beds. Any bed or series of beds with a distinctive response on any log, and which can be recognized over the area of interest, can be used as a marker for correlation (basal marker in Fig. 9; see also K, L markers, Fig. 17, "Shelf and Shallow Marine Sands", this volume).

In cases where the section is simple and laterally unvarying, the major units themselves may be distinctive enough to use as markers. For example, a laterally extensive carbonate unit within a dominantly shaly section could be employed. In other cases, unusual lithologies must be sought. Bentonites, where present, are commonly used (top of Fig. 9). Other examples are shales rich in organic debris, such as the Fish Scales Horizon of the Alberta plains. This unit is present over thousands of square kilometres, and is recognizable by its characteristic very high gamma ray reading, slightly high resistivity response, and high density-porosity

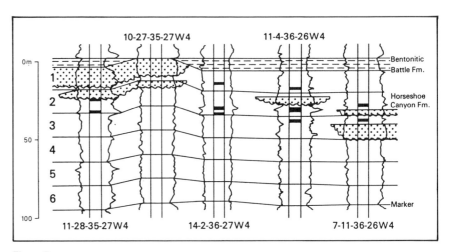

Figure 9
A cross-section (gamma-ray logs on left, resistivity logs on right) from the Upper Cretaceous Horseshoe Canyon Formation in central Alberta. The section between the bentonitic Battle Formation and the basal marker was subdivided into 6 equal slices. The slices were chosen to include but not subdivide the major channels (stippled) in this non-marine section, from Nurkowski and Rahmani (in press).

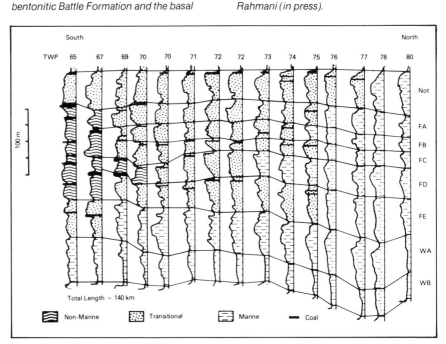

Figure 10
A north-south gamma-ray cross-section from the Lower Cretaceous Spirit River Formation near the Alberta-British Columbia border. Sequence analysis has allowed correlation of 8 genetic units in marine and transitional areas. Each sequence boundary represents a transgression which occurred over a short time interval compared to the regressive deposition of the sediment. The sequence boundaries, therefore, are taken to approximate time lines. The interpretation of depositional environments was made from cores, log curve shape analysis, palynology, and comparison to outcrop. From Cant (1983).

and neutron-porosity values. Other possible markers are tightly cemented zones, with high sonic velocities and density values, or shale beds with anomalously high radioactivity.

Many markers have the further advantage of approximating time lines. The Fish Scales Horizon has been dated paleontologically as occurring very close to the Upper-Lower Cretaceous boundary, and is taken to approximate this wherever it is found. Bentonite beds originate as ash falls, so are essentially isochronous.

Marker beds are most useful in sediment laid down in relatively low-energy environments such as lacustrine or some marine settings. In high energy fluvial and nearshore sediments, distinctive sediment types are likely to be dispersed by depositional processes.

2) Sequence Analysis. Sequence analysis involves the recognition and matching of distinctive log patterns such as the fining-upward or coarsening-upward sequences shown in Figure 6. In many cases, these sequences are prominent on logs and can be traced over wide areas. Sequences defined in this fashion may cut across lithologic and facies boundaries as shown in Figure 10. In this case several of the sequences (FA to WA) pass laterally from shoreline deposits capped by coal (south end) into marine coarsening-upward deposits (north end).

The major strength of this method of correlation is that well-chosen sequences are natural sedimentary units. Data collected from within a unit may be very meaningful because any patterns observed can be fitted into the overall depositional framework established by the sequence. Correlation of sequences is an example of "event" correlation. It has been suggested that time-significant correlations can be established by this method, and this has been partly verified paleontologically. Whether or not the correlations established by sequence analysis are precisely time-markers is difficult to judge, but these correlations appear to be closer to true time-lines than those defined by any other method.

The weakness of sequence analysis is that it cannot be applied in many sections. In non-marine sediments, the method commonly breaks down because of channelling and laterally-restricted sediment bodies.

3) Slice Techniques. Where no other method can be applied, an interval can be subdivided by establishing arbitrary slices, either of constant thicknesses, or of thicknesses proportional to the thickness of the entire interval. This method is not precise in that slices may cut through natural units, but it may be the only possible means to subdivide an interval. Slices should be chosen with some knowledge of the geology. For example, if most sand bodies are 30 m thick or more, to choose slices less than 30 m thick would complicate the results

unnecessarily. Another way of establishing slices is to arbitrarily extend naturally-occurring sequences or marker bed correlations laterally into zones lacking them.

Slice techniques are most useful in non-marine sediments where other techniques do not work well because of channelling and differential compaction. In the Upper Cretaceous Horseshoe Canyon Formation, the distribution of sandstones and coals has been documented by Nurkowski and Rahmani (in press) by slicing an interval between a bentonitic marker and a persistent shaly marker (Fig. 9). In the Athabasca Oil sand deposit, Flach (in prep.) has also used a slice technique to subdivide the McMurray Formation. By noting the stratigraphic position below a marker horizon and thickness of each lithology, the data is in a form of maximum utility when computerized. The thicknesses of slices can be varied easily, and lithologic maps produced rapidly until patterns emerge.

A good example of subdivision of an interval using both marker beds and slice techniques has been published by Wermund and Jenkins (1970). They used marker-bed correlation for major subdivision of a thick pile of deltaic sediments, but subdivided between markers by creating slices of equal thickness. This allowed them to map lithologies in each slice to determine the effects of earlier deposits on the facies patterns developed in later slices.

SUBSURFACE FACIES ANALYSIS
Subsurface facies analysis depends heavily on the availability of cores. Without sufficient core material, interpretations must be generalized and imprecise. However, subsurface facies analysis is more than simply core examination. The interpretation made from cores can be extended farther than core coverage allows by use of log interpretation, and can be put into a larger context by cross-sections and maps prepared from log data.

Log Curve Shapes
A great deal has been written about the interpretation of log (gamma ray and SP) curve shapes in terms of depositional environment (e.g., Pirson, 1970; Selley, 1978). Much of the published literature is extremely simplistic, using a naive "pigeon-hole" approach to deposi-

tional environments; for example labelling every "bell-shaped" gamma-ray or SP curve as a meandering stream deposit (the left half of a "bell" can be seen in Figs. 6 and 11). The most typical patterns seen on these logs are shown in Figure 11 with some depositional settings indicated in which each curve could be generated. No pattern is unique to a particular depositional environment, so interpretation on the basis of curve shapes alone in the absence of other data is extremely dangerous. Calibration of log curve shape to depositional environments determined from cores can be very successful. Curve shapes on logs from wells with no core can then be interpreted. This is a very useful method of analysis which is widely used in many subsurface studies. The method is very powerful where an appropriate facies model is used. Laterally varying log patterns can be interpreted in terms of the lateral variation of different types of deposits in the facies model. It is a matter of judgement as to how far this calibration can be applied, both stratigraphically and geographically.

The log curve shapes of Figure 11 can clearly be thought of as *norms* (see "General Introduction", this volume) against which other log signatures can be compared. A log curve shape, by itself, however, has no predictive capability until it is linked by a genetic interpretation to a facies model. When the correct facies model is combined, the log curve shape becomes a powerful tool which can be used to *predict* the distribution of facies laterally (see Fig. 10). It also becomes a *guide for observations* both for cores and for well logs. For example, a bell-shaped log pattern implies a core in the same interval may show sedimentary structures typical of fluvial, tidal, or deep sea channels (Fig. 11). A few critical observations can discriminate among these possibilities. In the Spirit River Formation (case history discussed below), a funnel-shaped log pattern acted as a *guide for observation* of the log. Determinations of the presence or absence of coal at the top of the sequence is a critical observation for mapping shoreline regression and environmental interpretation. Log curve shapes, combined with knowledge of the general environmental setting, can be used cautiously as a *basis for interpretation.* For example, if we know a rock unit is in general a delta deposit, a cylindrical gamma-ray pattern might be reasonably interpreted as a fluvial or distributary channel, an irregular pattern lateral to that, an overbank or interdistributary floodplain or marsh, and a funnel shaped pattern basinward of these as delta-front deposits.

Problems In Interpretation
Funnel-shaped patterns (Fig. 11) can result from progradation of a crevasse splay into an interdistributary bay in a delta complex (see "Deltas", this volume) or from progradation of a submarine fan lobe (see "Turbidites and Associated Coarse Clastic Deposits", this volume). However a crevasse-splay sequence would be a maximum of a few tens of metres thick while the submarine fan lobe sequence could be many hundreds of metres thick. The scale of the sequence is therefore an important criterion in interpretation. General information on the scales of sequences in each environment can be found in the appropriate papers in this volume.

The mechanism of formation of the log pattern is also an important factor to be considered. Log patterns can be the result of three different processes. First, some log patterns represent a single depositional sequence; for example, a bell-shaped pattern resulting from lateral migration of a fluvial point bar, or a funnel-shaped pattern from a single shale-to-carbonate shoaling-upward cycle. Second, other log patterns result from amalgamation of several depositional units; for example, a cylindrical pattern formed by the stacking of many braided river channel sequences, or an irregular pattern of a coarse-grained submarine canyon fill where many individual channel-terrace units are superimposed. Third, some log patterns result from deposition in environments where individual sequences are not formed; for example, a cylindrical pattern from crossbedded aeolian sands or an irregular pattern from a deep-water carbonate slope and apron.

In the first two cases (single depositional sequences and amalgamated sequences), log patterns are very sensitive to the mechanism of stacking of sequences. For example, because of later channelling, fluvial point bar sands may be superimposed, forming a compound sequence which does not represent one depositional unit. Braided river channel fills may be separated by lacustrine muds. In either case, the resulting curve shape may differ from the idealized example in Figure 11.

Other Difficulties In Interpretation
Two other major problems exist with interpretation of log curve shapes. Amalgamation of units from different depositional environments and deviations from the idealized facies model may cause difficulties. Figure 12 shows a log cross-section in the Lower Cretaceous Mannville Group of Alberta. The thick sharp-based sandstone in well 10D-29 has an almost cylindrical log pattern; the entire thickness of sand was interpreted as a deep fluvial channel deposit by Putnam (1982). Core examination suggested that the sandstone is made up of three amalgamated bodies (stippled in Fig. 12), of which at least the lower one is marine (Wightman et al., in prep.). The cross-section clearly shows that amalgamation of thinner units has created the thick

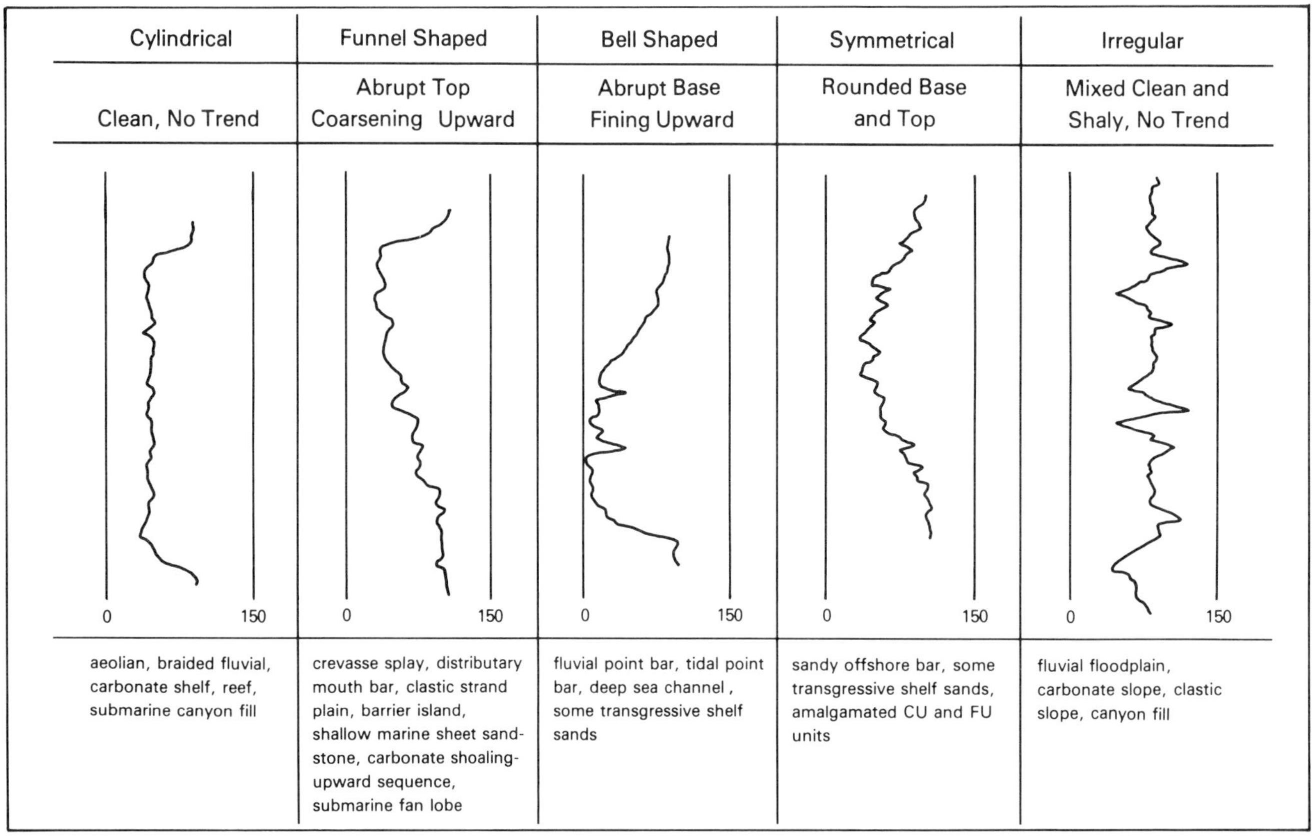

Cylindrical	Funnel Shaped	Bell Shaped	Symmetrical	Irregular
Clean, No Trend	Abrupt Top Coarsening Upward	Abrupt Base Fining Upward	Rounded Base and Top	Mixed Clean and Shaly, No Trend

| aeolian, braided fluvial, carbonate shelf, reef, submarine canyon fill | crevasse splay, distributary mouth bar, clastic strand plain, barrier island, shallow marine sheet sandstone, carbonate shoaling-upward sequence, submarine fan lobe | fluvial point bar, tidal point bar, deep sea channel, some transgressive shelf sands | sandy offshore bar, some transgressive shelf sands, amalgamated CU and FU units | fluvial floodplain, carbonate slope, clastic slope, canyon fill |

Figure 11
The most common idealized gamma-ray (SP) log curve shapes and at least some of the depositional settings in which they can originate. Several environments are listed under more than one curve, indicating they are somewhat variable. The limitations of this approach are discussed in the text.

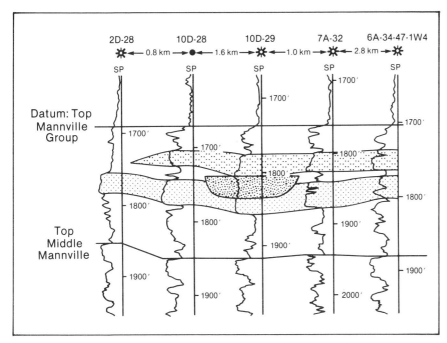

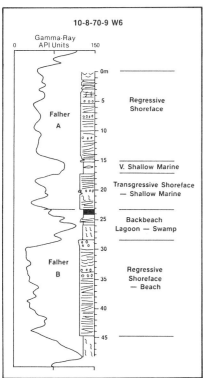

Figure 13
Gamma-ray log and core from the Spirit River Formation. The two thicker sandstones are both regressive shoreline deposits, but neither shows the funnel-shaped pattern of Figure 11. This is caused by deviations from the standard facies model – see "Barrier and Shoreline Sands" (this volume). The thinner sandstone in the FA sequence is transgressive in origin. In other wells nearby, the transgressive and upper regressive sandstones are amalgamated, further complicating interpretation.

Figure 12
An SP-log cross-section in the Lower Cretaceous Mannville Group of Alberta. In the central well, the sandstone with the sharp base and almost cylindrical log pattern has been interpreted as a fluvial channel. Core logging suggested that the sandstone is actually made up of 3 amalgamated bodies (stippled) as shown on this cross-section. The shaly interval between the sands has been removed by a channel in the central well. From Wightman et al. (in prep.).

sandstone which could not be correctly interpreted from logs alone.

Figure 13 shows a sandstone (FB) with an irregular to cylindrical gamma-ray log profile. From core logging, palynology, and the regional setting, this is known to be a littoral sandstone. The upper sequence of sedimentation (above the coal) consists of a basal transgressive sandstone and another regressive shoreline sandstone. The log patterns are irregular to roughly cylindrical in each case. Neither of the shoreline sand bodies has a log pattern which fits the idealized funnel-shaped pattern for a clastic shoreline deposit (Fig. 11). Deviations from the idealized facies model and the idealized log pattern make these sandstones difficult if not impossible to interpret without cores.

This example is from the Spirit River Formation, a case history discussed later in the paper when the reasons for the deviations from the standard facies models will be considered.

Other Methods
This section will mention briefly other specialized methods of facies interpretation commonly used in the subsurface. Palynology and micropaleontology can be applied to cuttings. Mineralogic or lithologic criteria such as the presence of glauconite or coal also have this advantage. Ichnology is a very useful tool in many clastic units where microfossils and body fossils are lacking, but requires core (see "Trace Fossil Facies Models", this volume).

Dipmeter logs are not very common, but can provide useful data where available. They may show dips increasing or decreasing upward, patterns which can aid interpretation if other data are available. In the McMurray Formation of Alberta, epsilon crossbeds (see "Sandy Fluvial Systems", this volume) can be detected by dipmeters, and their directions mapped.

In general, it must be emphasized that all available lines of data should be integrated to form a complete interpretation. While core logging is undoubtedly the most powerful method of analysis, integration into a larger scale picture is necessary. This can be accomplished by use of correlation techniques discussed previously to enable construction of cross-sections and maps. No single technique is adequate to uniquely define and interpret sedimentary facies in the subsurface.

CASE HISTORY — THE SPIRIT RIVER FORMATION
This Lower Cretaceous (Albian) unit is part of a major clastic wedge within the foreland basin of the Cordillera. The earlier non-marine deposits of the Cadomin and Gething were inundated by the Boreal transgression from the Arctic (Fig. 14). In this seaway, northward progradation of shoreline and shallow marine deposits and southward transgressions during periods of low sediment input created the sequences of the Spirit River Formation. In the study area in west-central Alberta (Fig. 14), the unit was the subject of detailed facies analysis (Cant, 1983, 1984). Well control is adequate throughout the study area (Fig. 15), but cores are restricted to some stratigraphic levels within the formation and to the centre of the study area. Lithologic determination was made by core examination, then calibrating cores to gamma-sonic logs.

308

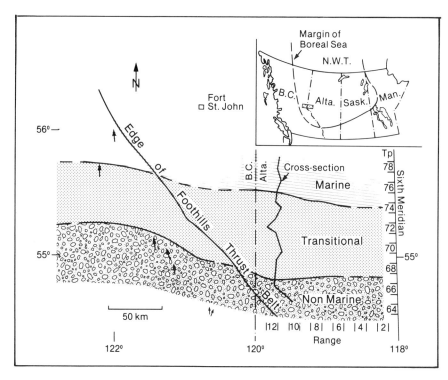

Figure 14
Location map of the study area in Alberta showing the foothills thrust belt to the west, the location of the cross-section in Figure 10, *and the generalized environments of deposition of the FA to FE sequences. On the inset, the extent of the Boreal Sea is outlined.*

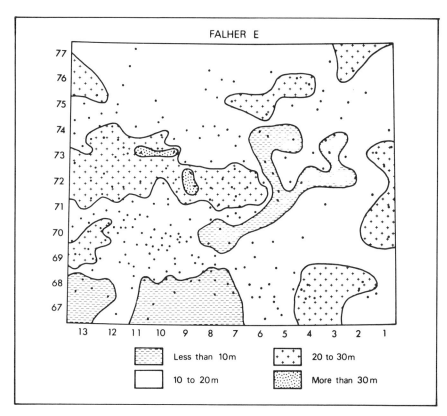

Figure 15
A map of the sandstone thickness in the FE sequence. The dots indicate the well control *used in the mapping and facies analysis in this project.*

The most important lithlogies present are sandstones and shales (separated by the gamma-ray log), coals and carbonaceous shales (identified by low sonic velocities), and conglomerates. Not all conglomerates are distinguishable from sandstones on logs. Very permeable matrix-free conglomerates show as zones of cleaner gamma-ray readings, and smaller diameter hole on the caliper log because of filter-cake buildup. Less permeable conglomerates with sandy matrix material are separable from sandstone only in core. Regional stratigraphic cross-sections were constructed (hung on the top of the unit to remove regional dip) on which sequences of sedimentation or cycles of sedimentation were identified. Correlation by sequence analysis of the dominantly coarsening-upward units allowed internal subdivision of the formation (Fig. 10). Several cycles (FA to FE) cannot be correlated into the southern part of the area where coals are abundant. Core logging reveals that the boundaries between sequences Not, FA, FB, FC, and FD in Townships 68, 69, 70, and 71 are surfaces of transgression, with basal marine sediments of each cycle overlying the upper non-marine deposits of the previous cycle (Fig. 13). Traced northward, the non-marine deposits (as interpreted from the presence of coals) disappear, and the cycles become more regular coarsening-upward, entirely marine units (Fig. 10).

Cores from the central part of the study area are interpreted as deposits of prograding shorelines or shoreface-beach deposits, capped by non-marine coastal plain muds and coals (Fig. 13). Locally conglomeratic channels and beaches are also present. Each cycle represents a regressive pulse of sedimentation, with totally non-marine deposits in the south, a transitional coastal zone with marine to non-marine sequences in the centre of the area, passing into fully marine deposits in the north (Fig. 10). The marine sand at the top of each cycle forms a seaward-thinning, shoreline-attached wedge extending a considerable distance into the seaway. In the lower cycles (WA, WB), the shorelines were so far to the south that non-marine deposits are virtually absent in the study area.

Because several transgressions terminated around Townships 68 and 69,

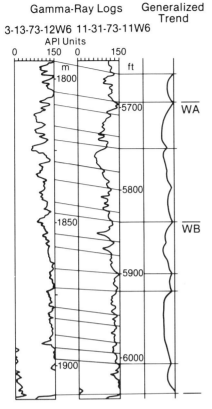

Gamma-Ray Logs

3-13-73-12W6 11-31-73-11W6

API Units

0   150 0   150

Generalized Trend

ft

WA

WB

Figure 16
Two logs from the WA and WB sequences showing very detailed correlations between the two. The generalized trend curve is an "eyeball" estimate of the curve shape. Some correlation lines which have been found to extend great distances are extended through to this curve.

the resulting sequence boundaries cannot be extended farther south. The non-marine deposits were subdivided by arbitrarily slicing them with divisions extended southward from the sequence boundaries. The thickness of each slice depends on the thickness of the sequence which was being extended, but also the thickness was varied proportionally to the entire thickness of the entire non-marine zone.

By using a cutoff halfway between a sand line and a shale line (2/3 sandstone — see Fig. 6), the total amount of sandstone and conglomerate in each slice was isopached. The resulting maps (Fig. 15) show that thickenings in the coarser sediment bodies dominantly trend east-west, and occur in the transitional zone of each cycle (Cant, 1983).

Neither of the shoreline sandstones shown in Figure 13 has the standard funnel-shaped log signature shown in Figure 11. The reason for this becomes

more clear in the context of the cycle. Near the limit of the transgression where this well is located, shoreline sands were laid down in very shallow water in high energy conditions. Marine shales are not present at the base of the sequence. Farther north, in deeper, quieter water, a more standard gradationally-based sand body was developed.

Other results of subsurface facies analysis include definition and correlation of minor (1 to 10 m) sequences (Fig. 16) within the marine parts of some cycles. The boundaries of these minor sequences slope down seaward and lap onto the basal surface of the cycle. These are interpreted as time lines, reflecting northward accretion of the sediments in each cycle (Cant, 1984). Subsurface methods in this case allowed clear definition of the detailed stratigraphy of the unit.

This case history serves to illustrate the procedures which yielded results in this clastic unit. These results probably could not have been obtained from outcrop study because of the scale of the units involved.

CONCLUSIONS

While subsurface tools, methods, and types of data differ from those of outcrop sedimentology, basic principles remain the same. Subsurface sedimentology can provide a larger-scale perspective of a rock unit or sequence by putting it into its areal context. It is particularly useful for investigating the geometries of facies and the relationship between facies. Log curve shapes mimic vertical trends in shaliness or grain size and therefore look like the familiar vertical sequences by which many facies models are summarized. It must be remembered that because: 1) there is not necessarily a unique relationship between log response and lithology, and 2) there is not necessarily a unique relationship between log responses and criteria used to define facies, log curve shapes or measurements do not necessarily directly reflect facies.

REFERENCES

SUBSURFACE METHODS

Allen, D.R., 1975. Identification of sediments — their depositional environment and degree of compaction — from well logs. *In* Chilingarian, G.V. and Wolf, K.H., eds., Compaction of coarse-grained sediments I. New York, Elsevier Publishing Co., p. 349-402.
A general discussion of well log fundamentals and interpretation of depositional environments.

Asquith, G.B., 1982. Basic well log analysis for geologists. American Association of Petroleum Geologists, Methods in Exploration Series, 216 p.
An excellent up-to-date description of the fundamental means of data collection in the subsurface. The book is directed at interpretation of fluids in the rock by the use of mathematical equations and calibrations. It provides a very clear explanation of the techniques and theory of each different type of well log.

Jageler, A.H. and Matuszak, D.R. 1972. Use of well logs and dipmeters in stratigraphic trap exploration. *In* King, R.E., ed., Stratigraphic oil and gas fields. American Association of Petroleum Geologists, Memoir 16, p. 107-135.
A discussion of correlation techniques and interpretation of dipmeter data.

Krumbein, W.C. and Sloss, L.L. 1963. Stratigraphy and sedimentation. San Francisco, W.H. Freeman and Co., Second Edition, 660 p.
Chapter 3 of this textbook provides some basic information on geophysical logs and the use of cuttings. Much of chapter 12 on stratigraphic maps is of use in subsurface work.

Merkel, R.H., 1979. Well log formation evaluation. American Association of Petroleum Geologists Continuing Education Course Note Series, Number 14, 82 p.
A shorter publication on the fundamentals of well log analysis, again directed mainly at the evaluation of the types of fluids in the rock.

Payton, C.E., 1977. Seismic stratigraphy – applications to hydrocarbon exploration. American Association of Petroleum Geologists, Memoir 26, 516 p.
A collection of papers, some of which discuss how seismic data can be used in facies analysis. The relationships between sonic log data and seismic data are discussed.

Pirson, S.J., 1970. Geologic well log analysis. Houston, Gulf Publishing Company, 377 p.
A somewhat out of date book on the uses of well logs in stratigraphy, sedimentology, petroleum geology and hydrogeology. It contains a very complete chapter on the processing and analysis of dipmeter records. The chapter on log curve shapes is somewhat simplistic, with some highly dubious methods included.

310

Rees, F.B., 1972. Methods of mapping and illustrating stratigraphic traps. *In* King, R.E., ed., Stratigraphic oil and gas fields. American Association of Petroleum Geologists, Memoir 16, p. 168-221.
An in-depth discussion of subsurface cross-sections and maps.

Selley, R.C., 1978. Concepts and methods of subsurface facies analysis. American Association of Petroleum Geologists, Continuing Education Course Note Series, Number 9, 82 p.
Lecture notes from a short course on subsurface methods. At least half the publication consists of basic sedimentology. Some very good examples of logs through different facies are included, but a simplistic labelling of log curve shapes mars the publication.

Serra, O. and Abbott, H.T., 1982. The contribution of logging data to sedimentology and stratigraphy. Society of Petroleum Engineers Journal, v. 22, p. 117-131.
An interesting, thought-provoking article on statistical analysis of log data, a particularly useful technique for use with computers. The authors do not clearly distinguish "facies" from "lithology", but their basic methods seem to be very useful. Recommended only for those involved in an intensive study.

EXAMPLES OF SUBSURFACE STUDIES

Numerous examples of subsurface studies have been published by the Canadian Society of Petroleum Geologists in their bulletins and memoirs. Few papers, however, specifically discuss the methods used in subsurface analysis. The papers listed below illustrate specific features referred to in the text.

Cant, D.J., 1983. The Spirit River Formation: a stratigraphic-diagenetic gas trap in the Deep Basin of Alberta. American Association of Petroleum Geologists, Bulletin, v. 67, p. 577-587.

Cant, D.J., 1984. Development of shore-line-shelf sand bodies in a Cretaceous epeiric sea deposit. Journal of Sedimentary Petrology, v. 54, p. 541-556.
These papers discuss in more detail the case history described in this paper.

Flach, P.D., in prep. Regional subsurface geology of the Athabasca Oil Sands Deposit — North Sheet. Alberta Research Council Bulletin.

Hsu, K.J., 1977. Studies of Ventura Field, California, 1: Facies geometry and genesis of Lower Pliocene turbidities. American Association of Petroleum Geologists, Bulletin, v. 61, p. 137-168.

Nurkowski, J.R., and Rahmani, R.A., in press. An Upper Cretaceous fluvio-lacustrine coal-bearing sequence, Red Deer Area, Alberta, Canada. *In* Rahmani, R.A., and Flores, R.M., eds., Sedimentology of coal and coal-bearing sequences. International Association of Sedimentologists, Special Publication 7, 1984.
This paper illustrates the use of marker beds and slice techniques for correlation.

Putnam, P.E., 1982. Aspects of the petroleum geology of the Lloydminster heavy oil fields, Alberta and Saskatchewan. Canadian Society of Petroleum Geologists, Bulletin, v. 30, p. 81-111.

Wermund, E.G. and Jenkins, W.A., 1970. Recognition of deltas by fitting trend surface to Upper Pennsylvanian sandstones in North-Central Texas. *In* Morgan, J.P., ed., Deltaic sedimentation – modern and ancient. Society of Economic Paleontologists and Mineralogists, Special Publication 15, p. 256-269.
A good example of the use of markers and slice techniques for correlation and preparation of maps.

Wightman, D.M., Pemberton, S.G., and Singh, C., in prep. Depositional modelling of the Upper Mannville, East-Central Alberta: implications for the recognition of marine shoreline deposits. American Association of Petroleum Geologists, Bulletin.

Seismic-Stratigraphic Facies Models

THOMAS L. DAVIS
Department of Geophysics
Colorado School of Mines
Golden, Colorado 80401

INTRODUCTION

Seismic stratigraphy involves the recovery of stratigraphic information from reflected seismic signals. Commonly the patterns of reflections may delineate rock bodies with distinctive geometries: the relationship of different geometric patterns laterally and vertically may enable conclusions to be drawn concerning depositional environments, albeit on a large scale.

It is impossible to review all aspects of seismic facies modelling here, and I have chosen to present three case histories to give some feeling for the scope of the technique. For details of the method, what the seismic trace is, and how it can be interpreted, the reader is referred to the very informative, entertaining and approachable book by Anstey (1982), or the short book by Sheriff (1980). On a much more technical level, the application of seismic stratigraphy to hydrocarbon exploration is considered by many authors in the Memoir edited by Payton (1977). Many examples of seismic lines, in a variety of geological settings, have been presented recently by Bally (1983) in three large-format volumes – these make up an extremely useful and instructive compilation.

Information condensed within seismic lines is often overwhelming within the total framework of subsurface stratigraphy. A seismic-stratigrapher must focus on selected stratigraphic settings in order to recognize stratigraphic anomalies. Anomaly recognition requires complimentary geological modelling of the type discussed in most of the papers in this volume. Use of seismic data to establish stratigraphic relationships is dependent on geological facies modelling. Once established, facies may be further documented, refined and expanded upon by proper seismic-stratigraphic interpretations.

Within relatively thin stratigraphic sequences of interior basins the seismic definition of facies requires a perceptive eye and a substantial knowledge of geological environments and facies models. A seismic wavelet (see Sheriff, 1980; Anstey, 1982) displayed in travel time may represent 30 to 50 m or more of geologic strata, and hence the scale of modelling is rather greater than most of the other models in this volume. Strata 30 to 50 m in thickness may encompass substantially different geologic environments, and the term *facies* refers to contemporaneous lithologic changes within these environments. As examples of seismic-stratigraphic facies modelling, three case studies are given in this paper. In each case accurate geologic facies modelling of these systems prior to seismic definition increases the effectiveness of seismic to further delineate facies. A wealth of information awaits the individual who is willing to coordinate seismic and stratigraphic data into geological models and subsurface interpretations.

SEISMIC REFLECTIONS – THEIR ROLE IN FACIES MODELLING

Seismic reflections are generated by changes in acoustic impedance: the product of interval velocity and bulk density for a geologic medium (Sheriff, 1980; Anstey, 1982). The product ratio across an acoustic boundary yields reflected information which is displayed in terms of a seismogram or seismic section. Polarity and strength of the reflected signal is controlled by the impedance ratio or contrast across the acoustic boundary. If the acoustic impedance ratio is unity no contrast exists at the boundary and the contact is acoustically transparent no matter how geologically profound it "really" is. Acoustic impedance or "reflectivity" interfaces generate reflections. Figure 1 illustrates this concept. To properly track the unconformity surface one would have to correlate from a peak to an

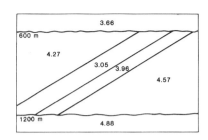

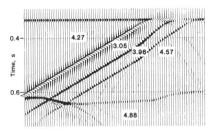

Figure 1
Sesmic model of an angular unconformity. The polarity and amplitude or strength of the seismic event representing the unconformity surface is controlled by the acoustic impedance ratio at the boundary. Velocity is labelled in meters/millisecond.

acoustic trough and across a zone of no reflection. Note that the peak part of the signal is coloured black, to help the eye correlate peaks along the seismic line. "Proper" correlation and interpretation of features like that portrayed would be a "challenge" to anyone without well control to rely on. Even with the well control it is up to the geophysicist to realize the need for good velocity and density control to help solve specific interpretational problems. A lot can be learned by rather simplistic seismic modelling, and the reader is referred to Sheriff (1980), Anstey (1982), Ryder *et al.* (1981), Bally (1983), and Jain and deFigueiredo (1982). It is most important to include as much information as possible in the interpretations and to base these interpretations on sound geological concepts and models. Thus geological and seismic modelling or facies definition must be coordinated.

SEISMIC-STRATIGRAPHIC EXAMPLE 1 – VALLEY FILL

Syndepositional tectonics and sea level changes controlled the distribution of many reservoir systems in the Western Interior during Cretaceous time. A

312

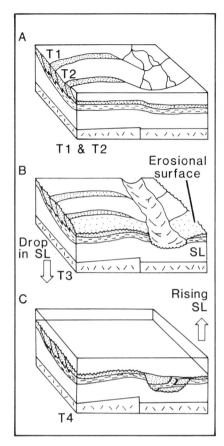

Figure 2

A) Block diagram showing deposition of regressive Newcastle sandstone. Shoreline prograded from position at time 1 (T1) to position at time 2 (T2). Inferred basement movement is shown. B) Block diagram of area during time 3 (T3). A drop in sea level caused a regional erosional surface and an incised drainage. C) Block diagram showing deposits in areas of incised drainage as valleys filled during a rising sea level.

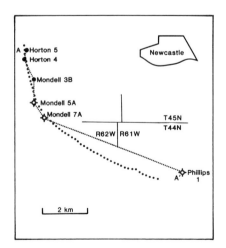

Figure 3

Newcastle seismic line location map and well cross-section A-A'. Newcastle is in north-eastern Wyoming.

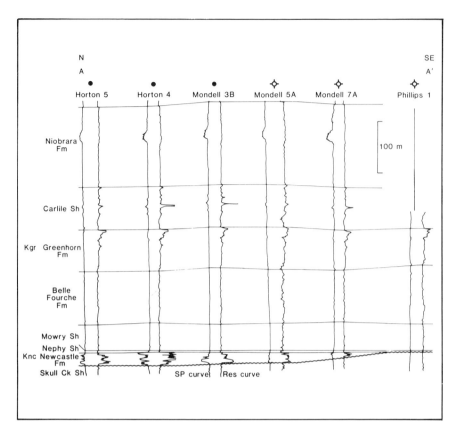

Figure 4

Electric log (SP - Resistivity) cross-section from wells along seismic line. Note thickness changes in the Newcastle Formation.

depositional model for facies distribution incorporating tectonics and sea level changes was prepared by Weimer *et al.* (1982) for the Newcastle Formation in the east-central Powder River basin of Wyoming. Incision of fluvial drainages occurred during an Albian sea level drop 97 million years ago and the fill of valleys occurred during a subsequent sea level rise (Fig. 2). Major petroleum production in the southeast Powder River basin is from the fluvial meander-belt sandstones of the valley-fill deposits. Recurrent movement on basement fault blocks controlled valley-fill distribution. During the low-stand of sea level 97 million years ago major drainage patterns were incised into the low structural area.

A seismic line (Fig. 3) was shot by the Colorado School of Mines southwest of Newcastle, Wyoming where well data indicated a southward wedge-out of the Newcastle along the line of traverse (Fig. 4). Synthetic seismograms (see Anstey, 1982, p. 52 and Fig. 5 of this paper) derived from sonic logs from wells along the line of traverse were used to identify the Newcastle signature

(Figs. 6 and 7), so that it could then be identified on the seismic line (Fig. 8). Lateral changes in amplitude of the Newcastle appear to be caused by changes in net sandstone and thickness. Large amplitudes define zones of thick high net sandstone content whereas low amplitudes define zones of low net sandstone content (Fig. 8). The Newcastle valley fill sequence can be identified by seismic on the down-thrown side of a basement fault zone (Figs. 9 and 10). Figure 9 shows the seismic line, and in Figure 10 the interpreted faults have been added and Knc identified on the left. Small amplitudes and loss of reflection character indicate that Newcastle channel sandstones are absent from the southeast end of the line. Basement faults, channel sandstones and channel margin mudstone facies can be identified along the seismic line. Seismic can then be coordinated with geologic facies models to explore for reservoir facies within the Newcastle Formation in the Powder River basin. As in Figure 1 delineation of the unconformity surface from seismic data alone is impossible.

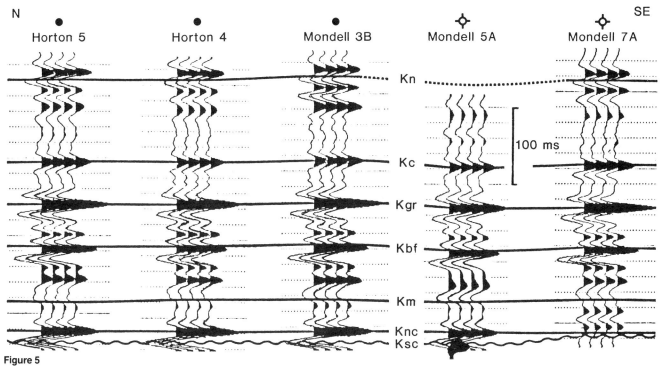

Figure 5

Cross-section of synthetic seismograms derived from sonic logs along Newcastle line. Note decrease in amplitude of Newcastle

reflector, which corresponds to decrease in sandstone content. Location of wells shown on Figure 3. Horizons shown are: Kn - Nio-

brara; KC - Carlile; Kgr - Greenhorn; Kbf - Belle Fourche; Km - Mowry; Knc - Newcastle; Ksc - Skull Creek.

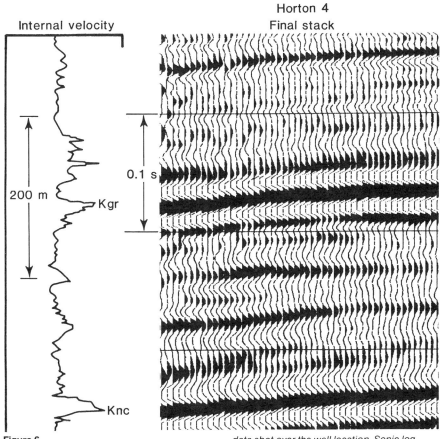

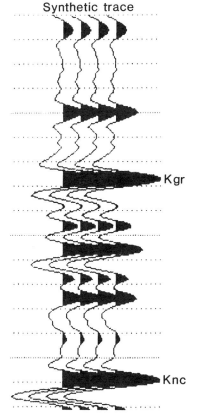

Figure 6

Synthetic seismogram (right) from Horton 4 well and its comparison to actual seismic

data shot over the well location. Sonic log shown on left. Approximately 26m of Newcastle sandstone is present in this well.

Note the high amplitude Newcastle (Knc) seismic signature.

Mondell 7A

Interval velocity | Final stack | Synthetic trace

0.1 s

200 m

Kgr

Knc

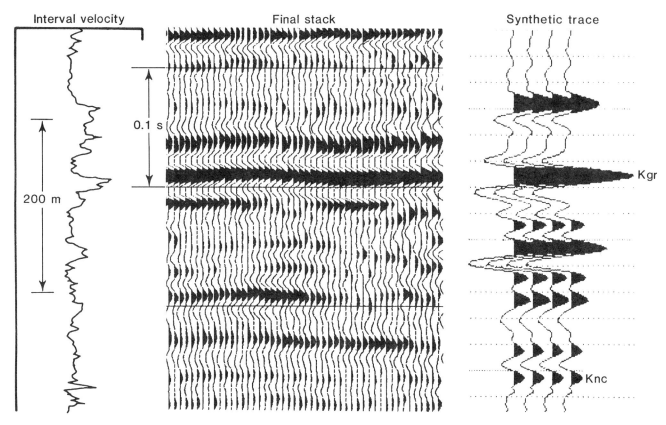

Figure 7
Synthetic seismogram (right) from Mondell 7A well. Sonic log shown on left. Approxi-

mately 9m of Newcastle sandstone is present in the well. Note "dim" Newcastle event on seismic. Dimming occurs because net sand-

stone content and thickness of the Newcastle is decreased in this well as compared to the Horton 4 well; see Figure 6.

4   3B   5A   7A

0.4

200 m

Time, s

Knc

0.6

Kg

Knc

0.8

Ꝑs

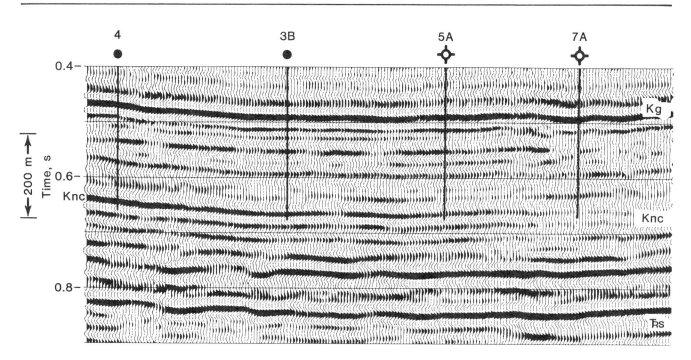

Figure 8
Seismic data showing amplitude variation in

Newcastle event from producing wells where the Newcastle is thick (Horton 4, 26m) to the

dry holes where the Newcastle is thin (Mondell 7A, 9m).

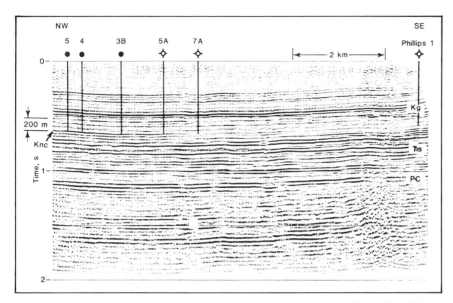

Figure 9
Newcastle seismic line, located in Figure 3. Marker horizons are Cretaceous Greenhorn (Kg), Newcastle (Knc), Triassic Spearfish (Trs) and near-basement (PC). Interpretation is shown in Figure 10.

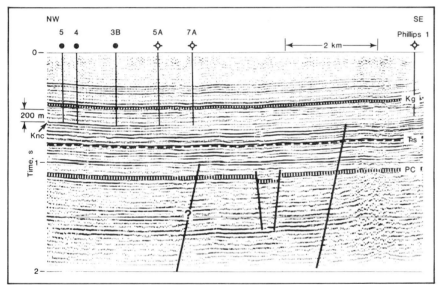

Figure 10
Interpreted Newcastle seismic section. Note amplitude decrease of the Newcastle (Knc) event to the southeast, and basement-controlled faults. Uninterpreted section shown in Figure 9.

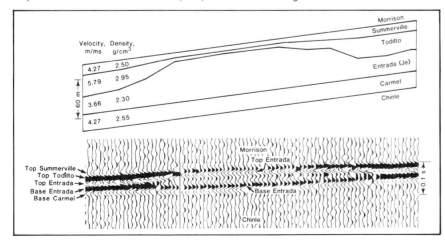

SEISMIC-STRATIGRAPHIC EXAMPLE 2 – EOLIAN SAND DUNES

Vincelette and Chittum (1981) reported on Jurassic Entrada oil fields in the San Juan basin. A seismic model suggests that thick Entrada eolian dune fields can be detected seismically (Fig. 11). With true relative amplitude, wavelet-processing and migration techniques applied (Anstey, 1982), the correspondence between the modelled data and the actual seismic data is striking (Fig. 12). Observations indicate the presence of a Todilto dim spot over the crestal portion of the dune complex and the presence of a doublet where the Entrada thickens. The Entrada is the reservoir system; Todilto the source rock. Accurate delineation of the topographic relief and closure on top of the Entrada is essential to the generation of Entrada prospects. Seismic can play a key role in delineating these traps. Modern acquisition and processing techniques now enable greater accuracy in delineating the presence of a dune complex and the associated topographic relief. With probably a large number of dune complexes to explore for in the San Juan basin, seismic is a primary exploration tool used to minimize drilling risk. Entrada topography and structure due to basement-controlled faulting can be detailed seismically. Recurrent movement on the basement-controlled fault systems may have the effect of folding the overlying Entrada, thereby enhancing, modifying, or destroying potential closures due to topography of the Entrada sand ridges. Seismic enables the delineation of basement structure.

SEISMIC-STRATIGRAPHIC EXAMPLE 3 – CARBONATE PALEOSHORELINE

Within the Mississippian of the Williston basin, several oil fields can be related to the development of stratigraphic traps which reflect stillstands and stable shoreline positioning during a regressive sequence. Porous reservoir rocks generally grade into tight evaporites in an updip direction, providing a trap. The Wiley field in the northeastern Williston

◀ Figure 11
Seismic line illustrating modelled seismic response of a Jurassic Entrada sand dune complex. Velocities and densities used in the modelling are determined from sonic and density logs respectively.

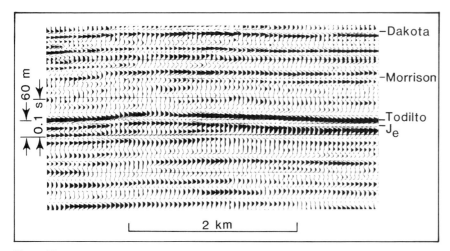

Figure 12
Seismic data over an Entrada field. Note the similarity to the modelled result (Fig. 11).

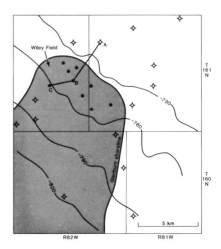

Figure 13
Wiley field, Bottineau County, North Dakota. Production is from the Mississippian Glenburn member of the Mission Canyon Formation, shown with dark shading (see Fig. 14). A re-entrant in the paleoshoreline forms the trap at Wiley. Updip seal is supratidal anhydrite, shown white. Reservoir is intertidal porous and permeable dolomites and limestones. Structural dip is to the southwest. Structure contour map on Base of State "A" marker in metres relative to sea level is superimposed.

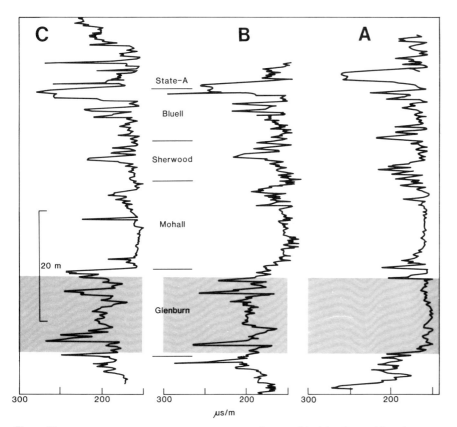

Figure 14
A sonic log cross-section illustrating the facies change that forms the trap at Wiley. Line of section shown on Figure 13. Porous and permeable dolomites and limestones have high travel times in wells B and C; the non-porous, impermeable anhydrite in well A has a much lower travel time.

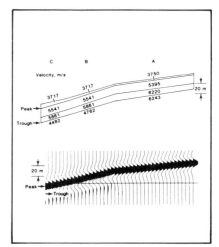

Figure 15
A seismic model of the Glenburn facies change that controls production at Wiley. Velocities from sonic logs (see Fig. 13).

basin, North Dakota, is an example of a stratigraphic trap related to a re-entrant in the paleoshoreline of the Glenburn member of the Mission Canyon Formation (Fig. 13). Wiley has produced approximately 10 million barrels of oil. Figure 14 illustrates a sonic log (see

"Subsurface facies analysis", this volume) cross-section across the facies change which forms the trap at Wiley. A seismic model of the porosity development in the Glenburn member is illustrated on Figure 15, where porosity development is shown by a trough

development on the model. A seismic line which traverses the Glenburn paleoshoreline shows the trough development (Fig 16). Seismic enables the delineation of the facies transition which forms the trap at Wiley.

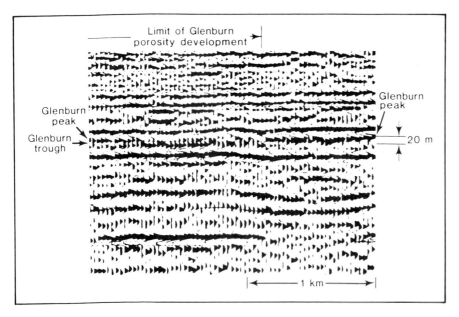

Limit of Glenburn
porosity development

Glenburn
peak

Glenburn
peak

Glenburn
trough

20 m

1 km

Figure 16
*Seismic line that crosses the Glenburn
paleoshoreline. Development of a seismic
trough is a direct indication of the presence
of Glenburn reservoir facies.*

SUMMARY

Three case studies of sesmic-
stratigraphic facies models have been
presented. In each case the success of
seismic-stratigraphic facies modelling is
dependent on the integration of seismic
with other subsurface information to
recognize depositional systems and to
establish the influence of regional and
local stratigraphic and structural controls on these systems. Applications of
seismic-stratigraphy abound in mature
exploration areas where abundant well
control may exist, as we explore for the
subtle trap or a better understanding of
stratigraphic systems. Studies of mature
exploration basins and selected field
areas hold the key to furthering our
understanding of the applications of
seismic-stratigraphy.

REFERENCES

Anstey, N.A., 1982. Simple seismics. Boston,
International Human Resources Development Corporation, 168 p.
A very useful and amusing introduction to
the subject.

Bally, A.W., 1983. Seismic expression of
structural styles. American Association of
Petroleum Geologists, Studies in Geology
Series No. 15, 3 volumes.
Three large-format volumes showing
many examples of seismic lines in stable,
extensional, convergent and strike-slip
situations.

Jain, K.D., and deFigueiredo, R.J.P., eds.,
1982. Concepts and techniques in oil and
gas exploration. Society of Exploration
Geophysicists, 289 p.

Payton, C.E., ed., 1977. Seismic stratigraphy -
applications to hydrocarbon exploration.
American Association of Petroleum Geologists, Memoir 26, 516 p.
A collection of technical papers on many
aspects of seismic stratigraphy, especially
fundamentals of interpretation, stratigraphic interpretation, and stratigraphic models from seismic data.

Ryder, R.T., Lee, M.W., and Smith, G.N.,
1981. Seismic models of sandstone stratigraphic traps in Rocky Mountain basins.
American Association of Petroleum Geologists, Methods in Exploration Series, 77 p.

Sheriff, R.E., 1980 Seismic stratigraphy. Boston, Mass., International Human Resources Development Corporation, 227 p.
Good introduction to the subject for the
non-specialist.

Vincelette, R.R., and Chittum, W.E., 1981.
Exploration for oil accummulations in
Entrada sandstone, San Juan basin, New
Mexico. American Association of Petro-
leum Geologists, Bulletin, v. 65, p.
2546-2570.

Weimer, R.J., Emme, J.J., Farmer, C.L., Anna,
L.L., Davis, T.L., and Kidney, R.L., 1982.
Tectonic influence on sedimentation, early
Cretaceous, east flank Powder River basin,
Wyoming and South Dakota. Colorado
School of Mines Quarterly, v. 77, no. 4,
61 p.

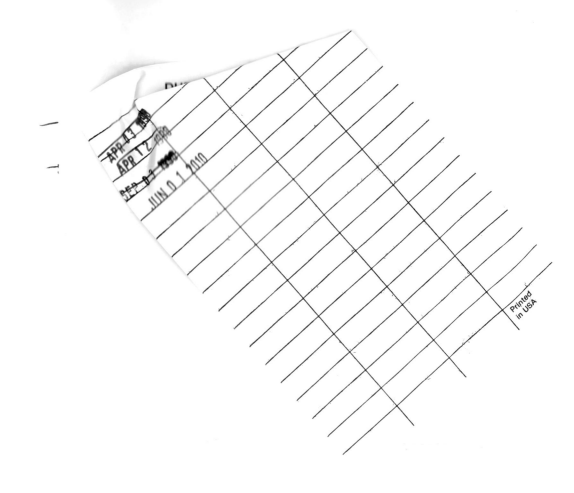

Printed
in USA